Basic physics

of atoms and molecules

New York · *John Wiley & Sons, Inc.*

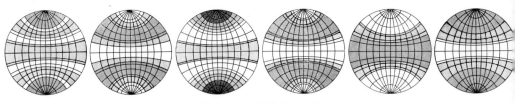

London · *Chapman & Hall, Ltd.*

U. Fano *and* **L. Fano**

Physicists

National Bureau of Standards

Basic physics
of atoms and molecules

Library of Congress Catalog Card Number: 59–6765

Printed in the United States of America

To Mother

Preface

"I know your Schroedinger equation, and I have even used it, but don't tell me I can *understand* it." This challenge, flung by a late and most illustrious chemist, has spurred the attempt to produce a digestible explanation. Everybody knows that matter consists of nuclei and electrons, but only people who have been put through the grind of theoretical physics seem to have a feel for how these things hang together and function just as they do. Why are atoms just so big? What is the affinity that makes them stick together in just certain groups? What makes a molecule act as it does? Our chemist friend could calculate the answers to many such questions, but seemed to have trouble in fitting the mathematical apparatus of atomic physics with the ordinary facts of macroscopic Nature.

The principles of quantum physics were discovered some thirty years ago, through a struggle that led to new attitudes and new mathematical tools. We feel that quantum physics is no more abstract than Newtonian mechanics, but it took a long time before Newtonian mechanics appeared as plausible as it does today. This book attempts to make quantum physics a little more plausible to a few more people.

A puzzle is no longer a puzzle when it is all fitted together and presents an obvious unity. The pieces of the puzzle of atoms did not fit together according to the schemes learned in previous experiences. Somehow a fitting was laboriously achieved and only then did the novelty of the game come to the fore. With hindsight, one can try to show from the beginning the novel properties of the pieces and then solve the puzzle systematically. The thrill of discovery is perhaps lost, but the game might be mastered efficiently. We have tried to tell the story of atoms in this "economical" way, but the road still seems rough and wearing. We hope that some better efficiency expert will take a crack at it.

This book is directed primarily to research workers in the natural sciences and presupposes, therefore, only a general knowledge of physics and mathematics. We have tried to develop ideas and establish laws through inductive analysis of experiments and only then to formulate the mathematical symbols, equations, and calculations that represent them. Since mathematics is a shorthand language, the preliminary reasoning in English is a costly proposition. As starting points of the inductive analysis we have chosen a few experiments that appear to illustrate most directly the characteristic properties of atomic systems. Some of these experiments are not accurate or easy to perform and therefore did not play a significant role in the historical development of quantum physics. That is, the experiments have been chosen for their pedagogical value; the conclusive evidence for quantum theory comes from its agreement with all the results of a vast array of accurate experiments.

This book intends to give a qualitative picture of the properties of atoms rather than to teach how to calculate the solutions of quantum mechanical problems. It might serve as a basis for an introductory course on the structure of matter in a graduate school, for example, of engineering or chemistry. We also feel that the introductory course on atomic physics for physics students at the junior level can profitably follow the line of this book, but in this case many details should be added. Chapters 5 to 16 and Appendix VIII have been covered in a 3-credit senior level course of quantum mechanics.

The fundamental concepts of quantum physics are presented in Chapters 6 to 9, and are subsequently elaborated through application to some basic problems of atomic mechanics. Effective application to a wide variety of problems should utilize the mathematical methods of matrix and operator algebra; these methods can be introduced, after Chapter 9, following the lines indicated in Appendix VIII. The material in this Appendix should also help the student who wants to continue the study of quantum mechanics utilizing any of the numerous available textbooks. Among these the following may be noted:

L. I. Schiff, *Quantum Mechanics*, McGraw-Hill Book Co., New York, 1949, a compact and comprehensive treatise;

D. Bohm, *Quantum Theory*, Prentice-Hall, Englewood Cliffs, N. J., 1951, with extensive discussion of principles and techniques;

V. Rojansky, *Introductory Quantum Mechanics*, Prentice-Hall, Englewood Cliffs, N. J., 1946, with a detailed study of numerous well chosen elementary examples and problems;

H. A. Kramers, *Quantum Mechanics*, Interscience, New York, 1957;

E. Persico, *Quantum Mechanics*, Prentice-Hall, Englewood Cliffs, N. J.;

F. Mandl, *Quantum Mechanics*, Academic Press, New York, 1954.

The following books have been designed especially for application to chemistry:

L. Pauling and E. B. Wilson, *Introduction to Quantum Mechanics*, McGraw-Hill Book Co., New York, 1935;

H. Eyring, J. Walter, and G. E. Kimball, *Quantum Chemistry*, John Wiley, New York, 1944.

W. Kauzmann, *Quantum Chemistry*, Academic Press, New York, 1957.

A qualitative but extensive interpretation of properties of matter on the basis of atomic physics is given by

F. O. Rice and E. Teller, *The Structure of Matter*, John Wiley, New York, 1949.

This book has been written during the tenure by one of us of a Rockefeller Public Service Award at the University of Rome, Italy. Extensive preliminary work had been done in previous years. Many ideas date to our earlier association with the geneticists of the Carnegie Institution of Washington. The activity at the National Bureau of Standards has provided a continuous stimulus and an invaluable opportunity to develop ideas in the context of practical problems. Various lines of approach to quantum physics were tried out in courses at the National Bureau of Standards, at the George Washington and Georgetown Universities, and at the University of California (Berkeley), and were developed during extended visits at the University of Colorado Medical School and at the Institute of Theoretical Physics of the University of Copenhagen. We wish to thank all these Institutions and the numerous friends who contributed generously time and suggestions.

U. FANO
L. FANO

December, 1958

Contents

PART 2   Aggregates of particles

Appendices

PART 1

Basic facts and concepts

Initial evidence regarding atoms

The idea that matter is an aggregate of very small but stable units, called "atoms," remained a speculation until the fundamental laws of chemistry were discovered in the early 1800's. Chemical experimentation is macroscopic rather than atomistic in that it deals with amounts of matter whose structure appears continuous and homogeneous despite its particulate nature. The particulate nature of matter is not directly manifest as long as one observes effects due to the collective action of very large numbers of particles. Nevertheless, one can draw from chemical experimentation definite inferences concerning the existence, the classification, and many properties of atoms. Additional inferences about atoms have been drawn from macroscopic experimentation on the transport of electricity by matter. Different kinds of atoms were shown to contain a single kind of carrier of negative electricity with small mass, —the electrons, whereas positive electricity is associated with a heavy constituent characteristic for each kind of atoms. This chapter reviews briefly the main lines of evidence provided by macroscopic experimentation.

1.1 Evidence from Quantitative Chemical Analysis

Chemistry begins with the identification of "chemical substances" whose quantitative properties have fixed values under any given set of external conditions. For example, the density and the specific heat of distilled water are always the same at given temperature and pressure. Most chemical substances can be broken down into other substances, but this process of breakdown (chemical analysis) reaches an ultimate limit. Substances that cannot be further analyzed are called "chemical elements."

Different chemical elements combine to form innumerable "compound" substances according to definite rules. The first rule is called the *law of constant proportions:* "When chemical elements are brought together under favorable conditions to form a specific compound, the proportion in weight of the combining elements is always the same." When any compound is broken down into elements, the proportion in weight of the resulting elements is also the same. For instance, when hydrogen and oxygen combine to form water, 1 g of hydrogen combines with 8 g of oxygen; when water is decomposed, eight-ninths of its weight is oxygen, one-ninth hydrogen.

Experimenting with two elements, bringing them together under different conditions to form more than one compound, shows that their combinations obey the *law of multiple proportions:* "When two elements combine together in different ways to form more than one compound, the weights of one element which combine with a definite weight of the other always bear a simple ratio to one another," for example, 1 g of hydrogen combines with 8 g of oxygen to form water and with $16 = 2 \times 8$ g of oxygen to form hydrogen peroxide. A striking example is offered by the series of compounds of nitrogen and oxygen: 14 g of nitrogen can combine alternatively with amounts of oxygen weighing respectively 1×8, 2×8, 3×8, 4×8, or 5×8 g. The fact that the amounts of oxygen which combine with the same amounts of nitrogen bear such simple ratios to one another is *substantial evidence that oxygen consists of discrete particles or building blocks* 1, 2, 3, 4, or 5 of which can combine with the same quantity of nitrogen.

Because the examination of any amount of a chemical substance does not reveal in it the existence of discrete particles of its component elements, one concludes that such particles are small enough to escape direct observation. The experimental chemical evidence is then brought into order by assuming that each element consists of identical submicroscopical particles, called "atoms" from the Greek word for "indivisible."

The formation of a compound from two or more elements in *fixed weight proportions* is attributed to the formation of a large number of submicroscopical identical aggregates of atoms of the different elements. Each aggregate consists of a set of atoms in simple numerical proportions. Each aggregate is the smallest unit of the compound substance and is called a "molecule." A chemical reaction affecting a ponderable amount of matter results from the occurrence of identical transformations at the molecular level in which all atoms are regrouped into new identical sets.

Further evidence on the molecular structure of chemical substances derives from measuring the volume of gaseous substances which take part in chemical reactions. When two gaseous elements are brought together to form a compound, not only the weights of the substances entering into the reaction are governed by simple laws but also their volumes. Gay-Lussac formulated the law: "In every gas formed or decomposed, the volumes of the component and of the compound gases bear simple ratios to one another." [1] Thus, for instance, a volume V of oxygen combines with a double volume $2V$ of hydrogen to form a volume $2V$ of water vapor. The reduction in total volume from $3V$ to $2V$ resulting from the chemical combination corresponds to the aggregation of hydrogen and oxygen atoms into compound molecules of water.

The fact that the volumes of gases taking part in the reaction are in *simple* ratios indicates that the volume of a gas is related to the *number* of particles contained in it. This consideration led to *Avogadro's law:* "Equal volumes of different gases under the same conditions of temperature and pressure contain the same number of molecules."

The application of Avogadro's law to the formation of water vapor from hydrogen and oxygen shows that 2 molecules of hydrogen and 1 of oxygen are required per every 2 molecules of water which are formed. Since the amounts of hydrogen and oxygen involved are in a weight ratio of approximately 1 to 8, it follows that the molecules of hydrogen, oxygen, and water are in a weight ratio of 1:16:9. This and other methods serve to determine the relative weights of most kinds of molecules. Finally, since only 1 molecule of oxygen is required for the formation of every 2 molecules of water, each of which contains oxygen, it follows that an oxygen molecule must contain at least 2 oxygen atoms. Thus, the detailed study of weight and volume relationships of different gaseous atoms forming different compounds indicates the number of atoms entering into each molecule. Analogous studies for liquid and solid substances yield the usual chemical formulas.

---

[1] The law of Gay-Lussac and the subsequent law of Avogadro pertain to "perfect" gases; real gases behave approximately like perfect gases when they are sufficiently rarefied.

A table of relative weights of all kinds of known atoms and molecules can thus be prepared. The weight of the lightest kind of atom, namely hydrogen, was originally taken as the unit weight since the absolute weight of no atom or molecule was known. At a later time, it appeared that the weight of an oxygen atom was more useful as a standard of reference and this weight was taken to be exactly 16; the corresponding weight of a hydrogen atom is then 1.008. The relative weights of atoms and molecules determined in this way are called, respectively, "atomic" and "molecular" weights.

To determine the absolute weight of atoms one should know the actual number of atoms contained in a given amount of matter. However, this knowledge is not required for the study of most macroscopic phenomena, it being sufficient to know that one "mole" of any substance, namely, an amount weighing a number of grams equal to the molecular weight, contains a standard number N of molecules. Similarly, an amount of any element weighing a number of grams equal to its atomic weight contains N atoms. This number N is called "Avogadro's number" and may remain unspecified for many purposes. Avogadro's law is completed by the knowledge that one mole of any gas at 0°C and atmospheric pressure (760 mm mercury) has a volume of 2.242×10^4 cm^3.

The value of N may be determined by experimentation with certain macroscopic phenomena which depend on the size of the molecules. These methods are indirect and could not be utilized until a molecular theory of the phenomena had been developed. The first determination of N, due to Loschmidt, relied on the connection between the heat conduction, or the viscosity, of a gas and the rate at which molecules intermix. This rate depends in turn on the distance which a gas molecule travels before colliding with another molecule, and thereby depends on the size of individual molecules. The size of atoms turns out to be of the order of a few Angstrom (1 A $= 10^{-8}$ cm). The value of N is known today with an accuracy of better than 1 part in 10,000 and is 6.025×10^{23}. A determination of N by direct observation of an atomic effect will be described in the next chapter.

The volume of a given mass of liquid or solid material depends but little on external variables, such as pressure or temperature. This volume, divided by the number of atoms or molecules in the given mass, may then be regarded loosely as the volume occupied by a single atom or molecule. For example, 18 g of water constitute 1 mole and have a volume of 18 cm^3; to each water molecule corresponds then a volume of $18/6.025 \times 10^{23}$ cm$^3 = 3 \times 10^{-23}$ cm$^3 = 30$ A^3. One mole of iron weighs 56 g and occupies 7.2 cm^3, which yields a volume of 12 A^3 per atom.

1.2   Evidence from Electrolysis

Electricity can flow through aqueous solutions of acids, salts, or bases, interposed between two pieces of metal (electrodes) at different potential. Chemical substances, for example, hydrogen and oxygen, separate out of the solution at the surface of the electrodes. This phenomenon, called electrolysis, involves a transport of matter associated with the transport of electricity.

Faraday observed that the weights of substances separated and the quantity of electricity transported during their separation obey the following law: "The quantity of electricity is proportional to the weight of substance and independent of other factors; it is equal to a constant (Faraday's constant) $F = 9.652 \times 10^4$ coulombs,[2] or to a small multiple of it, per every mole of material separated." This result indicates that each *atom can carry only a fixed quantity of electricity*,

$$ e = \frac{F}{N} = 1.602 \times 10^{-19} \text{ coulombs} = 4.803 \times 10^{-10} \text{ esu}, \qquad (1) $$

or a small multiple thereof. This quantity of electricity can be of either sign.

Faraday's law may be formulated in terms of the ratio of the quantity of electricity Q transported through the solution to the weight M of a chemical element separated at one electrode. Since the weight in grams of a mole of atoms equals the atomic weight A of the element, Faraday's law reads

$$ \frac{Q}{M} = n\frac{F}{A} = n\frac{e}{m}\frac{\text{coulomb}}{\text{gram}}, \qquad (2) $$

where n is a small integer and m is the absolute weight of each atom. The ratio Q/M is called the specific charge carried by each atom.

Often there are separated at the electrodes not just atoms of one element but molecular groups of atoms, for example, sulfate groups. Faraday's law also holds in this case; only the atomic weight A must be replaced with the molecular weight of the group.

The number n in Eq. 2 equals the chemical valence of the atom or group of atoms in general; for example, it is 1 for hydrogen, 2 for sulfate, 3 for aluminum.

The atoms, or groups of atoms, that carry electricity to the electrodes are called "ions." An ion is represented by its chemical symbol with a

---

[2] The coulomb is the unit of quantity of electricity in the MKQS system, the esu in the CGS system; their ratio is 1 coulomb $= 2.9979 \times 10^9$ esu.

superscript consisting of a number of $+$ or $-$ signs equal to the number of units e of electricity which it carries. For example, the hydrogen ion is indicated by H^+, the oxygen ion by O^{--}, the sulfate ion by SO_4^{--}.

1.3 Transport of Electricity Through Gases

Gases have a very low electrical conductivity under ordinary conditions but, when a sufficiently high potential difference is applied between two electrodes separated by a gas or vapor at sufficiently low pressure, a luminous discharge takes place and electricity flows readily through the gas. Since these phenomena occur even in gases of high purity, it appears that electricity is carried by gas molecules turned into ions.

The low conductivity of ordinary gases indicates that a minimal fraction of all molecules carries any charge under ordinary conditions. When a low potential difference is applied between two electrodes in a gas, each of the few ions that are present migrates slowly to the electrode with opposite charge, its motion being hindered by innumerable collisions with gas molecules. When the potential difference is high, each ion is accelerated sharply. Moreover, when the gas pressure is low, the free acceleration between each two successive collisions lasts longer and the ions attain a high speed. The collisions are then violent and cause additional ionization, that is, separation of charges, in rough analogy to the separation of electric charges by the mechanical action of rubbing. Thus an intense flow of electricity results, under favorable conditions, through the snowballing production of new ions.

The carriers of electricity may be studied by piercing holes in the electrodes. Ions arriving at the electrodes are then carried by their inertia through the holes into a region where the gas pressure may be lowered and the ions may be subjected conveniently to analysis. A single hole, long and narrow, accepts only ions directed in a beam along its axis and makes it possible to evacuate the space beyond the electrode so that the beam travels on freely, undisturbed by collisions with gas molecules.

Experimentation with an arrangement of this kind, shown schematically in Fig. 1.1, reveals that electricity of different signs is transported in a gas discharge by quite different kinds of carrier.

Canal rays. Mass spectroscopy. Isotopes. In the conditions of Fig. 1.1, a luminous beam is observed to emerge from the canal in the negative electrode (cathode) but not from the positive one (anode). This beam is called "canal rays." It produces a glowing spot when it strikes a glass wall, provided the potential applied to the electrodes is sufficiently high.

The nature of canal rays is studied by subjecting them to electric and magnetic actions, passing the beam between the plates of a condenser or between the poles of a magnet.   As indicated in Fig. 1.1, the beam is deflected toward a negatively charged condenser plate.   This result confirms that the canal rays consist of positive charge carriers, presumably ions of the gas in the discharge tube, in agreement with the fact that they have been drawn through the negative electrode of the tube.   The beam is also deflected when passing through the poles of a magnet, in the same direction as a wire carrying a current parallel to the beam.

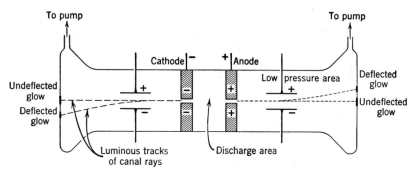

Fig. 1.1   Schematic setup for canal and cathode rays.   Canal rays are deflected toward the negative plate of a condenser, cathode rays toward the positive plate.

Any deflection of the beam is opposed by the inertia of its constituent particles.   Other conditions being equal, the deflection is inversely proportional to the mass of the charge-carrying particles and, of course, directly proportional to the electric charge of each particle.   Therefore, a measurement of the deflections, together with a knowledge of the electric and magnetic fields in the space traversed by the beam, serves to determine the charge-to-mass ratio, or specific charge, of the particles in the beam.   For particles of known velocity, measurement of the deflection in a single field, electric or magnetic, would suffice to determine the specific charge.   Concurrent measurement of both deflections gives the result irrespective of particle velocity.   A formula relating the specific charge to the deflections and to the fields is derived in Appendix I.

Each particle in a beam of canal rays is deflected by electric or magnetic fields according to its own specific charge.   A beam containing a mixture of particles with different specific charges can thus be resolved into homogeneous components, whereas specific charge measurements of ions by electrolysis, according to (2), yield only an average value, namely, the ratio of total charge to total mass.   Therefore, the determination of the specific charge of particles by electric and magnetic deflection constitutes an important analytic tool.   It is called "mass spectroscopy" because the charge of each particle may often be regarded as known, so that a measurement of specific charge amounts to an analysis and measurement of the mass of particles.[3]

The canal rays arising from a discharge in a gas consist of the various kinds of positive ions, atomic and molecular, that are generated in accordance with the chemical composition of the gas. For example, from a pure monoatomic gas, such as neon, one would expect only the ions Ne^+, Ne^{++}, Ne^{+++}, $\cdots$; since the atomic weight of neon, as determined by ordinary methods, is 20.2, the specific charge of these ions should be, according to (2), $9.652 \times 10^4/20.2$, $2 \times 9.652 \times 10^4/20.2$ $\cdots$ coulombs/gram, respectively. Experimental analysis of the canal rays from neon by mass spectroscopy fulfills this expectation only approximately. It reveals in fact a greater number of components than indicated above; namely, each of the beams expected with specific charge $n(9.652 \times 10^4/20.2)$ coulombs/gram is actually resolved into three components with somewhat different specific charges. Most kinds of positive ions, which are expected from chemical and electrochemical evidence to have a unique specific charge, turn out to be mixtures of components with different specific charges.

The different specific charges might reflect differences in charge, in mass, or in both of them. Differences in mass are more readily expected, since the masses of different atoms or ions bear no simple ratio to one another, but the charges of ions are otherwise known to be multiples of the elementary charge e. Assuming all charges to be multiples of e, neon atoms turn out to have atomic weight very close to one of the integers 20, 21, and 22. That is, the specific charges of all ions of neon are represented by the three formulas

$$n\frac{9.652 \times 10^4}{20.0}, \quad n\frac{9.652 \times 10^4}{21.0}, \quad n\frac{9.652 \times 10^4}{22.0} \text{ coulombs/gram.} \quad (3)$$

The mass analysis of ions from most chemical elements gives similar results.

It is concluded that the atomic weights determined by mass spectroscopy are the correct ones, whereas the values determined by ordinary chemical methods are generally averages taken over mixtures of atoms which have different masses but identical chemical properties. Atoms of the same chemical element with different masses are called "isotopes,"

---

[3] Mass spectroscopy techniques are very accurate. The main limitation to their absolute accuracy stems from uncertainty in magnetic field determination (nearly one part in 10,000). Relative measurements are accurate to the order of one part in 1,000,000.

from Greek words meaning "in the same place," because they belong in the same place in Mendeleev's periodic chart of chemical elements. The isotopes of each chemical element found in nature range in number from one to ten, and their atomic weights are represented to within ten percent by integers, called "mass numbers," each of which differs from the next one by one or two.[4]

Cathode rays. Electrons. As mentioned before, no luminous beam is observed to emerge from a canal in the positive electrode of a gas discharge tube, as would be expected if the discharge involved equally positive and negative ions. Nevertheless, the transport of electricity through the gas requires that some carriers of negative charge reach the positive electrode (anode). These carriers become manifest beyond the anode only when the gas pressure is very low, of the order of 10^{-6} atmospheres; a glow is then observed on a glass wall behind the anode. A small screen interposed between the anode and the wall casts a shadow on the glow, thus showing that the glow is due to a radiation which originates from the gas discharge and is stopped by the screen. The radiation imparts a momentum to the screen, as demonstrated by an experiment where the screen is an element of a light paddle wheel.

The radiation persists and is studied more conveniently when the gas pressure is reduced in the tube. The phenomenon changes character when the pressure decreases below 10^{-6} atmospheres. Provided the negative electrode (cathode) is heated or has a pointed shape, a glow persists behond the anode and electricity flows between the electrodes, although the gas discharge no longer manifests itself. The electricity appears to be carried by a radiation which originates from the cathode, is attracted toward the anode, and is carried on by inertia if it fails to be stopped by the anode itself. This radiation is called "cathode rays."

Analysis of cathode rays by mass spectroscopy confirms that they consist of carriers of negative electricity and shows their specific charge to be orders of magnitude higher than that of ions and *always* equal to

$$1.7589 \times 10^8 \text{ coulombs/gram.} \tag{4}$$

The simplest interpretation of this result, confirmed by all subsequent evidence, is that each cathode ray particle carries one unit e of negative charge of the magnitude given by (1). The mass of these particles is then obtained from their specific charge and is

$$m = 9.108 \times 10^{-28} \text{ grams.} \tag{5}$$

---

[4] It is now known that isotopes of an element contain different numbers of neutrons, particles of atomic weight close to one. The residual departures of atomic weights from multiples of a basic unit have also been accounted for.

To this value corresponds a very low atomic weight (mass in grams of one mole of particles), namely, 1/1822. Accordingly, cathode ray particles cannot be identified with ions of any chemical substance. On the contrary, cathode rays with identical properties are obtained from whatever materials have been utilized in their preparation. The cathode ray particles are called "electrons."

1.4   Conclusions.   Energy Scale of Atomic Phenomena

Whereas in electrolysis atoms and molecular groups of atoms carry units of electricity of either sign, in a gas discharge they are seen to carry only units of positive electricity, the negative electricity being transported by electrons. The low mass of electrons and the lack of specificity of their origin suggest that they are ordinary constituents of all kinds of atoms. These circumstances indicate that each kind of atom has a characteristic part carrying a positive electric charge which is ordinarily neutralized by a complement of electrons with negative charge. Loss of one or more electrons changes an atom into a positive ion, capture of one or more electrons changes it into a negative ion. Picturing positive ions as incomplete structures and negative ions as overloaded structures accounts for the fact that positive ions exist amongst the violent collisions of a gas discharge, whereas negative ions are not readily found there.

To remove an electron from an atom all the way to infinity, one must overcome the electric attraction of the positive ion that is left behind. It is of interest, for purpose of orientation, to evaluate the amount of energy required for this process. Suppose that one starts with the electron with a charge $e = 1.60 \times 10^{-19}$ coulombs at 2 A $= 2 \times 10^{-8}$ cm from the center of a positive ion. At this position the electric potential V is 7.20 volts [5] and, therefore, the potential energy of the negative electron is $-eV = -1.60 \times 10^{-19} \times 7.20 = -11.5 \times 10^{-19}$ joules. Work equal to this energy has to be performed to remove the electron.

It is also of interest to compare this energy with the energies involved in chemical reactions. If 11.5×10^{-19} joules were spent to remove one electron from each atom of one mole of a monoatomic substance, the total energy expenditure would be $NeV = 6.02 \times 10^{23} \times 11.5 \times$

---

[5] The volt is the unit of electric potential in the MKQS system; the unit of potential in the CGS system equals 300 volts. The calculation of atomic potentials is simplest in the CGS system, where $V = e/r$; with $e = 4.80 \times 10^{-10}$ esu and $r = 2 \times 10^{-8}$ cm, V equals 2.40×10^{-2} CGS units, that is, 7.20 volts. The joule is the unit of energy in the MKQS system and equals 1 coulomb $\times$ 1 volt; the CGS unit of energy is the erg, equal to 10^{-7} joule; the thermal unit of energy is the calorie, equal to 4.184 joules.

$10^{-19} = 6.92 \times 10^5$ joules $= 165$ kcal. This energy of 165 kcal/mole is of the order of magnitude of the energies released in the formation of chemical bonds. That is, the energies involved in the formation and in the transformations of molecules are comparable to the electric potential energy of electrons at the periphery of atoms.

The potential energy of an electron at a point where the electric potential is one volt is a convenient unit of energy for atomic physics. It is called the "electron volt," [6] indicated by ev, and amounts to

$$1 \text{ ev} = 1.60 \times 10^{-19} \text{ coulomb} \times 1 \text{ volt}$$

$$= 1.60 \times 10^{-19} \text{ joules} = 1.60 \times 10^{-12} \text{ ergs}$$

$$= 23 \text{ kcal/mole.} \tag{6}$$

In a beam of cathode rays generated with a potential difference of 10,000 volts between cathode and anode, each electron arrives at the anode with a kinetic energy of 10,000 ev $= 10$ kev.

PROBLEMS

1.1 How many atoms are there in 1 g of iron? (Atomic weight $A_{Fe} = 55.84$.)

1.2 Calculate the number of molecules per cm^2 if 1 g of water were spread uniformly over the earth's surface.

1.3 A layer of BF_3 gas contains 0.003 g per cm^2 of area. Calculate: (a) its thickness (assuming normal pressure and temperature); (b) the number of B and F atoms per cm^2 of the layer; (c) the number of electrons per cm^2.

---

[6] The term volt is often used colloquially, though incorrectly, instead of electron volt.

chapter 2

The detection
of atomic events

Atoms and events involving individual atomic particles are not usually accessible to direct observation because of their small size. However, since the beginning of this century, methods have been developed to detect the effects of individual atomic events.

It is helpful for this purpose that the concentration of electricity on electrons and ions—indicated by the specific charge (4) and (2) in Chapter 1—is enormous compared with the concentrations dealt with in macroscopic experiments of electrostatics. When a macroscopic body is charged, for example, with negative electricity, it acquires ordinarily a number of extra electrons that is but an infinitesimal fraction of the number of its atoms. That is, a very small percentage increase of the number of electrons yields a macroscopically measurable electrical effect. The addition or loss of a single electron may affect appreciably the electric force acting on a particle of matter large enough to be observed visually. Millikan observed such an effect and thereby measured the charge e of an electron.

The detection of atomic particles is also facilitated when each particle carries a large amount of energy. Particles with kinetic energies of the order of one million electron volts (Mev) first became available through the discovery of natural *radioactivity*, that is, of the spontaneous emission of penetrating radiations by certain heavy elements. Procedures of mass spectroscopy show that the α rays from radioactive substances consist of He^{++} ions (α particles) and the β rays of electrons. (There are also high-frequency electromagnetic radiations called γ rays.) Compared with the beams of canal and cathode rays of the early 1900's, beams of α and β rays contain few particles with high energy per particle, which made it possible to detect visually the arrival of individual particles on a luminescent screen. Individual fast charged particles can also be detected through the ionization which they produce by collisions with the molecules of a gas.

The detection of single atomic events permitted a direct confirmation of inferences about atoms and atomic particles that had been derived from macroscopic experiments. The Millikan experiment is described briefly below as an example of direct measurement of atomic properties. More important, however, were experiments providing entirely new evidence. Typical among these were experiments in which one observes the effect of single collisions between incident particles and atoms of a test material. Such experiments utilize techniques, surveyed in Sect. 2.2, for detecting the passage or the arrival of atomic particles. The experiments also involve tests to ensure that the observed phenomena are in fact due to single collisions (Sect. 2.3).

2.1   Millikan's Oil Drop Experiment

Millikan gave the first direct demonstration of the existence of an elementary unit of charge and at the same time the first direct measurement of this charge.

A fine spray of microscopic oil droplets is introduced between the plates of a condenser (Fig. 2.1), where the motion of a single droplet may be followed through a microscope. The system is thermostated to eliminate convection currents. In the absence of disturbing effects, a falling droplet quickly attains a uniform velocity, which is limited by the viscosity of air and obeys a law given by Stokes.

Most droplets acquire an electric charge through friction in the process of spraying or through other causes. By applying an electric field between the plates of the condenser the fall of any one droplet can be altered, stopped or reversed. By comparing the motion of a droplet with and without a known electric field the charge of the droplet can be determined. When a droplet is held at rest, the electric force balances exactly the weight of the droplet suspended in air.[1]   The electric force equals the known field strength (potential of the condenser divided by its plate spacing) times the electric charge of the droplet which is to be measured.   The weight of each droplet is not known directly because its size is too small to be measured visually.   The size and weight are therefore determined by a separate measurement of the limiting velocity of fall with the electric field switched off and by application of the Stokes law.   The accuracy of the whole procedure is limited to the order of one percent by the accuracy with which the viscosity of air is known.

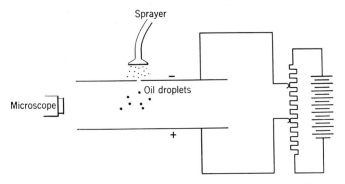

Fig. 2.1   Millikan's method for measuring the elementary charge.

The charge of each droplet, measured in this manner, is observed to vary abruptly from time to time, especially when the air is slightly ionized, for instance, by irradiation.   For each droplet and at each time the charge is always found to be a small multiple of an elementary charge $e = 1.60 \times 10^{-19}$ coulomb, of either sign.   This is the unit charge (1) of Chapter 1, which is carried by an electron or by a monovalent ion.   This experiment, taken together with the determination of Faraday's constant F by electrolysis, constitutes a direct determination of Avogadro's number $N = F/e$.

2.2   Methods of Detection of Charged Particles

Charged particles, electrons or ions, are detected primarily through the light, the ionizing action or the photographic action which they produce while traversing suitable materials.   Certain luminescent materials transform into light a substantial fraction of the kinetic energy

---

[1] The droplet acts somewhat as the needle of an extremely sensitive electrometer. The sensitivity relates to the minimal capacity of the droplet, of the order of 10^{-17} to 10^{-16} farad.

of an incident charged particle; this fraction may be so constant that the amount of light emitted serves as a measure of the particle energy. Scintillations produced by the arrival of individual particles on a screen

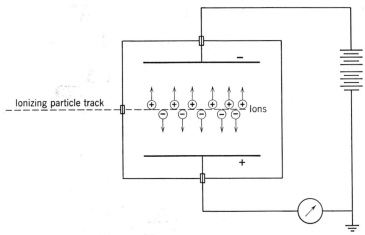

Fig. 2.2   Ionization chamber.

were observed visually for many years. In recent years, scintillations are detected, measured, and recorded by electronic devices. Particles which do not have sufficient energy to produce a detectable scintillation may be first accelerated by attraction toward a grid at a suitable potential. The arrival of successive particles on a detector may be distinguished, of course, only if the process of detection and recording is

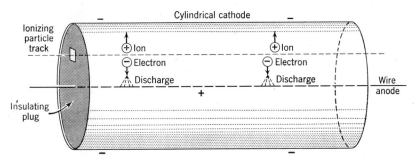

Fig. 2.3   Schematic proportional counter. The discharge is due to the strong field in the proximity of the wire anode.

sufficiently fast as compared to the rate of arrivals. Modern electronic techniques "resolve" arrivals separated by intervals of the order of 10^{-9} sec.

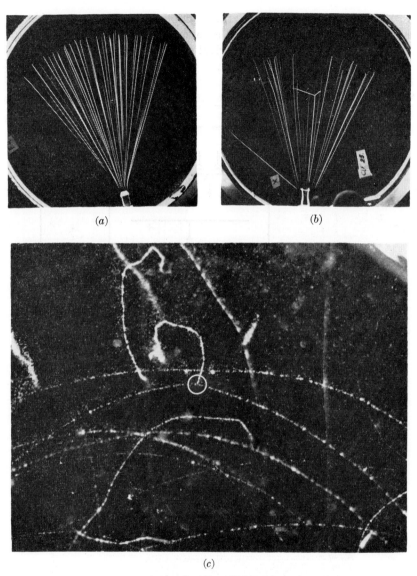

(a)   (b)

(c)

Fig. 2.4 Examples of cloud chamber pictures.

(a) α rays in hydrogen.

(b) α rays in fluorine showing a sharp deflection and recoil of a fluorine atom.

(c) β-ray track which forks where an atomic electron has recoiled with high energy.

(d) β-ray tracks resolved into separate droplets.

(a) and (b) Courtesy J. K. Bøggild, from *Atlas of Typical Expansion Chamber Photographs*, Pergamon Press, London, 1954. (c) Courtesy H. Maier-Leibniz, Technische Hochschule, München. (d) Courtesy E. V. Hayward, University of California.

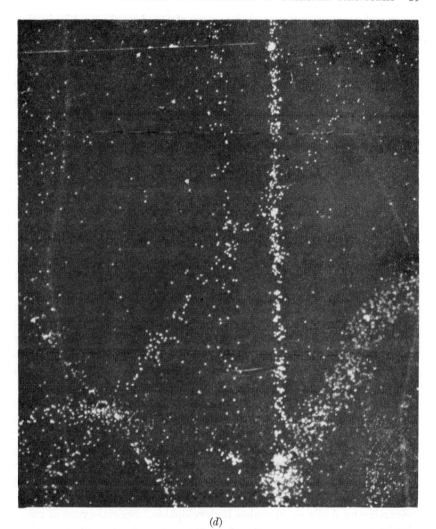

(d)

Fig. 2.4   (*Continued*)

Ionization, that is, production of ions, takes place along the track of a charged particle through a gas, provided the particle has sufficient energy. (This is the effect which starts a discharge in a gas.) Electrons are knocked off gas molecules by the impact of a charged particle; gas molecules are thereby changed into positive ions and the ejected electrons attach themselves to other molecules, changing them into negative ions, unless they are attracted first to a positive electrode. The ionization due to the passage of a single particle can be detected electrically by attracting the charges of opposite sign to two electrodes. In an "ionization chamber" (Fig. 2.2), one merely observes the potential change on the electrodes which results from the deposition of the bunch of electric charges generated by the passage of a single charged particle. For example, if an α particle generates 100,000 ions of either sign, which are collected on electrodes with a capacity of 10^{-11} farad, the potential change of these electrodes amounts to 1.60 millivolts.

In other instruments, the ionization is amplified in the gas itself, before the charge is deposited on the electrodes; the anode is made of thin wire so that the electrons are sharply accelerated when they approach it and start a secondary discharge. When this discharge remains limited to the vicinity of its starting point, the device is called a "proportional counter" (Fig. 2.3). When the discharge spreads to the whole space between the electrodes, the device is called a "Geiger counter." Geiger counters are characterized by a high potential applied to their electrodes, nearly sufficient to produce a spontaneous discharge; therefore, the discharge is readily triggered, even by a single ionization produced by an incident particle.

The ionization trail of a charged particle may be made visible by the "cloud chamber" method, originally developed by C. T. R. Wilson about 1911. In a gas supersaturated with a vapor, each ion acts as the center of condensation of a droplet. The passage of a particle through a chamber with the proper conditions of supersaturation leaves, therefore, a trail of droplets forming a visible cloud (Fig. 2.4).

The cloud chamber technique has the advantage of providing a pictorial record of events. It shows not only the rate of ionizations and the occurrence of deflections but also secondary effects of collisions with gas atoms when the atoms or some of their electrons recoil fast enough to form side tracks (Fig. 2.4b and c). These advantages are shared by the emulsion technique, which relies on the photographic action of fast charged particles, analogous to their ionizing action in gases. A particle traversing an AgBr grain makes it developable. Special types of emulsion have been prepared in recent years which, upon development, show tracks of fast charged particles as trails of darkened grains (Fig. 2.5). The developed emulsion must be examined under a microscope because the very high density of the materials in the emulsion, as compared with cloud chamber gases, makes the particles' tracks much shorter. (For example, an α particle track is several centimeters long in a cloud chamber at atmospheric pressure, but only of the order of 10^{-3} cm in an emulsion.)

Still another technique has been developed for the observation of very high-energy particles whose trails extend over centimeters of a liquid.   Under suitable conditions the ions produced by a particle in a liquid act as centers of formation of bubbles much like ions in the gas of a cloud chamber lead to formation of droplets.   The "bubble chamber"

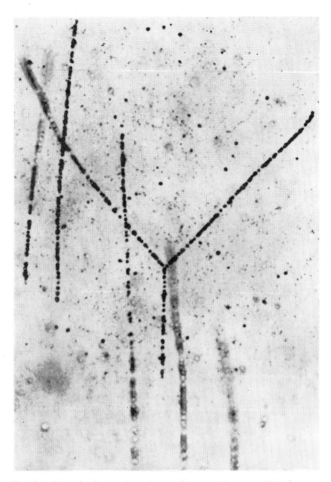

Fig. 2.5 Tracks of fast hydrogen ions in emulsion.   One ion collides with a hydrogen atom in the emulsion and knocks it off sharing its energy with it in nearly equal parts.   (Courtesy C. F. Powell, from Powell and Occhialini, *Nuclear Physics in Photographs*, Clarendon Press, Oxford, 1947.)

technique, based on this principle, provides pictorial records of events quite analogous to those obtained from cloud chambers or emulsions but extending over much larger masses of matter.

2.3   Elementary Collision Processes and Their Quantitative Observation

The study of particle tracks, by the methods indicated above, gives evidence on the interactions between a particle and the material which it traverses. Many properties of particle tracks result from a multitude of collisions between a particle and different atoms or molecules. Among these properties are, for example: the total amount of ionization produced by an α particle in the gas of an ionization chamber; the total length of a particle track which depends on the initial energy of the particle and on its average rate of energy dissipation through successive collisions; the progressive curvature of tracks, which also results from successive collisions. On the other hand, there are events occurring infrequently along tracks, such as occasional sharp deflections or even forks (see Fig. 2.4b and c), which appear to originate from collisions with single atoms or molecules of the material. These events are called "elementary processes" and provide direct evidence regarding the properties of atoms and atomic particles. Multiple processes also provide such evidence, but only through elaborate theoretical analysis.

Elementary processes must occur with a frequency proportional to the number of encounters between a particle and the atoms in the material. To test whether a certain process is elementary one must verify: (a) that it occurs with a uniform frequency along the track, as long as the properties of the particle and of the material remain constant; and (b) that its frequency per unit track length is proportional to the density of the material traversed, again as long as the relevant properties of the material are independent of its density. A progressive reduction of the density of a material draws successive elementary processes farther and farther apart along the track; therefore, multiple processes such as the slowing down of β particles can be resolved into elementary processes of energy loss in a gas at low pressure (see Fig. 2.4d).

Since the frequency of an elementary process in a given length of track is proportional to this length and to the density of the material, the significant quantity to be derived from the observation of elementary processes is their frequency per unit track length per unit density of the material. This quantity relates immediately to collisions with individual atoms (or molecules) when the density is expressed as the number of atoms (or molecules) per unit volume of the material. For example, we shall discuss in the next chapter sharp deflections of α-particle tracks which are observed occasionally in cloud chambers (Fig. 2.4b). These deflections are studied quantitatively with the arrangement shown schematically in Fig. 2.6 and are verified to be elementary processes. One measures first the number n_0 of α particles received per unit time by the detector when placed so as to intercept the whole incident beam. Then one inserts in the beam a thin metal foil and one measures the number n of particles received per unit time when the detector is placed so as to intercept particles deflected in a certain direction. The frequency of the elementary processes which are scored is n/n_0, and is proportional to the thickness t of the foil and to its density d. The ratio

$$S = \frac{n/n_0}{td} \tag{1}$$

is independent of the foil thickness and density. When d is expressed as number of atoms per unit volume, S represents the frequency of deflection toward the detector by collision with a single atom. Throughout atomic and nuclear physics one utilizes particle detectors to study elementary processes resulting from collisions with single atoms (or molecules) and one expresses the quantitative results by Eq. 1.

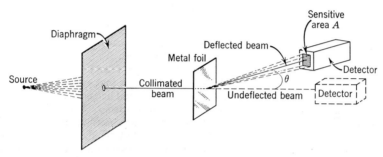

Fig. 2.6 Observation of particles which have undergone large-angle deflection. After insertion of the metal foil, the detector has been rotated by an angle θ in the plane perpendicular to the paper.

The significance of the frequency S is visualized by the following geometrical model. If, in a layer of material of thickness t and density d (atoms per unit volume), each atom carried a target of area S, the aggregate area of all targets would constitute a fraction Sdt of the area of the layer. Provided this fraction is much smaller than one, that is, provided the layer is so thin that no target is screened by another one, the frequency n of hits on the targets by a beam of n_0 particles would be just n_0Sdt, that is, it would equal the frequency of the observed atomic events. For this reason one talks of the frequency of collision processes *as though* it were the frequency of hitting targets of area S. This figure of speech has proved convenient and S, as defined by (1), is called the "effective target area" or, more commonly, the "effective cross section" of an atom for occurrence of the elementary process that is being considered.

In the experiment of Fig. 2.6 and in many others, the observation of a collision process involves the detection of particles traveling in certain directions from the point of collision. The frequency of detection S depends, then, on the sensitive area A of the detector and on its distance r from the point of collision, which are incidental characteristics of the detector. More specifically, S is proportional to the solid angle $\Omega = A/r^2$ subtended by the sensitive area of the detector, provided this angle is sufficiently small. The ratio

$$\sigma = \frac{S}{\Omega} = \frac{n}{n_0} \frac{r^2}{tdA} \tag{2}$$

is the parameter of greatest intrinsic significance to be derived from the experimental data. This ratio represents the frequency—per unit track of the incident particle and per unit density of the material (one atom per unit volume)—of elementary processes from which a particle emerges traveling within a unit solid angle about a given direction. The frequency σ is called the "effective cross section per unit solid angle" or also, briefly, the "differential cross section" of the collision process under consideration. It depends, of course, on such variables as the angle between the directions of observation and of incidence, or the energy of the incident particles, but it is independent of n_0, t, d, A, and r, because any change of these variables is compensated by a change of the observed frequency n.

PROBLEMS

2.1 The α particles of a very thin source of polonium produce 1.2 scintillations per second per cm^2 of a screen at 1 m from the source in an evacuated vessel. Calculate the number of particles emitted per second by the source.

2.2 Calculate the current carried to the electrodes of a large ionization chamber when the source of Problem 2.1 is placed in it. Consider that each α particle dissipates an energy of 5.2×10^6 ev and that one positive and one negative ion are produced, on the average, per every 34 ev of energy dissipation.

2.3 In a hydrogen bubble chamber traversed by high energy particles (π^- mesons), 60 events were scored in which a track stopped abruptly and a pair of separate V-shaped tracks (due to Λ^0 and θ^0 disintegrations) appeared as secondary effects. The track length observed was 21,000 meters. Calculate the cross section for the production of these events in the collision of the track particles with H atoms. (The hydrogen density in the chamber was 0.057 g/cm^3.)

2.4 A neutron beam from a nuclear reactor experiences a 2 percent loss of intensity when it traverses the BF$_3$ layer of Problem 1.3, which contains 2.7×10^{19} molecules/cm^2. This loss increases to 5 percent when the concentration of the boron isotope of atomic weight 10 in the BF$_3$ is enriched from its normal proportion of 18 percent to 45 percent. Show that the neutron loss is due almost entirely to the isotope B^{10} and calculate the cross section of its collision with neutrons.

chapter 3

The structure of atoms discovered by Rutherford

About 1910, Rutherford discovered the main features of atomic structure by studying the passage of α particles through matter. The high energy of α particles enables them to penetrate through very numerous layers of atoms and thus to serve as sharp probes of atomic structure. Rutherford studied the sharp deflections experienced occasionally by α particles traversing atoms. He accounted for these deflections in great detail by assuming that the mass and the positive electric charge within each atom are highly concentrated within a "nucleus" over 10,000 times smaller in diameter than a whole atom. The positive charge of the nucleus is a characteristic of the atoms of each element; it equals the elementary charge e multiplied by the "atomic number" of the atom, which is its number in the sequence of chemical elements in Mendeleev's periodic system. Rutherford's results and conclusions were confirmed by all subsequent evidence.

The mass and positive charge in an atom being so concentrated, the bulk of an atom's volume, which we will call its "body," must consist of its light weight, negatively charged fraction, namely, of electrons. In order that the negative charge of the electrons balance the positive charge of the nucleus, the body of a neutral atom with atomic number Z must consist of Z electrons. Thus the body of electrons which a nucleus draws around itself depends on the charge rather than on the mass of the nucleus.

The chemical behavior of atoms, that is, their aptitude to become attached to or separated from other atoms, may be expected to be a property of the outer portion of the body. This accounts for the existence of isotopes, species of atoms with different mass but almost identical chemical properties. In general, most physicochemical properties of each kind of atoms, including their size and stability, should be accounted for as properties of its body of electrons. A preliminary discussion of the structural stability of the body will be given at the end of this chapter.

3.1 Qualitative Analysis of α-Particle Scattering

Cloud chamber pictures of α-particle tracks, such as those of Fig. 2.4, show that these particles traverse a few centimeters of gas at ordinary pressure before the end of their track. Given the gas density and the size of molecules, one estimates that an α particle collides with molecules roughly 100,000 times before the end of its track. The pictures show that hardly any of these collisions results in appreciable deflection of the α particle.

Substantial deflections should result normally from collisions between bodies of comparable mass, such as an α particle (He^{++} ion) and a gas molecule, if these bodies are impenetrable to one another. It follows that the α particles penetrate through most of the molecules with which they collide. The collisions without deflections lead, however, to the ionization shown in the cloud chamber pictures. The initial kinetic energy of α particles is dissipated progressively in the course of the collisions, as shown by the increasing deflection of tracks in a magnetic field.

A few sharp deflections are noticed here and there along α-particle tracks. An experimental arrangement of the type indicated in Fig. 2.6 showed to Rutherford and his co-workers that when an α-particle beam traverses a thin metal foil, a small fraction of it is sprayed ("scattered") all around, even in backward directions. This "large-angle scattering" must be due to elementary collision processes because its frequency meets the criteria given in Sect. 2.3.

Rutherford considered what in the atoms could be responsible for the large-angle scattering. Firstly, atomic electrons cannot deflect an α particle sharply because of their small mass.[1] Therefore, the large-angle scattering must result from interaction between the α particle and the heavy, positively charged portion of atoms.

The scarcity of sharp deflections indicated to Rutherford that the heavy, positively charged portions of the α particles and of atoms merely pass by each other without much mutual disturbance in the great majority of collisions. Therefore, these heavy portions should be small. On the other hand, positive charges that are highly concentrated repel each other very strongly when they happen to approach closely. The electric repulsion may then suffice alone to cause sharp deflections despite the high kinetic energy of the α particles.

Rutherford followed up in detail the consequences of this hypothesis. He calculated the probability of large-angle scattering as a function of the α-particle energy and of the scattering angle.[3] Experimental determinations of this functional dependence agreed outstandingly with the results of the calculation and thus gave evidence that the positive charges and the masses of atoms are concentrated in very small nuclei.

3.2 Calculation of the Scattering Probability

The motion of an α particle traversing an atom was treated by Rutherford according to ordinary mechanics. He regarded the α particle as a pointlike body with the mass of a He^{++} ion, and assumed the positive charge and mass of the scattering atom to be concentrated in a pointlike nucleus. The positive charges of the α particle and of the nucleus may be expressed in terms of the elementary charge e and indicated by ze and Ze, respectively; the values of z and Z need not be specified initially. The motion of the α particle is then affected only by the electrostatic repulsion exerted on it by the nucleus.[2]

The force between an α particle and the nucleus influences their motion with respect to one another. Its effect is conveniently calculated in a frame of reference attached to the center of mass of the two bodies. If the atomic nucleus is much heavier than the α particle (an atom of Au is 50 times heavier than a He^{++} ion), the center of mass coincides approximately with the position of the nucleus; one may then calculate approximately as though the nucleus were at a fixed position and only

---

[1] In a collision between bodies with masses M and m, with $M \gg m$ and the light body initially at rest, conservation of momentum and energy requires that the fractional change $\Delta P/P$ of the momentum of the heavy body cannot exceed the order of magnitude of m/M, which is about $1/7300$ for an α particle and an electron.

[2] The attraction exerted by the atomic electrons on the α particle counteracts the nuclear repulsion and is called "screening effect." It may, however, be disregarded in a calculation of large-angle scattering.

the α particle moved, whereas in practice the nucleus recoils.   Here we shall regard the nucleus as fixed, but Appendix II shows that the exact calculation differs only by a minor adjustment.

The repulsion by the nucleus forces the α particle to follow a path of the type indicated in Fig. 3.1.   The Coulomb law of force between electric charges (whether attraction or repulsion) has the same analytical form as the law of gravitational attraction.   In either case of repulsion

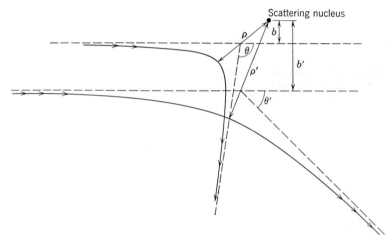

Fig 3.1   Scattering of α particles by a nucleus.   The track with small impact parameter b is deflected by the large angle θ, the track with impact parameter b' by the angle θ'.   The distances of closest approach of the α particles to the nucleus are ρ and ρ'; $\rho = b \left(\mathrm{tg}\tfrac{1}{2}\theta + \dfrac{1}{\cos\frac{1}{2}\theta} \right)$.   Approximate scale $b = 1.8 \times 10^{-12}\mathrm{cm}$ for a 4 Mev α particle scattered by a gold nucleus.

or attraction, the incident particle follows a Kepler orbit which is a hyperbola.   The parameters of the orbit, and in particular the total deflection θ experienced by the α particle, depend on the magnitudes of the charges ze and Ze, on the mass m and velocity v of the α particle, and on the distance b shown in Fig. 3.1 and called "impact parameter."   This is the distance of the initial line of flight of the α particle from the atomic nucleus.   The smaller b is, the larger becomes the repulsion and the larger the deflection.   In the event of a head-on collision ($b = 0$) the α particle continues in a straight line until its kinetic energy is spent and the repulsion forces it back in the direction from where it came ($\theta = 180°$).   Appendix III shows that the deflection is related to the impact parameter by

$$\mathrm{tg}\tfrac{1}{2}\theta = \frac{zZe^2}{mv^2b}. \tag{1}$$

For α particles of given velocity colliding with atoms of a given kind, the deflection depends only on the impact parameter.

All particles whose initial line of flight was aimed so as to pass within a distance b from a nucleus are deflected by an angle larger than θ, where θ is related to b by (1). Therefore, a circle of radius b and area πb^2 around a nucleus constitutes an aiming target for collision processes with deflection larger than θ. In Sect. 2.3 the observed frequency of any elementary collision process was represented as an "effective target area" or "cross section," as though there were a corresponding aiming target attached to each atom. Rutherford's calculation associates with deflection toward a given detector an actual target of definite size and shape. The calculation and the underlying hypotheses are to be tested by comparing the calculated size of targets with the magnitude of the effective cross sections derived from the observed frequency of deflections.

The comparison is performed conveniently for the differential cross section (2), Chapter 2, pertaining to scattering per unit solid angle about a direction of given obliquity θ. Deflection angles comprised between θ and $\theta + \Delta\theta$ correspond to impact parameters between b and $b - \Delta b$, where

$$b = \frac{zZe^2}{mv^2}\ \frac{1}{\mathrm{tg}\frac{1}{2}\theta} \qquad (2)$$

according to (1), and $b - \Delta b$ is similarly related to $\theta + \Delta\theta$. A direct relationship between Δb and $\Delta\theta$ follows from (2) by differentiation and is

$$\Delta b = \frac{zZe^2}{mv^2}\ \frac{1}{\sin^2\frac{1}{2}\theta}\ \frac{1}{2}\Delta\theta. \qquad (3)$$

The impact parameters between b and $b - \Delta b$ cover a ring-shaped target of area $S = 2\pi b\ \Delta b$. The directions with obliquity between θ and $\theta + \Delta\theta$ cover a ring-shaped conical region of solid angle $\Omega = 2\pi \sin\theta\ \Delta\theta$ (see Fig. 3.2). The differential cross section is therefore

$$\sigma = \frac{S}{\Omega} = \frac{2\pi b\ \Delta b}{2\pi\ \sin\theta\ \Delta\theta} = \frac{b\ \Delta b}{\sin\theta\ \Delta\theta} \qquad (4)$$

Fig. 3.2 Area $A = 2\pi r \sin\theta\ r\ \Delta\theta$ of a ring-shaped detector which intercepts, at a distance r from the point of scattering, all particles deflected by angles between θ and $\theta + \Delta\theta$. The detector covers a solid angle $\Omega = A/r^2 = 2\pi \sin\theta\ \Delta\theta$.

This cross section is expressed in terms of ze, Ze, m, v, and θ by expressing b and Δb according to (2) and (3); it is also convenient to express $\sin\theta$ as $2 \sin\frac{1}{2}\theta \cos\frac{1}{2}\theta$.

The final formula by Rutherford gives the number n of α particles received by a detector at obliquity θ divided by: (a) the number n_0 of particles incident on a metal foil; (b) the thickness of the foil; (c) the density d of the foil expressed in atoms per unit volume; and (d) the solid angle Ω subtended by the detector:

$$\sigma = \frac{n}{n_0 t d\Omega} = \left(\frac{zZe^2}{2mv^2}\right)^2 \frac{1}{\sin^4 \frac{1}{2}\theta}. \tag{5}$$

3.3 Comparison with Experimental Results

The number of scattered particles as given by (5) is a sensitive function of the α-particle velocity and of the scattering angle, since it depends on v^4 and $\sin^4 \frac{1}{2}\theta$. Geiger and Marsden performed experimental

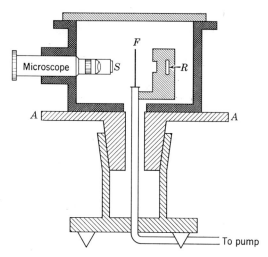

Fig. 3.3 Apparatus for the study of α-particle scattering, after Rutherford's drawing. The luminescent screen S and the microscope turn with the platform A around the source of particles R and the scattering foil F.

measurements of the number of scattered particles for large-angle scattering with the arrangement of Fig. 2.6, shown in better detail in Fig. 3.3. Thereby they subjected the Rutherford formula to tests extending over a wide range of values of expression (5). The tests showed remarkable agreement with the theoretical formula and thus gave strong support to Rutherford's theory of large-angle scattering and to the underlying assumption of the nuclear structure of atoms.

For given values of v and θ, and considering that m and e are known, an experimental determination of σ yields then a value of the product zZ, which was initially unknown. Experiments with foils of different elements show that the values of zZ increase smoothly as one progresses from element to element along the periodic system of chemistry. Moreover, these values coincide, to within the experimental uncertainty, with the product of the atomic numbers of helium and of the foil element. The values z and Z are therefore taken to represent, respectively, the *atomic numbers* of these two elements. Since helium has atomic number 2, an ion He^{++} is completely stripped of electrons, that is, α particles are *bare nuclei* of helium.

The number of observed particles scattered by small angles θ may fall below the value predicted by (5) owing to the screening effect of the attraction exerted by the atomic electrons on each α particle. Departures are also observed for very large deflections when the impact parameter (2) drops below 10^{-12} cm. These departures are attributed to non-electric forces between the α particle and the nucleus of an atom, which become appreciable for sufficiently close approach of the two particles. A different type of departure from Rutherford's result, which occurs only in the scattering of α particles by helium atoms, will be described in Chapter 17.

3.4   The Structural Stability of Atoms

The electrons which constitute the body of an atom are subject to electric attraction by the nucleus, which thereby tends to contract the volume of the atom. Each kind of atom maintains, nevertheless, a rather well-defined volume, which shrinks hardly at all even under the influence of strong pressures. These facts suggest that the body of an atom has a tendency to expand and that its volume adjusts itself so that the tendency to expand balances the inward pull exerted by the nucleus. External pressures would then cause only small readjustments of this balance.[3]

This surmise is confirmed by data on the size of "isoelectronic sequences" of ions, that is, of sequences of ions of different elements but with equal numbers of electrons. (For example, F^-, Na^+, Mg^{++}, Al^{+++} constitute a sequence of ions with ten electrons.) These data are derived from the density and structure of crystals containing ions, and show that, as the nuclear charge increases from one ion to the next of the sequence, the size of the "body" shrinks. The radii of F^-, Na^+, Mg^{++} and Al^{+++} are, respectively, 1.36, 0.95, 0.65, and 0.50 A. On the other hand, in the sequence of neutral atoms along the periodic sys-

---

[3] Pressures available in the laboratory are small as compared to the pull of nuclear attraction. For example, a pressure of 1000 kg/cm^2 performs work equal to 10^9 ergs per cm^3 of contraction of a material. Translated in atomic units, 10^9 ergs/cm^3 equals 6×10^{-4} ev/A^3. The data in Sect. 1.4 show that the nuclear attraction performs work at a rate of at least 10 ev per A^3 of contraction of the atomic volume.

tem, the nuclear attraction increases but the number of electrons also increases, and the atomic volume shows no strong trend of uniform increase or decrease.

Notice that atoms of hydrogen, which have the atomic number $Z = 1$ and hence a single electron, have the same qualitative properties as other atoms. Hence the expansive tendency of the "body" of electrons does not appear to result from interactions among different electrons but to be a property of even a single electron. The evidence considered thus far does not suffice to define this property more precisely or to relate it to other, more general phenomena. This will be done progressively in the following chapters.

Following Rutherford's success in calculating the α-particle scattering by treating particles as pointlike bodies according to the ordinary methods of mechanics, it was a natural step to calculate the motion of electrons by a similar treatment. According to this point of view, an electron could move around a nucleus, under the influence of its electric attraction, on a stable circular or elliptical orbit. The centrifugal force of the motion on such an orbit would exactly balance the attraction and prevent the electron from "falling" onto the nucleus, just as it prevents planets from falling onto the sun. This treatment of the mechanics of atomic electrons is called the "planetary model" of atomic structure.

The planetary model fails, however, in that it provides no reason why the radii of the orbits should be of any particular order of magnitude, or why all atoms of the same element should have the same size. Moreover, the stability of orbits in the planetary model is deceptive, in that the model presupposes the absence of any substantial interaction with other physical systems. In fact, the solar system itself would collapse with a release of energy if the planets were pushed in by an external pressure. Still further, the motion of an electron around the nucleus constitutes a high-frequency variable current which should act as an antenna and radiate energy away; this energy dissipation should lead by itself to rapid collapse of the electron onto the nucleus. Finally, atoms would be flat according to the planetary model, at least in the case of hydrogen, contrary to evidence.

The concepts and laws derived from macroscopic experiments thus appear inadequate to account for the properties of atoms, particularly for their stability. Bohr realized this failure very soon after Rutherford's discovery. In time, the interpretation of new experiments revealed physical relationships which are not brought out by macroscopic investigations. New concepts and laws were then formulated which account for atomic as well as for macroscopic phenomena.

PROBLEMS

3.1   A beam of α particles of 5 Mev kinetic energy traverses a gold foil; 1 particle in 800,000 is scattered so as to hit a surface of 0.5 cm^2 at 10 cm from the point of traversal of the foil and in a direction at 60° from the beam axis.   Calculate: (*a*) the foil thickness t; (*b*) the distance ρ of closest approach to a nucleus by the particles which hit the detector's surface; (*c*) the change in the number of particles hitting the detector, when the gold foil is replaced with a silver foil with an equal number of atoms per unit area.

chapter 4

Energy levels
of atoms and radiation

As we have seen, bombardment of matter with high energy α particles serves to probe into the innermost structure of atoms. Bombardment with particles of low energy, particularly electrons, serves to study the properties of the outer layers of atoms. Observations on the emission and absorption of light [1] by single atoms or atomic particles contribute much to the same study.

Bombardment of atoms with low energy electrons shows that atoms do not absorb just any small amount of energy. Each atom has a sequence of metastable ("stationary") states with energies at various levels, of the order of 1 to 10 ev above that of the ordinary state; an atom can absorb only the energy required to raise it to one of these levels or to break it up into an ion and a free electron.

In energy exchanges between atomic systems and light, or other electromagnetic radiation, the amount of energy exchanged is strictly

---

[1] "Light" is intended here to include infrared and ultraviolet as well as visible light. Radio waves (including microwaves) and X rays are included with light in the broader term "electromagnetic radiation."

related to the radiation frequency. Radiation of frequency ν gives to atoms, or takes from atoms, in each elementary process only a definite amount of energy E, equal to ν multiplied by a constant h called Planck's constant, $E = h\nu$.[2,3] The discontinuity of energy exchanges shows that the energy transported by radiation of given frequency has itself a discrete set of energy levels.

The discontinuities in the energy levels of atoms and radiation escape detection in macroscopic experiments where one observes only the aggregate amount of energy transferred in a multitude of atomic processes. These discontinuities, and in general the novel characteristics of atomic phenomena, are called "quantum effects." "Quantum physics" is the study of phenomena where quantum effects are apparent; "macroscopic" or "classical" physics is the study of phenomena where quantum effects fail to stand out. Concurrent study of the quantum properties of matter and radiation helps toward their over-all understanding.

Free atoms absorb or emit radiation as they pass from one to another stationary state, the energy difference between the two states being related to the radiation frequency by $E = h\nu$. In these processes, atoms act as radio antennas carrying oscillating currents of frequency ν. The spectral analysis—analysis into components of different frequencies —of the radiation emitted or absorbed can be performed with high accuracy and provides a wealth of information about the stationary states of atoms.

The following sections outline the experiments which show the existence of energy levels and their properties. The connection between the quantum properties of radiation and its macroscopic properties will be discussed in the next chapter.

A final section of this chapter describes the set of energy levels of the hydrogen atom and of ions with a single electron. The qualitative interpretation and quantitative calculation of these levels constitute a main problem of atomic theory. In 1913, Bohr succeeded first in calculating the levels by complementing the planetary model with suitable postulates; a satisfactory solution of the whole problem, to be given in Chapter 14, was obtained only in 1926.

---

[2] The frequency of electromagnetic radiation is the frequency of oscillation of the force which the radiation exerts on electric charges. The frequency equals the light velocity c divided by the wavelength λ. Therefore, the relationship $E = h\nu$ may also be written $E = hc/\lambda$.

[3] The Compton effect and analogous processes of radiation scattering fulfill this rule insofar as they are regarded as two-step processes in which atoms first take up a certain amount of energy and then release a part of it.

4.1 The Photoelectric Effect

The "photoelectric effect" is the release of electrons from matter under the influence of light or of other electromagnetic radiation. It occurs at the surface of a number of substances, particularly alkaline metals, when exposed to visible light. Light in the far ultraviolet produces it in all substances. Since light delivers energy to any material by which it is absorbed, it is understandable that some of the energy thus available serves to remove electrons, as thermal energy does in a hot wire.

The photoelectric effect appears, in the first place, as a release of negative electricity. Mass spectroscopy procedures verify that the negative electricity consists of *electrons*. Procedures analogous to mass spectroscopy determine the kinetic energy of the "photoelectrons" ejected from the material.

Figure 4.1 shows a schematic "photocell" for the analysis of photoelectrons. Light is directed through a window onto the surface of a

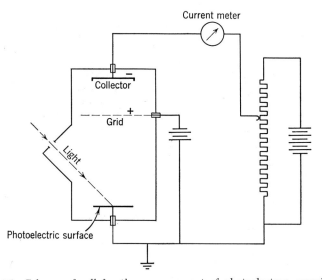

Fig. 4.1 Scheme of cell for the measurement of photoelectron energies.

material under study in an evacuated vessel. Electrons, if any are released from the surface, are sucked up by a positive grid and may pass through its holes to reach a collecting electrode. A current meter measures the rate at which the photoelectrons reach the collector. If a negative potential difference of V volts is applied between the collector and the emitting surface, the collector repels the electrons and will receive only those which have left the surface with a kinetic energy of at least

V electron volts, whereas lower energy electrons are turned back. Measuring the collector current i as a function of the potential V yields thereby an analysis of the energy distribution of the photoelectrons.

The experiments show that the energy and the number of the photoelectrons depend, respectively, on the color and on the intensity of the incident light. Other conditions being equal, the intensity of the photo-

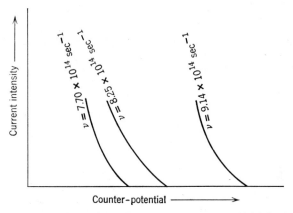

Fig. 4.2 Photoelectric current intensity versus counter-potential for incident light of different frequencies. (Adapted from Millikan, 1916.)

electric current is proportional to the intensity of the incident light. On the other hand, the energy distribution of the photoelectrons depends on the color, that is, on the frequency (or wavelength) of the light.

In the first place, no photoelectric effect whatsoever is observed unless the incident light contains spectral components of color sufficiently far in the direction of ultraviolet. The light may be filtered preliminarily through a "monochromator," which lets through radiation with frequency very close to any desired value of ν. By varying ν, the photoelectric current is found to appear only if ν exceeds a *threshold* value ν_0, which depends exclusively on the chemical nature of the photoelectric surface. For example, the threshold frequency is 6.0×10^{14} cycles/sec for sodium, 12.1×10^{14} for nickel, and 11.7×10^{14} for gold. In particular, the threshold is wholly independent of the light intensity. Electromagnetic radiation is thus shown to have a *potency* which depends on its frequency. High-frequency (short wavelength) radiation achieves effects which lower frequency radiation cannot achieve, *no matter how intense it is.*[4]

---

[4] Experiments on the chemical and biological actions of electromagnetic radiation also show very clearly that short-wave (high-frequency) radiation achieves effects that lower frequency radiation does not achieve even upon delivery of much larger amounts of energy.

This finding is extended by the analysis of photoelectron energies, performed by observing the function $i(V)$ of the photoelectric current versus counter-potential. For incident light of any given frequency ν, above the threshold ν_0, $i(V)$ decreases as the counter-potential V increases, and vanishes at, and above, a definite potential V_t which stops all photoelectrons (see Fig. 4.2). The value of V_t may be measured for various frequencies and plotted against ν. The result, shown in Fig. 4.3, is a straight line, whose slope has the same value, 4.135×10^{-15} volt sec,[5] for all photoelectric surfaces. That is, plots corresponding to dif-

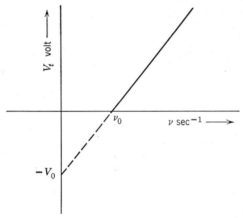

Fig. 4.3 Plot of the counter-potential V_t necessary to stop all photoelectrons emitted by a given material under the influence of light of frequency ν. For light of frequency smaller than ν_0, no photoelectrons are emitted. The slope of the plots is the same for all materials while ν_0 is a characteristic of the material and the extraction potential $-V_0$ equals $4.135 \times 10^{-15}\, \nu_0$.

ferent surface materials yield parallel lines, with different intercepts ν_0.

For $\nu_1 < \nu_0$ there are, of course, no photoelectrons and hence no measurable value of V_t. If the plot of Fig. 4.3 is nevertheless extrapolated to the axis $\nu = 0$, one finds a negative intercept $V_0 = 4.135 \times 10^{-15}\nu_0$. The value V_0 thus determined coincides with a characteristic of the surface material which is known from other phenomena, namely, the "extraction potential" or "work function." This is the electric potential which holds electrons within a metal and prevents them from escaping out of its surface.[6]

The energy which each photoelectron receives from the radiation

---

[5] When frequencies are measured in reciprocal seconds, the slope, which represents the ratio potential/frequency, is expressed in volt/sec^{-1} = volt sec.

[6] The difference between the value of V_0 for different metals causes electrons to pour through the contact surface between two metals in the Volta effect. It also causes hot surfaces of different metals to release electrons at different rates in the thermionic effect.

consists then of two parts. One portion is spent in extracting the electron from the surface and amounts to *at least* eV_0, that is, at least V_0 electron volts. The other portion becomes kinetic energy of the electron and amounts to *no more* than eV_t, that is, than V_t electron volts, because no photoelectron surmounts a counter-potential greater than V_t. Einstein surmised in 1905 that each electron receives an amount of energy exactly equal to $eV_0 + eV_t$; those electrons which were bound within the material by more than the minimum energy eV_0 emerge with correspondingly reduced kinetic energy.

This surmise is confirmed by observations on the photoelectric effect produced in monoatomic gases and metal vapors rather than on solid surfaces. The threshold frequency ν_0 lies in the ultraviolet, often in the far ultraviolet, for gases and vapors. It is found here that all photoelectrons are released with the same kinetic energy eV_t, and that all appear to have spent the same energy eV_0 in breaking loose from an atom.[7] It is also verified, by varying the density of the gas, that the photoelectric effect results from elementary processes of interaction between light and single gas atoms, since it meets the criteria of Sect. 2.3.

According to Einstein's interpretation, the total energy received by each electron is proportional to the radiation frequency, because $eV_0 + eV_t = e(V_0 + V_t)$ and $V_0 + V_t$ equals the frequency ν multiplied by 4.135×10^{-15} volt sec, as shown in Fig. 4.3. This relationship is expressed by Einstein's equation

$$E = eV_0 + eV_t = h\nu, \tag{1}$$

where the proportionality factor

$$h = 4.135 \times 10^{-15} \text{ ev sec} = 6.625 \times 10^{-27} \text{ erg sec} \tag{2}$$

is called the "Planck constant."

All subsequent evidence has confirmed that energy exchanges between atomic systems and electromagnetic radiation obey Eq. 1. That is, electromagnetic radiation energy is always absorbed or emitted in discrete amounts of magnitude proportional to the radiation frequency. The elementary quantity of radiation $h\nu$ is called a "photon" or "light quantum."

The subdivision of radiation energy into finite units escapes detection in all macroscopic experiments that fail to bring out the effects of interaction between radiation and single atomic particles. This discontinu-

---

[7] To be exact, photoelectric processes in which electrons require different energies for extraction occur also in gases. Here, there is a number of different possible extraction energies $V_0, V_1, V_2 \cdots$ and only the lowest one, V_0, is relevant as long as $h\nu < eV_1$. In solids the different possible extraction potentials are not separated because of interaction among atoms.

ous structure of radiation energy had been inferred by Planck in 1900, before Einstein's interpretation of the photoelectric effect, from an analysis of the thermal equilibrium between matter and radiation. His discovery showed that discontinuities akin to the atomic structure of matter are more widespread than had been expected.

The discontinuous or "atomistic" structure of radiation and matter are similar only insofar as photons, like atomic particles, enter elementary processes or emerge from them as single, individual units. Otherwise, the properties of matter and radiation are quite different. An atom occupies a certain portion of space and no other atom can be crowded in it without profound disruption to both atoms; therefore, one cannot raise the density of a solid material much above its normal value without crushing its atomic structure. The intensity of electromagnetic radiation in any region of space is subject to no analogous limitation.

The relationship between energy transfer and oscillation frequency, which is revealed by the photoelectric effect, links the energy and time variables of phenomena in a previously unsuspected manner. One sees here and in the following that the energy transferred in an elementary process is strictly related to the oscillation frequency of the incident light and of electric currents within atoms. The delivery of a large amount of energy in a single process requires a rapidly varying action, and, conversely, any rapidly varying action is capable of delivering a large amount of energy. The implications of this connection will emerge in the following chapters.

4.2   Inelastic Collisions of Electrons with Atoms

An elastic collision between two bodies is one in which the internal energy of each body remains unchanged, whereas in an inelastic collision the internal energy usually increases at the expense of kinetic energy. If an electron collides with an atom at rest and the collision is elastic, the atom hardly recoils because it is much heavier than the electron and takes up a negligible fraction of the electron's kinetic energy. Therefore, if an electron emerges from a collision with a substantial energy loss, the collision must have been inelastic and the energy must have been absorbed by the atom. Observation of the energy losses experienced by electrons serves to study the energy absorption by atoms.

Equipment for this study consists of three main parts, as shown schematically in Fig. 4.4:

(1) A device to produce a beam of electrons with uniform kinetic energy. This device, called an "electron gun," may consist of a hot wire ("filament") which releases large numbers of electrons with low velocity,

of a grid at a potential positive with respect to the filament which attracts the electrons and lets them through, and of collimating slits or pinholes in diaphragms which let through only electrons traveling in a given direction. The energy of the electrons in the beam is determined by the potential of the grid. The electron gun is evacuated to avoid collisions of the electrons with gas molecules.

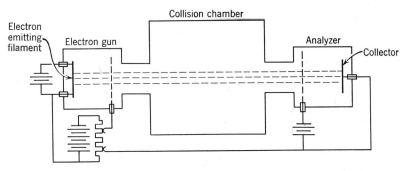

Fig. 4.4 Scheme of apparatus for the measurement of energy losses of electrons in a gas.

(2) A collision chamber, containing a rarefied monoatomic gas or vapor. At a pressure of 0.01 mm Hg, electrons travel on the average about 1 cm before colliding with gas molecules; the probability for an electron to experience repeated collisions in traversing the chamber may thus be minimized by keeping the pressure low.

(3) A device to analyze the kinetic energy of electrons which have traversed the chamber. This device may be of the simple type indicated in Fig. 4.1 for a photocell, that is, it may consist only of a collector at a variable negative potential.

Additional devices may be attached to the collision chamber to analyze any by-products of the collisions.

The energy levels of atoms. Franck and Hertz performed in 1914 the first experiment to observe elementary processes of inelastic collision between electrons and atoms. The experiment showed, first of all, that electrons with kinetic energies up to a few electron volts experience only elastic collisions against atoms.[8] As the electron energy is increased, all collisions remain elastic until the energy reaches a threshold value E_1 which is characteristic for the chemical species of atoms in the collision chamber, for example, 4.9 ev for Hg, 1.6 ev for Cs, 16.6 ev for Ne.

---

[8] This result holds only for collisions against isolated atoms; inelastic collisions occur at lower energies when atoms are grouped in diatomic or polyatomic molecules.

When the energy exceeds the threshold E_1, many electrons emerge from the chamber with kinetic energy reduced by an amount just equal to E_1, whereas the others lose no significant amount of energy (Fig. 4.5). This means that many electrons have experienced inelastic collisions in which a fixed amount of energy E_1 is transferred from one electron to

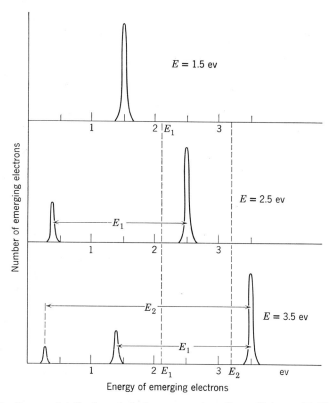

Fig. 4.5 Energy distribution of electrons emerging after collisions with Na atoms. The incident electron energies are $E = 1.5$ ev, $E = 2.5$ ev, and $E = 3.5$ ev for the three plots. The first two excited levels of Na lie at $E_1 = 2.1$ and $E_2 = 3.2$ ev.

the internal energy of an atom. The number of electrons that have lost energy is proportional to the density of atoms in the collision chamber—provided this density is sufficiently low; according to the criteria of Sect. 2.3, the inelastic collisions are thus shown to be elementary processes between one electron and one atom.

New types of inelastic collisions set in successively, when the energy E of the bombarding electrons is raised above successive thresholds E_2, E_3, $\cdots$. Electrons emerge from the chamber with energies reduced to

$E - E_2, E - E_3, \cdots$ showing that collisions have occurred with energy transfers $E_2, E_3, \cdots$ (Fig. 4.5).

The lack of inelastic collisions at subthreshold bombarding energies shows that the atoms are left after the collisions in unchanged states of internal energy. When inelastic collisions take place, at higher bombarding energies, the energy lost by an electron in an inelastic process must have been retained by an atom which is thereby left in a new state of internal energy. To each of the discrete energy losses of the electrons must correspond a different state of internal energy of the atoms. All atoms of the same element possess a characteristic, discrete set of states with different levels of internal energy, in which they can exist after collisions. These states are called "stationary states," because an atom can pass from one of them to another only through a mechanism of interaction that provides for the transfer of the required amount of energy. (By contrast, the internal energy of macroscopic bodies appears to be a continuous variable which may change ever so little.) The stationary state of lowest energy, which is the normal, stable state of a free atom, is called the "ground state"; the others are called "excited states" because their higher level of internal energy implies a more active internal motion.

The threshold energies $E_1, E_2, E_3, \cdots$ are called "critical potentials." [9] The differences between successive critical potentials decrease rapidly to a point where critical potentials can no longer be distinguished by analyzing the energies of electrons emerging from the chamber. The analysis of energy levels can, however, be continued by observing byproducts of inelastic collisions.

Radiation emission. Light emerges from the collison chamber of Fig. 4.4 when inelastic collisions set in for bombarding energies above the first threshold E_1. The intensity of this light is proportional to the current of bombarding electrons; its frequency depends only on the threshold energy according to an equation equivalent to (1), namely $\nu_1 = E_1/h$. We have here a situation reciprocal to that encountered in the photoelectric effect: in the photoelectric effect radiation of frequency ν makes available to matter amounts of energy $E = h\nu$; here atoms with excitation energies E_1 available for release emit radiation of frequency $\nu = E_1/h$. We conclude that, after electron bombardment, atoms emit radiation energy one photon at the time just as they absorb it in the photoelectric effect.

---

[9] The term "potential" refers to the accelerating potential applied to the grid of the electron gun; a critical potential should accordingly be expressed in volt, rather than in electron volt or in other energy units.

When the energy of the bombarding electrons is raised progressively above the successive thresholds E_2, E_3, $\cdots$, one observes, in general, the emission of light with new frequencies, first, $\nu_2 = E_2/h$ and $\nu_{21} = (E_2 - E_1)/h$, then, $\nu_3 = E_3/h$, $\nu_{31} = (E_3 - E_1)/h$, etc. Thus atoms return from excited states to the ground state either in a single jump or in successive steps through intermediate levels, if any. In every transi-

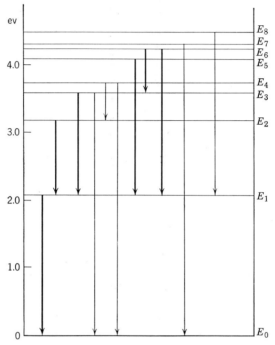

Fig. 4.6 A few energy levels and radiative transitions for sodium. The frequencies of the emitted lines are $\nu_{ij} = (E_i - E_j)/h$.

tion process accompanied by radiation emission, the radiation frequency equals the energy difference of the initial and final state divided by the Planck constant h (Fig. 4.6).[10]

When a critical potential is detected through the onset of light emission of a specific frequency, it is often called a "radiation potential." The measurement of radiation potentials permits a better analysis of atomic energy levels than the measurement of electron energies after collisions. However, the precision of this measurement is still greatly limited by the poor homogeneity of the energies of bombarding electrons

---

[10] All emission processes consistent with this rule do not take place with comparable intensity. Many of them are hardly observable.

for a given potential setting of the electron gun. By far the best analysis
of levels is provided by the study of light emission irrespective of the
method of excitation (see Sect. 4.3.).

Ionization. Positive ions appear in the collision chamber of the
experiment of Fig. 4.4, when the bombarding electron energy exceeds a
new critical potential, somewhat higher than the potentials considered
thus far. The presence of positive ions is demonstrated by inserting a
negatively charged grid in a wall of the chamber and analyzing by mass
spectroscopy the particles flowing through the grid. That electrons
have been ejected from the atoms in the chamber is confirmed by an
increase in the flow of electrons out of the chamber.

As the energy E of the bombarding electrons is increased, starting from
a low value, no ions are detected until E reaches a threshold E_I, but
thereafter the yield of ions rises sharply. The threshold E_I, expressed
in volt of accelerating potential, is called the "ionization potential" of
the element and coincides with the extraction potential V_0 determined
according to Fig. 4.3 from the photoelectric effect in free atoms of the
same element. The energy E_I is also called the "binding energy" of the
electron which is ejected, because it represents the energy required to
release the electron by breaking the bond which was holding it within
the atom.

The variations of the ionization potential from one chemical element
to another are indicated in Fig. 4.7 and follow a periodic pattern in accordance with chemical classification. The lowest ionization potentials

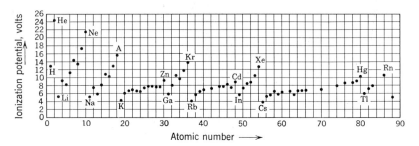

Fig. 4.7   Ionization potentials of the elements.

are observed in alkali atoms (3 to 6 volts), the highest in rare gases (up
to 24 volts). On the whole the ionization potentials decrease slightly
from one row to the next of the periodic system.

When ionization takes place, electrons emerge from the collision chamber with a continuous distribution of energies. Two electrons emerge
from each ionizing collision, one that had arrived from the electron gun

and one released from the atom; these electrons share in any proportion the energy $E - E_I$ available after the ionization requirement.

If the energy of the bombarding electrons is raised further above the ionization threshold E_I, the yield of ions from any element but hydrogen shows successive steplike rises at higher critical potentials. These rises are often accompanied by the onset of light emission with new frequencies, indicating the occurrence of ionizing collisions in which the residual ion is left in an excited state; the light is emitted by the ion as it drops to a state of lower energy. Other critical potentials mark the appearance of doubly or multiply charged ions.

Further critical potentials. X rays. Critical potentials of the order of 100 volts exist for all elements except hydrogen and helium. They are in fact very numerous and difficult to analyze owing to the variety of possible degrees of ionization and excitation of the residual ions. The ionization yield reaches a maximum in most elements for bombarding energies of the order of 100 ev. It decreases at still higher energies, because the incident electrons move so fast that their collisions with atoms are fleeting and allow little opportunity for energy transfers.

At accelerating potentials of the order of 1000 volts or more, critical potentials are still observed in elements with atomic numbers of the order of 10 or more. They are detected as radiation potentials, marking the onset of the emission of electromagnetic radiation with new frequencies in the X-ray range. These critical potentials correspond to ionizing collisions in which the residual ion is left in a state of very high excitation, so that it has a large amount of energy available to emit photons of high-energy radiation. The values of these high critical potentials form a simple pattern characteristic for each element; they lie singly or in small groups widely separated from one another, differing by factors as large as 5 or 10.

The wide separation between groups of critical potentials indicates that the electronic "body" of atoms and ions has levels of excitation energy of quite different magnitude. One surmises readily that excitations of higher and higher order of magnitude affect deeper and deeper layers, or "shells," of the body of electrons, which are held with increasing stiffness by the nuclear attraction. Increasing stiffness expresses itself, of course, in the increasing frequency of the oscillating current which must be the source of the X-ray emission. This surmise is borne out by the variation of the X-ray critical potentials from one element to the next along the periodic system. As mentioned before, the lower critical potentials, including the first ionization threshold E_I, vary in cycles corresponding to the periodicity of the chemical elements; they appear to involve disturbances of the outer layers of atoms which are the seat of chemical properties. On the contrary, each X-ray potential rises monotonically by a small fraction from one element to the next (see Fig. 4.8), showing no relation to chemical periodicity but a direct relationship to the strength of the nuclear attraction upon the electrons. For each element the values of the X-ray potentials and of the frequencies of the emitted X rays are also practically independent of the state of chemical aggregation of the element, whereas the lower potentials are greatly altered by chemical combination.

The highest critical potential of each element, called K potential, is of the order of $10Z^2$ volts (Z is the atomic number). Next is a group of three potentials, called the L potentials, lying 5 to 10 times lower than the K potential. As seen in Fig. 4.8, each group of X-ray potentials rises rapidly with increasing Z, and new groups

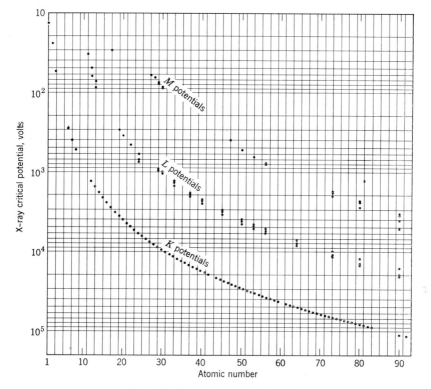

Fig. 4.8   X-ray critical potentials.

appear in the range of energies where observations are convenient. This indicates that, as the number of electrons increases, more and more of them are drawn in to form new recognizable layers of the atomic body. The systematics of this process will be analyzed in Chapter 18.

4.3   Evidence from Spectroscopy

This section outlines the type of information obtained from the spectroscopic analysis of the light absorbed or emitted by free atoms in a gas or vapor.

"Spectroscopy" means, in general, the analysis of electromagnetic radiation into components with different frequencies of oscillation. The simplest spectroscopes utilize a glass prism which deflects light of different colors by different angles; components of different colors that arrive on a prism in a parallel beam are projected onto different points of a screen. Diffraction gratings and other devices can be utilized instead of prisms to provide a more accurate analysis. X-ray spectroscopy relies primarily on suitable diffraction gratings, which we need not discuss here, and is otherwise analogous to light spectroscopy.

All forms of matter emit electromagnetic radiation when they have been brought to a state of excited internal motion. Excitation may result from bombardment by electrons, ions, or atoms, or simply when high temperature increases the violence of ordinary collisions between atoms. Favorable conditions for intense excitation of free atoms occur in gaseous discharges, including arcs and sparks. Radiation emitted by a substance and analyzed with a spectroscope spreads out on the spectroscope screen in a pattern which constitutes the "emission spectrum" of the substance.

The spectral analysis of the absorption of radiation utilizes a radiation source with a frequency spectrum as smooth and uniform as practicable. This spectrum is analyzed and displayed on a screen. When a vessel containing a test substance is inserted between the source and the spectroscope, it absorbs preferentially radiation of certain frequencies. Shadows appear on the spectroscope screen in correspondence to those frequencies. The set of shadows constitutes the "absorption spectrum" of the substance.

The gross features of the emission and absorption spectra may be anticipated from the results of the preceding sections. Atoms are normally in their ground state and therefore can absorb only radiation of such frequencies as will bring them to one of their excited stationary states or to an ionized state, in which an electron has been removed from the atom. The excited states form a sequence, with energies $E_1, E_2, \cdots$ higher than the ground state. Accordingly, the absorption spectrum will contain localized shadows at a sequence of frequencies $\nu_1 = E_1/h$, $\nu_2 = E_2/h \cdots$ such that the corresponding photon energies $h\nu_1$, $h\nu_2 \cdots$ are exactly sufficient to raise atoms to their various excited levels. This set of localized shadows constitutes the "line" or "discrete" absorption spectrum. The lines of this spectrum have, in general, quite different intensities; many of them are usually so weak as to be unobservable. On the other hand, the lines are very sharp, and appear distinctly in much greater number than the excited levels distinguishable by the Franck-Hertz procedure.

Absorption of radiation in a process that brings an atom to an ionized state constitutes a photoelectric effect. This process occurs for radiation of all frequencies in excess of the threshold

$$\nu_0 = \frac{eV_0}{h} = \frac{E_I}{h}, \tag{3}$$

where V_0 is the extraction potential of Eq. 1 and $E_I = eV_0$ is the binding energy of the electron to be ejected. Accordingly, the absorption spectrum contains an extended shadow or "band," limited on the low-frequency side by a sharp edge at the frequency ν_0. Ionization processes which leave the ion in one of its states of excitation with levels E_1', E_2', $\cdots$ can be produced by absorption of radiation with frequencies in excess of other thresholds $\nu_1' = (eV_0 + E_1')/h$, $\nu_2' = (eV_0 + E_2')/h$, $\cdots$. There will thus be additional extended shadows, superposed on one another, marked by sharp edges at the frequencies ν_1', ν_2', $\cdots$. This set of bands constitutes the continuous absorption spectrum, or "absorption continuum." It extends into the X-ray range of frequencies, in correspondence to excitation energies E_i' of the order of thousands of electron volts.

The emission spectrum of the atoms of each element consists of lines and bands like the absorption spectrum, but contains many more of them. Each line or band of the absorption spectrum also appears in emission. These lines are emitted by atoms dropping from excited states to the ground state. The bands are emitted when a free electron becomes attached to an ion to form a neutral atom in the ground state (inverse process to the photoelectric effect). The other lines, which do not appear in the absorption spectrum, are emitted by atoms dropping from an excited state to another one at a lower energy level. The frequencies of all lines in the emission spectrum are given by the formula

$$\nu_{ik} = \frac{E_i - E_k}{h}, \tag{4}$$

where E_i and E_k indicate the energies of any two stationary states with $E_i > E_k$. The intensities of all lines represented by this formula differ from one another, in general, up to many orders of magnitude, the majority of them too weak to be observed. Nevertheless, there are spectra with thousands of observed lines. The continuous emission spectrum contains also numerous bands, emitted in processes in which a free electron becomes attached to an ion to form a neutral atom in one of its various excited states.

The spectra of all elements have the features just indicated. Many spectra were analyzed long before the existence of atomic energy levels was demonstrated directly by the Franck-Hertz experiment. It was noticed by Rydberg and Ritz that the reciprocal values of the measured wavelengths of numerous spectral lines can be represented by a "combination principle," in the form

$$\frac{1}{\lambda_{ik}} = \tau_i - \tau_k, \tag{5}$$

that is, as differences of a smaller number of quantities τ_i, τ_k $\cdots$, called the "spectral terms." Initially, this representation had only the advantage of compactness, but after Einstein's interpretation of the photoelectric effect, it was realized that each term must correspond to an energy level. Equations 4 and 5, together with $\nu = c/\lambda$, show that the energy levels are related to the spectral terms by

$$E_i = hc\tau_i. \tag{6}$$

Extensive and accurate tables and diagrams of energy levels have been prepared from the analysis of spectra, primarily emission spectra. A sample level diagram is shown in Fig. 4.6. The arrows in the diagram indicate the transitions actually observed in the emission spectrum. The presence or absence of the lines corresponding to the various conceivable transitions, and the relative intensities of the observed lines provide a basis for the classification of energy levels. This classification had great importance for the development of atomic mechanics and will be discussed in Chapter 18.

4.4 Energy Levels of the Hydrogen Atom and of Related Systems

Because the "body" of a hydrogen atom consists of a single electron, its properties should be accounted for most simply, from general principles. The special position of hydrogen in the periodic system of elements attracted much work to measurements of the hydrogen spectrum and to analysis of the numerical data thus obtained. This analysis led to the early discovery of an empirical formula which represents the spectral terms of hydrogen.

In 1885, Balmer recognized that the wavelengths of the four brilliant lines in the visible spectrum of hydrogen can be represented by

$$\frac{1}{\lambda} = R\left(\frac{1}{4} - \frac{1}{n^2}\right), \tag{7}$$

where $R = 109{,}678$ cm^{-1} is called the "Rydberg constant," and n equals, respectively, 3, 4, 5, and 6 for the four lines. This observation led Rydberg to discover the combination principle showing that all wavelengths of the line emission spectrum, from the infrared to the far ultraviolet, are represented quite accurately by (5) with the spectral terms

$$\tau_n = -R/n^2, \tag{8}$$

where n is any positive integer. In the representation (5) the wavelengths of the series of Balmer lines are indicated by λ_{n2}; this series continues in the near ultraviolet for $n > 6$. Other series of lines are known whose wavelengths are indicated by $\lambda_{nn'}$, with $n' = 1, 3, 4, 5, 6, 7$ and $n > n'$; the series with $n' = 1$ lies in the far ultraviolet, those with $n' \geq 3$ lie in the infrared. The lines of each series "converge," that is, become increasingly close to one another as n increases and they approach a limit which coincides with the edge of a band. The wavelengths of these edges are accordingly represented by

$$\frac{1}{\lambda_{\infty n'}} = \tau_\infty - \tau_{n'} = \frac{R}{n'^2}. \tag{9}$$

The absorption spectrum of hydrogen atoms consists of a single series of lines, namely, the Lyman series in the far ultraviolet, and of a continuous band beyond the limit of this series. The ionization potential of hydrogen is, therefore, according to (4) and (8),

$$V_0 = -\frac{hc\tau_1}{e} = \frac{hcR}{e} = 13.6 \text{ volts.} \qquad (10)$$

The formula

$$E_n = hc\tau_n = -\frac{hRc}{n^2} = -\frac{13.6}{n^2} \text{ ev.} \qquad (11)$$

represents the energy levels of the stationary states of the hydrogen atom, in a scale where $E = 0$ indicates the energy of the atom after dissociation into an electron and a nucleus with zero kinetic energy. The energy levels measured from the ground state are given by $E_n - E_1$.

Analysis of the hydrogen spectrum with very high resolution shows that most of the lines considered above are actually clusters of lines whose frequency differences are of the order of one part in a million. The details of the spectrum, called its "fine structure," and further details called "hyperfine structure," will be considered in Chapter 16.

The ions He^+, Li^{++}, Be^{+++}, etc., are isolectronic to H, that is, their "bodies" consist also of a single electron. Their spectra are found to have the same structure as the H spectrum, but with all frequencies scaled up approximately in proportion to the squared atomic number Z^2 (that is, by a factor of 4 for He^+, of 9 for Li^{++}, etc.). Accordingly, their energy levels are given by a modification of (11), namely

$$E_n = -Z^2 \frac{hcR}{n^2} = -Z^2 \frac{13.6}{n^2} \text{ ev.} \qquad (12)$$

To be exact, the energy levels are fitted best by (12) with values of the Rydberg constant differing from one another by small fractions, of less than one part in a thousand. These different values are indicated respectively by R_H, R_{He}, R_{Li}, etc. The spectrum of the hydrogen isotope of atomic weight two (deuterium) is also fitted best by an appropriate value of R, called R_D. As will be seen, these differences result from the differences in the nuclear mass among the various atoms and ions with a single electron.

The line spectra of all atoms consist, like that of hydrogen, of series of lines converging to the edges of continuous bands. The resemblance to hydrogen stems from the circumstance that any atom, when it is nearly ionized, may be visualized as consisting of a single electron loosely bound to a residual ion. To the extent that the electron is already removed out of the "body" of this residual ion, and the ion acts on it as though it were a unit positive point charge, the loosely bound electron should behave like the electron of a hydrogen atom.

Bohr's theory of the Rydberg constant. In 1913, Niels Bohr obtained a remarkable theoretical success by a modification of the planetary model. As pointed out in Sect. 3.4, the planetary model provides no basis to explain why the orbit of an electron around a nucleus should be of any particular size. Bohr considered which sizes of circular orbits would correspond to the experimental evidence regarding the hydrogen spectrum. He considered in particular very large orbits, corresponding to states of high excitation, because any departures from the laws of macroscopic physics should have least influence when an atom becomes very large.

According to the planetary model, the electron may follow a circular orbit of any radius r. To each radius corresponds an energy E and a frequency of revolution ν which will be given explicitly below as a function $\nu(E)$. The electron following such an orbit should emit radiation of frequency ν continuously, and its energy E should decrease progressively to compensate for the loss of energy through irradiation.

On the other hand, experiments show that energy is in fact radiated away in photons $h\nu$. Each actual emission process is accompanied by a jump from an energy level E_n to a lower level which is most frequently E_{n-1}. To preserve a connection between these facts and the planetary model, Bohr postulated that the energy difference between successive levels be related to the frequency of planetary revolution by

$$E_n - E_{n-1} = h\nu(E_n). \tag{13}$$

He solved this equation for E_n as a function of n, with the approximation $n \gg 1$.

The explicit relationship between ν and E is derived as follows: A circular orbit is stable if the centrifugal force on the electron balances the electric attraction exerted on it by a nucleus with charge Ze, that is, if

$$\frac{mv^2}{r} = \frac{Ze^2}{r^2}, \tag{14}$$

where m and v are the mass and velocity of the electron. The electron energy consists of kinetic energy and of a potential energy which represents the attraction by the nucleus and is, accordingly, negative,

$$E = \tfrac{1}{2}mv^2 - \frac{Ze^2}{r}. \tag{15}$$

Combination of (15) and (14) yields

$$E = -\tfrac{1}{2}mv^2 = -\frac{1}{2}\frac{Ze^2}{r}. \tag{16}$$

The frequency of revolution equals the velocity divided by the length $2\pi r$ of the orbit and can be expressed in terms of E by means of (16),

$$\nu = \frac{v}{2\pi r} = \sqrt{-\frac{2E}{m}}\frac{1}{2\pi}\left(-\frac{2E}{Ze^2}\right) = \frac{(-2E)^{3/2}}{2\pi\sqrt{m}\,Ze^2}. \tag{17}$$

Bohr's postulate (13) becomes then

$$E_n - E_{n-1} = \frac{h}{2\pi\sqrt{m}\,Ze^2}(-2E_n)^{3/2}. \tag{18}$$

For large values of n, that is, for large orbits, the difference $E_n - E_{n-1}$ may be represented approximately as a derivative dE/dn, so that (18) is replaced with the differential equation

$$\frac{dE_n}{dn} = \frac{h}{2\pi\sqrt{m}\,Ze^2}(-2E_n)^{3/2}, \tag{19}$$

whose solution is

$$E_n = -\frac{2\pi^2 m Z^2 e^4}{h^2 n^2}. \tag{20}$$

One arrives at the same result from an alternative form of Bohr's postulate, which requires the orbit of the nth stationary state to fulfill the condition

$$2\pi rmv = nh. \tag{21}$$

The result (20) coincides with the experimental formula (12) provided that

$$R = \frac{2\pi^2 m e^4}{h^2 c}. \tag{22}$$

Entering here the values of e, h, m, and c, given respectively by Millikan's experiment, by the photoelectric effect, by mass spectroscopy, and by measurements of the light velocity, yields approximately $R = 109{,}700$ cm^{-1}, in very good agreement with the experimental value of the Rydberg constant.

The agreement is carried further by considering that the nucleus is not to be regarded as fixed in the planetary model, but rather as moving together with the electron about their common center of mass. As shown in Appendix II, this effect is taken into account by replacing the mass m of the electron with the reduced mass $m_N = m M_N/(m + M_N)$, where M_N is the mass of a nucleus N. Replacing then in (22) m with the values of m_H, m_D, m_{He}, etc., for the nuclei of H, deuterium, He, etc., one obtains values R_H, R_D, R_{He}, etc., whose ratios agree very well with those of the experimental values of the Rydberg constant.

This calculation of energy levels, utilizing only the planetary model, Eq. 17, and Bohr's postulate (13), constituted a remarkable success of atomic theory. This success did not do away with the unrealistic aspects of the planetary model. It demonstrated the possibility of deriving significant results by somewhat tentative procedures, combining macroscopic theory with qualitative findings of atomic experimentation. Such procedures, developed further primarily by Bohr and by Sommerfeld, proved very useful until they were replaced in the mid-twenties by quantum mechanics.

PROBLEMS

4.1   The threshold wavelength λ_0 for photoelectric effect in tungsten is 2700 A. Calculate the maximum kinetic energy K_M of electrons ejected from tungsten by light of $\lambda = 1700$ A.

4.2   An electron with negligible initial energy falls through a difference of potential and produces radiation when it hits a target. Find the minimum potential difference required to produce: (a) X rays of 0.6 A wavelength; (b) light of 6000 A; (c) microwaves of 6 cm.

4.3   An electron with 4 ev kinetic energy collides with a mercury atom at rest and is deflected by 90°. Calculate its loss of kinetic energy, taking into account the conservation of momentum in the collision.

4.4   Atomic hydrogen is bombarded with electrons in a Franck-Hertz experiment. Emission of the red (lowest frequency) line of the Balmer series is observed, but the other lines of that series do not appear. This observation fixes an upper and a lower limit to the kinetic energy K of the bombarding electrons. Calculate these limits assuming the atoms to be initially in their ground state and disregarding their recoil.

4.5   In the experiment of Problem 4.4, the first two lines of the Lyman series L1, and L2, are observed besides the Balmer line B1. The relative numbers of photons of these three lines are $N_{L1}:N_{L2}:N_{B1} = 6:1:2$. Find the ratios among the numbers, C_n, of collisions that raise the atoms to their various excited energy levels E_n ($n = 2, 3, 4, \cdots$).

4.6   Calculate the ratio of the energy levels with the same quantum number in the spectra of the two isotopes of Li^{++} with atomic weights 6.0 and 7.0.

chapter 5

Macroscopic and quantum properties of electro- magnetic radiation— initial survey

The quantum properties of electromagnetic radiation, described in the preceding chapter, appear quite novel from the point of view of macroscopic electromagnetism. We begin now to consider how the macroscopic and atomistic properties of radiation hang together, and how the laws of macroscopic electromagnetism should be adjusted to attain a comprehensive formulation of macroscopic and quantum phenomena. The concepts and methods to be developed for the treat- ment of radiation have general validity throughout atomic physics.

The macroscopic description of a system need not *a priori* remain meaningful at the atomic level. In the example of gas mechanics, pres- sure is a macroscopic variable which is meaningless with regard to one or a few molecules. The mechanics of individual molecules develops on foundations independent of macroscopic gas mechanics, and macroscopic gas mechanics may be established as a statistical description of the col- lective behavior of an assembly of gas molecules with known individual behavior. With regard to electromagnetism, the situation is quite dif- ferent. The concepts and laws of macroscopic electromagnetism remain

54

meaningful at the atomic level; they only need reinterpretation and broadening.

The applicability of macroscopic electromagnetism to elementary processes emerges from the fact that its results prove valid at any low level of light intensity. That is, one may experiment at extremely low intensity and let the effects of numerous atomic processes of emission and absorption accumulate for a long time so that their aggregate effect be detectable by macroscopic devices, for example, by photographic plates. Under these conditions, the elementary processes of emission and absorption by atoms must occur independently of one another within separate intervals of time. Yet the final results of any such experiment, on refraction, polarization, interference, etc., of light, verify the predictions of macroscopic electromagnetism. Similar experiments, in which one observes separately the effects of single elementary processes, give basic information for the modification and extension of the macroscopic laws, as will be shown in later chapters.

Passing references have been made in the last chapter to general properties of radiation, such as its emission and absorption by electric currents. Section 5.1 gives a sketchy review of the main relevant facts of macroscopic electromagnetism, starting with the general question of energy exchanges between electric currents and the space surrounding them. Quantum effects will be discussed in Sect. 5.2.

5.1   Relevant Elements of Macroscopic Electromagnetism

The space surrounding an electric current is the seat of a magnetic field, whose presence is detected, for example, by the orientation of a magnetic needle. The onset of a current in an electric circuit and of the associated magnetic field is never abrupt, but is marked by a lag due to self-induction. During this lag, the current generator performs work to establish the current against the opposition of self-induction. The energy provided by this work is regarded as stored in the magnetic field which is being established. Indeed, when the current generator is switched off, self-induction has a reverse effect: The current keeps running for a while, despite the resistance of the circuit, and dies off gradually together with the magnetic field. In this phase of the phenomenon, energy is returned by the field to the circuit.

Both the start and the disappearance of the magnetic field in the space surrounding a current are associated with further electric actions. For example, an electric current is driven temporarily in a circuit adjacent to one in which a current starts or dies off. This effect of electromagnetic induction underlies the common a-c transformer action, in which an oscillating current is pumped in a coil of wire (the "primary" winding) and a current is obtained in another coil (the "secondary" winding).

Little energy is dissipated away from the space surrounding a current in the course of induction processes, provided the rates of change of current intensity remain low, as in ordinary a-c phenomena. The energy spent by currents in one phase of a process is almost entirely returned to currents in another phase. Roughly speaking, the dissipation remains low because the electromagnetic equilibrium is never greatly disturbed by slow variations of currents. This does not hold in the case of sharp current variations, as illustrated by a mechanical analog: A slow inflation of a balloon proceeds reversibly without energy dissipation, but a sudden deflation by a puncture results in dissipation by the sharp noise which propagates away.

Rapid variations of electric currents lead to substantial energy dissipation. The more rapid the current variations, the less readily can the magnetic and electric forces in the surrounding space readjust to follow the current variations. This unbalance leads to energy transfer away from the current. A very rapid current increase requires an especially large expenditure of energy, and a very rapid decrease draws only an especially low return of energy. The reactions caused by a sharp electromagnetic unbalance in a portion of space overshoot the equilibrium, just as in the phenomena of elastic unbalance. Thereby the disturbance fails to subside and propagates from one point to the next, farther and farther away.

The transport of energy by a rapidly varying electromagnetic disturbance is called electromagnetic radiation. It results from any rapid variation of electric current, such as takes place in a radio antenna. The higher the rate of change of the current, the higher is the rate of energy dissipation through radiation.

Electromagnetic radiation exerts the same kind of action on matter as electromagnetic induction. It exerts a force on all electric charges and on all currents. The work performed by this force absorbs the energy of radiation and returns it to matter. Thus the energy, which, we said, is dissipated by a radio antenna, is in fact generally returned to matter, somewhere, sometime, often a great distance away.

An electromagnetic disturbance which propagates as radiation maintains the pattern of time variations of the current from which the radiation originates. The work performed by the disturbance on a given portion of matter, that is, the rate of energy absorption, depends on the displacement which the disturbance impresses on the charges (and currents) within this matter. This displacement depends in turn on the readiness with which the charges can follow the pattern of variation impressed by the radiation source. The "tuning" of a radio receiver consists of adjusting the circuit of its antenna so that it oscillates most readily with the frequency of a given transmitter. Patterns of sinusoidal oscillation [1] are often utilized; they are characterized by the frequency of oscillation. The time variation of any electromagnetic disturbance may be treated as a combination of sinusoidal oscillations of different frequencies (see Appendix IV).

The phenomena outlined in the preceding paragraphs obey laws formulated by Maxwell in the 1850's. In Maxwell's formulation, radiation and other electromagnetic phenomena are described by the strength and direction of the electric and magnetic field at each point of space and at each instant of time. The electric field is defined as the electric force acting on a test charge divided by the magnitude of the charge, in the limit where the test charge is vanishingly small and therefore does not disturb the phenomena under consideration. (Notice that this limit of a vanishingly small charge is unrealistic from the atomic point of view.) The magnetic field is defined similarly in terms of the force acting on a test current or on a test magnetic needle.

In the absence of charges and currents, that is, for radiation in empty space, Maxwell's equations are relationships among the rates of variation of the electric and magnetic field from point to point and in the course of time. Unless the variations from point to point of the electric field fulfill certain conditions, the magnetic field is bound to vary in the course of time, that is, there is no electromagnetic equilibrium. Similarly, the electric field varies in the course of time unless the variations of the magnetic field from point to point fulfill certain conditions. Energy is stored in any region of space where the electric and magnetic field have non-zero strength. Energy flows through space when the fields vary in the course of time.

In a region of space where there are electric charges and currents, Maxwell's equations relate the rates of variations of the fields not only among themselves but also to the charges and currents. Electromagnetic equilibrium is possible only if the distributions in space of charges and currents remain constant in the course of time. Any variation of charges and currents generates a traveling electromagnetic disturbance and conversely the fields tend to disturb the charges and currents since they exert forces on them. Thereby radiation, a phenomenon that exists in empty space, interacts with the charges and currents which exist in matter. Radiation and matter are treated initially as separate, inde-

---

[1] The intensity i of a current that oscillates sinusoidally is represented as a function of the time t by $i(t) = i_0 \sin (2\pi\nu t + \phi)$, where i_0 is the amplitude (peak value of the intensity), ν the frequency and ϕ the phase of oscillation at the time $t = 0$.

pendent systems, in macroscopic and also in quantum physics; their interaction is introduced as a mechanism which causes energy exchanges between the two systems.

Maxwell's formulation was based on evidence obtained with slowly varying currents and fields. In the succeeding century electrical circuits have been developed which oscillate with frequencies up to the order of 10^{10} cycles/sec. The radiation emitted and absorbed by these circuits behaves according to Maxwell's equations.

Light and X rays have been identified as electromagnetic radiation with oscillation frequencies beyond the limits attained by electrical circuits. The identification rests on the fact that these radiations propagate according to Maxwell's equations and, in particular, travel in empty space with the velocity predicted by Maxwell for electromagnetic disturbances. (Prior to Maxwell, light was known to be an oscillatory phenomenon of very short wavelength and high velocity—and hence of extremely high frequency—but its nature was otherwise unknown.) All phenomena of emission, propagation, and absorption of light, in which light interacts with macroscopic amounts of matter, can be interpreted in terms of submicroscopic currents within matter.

Because atoms and molecules are lighter and stiffer than macroscopic portions of matter, and because they contain charged particles, it is understandable that they can be the seat of oscillating currents of extremely high frequency. Thus light is seen to differ from lower frequency radiation in that it is generated, modified, and absorbed by atomic electric currents rather than by macroscopic ones. (Interaction of radiofrequency radiations with atomic currents are also observed, see Sect. 7.2.) The selective absorption or emission of light of specific frequency by a material, for example, by a monoatomic gas, means therefore from the macroscopic point of view that currents readily oscillate with those frequencies within the atoms or molecules of the material.

5.2   Discussion of Quantum Properties

The first quantum property of radiation which has been described in Chapter 4 is the discontinuity of the amounts of energy exchanged between radiation and atoms, or atomic particles. For example, when a mercury atom emits light in a transition from its first excited state to the ground state, it gives up its excitation energy of 4.9 ev in a single process. This energy may be absorbed by another mercury atom which thereby becomes excited. Notice that the time between emission and absorption is very long if the two atoms are far from one another. During this time the energy is regarded as stored in the electromagnetic field of the radiation. The light emitted by mercury atoms in this transition is shown by spectroscopic analysis to have a wavelength of 2537 A. To this wavelength corresponds, according to macroscopic electromagnetism, a frequency of 1.18×10^{15} cycles/sec, equal to the energy of 4.9 ev divided by Planck's constant h.

The electromagnetic field of a radiation characterized macroscopically by a frequency ν is always found on the atomic scale to store energy in photons of magnitude $h\nu$. The field is then said to have discrete energy levels, just like atoms do, the levels being separated by equal amounts $h\nu$.

According to macroscopic electromagnetism, the energy stored in the field is a continuous variable, like the mechanical energy of a macroscopic body. The existence of separate energy levels of the field was overlooked in macroscopic electromagnetism, and did not in fact deserve attention because the difference between energy levels is too small to be of any macroscopic consequence. Macroscopically, the energy exchanged between matter and field appears to proceed with continuity in the course of time. Here, too, it is understandable that any discontinuity is of no consequence when, as in radio phenomena, the total quantity of energy transferred in a measurable time interval amounts to an exceedingly large number of photons. (A radio emission of 1 kw at 1000 kilocycles consists of 1.5×10^{30} photons per second.)

Macroscopic electromagnetism is nevertheless relevant to atomic phenomena because it accounts for the collective emission, absorption, and transmission of light, for example, by the free molecules of a gas. Let us then consider some typical situations in which macroscopic and atomic features appear simultaneously.

As we have seen, an electromagnetic disturbance preserves its pattern of time variation in the course of its propagation. This property has a determining effect on the distribution of energy at the atomic level. Consider an atomic transition which releases an amount of energy E as radiation of frequency ν. The radiation travels with constant frequency (unless it is modified by interaction with another oscillating current) and is eventually absorbed in an atomic process which takes up a photon of the same energy $h\nu = E$ as had been released initially. Thereby the energy originally available in an atom is not degraded or dispersed in different directions as a result of transmission by radiation. Macroscopically, the energy emitted by a radio antenna or by an assembly of atoms becomes distributed in all—or at least in most—directions around the source. The smoothness of this distribution represents a statistical average over a multitude of atomic processes; however, the energy radiated by one atom is picked up eventually by another atom in a particular direction.

A similar relationship prevails for the distribution in time of the energy emitted by a source. If an oscillating current is started in an electric circuit, for example, by shorting a condenser through an inductance, and is left to proceed freely, it radiates. Progressive loss of energy by radiation emission causes the current intensity to decrease as an exponential function of time;[2] the rate of energy emission also decreases exponentially. The emission is seen to proceed in this way when one observes macroscopically the light emitted by a large number of atoms after they have been excited. For example, one may look at the light emission by the canal rays, described in Sect. 1.3, which consist of ions emerging at high speed from an aperture; many of these ions are initially in an excited state and radiate as they fly on. Indeed the beam is made visible by its luminosity. As the ions travel away from the discharge where they have been excited, the variation in time of their rate of light emission is displayed as a variation of luminosity along the beam. The intensity of each spectral line emitted by the beam is observed to decrease exponentially at increasing distances from the origin of the beam, according to the macroscopic law. On the other hand, one may observe through a diaphragm the light emitted only at a particular spot along the beam; analysis of this light with a photoelectric cell shows it to consist of photons of the same energies as are received from the whole beam observed without the diaphragm. Here, again, the macroscopic distribution of intensity in the course of time represents a statistical average; each elementary process of photon emission appears to have occurred at a definite time instant. The frequency of photon detection decreases exponentially as the spot observed with the photoelectric cell is moved down the beam.

The relation between the smooth macroscopic distribution of light intensity and the sharply concentrated distribution which pertains to individual atomic processes is of fundamental importance. As pointed out at the beginning of this chapter, the macroscopic distribution should have a meaning for each single atomic process, because it remains unchanged in experiments at extremely low intensity levels, such that the emission processes by different atoms are widely separated in time. The nature of this relationship will be discussed in the next chapter.

Notice that the structure of radiation energy is analogous, in its combination of continuous and discontinuous aspects, to the structure of the "body" of atoms. The atomic "body" behaves macroscopically as

---

[2] An exponential function is one that varies by equal *fractions* in equal intervals of its variable. For example, a function that decreases exponentially with time is represented mathematically in the form $y = y_0 e^{-t/\tau}$; y decreases by a factor $1/e = 0.367$ whenever t increases by τ, where e is the number $2,718 \cdots$

a solid, continuous distribution of matter, but, on the other hand, its content of matter increases or decreases by one electron at a time, just as the energy content of radiation varies by one photon at a time.

Another analogy between the properties of radiation and atoms emerges from a discussion of cavity resonators. A cavity resonator is a device, consisting of a box with metallic reflecting walls, in which the electromagnetic field can oscillate with high intensity only at certain characteristic frequencies. These frequencies depend on the dimensions of the box, much as the characteristic frequencies of a vibrating string depend on its length. (The lowest frequency ν_1 of a cavity resonator is such that the corresponding wavelength $\lambda_1 = c/\nu_1$ is of the order of magnitude of the box dimensions.) Each of the characteristic frequencies decreases if the box dimensions are increased. From the point of view of quantum effects, the lowest energy amount, namely, one photon, of radiation that can be excited in a resonator has a minimum value $h\nu_1$ which is inversely related to the resonator's size. This means that each unit of radiation energy has a tendency to expand, similar to the tendency of the "body" of atoms, because its energy decreases if the resonator's size increases. Macroscopically, it is well known that radiation reflected by a wall exerts a pressure on it; therefore, radiation in a resonator performs work if it is allowed to expand pushing back the cavity walls. Atomistically, some of this work is performed at the expense of the energy of each photon, while the number of photons remains the same. It will be shown in later chapters that the stability of the "body" of atoms is due to the fact that each electron held within an atom must have a certain minimum kinetic energy inversely related to the atomic size, much as the energy of each photon in a resonator is inversely related to the cavity size.

The cavity resonator also illustrates a basic difference between the properties of radiation and of the "body" of atoms. The radiation intensity in a resonator can be raised beyond any limit, that is, the resonator can contain any number of photons, at least in principle, without any change in the frequency or other properties of the radiation. On the other hand, the addition of even a single electron to the body of an atom, if possible at all, changes altogether the energy levels and the chemical properties of the atom.

PROBLEMS

5.1 An oscillating current of frequency ν and mean square intensity $\langle i^2 \rangle$, flowing through a straight antenna of length $l \ll \lambda = c/\nu$, emits radiation. The radiation intensity I at a distance $r \gg \lambda$ in a direction forming an angle θ with the antenna is, according to macroscopic theory formulated in CGS units, $I(r, \theta) = \pi\nu^2 \langle i^2 \rangle l^2 \sin^2\theta / c^3 r^2$.

Calculate, with $\nu = 10^6$ cycles/sec, $\sqrt{\langle i^2 \rangle} = 1$ amp., $l = 10$m: (a) $I(r, \theta)$ at $r = 100$ km, $\theta = 60°$; (b) the mean number of photons/cm^2 sec corresponding to this intensity; (c) the total power radiated by the antenna.

5.2 Mercury atoms excited in a strong magnetic field emit light of undisturbed wavelength $\lambda = 1849$ A with the same macroscopic distribution of intensity as a radio antenna parallel to the field (see Problem 5.1). Consider the emission from a discharge in a magnetic field in a gas that contains 10^{-9} g of mercury vapor. A counter with a window area of 10^{-3} cm^2 at 10 m from the discharge in a direction forming a 60° angle with the magnetic field detects 100 photons/sec of 1849 A light. Regard each Hg atom as an antenna consisting of an electron oscillating with frequency $\nu = c/\lambda$ and mean square amplitude $\langle a^2 \rangle$; the correspondence with antenna characteristics is $\langle i^2 \rangle l^2 = e^2 4 \pi^2 \nu^2 \langle a^2 \rangle$. Calculate: (a) the total power radiated at 1849 A; (b) the total rate of photon emission; (c) the rate of photon emission per Hg atom; (d) the root mean square amplitude, $\sqrt{\langle a^2 \rangle}$, of oscillation for one atom.

chapter 6

The statistical aspect
of atomic physics

Light, even though it is emitted in separate processes by individual atoms, appears to obey the laws of macroscopic electromagnetism with regard to its emission, propagation, and absorption when it is observed with macroscopic devices. As seen in the last chapter, one can perform macroscopic experiments with light at exceedingly low levels of intensity without affecting their results. It remains to be seen if, and to what extent, individual atomic processes also obey macroscopic laws. This can be done by low-intensity experiments in which light is detected through devices that score the absorption of single photons.

Experiments of this type record light absorption events localized sharply in space and time, and so distributed at various points of space and instants of time that the aggregate distribution of light absorption obeys the macroscopic laws. Within this limitation, the single absorption events are distributed completely *at random*. Randomness means, specifically, that in different experimental runs under identical conditions the absorption events have different distribution in space and time. In aggregate, the photon absorptions have "statistical" features, such as averages, indices of fluctuation, etc., which reproduce from one to another experiment; the detailed distribution of individual observations does not reproduce.

Random distribution of single events is observed throughout atomic physics, with the limitation that the statistical distribution of a large number of events is reproducible and follows a definite law. For example, the Franck-Hertz experiment on inelastic collisions between electrons and atoms can be performed at low intensity detecting individual electrons which emerge from the scattering chamber with given deflections and given energy losses. The time intervals between the detection of successive electrons, and the sequence in which electrons emerge with various deflections and energy losses are quite random. Only the statistical features of the distribution of time intervals, deflections, and losses are reproducible. Similarly, the time intervals and directions of α-particle emission by a radioactive material are random, with a fixed average rate of emission and uniform distribution in all directions.

The theory of quantum physics regards the randomness of single atomic events as a fundamental primitive law. The objective of quantum theory becomes then to predict the probabilities of the various possible outcomes of any experiment in which single events are to be detected. The occurrence of any specific outcome in any particular experimental run is regarded as inherently unpredictable.

For many problems of radiation emission, propagation, and absorption, macroscopic electromagnetism provides the answer to the problem formulated according to quantum theory. For instance, if the macroscopic intensity of light of frequency ν at a certain position (expressed as incident energy per unit area per unit time) is indicated by I, the probability of recording one photon with an ideal detector of unit area equals $I/h\nu$ per unit time. To deal with the majority of problems of quantum theory, one must formulate the pertinent laws and develop methods of calculation.

The randomness of atomic events was gradually recognized as a primitive phenomenon in 1926 by Born, Bohr, and their collaborators. The adoption of this point of view resolved the apparent inconsistencies which had stood in the way of atomic theory. For example, the fact that atomic electrons in a stationary state do not radiate, even though they are certainly neither at rest nor in uniform motion, appeared inconsistent with electromagnetism, as long as theory was expected to assign to each electron at each instant a definite position and velocity. However, if a stationary state of the electrons is fully described by the probability distribution of their possible positions and velocities, the average current may well vanish (no radiation emission) while nevertheless the velocities have a non-zero mean square value (positive kinetic energy).

This point of view developed, historically, from a combination of partial experimental evidence, fragmentary methods of calculation, and intuition. Its soundness was proved when consistent theoretical methods developed from it and accounted in detail for the mass of experimental data on atoms and radiation available at the time.[1] Even today, no single experiment provides evidence leading unequivocally to the point of view of quantum theory. Section 6.1 describes a type of experiment which appears particularly instructive. Section 6.2 compares the roles of the concepts of probability in the analysis of atomic and of macroscopic phenomena.

6.1 Experiments on the Time Distribution of Atomic Events

The occurrence of single atomic events can be detected with counters, working on the principles indicated in Chapter 2. When the detection frequency is sufficiently low, one can record the instants of detection of successive events and analyze their distribution in time. Such a distribution is always strikingly irregular, as anyone can testify who has ever listened to the clicking of a Geiger counter as it receives radiation from a radioactive substance.

If a number of experimental runs is performed under identical conditions, the records of the instants of occurrence of successive events are quite different for the different runs. That is, the instants of occurrence of individual events are *not reproducible*. Only their cumulative distribution has statistical features, outlined below, which are well reproducible.

The absorption of single light photons can be recorded, for example, by means of a Geiger counter which is "photoelectric," that is, which has internal metal surfaces with low photoelectric threshold exposed to light arriving from outside the counter. We consider here an experiment performed by Meyer and Gerlach in 1913 with a device equivalent to a photoelectric Geiger counter but somewhat more elementary.

The Meyer-Gerlach apparatus was essentially the same as used by Millikan for his oil drop experiment described in Chapter 2 (Fig. 2.1.). The main innovation consisted in illuminating the particles under observation with ultraviolet light to produce photoelectric effects.

---

[1] Phenomena taking place within regions of space no larger than about 10^{-13} cm, and involving the nature of particles, such as electrons, have still not been organized successfully by theory. Those phenomena have no essential influence on the subject matter of this book.

Meyer and Gerlach also replaced Millikan's oil drops with metal grains whose photoelectric threshold is conveniently low. Whenever a single electron is ejected from a particle, the particle's charge increases by one unit e, the force exerted on it by the condenser changes suddenly, and so does the particle's motion. The emission of single photoelectrons can thus be observed visually through the microscope.

With this arrangement the observer can score the successive time instants at which photoelectric emission occurs from any one metal grain. The average rate of emission events per unit time, determined by scoring their total number over a great length of time, is proportional to the intensity of the light falling upon the grain, in agreement with the results of macroscopic experiments. The interest of the experiment lies in analyzing the time intervals which separate successive emission events.

For example, one may record the occurrence or non-occurrence of emissions during each one of a long series of equal time periods and also record for each of these periods the time elapsed since the last emission prior to it. The two scores turn out to be wholly *uncorrelated*. (Some notes about statistical distributions and about correlation tests are given in Appendix V.) The lack of correlation shows that the length of time since the last emission has no bearing upon the frequency of occurrence in later time periods.

Notice, again, that the scores obtained in separate, identical, experiments are different, but the lack of correlation is common to all experiments.

One may also measure a large number N of time intervals $\tau_1, \tau_2, \cdots \tau_N$, between successive emission events, classify these intervals according to their length, for example, according to whether they lie between 0 and δ sec, between δ and 2δ, 2δ and 3δ sec, etc., and then plot the number n of intervals in each class. In Fig. 6.1a, the number of intervals lying between 0 and 2 sec is plotted in correspondence to the abscissa $t = 1$ sec, the mid-point of this class of interval lengths; the next point is plotted in correspondence to the abscissa $t = 3$ sec, the mid-point between 2 and 4 sec, etc. The points in a plot of this type lie along an exponential curve [2] represented by

$$n = n_0 e^{-t/\tau}, \tag{1}$$

where n is the ordinate corresponding to the time t, n_0 the intercept of the curve on the ordinate axis, and τ is the mean length of all intervals, defined by

$$\tau = \frac{1}{N} (\tau_1 + \tau_2 + \cdots + \tau_N). \tag{2}$$

---

[2] See footnote 2 on page 60.

If various experiments are performed under identical conditions and their results are entered separately in the plot of Fig. 6.1, the various sets of points thus obtained do not coincide, in general; nevertheless, they all lie along the curve described by Eq. 1, within the limits of the statistical sampling error.

The main property of the statistical distribution shown in Fig. 6.1 and of its mathematical representation (1) is that the number of intervals in each class is a fixed fraction of the total number of intervals in

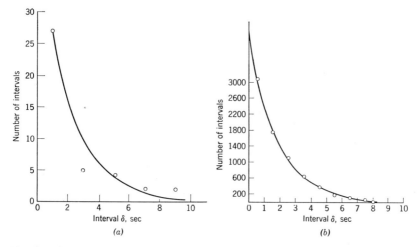

Fig. 6.1 Distribution of time intervals between successive elementary processes. Solid curves from Eq. 1; experimental points: (a) photoelectric emission (adapted from E. Meyer and W. Gerlach, *Ann. Physik*, **45**, 215, 1914); (b) α-particle emission (adapted from E. Rutherford, *Radioactive Substances and their Radiations*, Cambridge University Press, 1913, p. 190).

all classes of greater time length to within the experimental error. This fraction approaches δ/τ when the width δ of each class is much smaller than τ.

The experimental result represented by (1) may be stated as a mathematical law by saying that a photoelectric event has a *probability* dt/τ of occurring in a given metal particle within any infinitesimal time period dt. This probability is independent of the time elapsed since the previous photoelectric event and is proportional to the light intensity; otherwise it depends, of course, on the size of the particle and on the frequency of the light.

This probability law enables one to calculate the probability of observing m photoelectric events within a time period T. If a total number N of time periods is observed, the expected number n_m of periods in which

m events take place is given, according to Appendix V, by the Poisson distribution

$$n_m = Ne^{-T/\tau} \frac{(T/\tau)^m}{m!},$$ (3)

where $m! = 1 \times 2 \times 3 \times \cdots \times m$. This prediction is verified experimentally.

Experiments in which one records the time distribution of any elementary atomic process, such as collisions or the emission of radiations, yield invariably distributions represented by the same Eqs. 1 and 3 obtained in the Meyer-Gerlach experiment. In fact, the Meyer-Gerlach

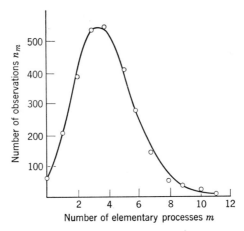

Fig. 6.2 Distribution of numbers of elementary processes observed in equal time periods. Solid curve from Eq. 3 with $T/\tau = 3.87$. (Experimental points from E. Rutherford, *Radioactive Substances and their Radiations*, Cambridge University Press, 1913, p. 189.)

experiment was not pushed to great accuracy, as shown by the small number of intervals entered in Fig. 6.1a. Figures 6.1b and 6.2 show extensive data from an experiment carried out by Rutherford and collaborators for the purpose of testing accurately the randomness of the times of α-particle emissions.

In the Meyer-Gerlach experiment the possible occurrence of photo-emission soon after the light has been switched on constitutes a striking consequence of the probability law. Within a finite, however short, time period Δt there is a finite probability $\Delta t/\tau$ that an electron be emitted from a given particle, even though the period Δt may be so short that the energy delivered to the whole particle by a weak light amounts to less than one photon $h\nu$ according to macroscopic laws. The macroscopic expression for the incident energy is $IS \Delta t$, where I is the light intensity and S the cross-sectional area of the particle. If, for example, $I = 10^{-10}$ watts/cm^2, $S = 0.1\mu^2 = 10^{-9}$ cm^2 and $\Delta t = 1$ sec, the energy delivered to the particle is $IS \Delta t = 10^{-19}$ joules $= 0.62$ ev. If the light wavelength is, for example, 3000 A, corresponding to a photon energy of 4 ev, the average number of photons available for absorption at the surface is 0.16 per sec. If the metal grains produce on the average 1 photoeffect per 10 photons available, the average rate of photoemissions is 0.016 per sec. Therefore, one photoelectron may have been emitted by the end of the first second after switching on, with a probability of 0.016, corresponding, on the average, to one success in 64 trials, even though the macroscopic value of the energy incident on the particle in each trial amounts to only 0.6 ev, which would be inadequate to eject an electron.

One concludes that the macroscopic expression of the light energy incident on a surface represents a statistical average. The actual arrival of energy experiences random fluctuations about the average. The metal particles in the Meyer-Gerlach experiment act as probe indicators of these fluctuations.

6.2   The Concept of Probability in Macroscopic and in Quantum Physics

Probability plays a role in various branches of physics, such as the statistical theory of gas mechanics, and in many familiar phenomena, such as dice or card games. Let us consider how probability is introduced in the analysis of macroscopic phenomena, before discussing its role in quantum physics.

The mathematical theory of probability derives logical consequences from an initial statement that a certain number of possible, mutually exclusive events are equally probable. We deal here not with the mathematical theory but with the physical considerations leading to an initial statement of equal probability.

The theory of a fair game of cards assumes that all possible initial distributions of cards among the players are equally probable. The card distribution derives from a multitude of accidental events in the course of shuffling the cards. One believes it plausible that adequate shuffling erases any correlation between the sequences of cards in a deck before and after shuffling, and consequently between the card distributions in successive games. Common experience supports this belief.

On the other hand, if one starts with a deck of cards in a given arrangement and if one controls and reproduces accurately the procedure of shuffling, one expects to obtain again and again the same card distribution among players. Accordingly, the equal probability of card distributions in a fair game rests on our intentional *failure to control and reproduce* the conditions affecting the operation of shuffling.

Similarly, the statistical mechanics of gases, in its "classical" form, rests on the assumption that all possible positions and velocities of each gas molecule are equally probable, subject to suitable restrictions, for example, that all molecules be within a given container and that their total energy be fixed. The equiprobability is assumed to result from a multitude of collisions among molecules. Nevertheless, it is also regarded as possible, in principle, to know the position and velocity of each molecule at a given time; in this event, statistical mechanics would not be applicable, just as the theory of a card game does not apply when shuffling is "rigged."

In other words, the distribution of playing cards or of molecules is regarded as unpredictable and *unreproducible* because of failure to control the numerous variables on which the distribution is known to depend.

With regard to the time distribution of the emission of photoelectrons in the Meyer-Gerlach experiment, these authors sought to identify the source of unreproducibility in the process of escape of electrons through the air surrounding each metal particle, but their explanation is not convincing. In other equivalent phenomena, for example, in the ejection of high-energy photoelectrons by X rays in gases, one knows of no variables which are responsible for the random distribution of the events. The same holds for all elementary processes of atomic physics, that is, for all processes involving individual particles or photons.

As no variables manifest themselves, whose control would eliminate or even reduce the randomness of elementary processes, one need not assume that such variables actually exist. Therefore, quantum mechanics regards the equiprobability of alternative events, such as the emission of a photoelectron in different short time periods of equal duration, as a physical fact which need not be a consequence of other facts, that is, as a primitive fact.[3] More generally, it regards as a primitive fact the limited reproducibility of observations of atomic events performed under identical conditions. Whereas in macroscopic physics any difference in the outcome of experiments is assumed to stem from

---

[3] The scientific procedure consists of assembling experimental evidence and of organizing it in our minds economically. Economy requires us to regard a minimum number of facts as fundamental, or primitive, the others as their logical consequences. During any period of the history of science, it depends on the evidence available at the time, on our analytical ability, and also to some extent on preference, which facts we regard as primitive.

actual differences in the experimental conditions, quantum mechanics makes no such general assumption.

Physics can make predictions only about those features of the outcome of experiments which are reproducible. In atomic experiments, statistical parameters of the results, such as the average rates of occurrence of certain events or the mean square values of departures from averages, are indeed reproducible. The variables of macroscopic phenomena, such as the intensity of the photoelectric current emitted by an illuminated metal surface, take reproducible values because they are statistical parameters of the same phenomena regarded from an atomistic point of view.

PROBLEMS

6.1   A counter registers the radiation from a radioactive source. The counts are recorded in ten-second intervals and it is found that in 10 percent of the intervals no counts are registered. Utilize the Poisson distribution law, Eq. 3, to calculate: (*a*) the mean time between successive counts; (*b*) the fraction of ten-second intervals in which three counts are registered.

6.2   A radioactive source is placed half-way between two identical counters A and B so that the average counting rates of A and B are equal. Six successive counts are registered. Calculate the probabilities of the following distributions of counts: (*a*) the first three in one counter and the next three in the other, i.e., in either sequence $AAABBB$ or $BBBAAA$; (*b*) alternation of successive counts in the two counters, i.e., in either sequence $ABABAB$ or $BABABA$; (*c*) all counts in the same counter, i.e., $AAAAAA$ or $BBBBBB$; (*d*) three counts in one counter and three in the other, in any sequence.

6.3   A counter detects radiation with a mean interval between counts $\tau = 5$ sec. The counter registers the number of counts, m, in each 15 sec period. The observation extends over N such periods. Calculate: (*a*) the mean $\langle m \rangle$ of the counts per period; (*b*) the mean square $\langle m^2 \rangle$; (*c*) the mean square deviation Δm^2. (Utilize Eq. 3; note that $mn_m = (T/\tau)n_{m-1}$ and that $\Sigma_{m=0}^{\infty} n_m = N$.)

6.4   A counter detects radiation from a distant radioactive source at a mean rate of N counts/sec. The counter is moved 2 percent closer to the source, so that the counting rate should increase by 4 percent. Estimate the time t required to verify the increase, taking as a criterion of significance that the observed counts should exceed Nt by three times the root mean square deviation of the expected number.

chapter 7

Analysis of radiation and particle beams; eigenstates and eigenvalues

Experimental observations establish relationships between physical variables, specifically between the variables one observes and the variables which define the initial conditions of the experiment. We have seen that observations of phenomena involving single atomic particles do not reproduce in detail in successive runs performed under identical conditions, but obey statistical laws. Therefore, the relationships among the variables of quantum physics, for example, between the energy and the position of an atomic electron, differ substantially from the corresponding relationships among macroscopic variables. This chapter will illustrate the nature of quantum variables and the relationships among them by discussing experiments on beams of electromagnetic radiation and of particles. (Throughout this book, "radiation" means electromagnetic radiation and "particle" a particle of matter.)

Consider, for example, the spectral analysis of the light emitted by atoms under bombardment by electrons. Upon filtration through a spectroscope the light becomes separated into components of different colors which emerge in different directions. The intensity of the different components may be measured by the response of photon counters at different positions along a screen. The average rate of scoring by a given counter is a measure of the intensity of one spectral component, but at any given time one cannot predict, in general, which counter will click next. However, if the light is initially made monochromatic by preliminary filtration through a spectroscope with a narrow exit slit, it is not further decomposed by a subsequent spectral analysis; one can then predict that every count will be scored by the detector at the right position on the screen.

In the various experiments we shall describe, analysis of a beam by a given device may show it to be homogeneous with respect to a certain characteristic; in this event, the beam is not subdivided into components, its entire intensity is scored by a single detector, and there is no uncertainty as to which one of several counters will score next. A result of this type merely verifies the effectiveness of a preliminary filtration. Alternatively, the beam may be found to be inhomogeneous; its intensity is then fractionated into different components and there is uncertainty as to the sequence of scoring by counters placed at the various exit channels of the analyzer. The fractionation is particularly clearcut when there are only a few components, as in the analysis of light polarization, rather than a large number, or even an infinity, of them as is often the case for spectral analysis. Particle beams are resolved in a small number of components when they are analyzed according to particle orientation with respect to a magnetic field (Sect. 7.2).

According to classical physics, the fractionation of a particle beam should attain an ultimate limit, when the particles are homogeneous in all their characteristics. Any further analysis should fail to subdivide the beam, so that the response of particle counters would be predictable in advance. Experiments to be described in Sect. 7.2 show that there is no such ultimate limit. A beam of particles can be fractionated again and again, indefinitely, by analyzers of different orientation, much like a beam of light can be fractionated further and further by successive filtration through crystals that transmit light of different polarizations.

The fractionation by polarization filters is readily understood in classical physics because, clearly, a light beam cannot be at the same time circularly polarized and linearly polarized. If it is circularly polarized after transmission through a certain crystal, it can be fractionated into linearly polarized components by filtration through a different crystal, and vice versa. Polarization filters of different kinds, or even only of different orientations, perform incompatible kinds of analysis. A light beam made homogeneous in the sense that it is characterized as right circularly polarized is clearly not linearly polarized and thus appears inhomogeneous when fractionated by a linear polarization filter. Circular and linear polarization constitute *incompatible characteristics* of a light beam.

The fact that a beam of particles cannot be made homogeneous in every respect implies that some characteristics of particles are incompatible, in the same sense as linear and circular polarization are incompatible. This conclusion was implicit in the finding that observations of atomic phenomena are not reproducible in detail even though the experimental conditions are controlled to maximum uniformity. Maximum uniformity of conditions means full homogeneity with respect to some characteristics. The fact that some of the possible experimental observations remain unpredictable means that these observations bear on characteristics incompatible with those that have been controlled in the preparation of the experiment. Incompatibility of particle characteristics constitutes a main quantum effect which escapes macroscopic observation. Examples of incompatibility will be given in this chapter and in the following ones.

Notice how the quantum properties of particles and of radiation complement each other. The incompatibility of certain radiation characteristics is known in classical physics. Classical physics predicts the intensity of beam components when linearly polarized light is analyzed for circular polarization. Classical physics fails, however, to show that light is absorbed one photon at a time and that the "intensity" of each component represents the average rate of photon absorptions by a counter. With regard to particles, classical physics defines the intensity of a beam component as the average number of particles flowing in it. On the other hand, classical physics fails to detect the incompatibility of particle characteristics and to provide rules to calculate the intensities in the fractionation of particle beams. Quantum mechanics describes incompatibility and calculates fractional intensities by methods that apply equally to radiation and to particles.

Quantum mechanics also treats on an equal footing characteristics of particles and radiation whose analytic representation is quite dissimilar in macroscopic physics. Some characteristics, like the energy of a particle or the frequency of radiation, are variables that assume definite numerical values in atomic as in classical physics. On the other hand, experimental analysis can make a beam homogeneous with respect to a characteristic such as circular polarization which is not identified usually by the numerical value of a parameter, although one could define a variable with two alternative values, namely 1 for circular dextro-rotatory and -1 for levo-rotatory polarization. In quantum physics, all characteristics of radiation and of particles are usually called "variables" in an extended sense; we shall thus speak of "compatible variables" and "incompatible variables." Numerical indices may be introduced to specify certain characteristics, where necessary, to facilitate a uniform treatment.

A state of particles or radiation which is identified by a specific value of a variable, or by one value of each of several variables, is called a "proper state" of that variable or variables. The half-German word "eigenstate" is currently used instead of "proper state." The specific value of the variable is called the "proper value" or "eigenvalue" corresponding to the eigenstate which it identifies.

The experimental fractionation of a beam is described in quantum mechanics by saying that the initial state of the beam is resolved into component states. If the initial state were an eigenstate of a certain variable, that is, if the beam were homogeneous with respect to that variable, the component states are eigenstates of a different variable. For instance, circularly polarized light is in an eigenstate of circular polarization; it can be resolved into linearly polarized components which are in eigenstates of linear polarization. The experiments on beam fractionation determine the probability of detecting a particle or photon in an eigenstate of a variable, when the beam was known to be in an eigenstate of another variable. Thus they establish probability relationships between eigenstates of different variables. These relationships constitute laws of quantum mechanics which replace, or at least supplement, the laws of macroscopic physics. Macroscopic laws are described by ordinary equations among the values of different variables, such as $\mathbf{F} = m\mathbf{a}$ or $x = x_0 + vt$. Quantum laws must take new forms to allow for the fact that a specific value of one variable is not, in general, associated uniquely with a specific value of another variable.

Examples of light beam analysis are discussed in Sect. 7.1, examples of particle beam analysis in Sect. 7.2. Conclusions and generalizations will be outlined in Sect. 7.3.

7.1 Light Beams

(a) *Frequency and photon energy.* Given a light beam which is not monochromatic, one may extract from it a monochromatic component of desired frequency by filtration through a "monochromator," that is, through a spectroscope provided with an exit slit at a suitable point of its screen. A monochromatic component delivers to matter, when it is absorbed, photons of uniform energy; therefore, monochromatic radiation is in a state characterized by a specific value of the photon energy, that is, in an eigenstate of photon energy.

Radiation filtered through a monochromator may be tested by filtration through a second monochromator identical to the first one; all of the radiation goes through the second filter if its slit is set in the same position as in the first filter, none goes through if the setting is different. For equal settings of the slit, a photon counter scores at equal rates whether it is placed behind the first or behind the second filter.

Spectroscopic analysis of a non-monochromatic beam may be regarded as a statistical analysis of the energy of photons absorbed from the beam. If the light intensity on a spectroscope screen is I_1 and I_2 at positions corresponding to frequencies ν_1 and ν_2, the relative probabilities of detecting photon absorptions at these positions are $I_1/h\nu_1$ and $I_2/h\nu_2$. These probabilities may be tested by low-intensity experiments, placing photon counters at the two positions.

According to macroscopic theory, radiation is described mathematically by the strengths and directions of the electric and magnetic fields at each point of space and at each instant of time. If the radiation is monochromatic, the fields vary at each point sinusoidally in the course of time. If the radiation is not monochromatic, the fields may be resolved into sums of sinusoidally varying components by the procedure of Fourier analysis outlined in Appendix IV. Each component of the fields which oscillates sinusoidally represents a monochromatic component of the radiation. The sum of the intensities of all monochromatic components equals the intensity of the whole radiation. This macroscopic calculation of the intensity of a monochromatic component of frequency ν amounts to a calculation of the probability that the energy of a photon absorbed equals $h\nu$.

Notice that monochromatic radiation constitutes an idealization, because a perfectly sinusoidal variation of any quantity in the course of time has no beginning and no end (see Appendix IV). Experimentally the spectroscopic analysis of radiation is also imperfect, because of theoretical limitations to the performance of monochromators, including the effect of the finite width of their exit slits. Thus one deals in practice with radiation whose photon energy is not exactly specified but is at best confined within a narrow range of values.

(b) Beam direction and photon momentum. Light may be collimated by filtration through diaphragms or focusing lenses, so as to travel in a given direction. Radiation thus collimated, when absorbed by matter, delivers to it a mechanical momentum in the direction of collimation. The magnitude of this momentum is known, from macroscopic theory and experiments, to equal the energy absorbed divided by the velocity of light $c = 3.00 \times 10^{10}$ cm/sec. It follows that each photon absorbed from monochromatic collimated radiation delivers to matter a momentum of magnitude

$$p = \frac{h\nu}{c}. \tag{1}$$

Therefore, monochromatic radiation traveling in a definite direction is in an eigenstate of photon momentum.

The direction of radiation and the momentum delivered by each photon absorption may be tested and retested experimentally like the frequency of radiation and the energy delivered by each photon absorption. Because the light velocity c is very large, the momentum (1) is very small even in the scale of atomic phenomena, except for very high frequencies. Experiments on the ejection of electrons from matter by an X-ray beam show clearly a prevalence of ejection in the direction of the beam, which results from the momentum delivered by each photon.

According to macroscopic theory, radiation which is monochromatic and monodirectional is described mathematically by electric and magnetic fields whose variations in space and time constitute a "plane sinusoidal wave." The name "plane wave" signifies that the fields vary from point to point along the direction of propagation and are uniform on any plane perpendicular to that direction. If a radiation is not monochromatic and monodirectional, its fields may be resolved into sums of components that vary as plane sinusoidal waves, by applying the procedure of Fourier analysis (Appendix IV) to the field variations in space as well as in time. Each component of the fields that varies as a plane sinusoidal wave represents a monochromatic monodirectional component of the radiation. The sum of the intensities of all these components equals the intensity of the whole radiation. The macroscopic calculation of the intensity of each monochromatic component amounts to a calculation of the probability that the momentum of a photon absorbed has magnitude and direction characteristic for that component.

Perfectly collimated monochromatic radiation constitutes an idealization, because a perfect sinusoidal variation in one direction and a perfect uniformity over planes perpendicular to it should extend to infinite distances. Experimentally, the directional analysis of radiation is also imperfect because of the effect of collimator edges, to be described in Chapter 10. Thus one deals in practice with radiation whose photon momentum is not specified exactly but is confined, at best, within narrow ranges of magnitude and direction.

(c) *Linear polarization.* According to macroscopic electromagnetism, the electric and the magnetic fields of radiation traveling in empty space or in an isotropic material are perpendicular to one another and to the direction of propagation. These limitations leave the direction of the fields undetermined within the plane perpendicular to the direction of propagation. The field direction need not remain constant at any one point in the course of time. Radiation whose electric field maintains a constant direction in the course of time is said to be polarized linearly in that direction. It is in an eigenstate of linear polarization, identified by the direction of the electric field.

Radiation emitted by currents that oscillate in a given direction is polarized linearly with its electric field in the plane defined by the direction of the current and by the direction of propagation (Fig. 7.1). Radiation from radio and television antennas is often polarized linearly.

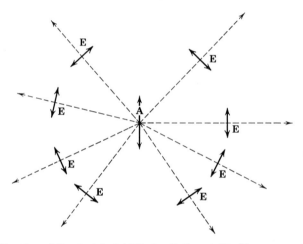

Fig. 7.1 Direction of the electric field **E** of radiation emitted by a current oscillating along the antenna **A**.

The currents within gas atoms which emit light are usually oriented in random directions. However, when atoms are subjected to a magnetic field, their internal currents are affected by the field and their frequencies of oscillation depend on their orientation; linearly polarized light emitted by currents parallel to the field may then be singled out by filtration through a monochromator (see Sect. 7.2.).

Light detectors such as photographic plates, photocells, or photon counters give usually a response independent of the polarization. However, the polarization of light can be analyzed, like its frequency, by suitable devices. A device that separates light with different polarizations and is followed by a diaphragm placed so as to let through only light in a state of specified polarization, serves as a "polarizer" filter to be utilized much like a monochromator.

Light with different linear polarizations is separated by means of materials whose properties are "anisotropic," that is, not uniform in all directions perpendicular to the beam axis. We consider here in

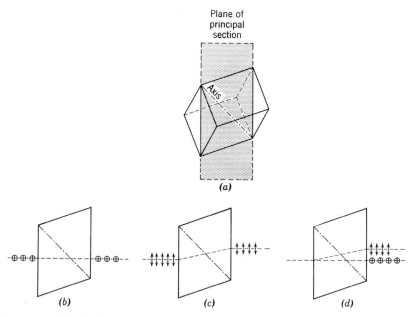

Fig. 7.2 (a) Iceland spar crystal with optical axis and principal section in the plane of the paper. In (b), (c), (d) the crystal is represented by its principal section. Light polarized with the electric field perpendicular to the principal section travels undisturbed, ordinary ray, Fig. (b); light with the electric field in the principal section is shifted, extraordinary ray, Fig. (c); light in any other state of polarization is split into an ordinary and an extraordinary ray, Fig. (d).

particular crystals of Iceland spar, whose electrons yield to the pull of an electric field by a displacement skew to the pull, unless the field is either perpendicular or parallel to an axis of symmetry of the crystal ("optical axis"). Figure 7.2a shows a spar crystal, its optical axis, and a "principal section," that is, a plane through the optical axis and perpendicular to a crystal face.

A light beam which enters a crystal as in Fig. 7.2b, at normal incidence along a principal section and with linear polarization perpendicular to this section, travels through undisturbed. If the direction of polarization lies on the principal section, the light experiences an anomalous refraction, it follows the path marked in Fig. 7.2*c* and emerges in a direction parallel to the direction of incidence but shifted sideways. If the direction of the electric field is oblique to the principal section, the incident light beam splits into two components which follow respectively the two paths of Fig. 7.2*d*. The component which follows the straight path is called "ordinary ray," the other "extraordinary ray."

When a diaphragm is placed behind the spar crystal, so as to let through either only the ordinary or only the extraordinary ray, the crystal acts as a "polarizer" filter. The transmitted light is linearly polarized in a direction respectively perpendicular or parallel to the principal section, independently of whether the incident light was linearly polarized or in what direction. The light is in an eigenstate of linear polarization defined by the orientation of the spar crystal.

The transmitted light may be tested with a second filter identical to the first one and equally oriented. All of the light goes through the second filter if its diaphragm is set in the same position as in the first filter; none of the light goes through if the settings are opposite. For equal settings of the filter a photon counter scores at equal rates whether it is placed behind the first or behind the second filter.

If the light incident on an Iceland spar filter is polarized linearly with its electric field $\mathbf{E}$ [1] oblique to the principal section, macroscopic theory calculates the intensity transmitted by the filter. The field $\mathbf{E}$ is analyzed into two components $\mathbf{E}_{\parallel}$ and $\mathbf{E}_{\perp}$, parallel and perpendicular to the principal section. If the direction of $\mathbf{E}$ forms an angle α with $\mathbf{E}_{\perp}$, the strength of $\mathbf{E}_{\perp}$ equals $E\cos\alpha$, whereas $E_{\parallel} = E\sin\alpha$. To the electric fields $\mathbf{E}_{\perp}$ and $\mathbf{E}_{\parallel}$ correspond two components of the incident light polarized linearly in the directions of these fields. The intensity of a light beam is proportional to the squared strength of the electric field. Accordingly, the relative intensities of the incident beam and of its two components polarized in the directions $E_{\perp}$ and $E_{\parallel}$ are $1:\cos^2\alpha:\sin^2\alpha$. The sum of the two component intensities equals the incident intensity.

The law of decomposition may be verified experimentally, for example, by utilizing a first crystal as a polarizer filter which passes the ordinary ray and turning the second crystal with respect to the first one by an angle α about the incident beam. If the intensity transmitted

---

[1] A vector, that is, a quantity having a magnitude and a direction, is usually indicated by a bold face character. The magnitude of the vector is indicated either by the same character in italics or by the bold face character between vertical bars, as, for example, $|\mathbf{E}|$. The square of a vector is defined as the scalar product of the vector by itself, for example, $\mathbf{E}\cdot\mathbf{E}$, and therefore equals simply the square of the vector's magnitude. However, in Chapters 14 and following it will be expedient to indicate the square of the angular momentum vectors by the bold face vector symbol followed by the exponent 2, for example, $\mathbf{l}^2$.

by the polarizer filter is called I, the intensity emerging from the second filter is $I \cos^2\alpha$ and $I \sin^2\alpha$, respectively, for its two settings, ordinary and extraordinary. The experiment may be performed at low intensity, observing the light with a photon counter.

Notice that an Iceland spar analyzer in a single fixed orientation, with the two alternative settings of its diaphragm, performs a complete analysis of the incident light into two component eigenstates with linear polarizations perpendicular to one another. The whole incident intensity is distributed between the ordinary and the extraordinary ray, whether or not the incident light was linearly polarized. An analyzer with different orientation performs a *different* analysis of the incident light into a different pair of alternative eigenstates of linear polarization. Analyzers with different orientation observe different "variables" which are incompatible in the sense indicated on page 74.

Without reference to macroscopic theory, one may draw from the experiments the following conclusions: (*a*) that light filtered as the ordinary ray of a "polarizer" crystal is in an eigenstate of linear polarization identified by the orientation of that crystal; (*b*) that light in this state may be resolved into two component eigenstates identified by the ordinary and extraordinary rays of a second ("analyzer") crystal; and (*c*) that the intensities of these components are proportional respectively to the squared cosine and the squared sine of the angle between the orientations of the polarizer and the analyzer.

The state of polarization of light changes in the course of propagation through various materials. For example, propagation through sugar solutions rotates the direction of linear polarization, that is, it changes light from one to another state of linear polarization. Filtration through other materials yields polarization other than linear, that is, it yields light whose electric field does not maintain at any one point a constant direction in the course of time. The change of direction takes place at a uniform rate when the light is monochromatic. When the electric field strength at any one point remains constant in the course of time and only its direction changes, the polarization is called "circular." *Right* and *left* circular polarizations correspond to opposite changes of direction.

Light of any polarization can be fractionated by suitable crystal filters into two components, one of which is right circularly and the other left circularly polarized. In general, to any state of polarization there corresponds another one *opposite* or *orthogonal* to it. Linear polarizations perpendicular to one another and circular polarizations with opposite directions (dextro-and levo-rotatory) are special orthogonal pairs of polarizations.

Light in any state of polarization can be analyzed experimentally into a pair of components with arbitrary orthogonal polarizations. Given a state of polarization, macroscopic theory calculates the intensities of its components corresponding to any set of orthogonal eigenstates. This calculation determines the probability of observing a photon with a counter placed behind any given analyzer.

Light in an eigenstate of polarization identified by a given orientation of analyzer crystals is split into two non-vanishing components by an analyzer with its crystals in different orientation. Two analyzers with crystals in different orientation perform incompatible types of analysis.

(d) Mathematical representation. Electromagnetic radiation is often conveniently analyzed into monochromatic, monodirectional, linearly polarized components. We give here, for purpose of illustration, the mathematical representation of one such component according to macroscopic theory.

If one chooses the direction of propagation of the radiation as the x axis, the direction of the electric field is perpendicular to it and may be taken as the y axis. The components of the electric field, at each point (x, y, z) of space and instant t of time, are then

$$E_x = 0$$
$$E_y = E_0 \sin\left[2\pi \left(\frac{x}{\lambda} - \nu t\right) + \phi \right] = E_0 \sin[2\pi(kx - \nu t) + \phi] \tag{2}$$
$$E_z = 0.$$

In this formula, E_0 indicates the peak strength of the electric field, ϕ the phase of oscillation at $x = 0$ and $t = 0$, $\lambda = c/\nu$ the wavelength, and $k = 1/\lambda = \nu/c$ the reciprocal wavelength or "wave number," that is, the number of waves included in a unit length. The magnetic field is directed along the z axis, and its single component H_z is proportional to E_y at all points and times; the value of H_z equals the value of E_y in the CGS system of units. E_y is a sinusoidal function of x, with period $\lambda = 1/k$, and of t with period $1/\nu$. The plot of E_y versus x at any instant t is obtained by sliding the plot at $t = 0$ along the x axis by the distance of propagation $\lambda \nu t = ct$.

The wave number relates to the momentum delivered by a photon, owing to (1), through the proportionality equation

$$p = hk, \tag{3}$$

which is analogous to the Einstein equation of photon energy, $E = h\nu$, and clearly derives from it.

The plane wave (2) may be represented with vector symbols without reference to a system of coordinates with particular orientation. The space coordinates of a point are then represented with a vector **r**, and the direction of propagation is represented, together with the magnitude of the wave number, by a "wave vector" **k**. The product kx in (2) is replaced by the scalar product

$$\mathbf{k} \cdot \mathbf{r} = k_x x + k_y y + k_z z, \tag{4}$$

and the peak electric field is represented in strength and direction by a vector $\mathbf{E}_0$. Equation 2 becomes

$$\mathbf{E} = \mathbf{E}_0 \sin[2\pi(\mathbf{k} \cdot \mathbf{r} - \nu t) + \phi], \tag{5}$$

and (3) takes the more complete vector form

$$\mathbf{p} = h\mathbf{k}. \tag{6}$$

According to (5) and (4), the electric field is a sinusoidal function of t and of each space coordinate x, y, or z. Therefore, $\mathbf{E}$ obeys the differential equation of the sine function with respect to each of these variables, namely,

$$\frac{\partial^2 \mathbf{E}}{\partial t^2} = -4\pi^2 \nu^2 \mathbf{E} \tag{7a}$$

$$\frac{\partial^2 \mathbf{E}}{\partial x^2} = -4\pi^2 k_x^2 \mathbf{E} \tag{7b}$$

$$\frac{\partial^2 \mathbf{E}}{\partial y^2} = -4\pi^2 k_y^2 \mathbf{E} \tag{7c}$$

$$\frac{\partial^2 \mathbf{E}}{\partial z^2} = -4\pi^2 k_z^2 \mathbf{E}. \tag{7d}$$

These equations state that the second rate of variation of the electric field $\mathbf{E}$ with respect to each variable is proportional to $\mathbf{E}$ itself, at all places and at all times. The proportionality constant is a function of the oscillation frequency or of a component of the wave vector.

The equations (7) belong to the mathematical class of "eigenvalue equations." An equation of this class requires that a function after being transformed in a specified manner—in this case, by taking a second derivative—turn out to be proportional to the function itself. The proportionality factor is called an "eigenvalue" of the equation and the solution of the equation is an "eigenfunction." In this example, the sinusoidal plane wave (5) is an eigenfunction of each of the equations 7; the corresponding eigenvalues are respectively: $-4\pi^2\nu^2$, $-4\pi^2 k_x^2$, $-4\pi^2 k_y^2$ and $-4\pi^2 k_z^2$. The mathematical representation of all eigenstates of quantum mechanical systems is derived from eigenvalue equations.

The four equations 7 may be combined utilizing the relationship between frequency and wavelength or wave number

$$\frac{\nu}{c} = \frac{1}{\lambda} = k, \qquad \text{that is,} \qquad \frac{\nu^2}{c^2} = k^2 = k_x^2 + k_y^2 + k_z^2. \tag{8}$$

Summing (7b), (7c), and (7d) and subtracting from the sum the equation (7a) divided by c^2, one finds

$$\frac{\partial^2 \mathbf{E}}{\partial x^2} + \frac{\partial^2 \mathbf{E}}{\partial y^2} + \frac{\partial^2 \mathbf{E}}{\partial z^2} - \frac{1}{c^2}\frac{\partial^2 \mathbf{E}}{\partial t^2} = 0. \tag{9}$$

This relationship, among the second rates of variation of $\mathbf{E}$ from point to point and in the course of time, constitutes the "wave equation." This equation is established by electromagnetic theory as a consequence of the Maxwell equations which interrelate the variations of the electric field and of the magnetic field. The wave equation holds for the macroscopic fields of any electromagnetic radiation in empty space, whether or not it is monochromatic or collimated.

Notice the chain of arguments which is followed here. For a plane monochromatic wave, characterized by a frequency and direction or by a wave vector, the wave equation holds as a consequence of the eigenvalue equations 7 and of the equation 8 relating frequency and wave vector. For radiation that has no definite wave vector or frequency, the wave equation holds nevertheless, because the radiation may be regarded as a combination of plane monochromatic components each of which obeys Eq. 9. This chain of arguments extends further, owing to the connection established by the photoelectric effect between the oscillatory properties of radiation and the mechanical properties of its photons. Equation 8 between frequency and wave vector may be expressed as a relation between photon energy and momentum,

$$\frac{E}{c} = \frac{h\nu}{c} = hk = p, \qquad \text{that is,} \qquad \frac{E^2}{c^2} = p^2 = p_x{}^2 + p_y{}^2 + p_z{}^2. \tag{10}$$

In view of the equivalence of (8) and (10), we may say that the wave equation represents the energy-momentum relation for the photons of monochromatic monodirectional radiation, that is, of radiation in an eigenstate of photon energy and momentum. The energy and the momentum components of photons do not have well defined values for radiation in a general state, that is, for radiation inhomogeneous with respect to these characteristics. The wave equation 9, which is valid for any state of radiation in empty space, represents implicitly the energy-momentum relation for photons even when these quantities have no definite values. It will be seen in following chapters that wave equations may represent relations among mechanical properties of particles as well as of photons.

Consider now the analysis of the plane linearly polarized wave (5) into components $E_\perp$ and $E_\parallel$ relating to a spar crystal analyzer. If the direction perpendicular to the principal section of the analyzer is indicated by a vector $\mathbf{P}$ of unit magnitude, the decomposition may be performed mathematically with vector symbols. The vector $\mathbf{E}_\perp$ has the direction of $\mathbf{P}$ and a magnitude equal to the component of the field $\mathbf{E}$ along $\mathbf{P}$, namely, to $\mathbf{E} \cdot \mathbf{P}$. We may then write

$$\mathbf{E} = \mathbf{E}_\perp + \mathbf{E}_\parallel, \qquad \mathbf{E}_\perp = (\mathbf{E} \cdot \mathbf{P})\,\mathbf{P}, \qquad \mathbf{E}_\parallel = \mathbf{E} - (\mathbf{E} \cdot \mathbf{P})\,\mathbf{P}. \tag{11}$$

Both linear polarizations $\mathbf{E}_\perp$ and $\mathbf{E}_\parallel$ are singled out experimentally by the analyzer as the polarizations of the ordinary and of the extraordinary ray. These characterizations may be summed up mathematically by a single equation, of the eigenvalue type (7) above. The equation is

$$(\mathbf{E} \cdot \mathbf{P})\,\mathbf{P} = a\mathbf{E}, \tag{12}$$

where a is a proportionality constant (eigenvalue) to be determined. One verifies that (12) has only two solutions, namely

$$\mathbf{E} = \mathbf{E}_\perp \qquad \text{for } a = 1 \quad \text{(full transmission in the ordinary ray),} \tag{13}$$

$$\mathbf{E} = \mathbf{E}_\parallel \qquad \text{for } a = 0 \quad \text{(no transmission in the ordinary ray).} \tag{14}$$

7.2   Molecular Beams

The analysis of beams of charged particles into components with different specific charge, described in Sect. 1.3, is an example of the type of analysis considered in this chapter. Here we concentrate on the analysis of beams of particles according to their magnetic properties, which arise from electric currents circulating within each particle.[2] For

---

[2] A particle may carry within itself a net *circulation* of electricity even though the average value of the net internal current in any one direction vanishes at all times.

particles that carry a net electric charge, like ions, the force exerted on this charge overshadows the magnetic interaction with internal currents. Therefore, the magnetic analysis is performed on beams of particles that carry no net electric charge.

Beams of particles with no net charge are usually called "molecular beams" even though they may consist of single atoms of gases or vapors, regarded as monoatomic molecules. Neutrons, which are particles with no net electric charge and with mass approximately equal to that of hydrogen atoms, may be regarded for this purpose as atoms with atomic number zero.[3]

A molecular beam is prepared by letting a minute amount of the desired material escape through a small aperture into an evacuated vessel. When the concentration of molecules in the vessel is about 10 million times lower than in atmospheric air, each gas molecule travels about one meter, on the average, without colliding with another molecule. The monoatomic molecules of metallic vapors are frequently studied in molecular beam experiments. The source of a beam consists then of a small oven containing a metal whose atoms evaporate and then leak out of a pinhole aperature.

The arrival of molecules can be measured by observing the accumulation of material deposited, if this accumulation is sufficiently large. More sensitive methods of detection are available, but they are not as simple as in the case of charged particles, except for neutrons, because each molecule carries no electric charge and little kinetic energy. Atoms of alkali vapors are conveniently detected through the ability of a hot tungsten wire to strip an electron from any alkali atom that falls upon its surface. The total amount of electricity thus collected by the wire measures the number of incident atoms. The alkali atoms leave the wire as positive ions; one could count these ions by accelerating them electrically to the point required to operate a counter.

Pencil-like beams of molecules can be obtained by inserting small aperture diaphragms in the path of the molecules. The molecules emerge from their source with various speeds, whose average value depends on the level of thermal agitation in the source. The velocities in a beam can be analyzed by means of shutter systems, for example, by the device of rapidly rotating disks shown in Fig. 7.3. The first disk stops all incoming molecules except those that reach it just when

---

[3] Neutrons are released as by-products of collisions among atomic nuclei, and emerge in particularly large numbers from nuclear reactors. They exist in a free state only for limited intervals of time because they are readily captured by almost any nucleus. They can be easily detected and counted through the phenomena which follow their capture, such as emission of α particles.

the small aperture in the disk passes in front of the entrance slit. The molecules flying on are collected on the second disk which rotates at the same speed as the first one. If the disks rotate by an appreciable amount while the molecules fly from the first disk to the second, the point of arrival of each molecule on the second disk depends on the speed of the molecule. The distribution of material collected at various

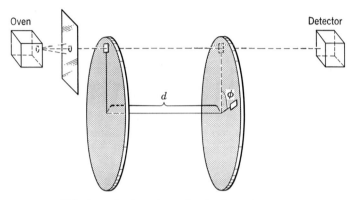

Fig. 7.3 Velocity selection of a molecular beam by rotating wheels.

points along the periphery of a wheel in an experiment of this nature measures directly the distribution of thermal velocities of the gas molecules emerging from a source.

If one carves a small aperture in the second disk, only molecules of a certain velocity reach the disk just in time to fly through the aperture. Fig. 7.3 shows the aperture in the second disk displaced by an angle of ϕ degrees with respect to the aperture in the first disk. If the disks rotate at n turns per second, the second aperture gets aligned with the entrance slit $\phi/n360$ seconds later than the aperture in the first slit. For a distance between the disks of d centimeters, molecules traveling with velocity

$$v = \frac{d}{\phi/n360} = \frac{nd360}{\phi} \quad \text{cm/sec} \tag{15}$$

find both disk apertures aligned. In this way a beam of molecules having a chosen velocity can be selected out of the incident inhomogeneous beam.

Molecular beams may thus be prepared in a state which is an eigenstate of velocity and direction, that is, an eigenstate of particle energy and momentum, analogous to radiation eigenstates of photon energy and momentum. From a practical standpoint, the energy and momentum of particles can only be made uniform to within finite limits, as in the analysis of radiation beams. For radiation it has been pointed out that, even from the standpoint of theory, an eigenstate of photon energy and momentum constitutes an idealization; we shall see in Chapter 10 that the same holds for particle beams.

(*a*) **Stern-Gerlach experiment.** A magnetic field exerts a force on any electric charge in motion; the force is perpendicular to the field and to the direction of flow of electric current. If the current flows in a closed loop, the forces exerted on the different portions of the loop tend to cancel out. No net force, but only a torque, remains if the magnetic field has the same strength and direction at all points of the loop. There is a net force if the field is not uniform.

Both the torque and the net force may be represented with good approximation in terms of a potential magnetic energy of the current loop. This energy is proportional to the strength of the magnetic field **H** in the middle of the loop and may be indicated as

$$- \mu_{\text{eff}} H. \tag{16}$$

The proportionality constant μ_{eff} indicates the effective magnetic moment of the current loop; it equals the current intensity in the loop multiplied by the projection of the area of the loop on a plane perpendicular to **H**, that is, the component of the magnetic moment of the loop in the direction of **H**.[4] (The current intensity is rated positive if it appears to circulate counterclockwise to an observer standing in the direction of the field.) The potential energy decreases if μ_{eff} increases owing to a change of orientation of the loop; the decrease of energy per unit angle of rotation equals the strength of the torque. The energy also decreases if the loop moves in a direction where H increases, for μ_{eff} positive (for $\mu_{\text{eff}} < 0$ the energy decreases if H decreases); the energy decrease per unit displacement of the loop equals the strength of the net force on the loop.

In 1921, Stern and Gerlach observed the deflection of a molecular beam in a non-uniform magnetic field. The deflection must be due to a net force acting on each molecule. Its magnitude determines the value of μ_{eff} of the molecules, since the variation of magnetic field strength encountered by the molecules along their path is a known design characteristic of the experiment.

---

[4] The magnetic energy of a current loop equals the flux of the magnetic field through the area enclosed by the loop, multiplied by the current intensity. Any current circulation may be analyzed into component currents along ideal loops, each of which contributes a component to the magnetic energy. Equation 16 represents the magnetic energy schematically and defines μ_{eff} as a convenient coefficient of proportionality.

The main tool of the experiment is a magnet whose shape is such that the magnetic field is strongly non-uniform as it is in the example of Fig. 7.4 within the V-shaped slot between the pole faces. A finely collimated beam of monoenergetic molecules is directed through the slot parallel to the pole faces. In the region traversed by the beam, the field points in a vertical direction and its strength increases as one

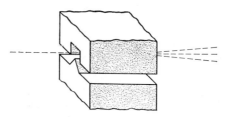

Fig. 7.4 Splitting of a molecular beam after traversing a Stern-Gerlach magnet.

approaches the lower pole edge. Even small deflections of the beam may be detected by observing its point of arrival on a distant screen beyond the magnet.

The following fundamental result is observed: A collimated mono-energetic beam of molecules which passes through a magnet of this kind either remains undeflected or, depending on the nature of the molecules, it splits into a small number of components that experience different deflections. For example, a beam of He atoms remains un-deflected, whereas a beam of H or Ag atoms splits into two components, a beam of oxygen molecules yields three, a beam of N atoms four, a beam of O atoms five components.[5] (A beam of neutrons is split into two components whose deflection is much smaller than in the other examples indicated here.)

The component beams hit the screen at *equally spaced* intervals, symmetrically distributed with respect to the point of no deflection,[6] that is, to the point of arrival in the absence of a magnetic field. The symmetry implies that the middle component beam remains undeflected if there is an odd number of components. If the number of components is even, there is no "middle" component, and the point of no deflection lies midway between the two components nearest to it.

---

[5] This statement must be qualified because the pertinent properties of the internal structure of the incident atoms and molecules may depend to some extent on the strength of the magnetic field to which they are subjected (see Chapter 16).

[6] This result holds insofar as the deflections are small so that each molecule is subjected to the same net force throughout the region between the pole faces, that is, insofar as the gradient of the magnetic field is uniform throughout the region traversed by the molecules.

Finally, the *intensities* of all component beams are *equal* provided the incident beam had not been subjected to previous magnetic actions.

One may observe experimentally the number, deflection, and intensity of the separate component beams. One may work at exceedingly low intensity and record the arrival of one molecule at a time for each component beam. The arrival of individual molecules is always subject to random fluctuations, but the probability of arrival per unit time at the point of collection of a beam is proportional to the macroscopic intensity of that beam.

The uniform deflection of the molecules of one component beam shows that their internal circulating currents are characterized by a single value of the constant μ_{eff} of Eq. 16. This value is obtained by a procedure analogous to that of Appendix I, from the observed value of the beam deflection, from the mass and velocity of the molecules, and from design characteristics of the deflecting magnet.[7] The circulation of intramolecular currents about a direction parallel to the magnetic field remains constant as a molecule flies on freely,[8] after leaving the magnet, as shown by the following experiment. A diaphragm is inserted at the exit of a Stern-Gerlach magnet, so as to let through only one among

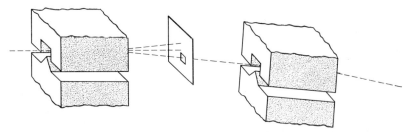

Fig. 7.5 Retest of a molecular beam with a second Stern-Gerlach magnet. A component beam is not resplit by a second magnet oriented equally to the first one.

the component beams. This component beam is allowed to travel on for a distance and then analyzed with a second Stern-Gerlach magnet equal to the first one and equally oriented (Fig. 7.5). The beam experiences *no further splitting* in the second magnet and is deflected to the same extent as in the first magnet.

---

[7] Call m the mass of a molecule, v its velocity through the magnet, l the length of magnet traversed and grad$H$ the rate of change of the field strength in a direction perpendicular to the beam. The force on a molecule is μ_{eff} grad$H$, the acceleration μ_{eff} gradH/m, the transverse velocity at the exit of the magnet $v_t = \mu_{eff}$ grad$H$ l/mv, and the deflection angle $\delta = v_t/v = \mu_{eff}$ grad$H$ l/mv^2. To a given observed angle δ corresponds the value $\mu_{eff} = (mv^2/l \text{ grad}H)\delta$.

[8] "Freely" means that all stray magnetic actions are screened off from the space where the molecules travel.

The main Stern-Gerlach experiment and this second experiment of retest analysis are analogous to the experiment of light beam splitting with an Iceland spar crystal and to the retest analysis with two crystal filters parallel to one another. The number of beam components varies, however, from one kind of atom to another.

These results are summarized by stating that the molecules of one component beam are in eigenstate of current circulation about the magnet axis, characterized by an eigenvalue of μ_{eff}. Since the component beams hit the screen at equally spaced points, symmetrically arranged with respect to the point of no deflection, the corresponding eigenvalues form an evenly spaced sequence and to each eigenvalue corresponds another one of equal magnitude and opposite sign. The largest of these eigenvalues is indicated for each kind of particle with the symbol μ and is called simply the "magnetic moment" of the particle. The difference between successive eigenvalues of the sequence is indicated by μ/j and the sequence of all eigenvalues is represented by

$$\mu_{\text{eff}} = \mu \frac{m}{j}, \tag{17}$$

where m is a number which varies in steps of one from $-j$ to j. The numbers j and m are integers when the number of beam components

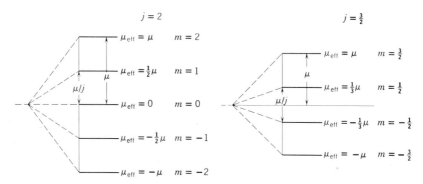

Fig. 7.6 Diagram of eigenvalues of μ_{eff} as determined by the separation of beam components in a Stern-Gerlach experiment.

is odd, so that there is an even number $2j$ of intervals between $\mu_{\text{eff}} = \mu$ and $\mu_{\text{eff}} = -\mu$, whereas j and m are half-integers when the number of beam components is even (Fig. 7.6). The numbers m and j are called "quantum numbers" like all the numerical indices which identify discontinuous features of quantum phenomena.

(b) *Repeated beam splitting in different directions.* In analogy with polarization experiments with the analyzer oriented differently from the polarizer, we consider the following schematic problem: One component beam has been filtered out of an initial molecular beam by means of a magnetic deflection followed by a selecting slit (as in Fig. 7.5). This component beam now enters "suddenly" [9] into another deflecting magnet whose field direction forms an angle θ with the direction of the field in the first magnet (Fig. 7.7). We call the first magnet a "polarizer" and the second one an "analyzer."

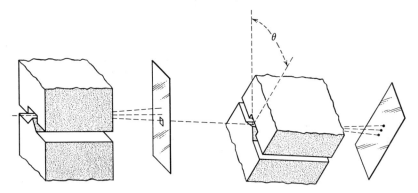

Fig. 7.7 Retest of a molecular beam with a second Stern-Gerlach magnet. A component beam is resplit by a second magnet oriented differently from the first one.

The second magnet splits the incident beam into a new set of component beams. These beams reach the end screen at a series of points aligned in a direction parallel to the field in the second magnet. The second magnet resolves as many component beams as the first one and the deflections are also equal in magnitude if the two magnets are identical except for orientation. However, the *intensities* of the component beams resolved by the second magnet are *unequal*, and depend

---

[9] Internal currents within an atom or molecule undergo a progressive readjustment if the molecule passes slowly from one place to another one where the magnetic field points in a different direction. A change of direction of the magnetic field is effectively "slow" or "fast," depending on the promptness of response of the intra-atomic currents.

A clear-cut study of the effect of two successive different magnetic fields upon molecules requires that the transition from the first to the second field be *sufficiently sudden*. Experimental arrangements to achieve this goal were developed by Stern and Phipps and especially by Frisch and Segrè. Without going into details, we assume that one can achieve in practice an ideally sudden transition from field-free space into the space between the poles of a magnet, or from one magnet into another one with different orientation.

upon the angle θ between the orientations of the analyzer and polarizer magnets.

This result is quite analogous qualitatively to the corresponding result of polarization analysis. A beam of molecules in an eigenstate of current circulation about the axis of one magnet can be fractionated into component beams of molecules in different eigenstates of current circulation about the *different axis* of another magnet. A component beam separated by the second magnet is split once more if retested with a further magnet parallel to the first one. Magnets with different orientation perform incompatible types of analysis.

The quantitative dependence of the component intensities upon the relative orientations of a polarizer and an analyzer is, however, different for light and for molecules. In the analysis of linearly polarized light with an Iceland spar crystal, the relative intensities of the ordinary

TABLE 7.1

PROBABILITY FORMULAS FOR TWO-, THREE-, AND FOUR-COMPONENT BEAM SPLITTING

$$P^{(1/2)}_{\bar{m}m}(\theta)$$

$\bar{m}$ \ m	$\frac{1}{2}$	$-\frac{1}{2}$
$\frac{1}{2}$	$\frac{1}{2}(1+\cos\theta)=\cos^2\frac{1}{2}\theta$	$\frac{1}{2}(1-\cos\theta)=\sin^2\frac{1}{2}\theta$
$-\frac{1}{2}$	$\frac{1}{2}(1-\cos\theta)=\sin^2\frac{1}{2}\theta$	$\frac{1}{2}(1+\cos\theta)=\cos^2\frac{1}{2}\theta$

$$P^{(1)}_{\bar{m}m}(\theta)$$

$\bar{m}$ \ m	1	0	-1
1	$\frac{1}{4}(1+\cos\theta)^2$ $=\cos^4\frac{1}{2}\theta$	$\frac{1}{2}(1-\cos^2\theta)$ $=2\sin^2\frac{1}{2}\theta\cos^2\frac{1}{2}\theta$	$\frac{1}{4}(1-\cos\theta)^2$ $=\sin^4\frac{1}{2}\theta$
0	$\frac{1}{2}(1-\cos^2\theta)$ $=2\sin^2\frac{1}{2}\theta\cos^2\frac{1}{2}\theta$	$\cos^2\theta$ $=(\cos^2\frac{1}{2}\theta-\sin^2\frac{1}{2}\theta)^2$	$\frac{1}{2}(1-\cos^2\theta)$ $=2\sin^2\frac{1}{2}\theta\cos^2\frac{1}{2}\theta$
-1	$\frac{1}{4}(1-\cos\theta)^2$ $=\sin^4\frac{1}{2}\theta$	$\frac{1}{2}(1-\cos^2\theta)$ $=2\sin^2\frac{1}{2}\theta\cos^2\frac{1}{2}\theta$	$\frac{1}{4}(1+\cos\theta)^2$ $=\cos^4\frac{1}{2}\theta$

$$P^{(3/2)}_{\bar{m}m}(\theta)$$

$\bar{m}$ \ m	$\frac{3}{2}$	$\frac{1}{2}$	$-\frac{1}{2}$	$-\frac{3}{2}$
$\frac{3}{2}$	$\frac{1}{8}(1+\cos\theta)^3$ $=\cos^6\frac{1}{2}\theta$	$\frac{3}{8}(1+\cos\theta)(1-\cos^2\theta)$ $=3\cos^4\frac{1}{2}\theta\sin^2\frac{1}{2}\theta$	$\frac{3}{8}(1-\cos^2\theta)(1-\cos\theta)$ $=3\cos^2\frac{1}{2}\theta\sin^4\frac{1}{2}\theta$	$\frac{1}{8}(1-\cos\theta)^3$ $=\sin^6\frac{1}{2}\theta$
$\frac{1}{2}$	$\frac{3}{8}(1+\cos\theta)(1-\cos^2\theta)$ $=3\cos^4\frac{1}{2}\theta\sin^2\frac{1}{2}\theta$	$\frac{1}{8}(1+\cos\theta)(1-3\cos\theta)^2$ $=\cos^2\frac{1}{2}\theta(1-3\sin^2\frac{1}{2}\theta)^2$	$\frac{1}{8}(1-\cos\theta)(1+3\cos\theta)^2$ $=\sin^2\frac{1}{2}\theta(3\cos^2\frac{1}{2}\theta-1)^2$	$\frac{3}{8}(1-\cos^2\theta)(1-\cos\theta)$ $=3\cos^2\frac{1}{2}\theta\sin^4\frac{1}{2}\theta$
$-\frac{1}{2}$	$\frac{3}{8}(1-\cos^2\theta)(1-\cos\theta)$ $=3\cos^2\frac{1}{2}\theta\sin^4\frac{1}{2}\theta$	$\frac{1}{8}(1-\cos\theta)(1+3\cos\theta)^2$ $=\sin^2\frac{1}{2}\theta(3\cos^2\frac{1}{2}\theta-1)^2$	$\frac{1}{8}(1+\cos\theta)(1-3\cos\theta)^2$ $=\cos^2\frac{1}{2}\theta(1-3\sin^2\frac{1}{2}\theta)^2$	$\frac{3}{8}(1+\cos\theta)(1-\cos^2\theta)$ $=3\cos^4\frac{1}{2}\theta\sin^2\frac{1}{2}\theta$
$-\frac{3}{2}$	$\frac{1}{8}(1-\cos\theta)^3$ $=\sin^6\frac{1}{2}\theta$	$\frac{3}{8}(1-\cos^2\theta)(1-\cos\theta)$ $=3\cos^2\frac{1}{2}\theta\sin^4\frac{1}{2}\theta$	$\frac{3}{8}(1+\cos\theta)(1-\cos^2\theta)$ $=3\cos^4\frac{1}{2}\theta\sin^2\frac{1}{2}\theta$	$\frac{1}{8}(1+\cos\theta)^3$ $=\cos^6\frac{1}{2}\theta$

and the extraordinary beams are $\cos^2\alpha$ and $\sin^2\alpha$ and are accounted for by macroscopic theory. For molecular beams there is a different intensity law depending on whether the beam is split into 2, 3, 4, $\cdots$ components. The theoretical deduction of these laws will be given after further analysis in the next chapter.

Each of the "relative intensities" of the component beams represents the probability that a molecule, having emerged from the polarizer magnet in the component beam identified by a quantum number m, will emerge from the analyzer magnet in the component beam identified by $\bar{m}$. This probability may be indicated as $P_{\bar{m}m}$. It is a function of the angle θ and it depends on m and $\bar{m}$ and on the number of beam components, that is, on the quantum number j of Eq. 17 which equals the largest value of m or $\bar{m}$. Table 7.1 gives analytical expressions that represent the experimentally determined probabilities $P_{\bar{m}m}^{(j)}(\theta)$ for the cases of two-, three- and four-component beams ($j = \frac{1}{2}, 1$, and $\frac{3}{2}$). In general $P_{\bar{m}m}^{(j)}$ is a function of $\cos\theta$ of degree $2j$. The table shows equal probability for a molecule in an eigenstate with $m = a$ to emerge in an eigenstate with $\bar{m} = b$, and for a molecule with $m = b$ to emerge with $\bar{m} = a$ ("reciprocity law"). The table also shows complete symmetry between deflections in opposite directions, characterized by values of m and $\bar{m}$ equal but with opposite sign.

(c) Magnetic energy eigenstates. Zeeman effect. Radio frequency spectra. The eigenstate of current circulation in an atom about the direction of a magnetic field **H**, with the eigenvalue μ_{eff}, is also an eigenstate of its magnetic energy with the eigenvalue $-\mu_{\text{eff}}H$. If the atom is otherwise in an eigenstate of its internal energy (it usually is in its ground state), it is also in an eigenstate of the total—internal plus magnetic—energy. Each internal energy level considered in Chapter 4 is modified by the addition of the magnetic energy

$$-\mu_{\text{eff}}H = -\mu H \frac{m}{j}, \tag{18}$$

which takes as many values as there are eigenvalues of μ_{eff}. That is, each level of the atom in the absence of the field is, in general, "split" into a number of different levels by the action of the field. The number of eigenvalues of μ_{eff} is a characteristic of each state of internal motion of the atom; specifically the values of both j and μ in (18) vary from one to another of these states. The examples given in the description of the Stern-Gerlach experiments, with regard to the number of component beams for various kinds of atoms, refer to the ground state of each atom.[10] Since the values of μ_{eff} for most atoms are of the order of 10^{-20} CGS units (that is, erg/gauss), the separation of levels of magnetic energy, for field strengths of 1000 to

---

[10] The description in this paragraph is schematized by disregarding deeper influences of the magnetic field on the internal structure of atoms, as indicated in footnote 5 on page 88 and discussed in Sect. 16.3. The eigenvalues of μ_{eff} are fixed, that is, independent of the strength of the magnetic field, only within certain ranges of this strength.

10,000 gauss is of the order of 10^{-17} to 10^{-16} erg, that is, 10^{-5} to 10^{-4} ev. This separation is, accordingly, orders of magnitude smaller than the separation of most levels of internal energy.

The splitting of the ordinary energy levels of internal motion brings about a modification of the optical line spectra described in Sect. 4.3. Consider the spectral line emitted or absorbed in a transition between two energy levels E_a and E_b of atoms of an element in the absence of a magnetic field. When a magnetic field is applied to the atoms, the levels E_a and E_b are split, respectively, according to (18), into levels $E_a - \mu_a H m_a / j_a$ and $E_b - \mu_b H m_b / j_b$, with different values of m_a and m_b. Therefore, the atoms emit or absorb no longer a single line of frequency $(E_a - E_b)/h$, but a number of lines of frequency

$$\frac{1}{h}\left[E_a - E_b - \left(\mu_a \frac{m_a}{j_a} - \mu_b \frac{m_b}{j_b} \right) H \right] \tag{19}$$

corresponding to different values of m_a and m_b. This splitting of spectral lines was first observed by Zeeman in the 1890's and is called Zeeman effect; it will be discussed further in Sect. 16.3. The Zeeman effect was of great help for the analysis of energy levels because it provided additional information on the properties of atoms in each level of excitation. Furthermore, since the energy levels in magnetic fields correspond to stationary states with net circulation of currents of fixed orientation, the transitions between any two states with certain values of m_a and m_b are accompanied by oscillating currents which have also particular orientations with respect to the magnetic field. Therefore, the light of any given spectral line emitted by atoms in a magnetic field has a particular polarization.

Transitions with absorption or emission of radiation are also possible between energy levels with the same value of internal energy E_a and different values of m_a. The radiation frequency corresponding to these transitions lies, for values of H available in the laboratory, in the radiofrequency range, often in the short-wave or microwave portions of this range. This phenomenon may be observed as the transition of an atom from one to another component of a molecular beam. Consider, for example, a molecular beam filtered through a polarizer magnet and thereby reduced to a single component with a certain value of m. The atoms in the beam can absorb or emit radiation and thereby pass into eigenstates with different values of m. Atoms that have experienced such transitions constitute new beam components and may be detected by retest analysis with another magnet (see Fig. 7.5).

Spontaneous emission of radiofrequency radiation is quite unlikely within the time spent by an atom in traversing the apparatus of Fig. 7.5. (As indicated in Chapter 5, the macroscopic intensity of radiation emitted by oscillating currents is a rapidly increasing function of the oscillation frequency.) Absorption of radiofrequency photons by atoms occurs when the atoms traverse a magnetic field, which splits their levels, and are simultaneously subjected to an oscillating electric field whose frequency equals the level separation divided by Planck's constant h. The action of the radiofrequency electric field also stimulates emission of radiation by the atoms, so that transitions with both absorption and emission of energy may be observed.

Devices for observing radiofrequency spectra very effectively have been developed particularly by Rabi and collaborators in the late 1930's. To increase the intensity of the beam, its components are not actually separated out by filters; thereby one eliminates the velocity selection of the molecules required for precision work with separate components. A molecular beam is passed through a first Stern-Gerlach magnet designed so as to refocus all components in a region of space where the magnetic field is uniform and parallel to the field in the magnet and where a radio-frequency electric field is applied. The beam passes then through a second (analyzer) Stern-Gerlach magnet, identical to the first one but with reverse orientation, which brings again all beam components to a second focus, on a detector. The refocusing works, however, only for molecules that traverse both magnets in the same beam component, that is, in the same eigenstate. Any transition with a change of m which takes place between the two magnets causes a loss of beam intensity at the second focus. Very extensive and accurate measurements of magnetic moments have been performed by this method.

7.3   General Scope of Eigenstate Analysis

The experiments with radiation and molecular beams show how to identify eigenstates of certain variables and how a beam in an eigenstate of one variable can be fractionated, also by experimental procedures, into component beams which are in eigenstates of another variable. In common language one says briefly that a state of a beam is resolved into component eigenstates. The concepts of eigenstate and of decomposition of eigenstates apply throughout quantum physics, even though direct experimental procedures of analysis are not available in the majority of cases. For purpose of illustration we mention here a few examples.

Consider the stationary state (energy eigenstate) of a hydrogen atom corresponding to the lowest energy eigenvalue, that is, the ground state. The existence of such a state is deduced from the Franck-Hertz and other experiments described in Chapter 4. The discussion of the statistical aspects of quantum phenomena in Chapter 6 indicates that, if the atom is in a stationary state, one should not expect with certainty to find its electron at any particular position within the atom. Suppose that an experiment were set up to test whether or not the position coordinates of the electron have certain values x, y, z at a particular time. The result would be a specific response if the coordinates have those values, and no such response otherwise. This experiment selects electrons in an eigenstate of the three position coordinates x, y, z. If the experiment were performed repeatedly on a large number of hydrogen atoms in their ground state, the specific response would be obtained in a fraction of all trials. This fraction measures the probability that the electron coordinates have the values x, y, z when a hydrogen atom is in its ground state. The same experimental device, with a different setting, might measure the probability that the coordinates have other values x', y', z'. Therefore, this device would perform the analysis of an energy eigenstate of the hydrogen atom into position eigenstates of its electron.

As another example, consider inelastic collisions of electrons with atoms in the Franck-Hertz experiment (Sect. 4.2). Each electron emerging from a collision may travel in any direction and have any one of various velocities, depending on the amount of energy transferred to the atom. The state of this electron is presumably determined by its initial state, which is an eigenstate of velocity and direction, and by the mechanics of collision. An experimental device that determines the velocity and direction of the electrons after collisions performs an analysis of the state of electrons emerging from collisions into eigenstates of velocity and direction.[11]

The polarization analysis of light beams illustrates the general procedure of analysis into eigenstates with particular clarity, because it resolves the incident beam into a *finite* number of *discrete* components. The analysis into eigenstates of variables with continuous eigenvalues, such as energies, positions, directions, etc., is less clear-cut, but not different in essence. These eigenstates often represent idealizations; for example, as mentioned before, rigorously monochromatic light, that is, light in an eigenstate of photon energy, cannot be prepared by realistic experimental procedures.

Returning now to the eigenstates of current circulation within atoms, there is a set of eigenstates of circulation of current about each direction of space. The sets pertaining to different axes are fully equivalent. The *reciprocity* property noticed in Table 7.1, namely that a molecule has equal probability of passing from an eigenstate with $m = a$ to one with $\bar{m} = b$ and of passing from $m = b$ to $\bar{m} = a$, is quite obvious in this case, because the two sets of states are interchanged by the irrelevant operation of interchanging the orientations of the polarizer and analyzer magnets. This reciprocity property is quite general. For example, the probability of finding the electron of a hydrogen atom at one point P, if the atom has been prepared in its ground state, is equal to the probability of finding the atom in its ground state if its electron has been placed at the point P. The reciprocity of probabilities rests in essence

---

[11] In the analytical treatment of α-particle scattering according to classical mechanics (Sect. 3.2), the direction of each α particle after scattering is a function of the impact parameter. The randomness of the α-particle direction derives, in that treatment, from the randomness of impact parameter, which was implicitly assumed by Rutherford to be of the card game variety (Sect. 6.2), that is, to derive from "failure" to control the "aim" of each particle. In fact, it will be shown in the following that this randomness is a quantum effect and that the aim cannot be controlled exactly, there being no state of a particle which is an eigenstate of both the direction and the impact parameter. Therefore, the calculation of Sect. 3.2 is not correct, but an exact quantum mechanical calculation yields the same cross section as was obtained by Rutherford.

always on the same ground, namely, that a quantum mechanical process of eigenstate analysis may function in reverse by interchanging the roles of the instruments that act as polarizer and analyzer, even though these instruments are not of the same kind.

Eigenstates of an atomic system corresponding to different values of the same variable are said to be *orthogonal* to indicate that they are *mutually exclusive*, since a variable which has one specific value certainly does not have any other value. Tests of mutual exclusiveness of eigenstates have been pointed out in the discussion of examples and are often obvious. For example, light with circular dextro-rotatory polarization is fully stopped by a filter that accepts only light with levo-rotatory polarization. The analysis of a state of a system into orthogonal eigenstates constitutes a listing of various alternative, mutually exclusive events that may ensue when the system is in that state, together with a listing of the probability of each of those alternative events.

Orthogonal eigenstates are said to form a "complete set" when there is no further state orthogonal to all states of the set. When a state is resolved into a complete set of orthogonal eigenstates, the probabilities pertaining to all these eigenstates add up to one.

Quantum mechanics deals usually with states of atomic systems which can be identified, at least in principle, as eigenstates of some physical variable. In some instances, the method of identification is obvious; for example, a state of linear polarization is an eigenstate of the polarization which is transmitted without loss of intensity as the ordinary ray by a spar crystal with a certain orientation. Often this method of identification is not practicable because it is not easy to design an analyzer that will respond with certainty to systems in the given state and and to those only. It is then preferable to identify a state through its analysis into a convenient set of eigenstates. Identifying a state with reference to a set of eigenstates amounts to an inversion of the process of analysis considered in this chapter. The inversion requires more data than a listing of the "intensity," that is, of the probability pertaining to each eigenstate of the set. The nature of the additional data and their mathematical representation will be discussed next.

PROBLEMS

7.1 A beam of nitrogen atoms, emerging unpolarized from a discharge tube, is split into four components by a Stern-Gerlach analyzer. Calculate the mean value and the mean square deviation of the quantum number m, by averaging over its values for the four components.

7.2 Under the influence of a magnetic field, the lowest energy level of the nitrogen atom splits into four adjacent levels. The magnetic moment of the atom in this group of eigenstates of current orientation is $\mu = 2.7 \times 10^{-20}$ erg/gauss. Assuming a magnetic field strength of 1000 gauss, calculate: (a) the energy separations among the levels; (b) the frequency of radiation that can be absorbed in the process of raising an atom from one of these levels to the next higher one.

7.3 A beam of atoms is fractionated by a Stern-Gerlach analyzer into three components, with quantum numbers $m = 1$, 0, and -1. Each component is then analyzed with a second magnet, as in Fig. 7.7, and thereby subdivided again into components with $\bar{m} = 1$, 0, and -1. Taking the probabilities $P^{(1)}_{\bar{m}m}(\theta)$ from Table 7.1, calculate for each value of m: (a) the mean value $\langle \bar{m} \rangle = \Sigma^1_{\bar{m} = -1} \bar{m} P^{(1)}_{\bar{m}m}(\theta)$, and (b) the mean square deviation $\Delta \bar{m}^2 = \langle \bar{m}^2 \rangle - \langle \bar{m} \rangle^2$.

7.4 Check that $y = x \exp(-\tfrac{1}{2}x^2)$ is an eigenfunction (see p. 83) of the equation $d^2y/dx^2 + x^2 y = Ky$, and calculate the corresponding eigenvalue K.

chapter 8

Interference
and superposition

In this chapter, we consider the relations among the probabilities of observing alternative atomic events, with the intent of discovering the laws which they obey. Such laws should enable us to calculate the probabilities to be expected under various conditions of observation; in particular, they provide a theoretical explanation of the experimental results on molecular beams which are given in Table 7.1.

The study of light polarization and of the orientation of intraatomic currents provides suitable examples for the determination of probability laws as well as for the process of eigenstate analysis. We shall consider the following problem: Suppose that a molecular beam emerging from a polarizer with orientation **P** is analyzed with a Stern-Gerlach analyzer whose field has a direction **A**, and that the intensities of the component beams separated by this analyzer are known. Suppose further that one has studied in a separate experiment the analysis of the eigenstates of **A** by a magnet with a different orientation **B**. What predictions can then be made about the analysis of the beam from the polarizer **P** with the magnet with orientation **B**? If the statistical results of this analysis were fully predictable from the given data, one would conclude that the analysis of the polarizer beam into component eigenstates of **A** provides all the relevant information and thereby identifies fully the state of orientation of the molecules emerging from the polarizer. It will be seen that such a single analysis is *not* adequate to identify the state of orientation. The analysis of atomic states and its reciprocal operation, namely a recombination which is called "superposition," involve a larger amount of information in full analogy to the corresponding procedures for electromagnetic radiation.

In electromagnetism, radiation components are combined by adding their fields rather than their intensities. The description of radiation

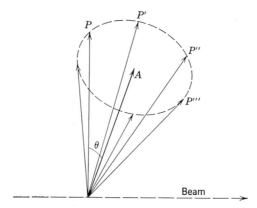

Fig. 8.1 Cone of polarizer directions **P**, **P′**, **P″**, etc., consistent with observations by an analyzer with axis **A**.*

by means of the electric and the magnetic field contains more information than is provided by the intensities of a set of component beams. For example, the intensities I_o and I_e transmitted as ordinary and extraordinary ray of a spar crystal do not identify the state of polarization of the incident light. This polarization is linear if the fields of the two rays oscillate in step, elliptical or circular if they are out of phase. The difference between the types of polarization consistent with the observation of I_o and I_e is revealed by analysis with a spar of different orientation. As shown in Sect. 8.1 the information provided by the additional analysis may be utilized to define a "phase difference" between the components I_o and I_e, without reference to the oscillations of the fields. It becomes then possible to represent the combination of radiation components independently of the macroscopic theory which has served thus

---

* Notice that in general the magnetic field may be oblique to the beam direction, even though Chapter 7 dealt explicitly only with fields perpendicular to the beam.

far as a guide but fails to account for the subdivision of radiation energy into photons.

For atomic systems, the identification of a state requires the same type of information as for radiation. For example, in the study of current circulation within atoms by magnetic beam-splitting (Sect. 7.2), the intensities of a set of component beams do not identify the initial state of current circulation. Specifically, in the experiment of Fig. 7.7, the intensities of the component beams emerging from the second (analyzer) magnet determine only the angle θ between the axes of the polarizer and the analyzer magnets; they are consistent with previous polarization by a magnet whose axis points in any direction at an angle θ with the analyzer axis (Fig. 8.1). To identify the axis of polarization of the incident molecules, it is necessary to perform a Stern-Gerlach analysis with a different orientation of the analyzer magnet. That is, the observation of *two* sets of component intensities is required to identify the state of the incident molecules.[1]

In general, two "incompatible" types of analysis are required to identify a state of radiation or of an atomic system.[2] Each experimental analysis determines the probability of response of an analyzer which detects only radiation or atomic systems in a given eigenstate; this probability will be called, for brevity, the probability of the eigenstate. Knowledge of the probability of each eigenstate of two complete orthogonal sets, for example, of the eigenstate sets of magnetic analyzers with two different orientations, can be translated into data about two independent characteristics of each eigenstate of a single set. These eigenstates are then regarded as *components* of the initial state. The two characteristics of each component eigenstate are called its "probability" and "phase." The difference between the phases of a pair of components specifies how to combine their contributions in calculating the probability of any end result, just as it does in the superposition of polarization eigenstates. That is, the state of an atomic system can be identified by its analysis into any one complete set of orthogonal eigenstates, but the identification must specify, besides the probabilities of the components, also their phase differences. The influence of phase differences upon the

---

[1] Two sets of observations are not quite sufficient in general to identify uniquely a state. The residual ambiguity is removed by a third observation (see Fig. 8.3).

[2] It is understood in this book, according to common practice, that a system is in a definite state ("pure state") when predictions can be made about it with maximum precision. One can always design a device, at least in principle, which detects a system with certainty if it is in a pure state, but with probability less than one if it is in any other state. Molecules with random orientation or unpolarized light are not in a pure state, according to this definition, because no orientation, or respectively polarization, analyzer will transmit them with certainty.

combination of components is called "interference effect," by analogy with optical interference.

This method of identifying the state of a system permits one to describe the variations of the state according to the "superposition principle," that is, by following the variations of a single set of component eigenstates. For example, it will prove particularly convenient to regard any state of an atom, or other system, as a combination of eigenstates of the energy, because these states remain stationary in the course of time. Throughout the analysis in eigenstates, one must keep track simultaneously of the changes of probability of each component and of the changes of phase. It will be shown in Sect. 8.2 how to carry out this simultaneous accounting by specifying for each component eigenstate one single complex number, called "probability amplitude" of the component. (Basic information on complex numbers is summarized in Appendix VI.) Each complex number has a magnitude equal to the square root of the probability of the component eigenstate and a phase which indicates how this eigenstate combines with others. The combination of components is represented by the addition of probability amplitudes, as it is represented in macroscopic electromagnetism by the addition of the electric and magnetic fields.

For the polarization of light and the circulation of currents within atoms, analysis of the experiments described in Chapter 7 suffices to determine the probability amplitudes which identify a state as a superposition of orthogonal eigenstates. The calculation of the probability amplitudes is discussed in Sect. 8.3 and explains the quantitative results of experiments described in Chapter 7, in particular the data of Table 7.1.

Interference effects are unknown in the classical mechanics of particles, principally because the conditions of macroscopic experimentation usually destroy the very possibility of interference. Combination of components under conditions which prevent interference is called "incoherent" superposition. The conditions required for interference are analyzed conveniently when component beams are actually separated and follow different paths, as described in Sect. 8.4. The most familiar examples of interference, with light or particle beams, arise actually from the combination of components traveling different lengths of path, rather than of components differing in polarization or current orientation. They will be described in Chapter 10.

8.1 Phase Differences

When a beam of light traverses an Iceland spar crystal and the two emerging rays, ordinary and extraordinary, have intensities I_o and I_e, the polarization of the beam [3] is not identified by the intensity ratio I_e/I_o. As mentioned above, identification requires an additional measurement of the ratio I_e'/I_o' with the spar crystal in a different orientation. (Only the ratios are relevant to the polarization, as the total intensity $I_o + I_e$ is the same for all analyzers.) The intensity pairs (I_o, I_e) and (I_o', I_e') are related as follows.

Suppose that the incident light is passed through two spar crystals A and B in succession; A transmits ordinary and extraordinary rays of intensities I_o and I_e, and B is turned around the beam axis by an angle $\alpha < 90°$ [4] with respect to A. If the extraordinary, or the ordinary, ray of crystal A is eliminated, the ordinary ray of B has intensity, respectively, $I_o \cos^2\alpha$ or $I_e \sin^2\alpha$, according to page 80. If crystal A is removed, so that its ordinary and extraordinary rays are not separated, the intensity of the ordinary ray of the second crystal, I_o', is *different*, in general, *from the sum* $I_o \cos^2\alpha + I_e \sin^2\alpha$ *of the intensities* that would be contributed by the rays separated by crystal A. (Similarly, the intensity I_e' of the extraordinary ray is not equal to $I_o \sin^2\alpha + I_e \cos^2\alpha$.) The difference $I_o' - (I_o \cos^2\alpha + I_e \sin^2\alpha)$ arises from interference; it depends, according to macroscopic theory, on the differences between the phases of oscillation of electric field components parallel and perpendicular to the principal section of crystal A.

Whatever be the formal interpretation of the difference $I_o' - (I_o \cos^2\alpha + I_e \sin^2\alpha)$, its magnitude varies depending on the polarization of the incident light, but it never exceeds $2\sqrt{I_o \cos^2\alpha \, I_e \sin^2\alpha}$, that is, twice the geometric mean of

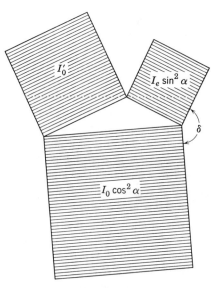

Fig. 8.2 Combination of component intensities in light polarization experiments.

$I_o \cos^2\alpha$ and $I_e \sin^2\alpha$. One can make a diagram, as in Fig. 8.2, in which the values of I_o', $I_o \cos^2\alpha$, and $I_e \sin^2\alpha$ are represented by the squares of the sides of a triangle. The diagram shows that the value of I_o' can be

---

[3] It is assumed here that the incident light has been prepared by filtration through an unknown polarizer; see footnote 2 on page 101.

[4] This restriction implies no loss of generality for the application considered here.

expressed in terms of the values of $I_o \cos^2\alpha$ and $I_e \sin^2\alpha$ and of the angle δ in the diagram,

$$I_o' = I_o \cos^2\alpha + I_e \sin^2\alpha + 2\sqrt{I_o I_e} \cos\alpha \sin\alpha \cos\delta. \qquad (1a)$$

Similarly one finds

$$I_e' = I_o \sin^2\alpha + I_e \cos^2\alpha - 2\sqrt{I_o I_e} \sin\alpha \cos\alpha \cos\delta. \qquad (1b)$$

These formulas may be transformed to define

$$\cos\delta = \frac{I_o' - (I_o \cos^2\alpha + I_e \sin^2\alpha)}{2\sqrt{I_o I_e} \cos\alpha \sin\alpha}, \qquad (2a)$$

or

$$\cos\delta = -\frac{I_e' - (I_o \sin^2\alpha + I_e \cos^2\alpha)}{2\sqrt{I_o I_e} \sin\alpha \cos\alpha}, \qquad (2b)$$

as a function of the measured values of I_o' (or I_e'), I_o, I_e, and α. The angle δ, which is thereby determined within a factor ± 1, coincides with the phase difference of the component eigenstates of linear polarization defined in macroscopic theory.

The name of "phase difference" is applied in quantum physics to the quantity δ as defined here, even though it is not implied that there is any observable characteristic of the component eigenstates which oscillates with any particular phase. The quantity $\cos\delta$ defined by (2) represents the information provided by a measured value of I_o' (or I_e') in addition to the information provided by I_o, I_e, and the knowledge of α. Once $\cos\delta$ is determined by observing I_o' with a particular value of α, Eq. 1 predicts the new value of I_o' to be observed with the spar crystal B reoriented to any different value of α.

Consider now a molecular beam and assume for simplicity that analysis with a Stern-Gerlach magnet A resolves the beam into two components only, with intensities $I_{\frac{1}{2}}$ and $I_{-\frac{1}{2}}$, that is, that the quantum number j, defined in eq. 17, page 90 is $\frac{1}{2}$.[5] Suppose that a second analyzer magnet B is placed behind the first one, with its axis $\mathbf{B}$ at an angle $\theta_{\mathbf{BA}}$ with respect to the axis $\mathbf{A}$ of the first magnet. If the component beams separated by A are eliminated in turn and analyzed separately by B, the beams of molecules emerging from B with the quantum number $\tilde{m} = \frac{1}{2}$ have respective intensities $I_{\frac{1}{2}} \cos^2\frac{1}{2}\theta_{\mathbf{BA}}$ and $I_{-\frac{1}{2}} \sin^2\frac{1}{2}\theta_{\mathbf{BA}}$, according to Table 7.1. If the magnet A is removed and the incident beam is analyzed directly by B, the beam of molecules emerging from B with $\tilde{m} = \frac{1}{2}$ has intensity $I_{\frac{1}{2}}'$ which differs, in general, from the sum

---

[5] It is assumed that the beam has been prefiltered with a Stern-Gerlach polarizer magnet of unknown orientation; see footnote 2, page 101.

$I_{\frac{1}{2}}\cos^2\frac{1}{2}\theta_{\mathbf{BA}} + I_{-\frac{1}{2}}\sin^2\frac{1}{2}\theta_{\mathbf{BA}}$.   That is, if one regards the state of orientation of the incident molecules as the combination of eigenstates of current circulation about **A**, the combination exhibits an effect of interference.   The effect is represented by a phase difference, defined, as in (2), by

$$\cos\delta = \frac{I_{\frac{1}{2}}' - I_{\frac{1}{2}}\cos^2\frac{1}{2}\theta_{\mathbf{BA}} - I_{-\frac{1}{2}}\sin^2\frac{1}{2}\theta_{\mathbf{BA}}}{2\sqrt{I_{\frac{1}{2}}I_{-\frac{1}{2}}}\cos\frac{1}{2}\theta_{\mathbf{BA}}\sin\frac{1}{2}\theta_{\mathbf{BA}}}. \tag{3}$$

The sign of δ remains undetermined by (3).   Its determination requires a separate experiment, except in the special cases $\cos\delta = 1$ and $\cos\delta = -1$, in which the phase differences $\delta = 0°$ and $\delta = 180°$ are respectively equivalent to $\delta = -0°$ and $\delta = -180°$.

Considering that the molecules have been prefiltered through a magnet of unknown orientation **P**, the measurement of the intensities $I_{\frac{1}{2}}$ and

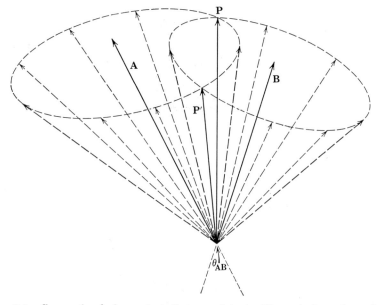

Fig. 8.3   Cones of polarizer orientations consistent with analysis performed by analyzers with orientation **A** or **B**.   The result of the combined analysis restricts the possible polarizer orientations to the cone intersections **P** and **P′**, which are symmetrical with respect to the plane **AB**.

$I_{\frac{1}{2}}'$ with the analyzer orientations **A** and **B** restricts the possible orientations of **P** to two directions, as shown in Fig. 8.3.   Since the same measurements determine $\cos\delta$ through (3) but leave the sign of δ undetermined, the two opposite values of δ must correspond to the two possible orientations of **P** in Fig. 8.3. The possible orientations **P** and **P′** are symmetric with respect to the plane **AB**. The special cases $\cos\delta = \pm 1$ arise when the cones of Fig. 8.3 are tangent and there is only one possible direction of **P**, coplanar with **A** and **B**.

Notice that the definition of a phase difference δ by means of (3) implies a value of $\cos\delta$ comprised between -1 and 1, which is true only if $I_{1/2}{}'$, $I_{1/2}\cos^2\frac{1}{2}\theta_{BA}$ and $I_{-1/2}\sin^2\frac{1}{2}\theta_{BA}$ fulfill the same triangular condition as $I_o{}'$, $I_o\cos^2\alpha$, and $I_e\sin^2\alpha$ in Fig. 8.2. It is a fundamental result of atomic experiments that this condition is always fulfilled.

Equation 3 provides the formulation of a law obeyed by the probabilities of eigenstates. Suppose, for example, that the polarizer prepares molecules in the state of orientation identified by $m = \frac{1}{2}$ with respect to the polarization direction **P**. Any one of these molecules passes through analyzer A and emerges in the component identified by the quantum number $\bar{m} = \frac{1}{2}$ with a probability which is indicated, according to Sect. 7.2, by $P_{\frac{1}{2}\frac{1}{2}}^{(\frac{1}{2})}(\theta_{AP})$. In this symbol, θ_{AP} indicates the angle between **P** and **A**, the superior index $(\frac{1}{2})$ indicates that we deal with molecules having sets of two orientation eigenstates, that is, with $j = \frac{1}{2}$, and the two subscripts $\frac{1}{2}$ refer to the eigenstates $m = \frac{1}{2}$ of P and $\bar{m} = \frac{1}{2}$ of A. The intensity $I_{1/2}$ in Eq. 3 equals the intensity I of the polarizer beam multiplied by the probability $P_{\frac{1}{2}\frac{1}{2}}^{(\frac{1}{2})}(\theta_{AP})$. Consider now the further analysis by the analyzer B. The factor $\cos^2\frac{1}{2}\theta_{BA}$ in Eq. 3 is the value of the probability $P_{\frac{1}{2}\frac{1}{2}}^{(\frac{1}{2})}(\theta_{BA})$. Therefore, the product $I_{1/2}\cos^2\frac{1}{2}\theta_{BA}$ may be indicated as $P_{\frac{1}{2}\frac{1}{2}}^{(\frac{1}{2})}(\theta_{BA})P_{\frac{1}{2}\frac{1}{2}}^{(\frac{1}{2})}(\theta_{AP})\,I$,[6] and similarly we have $I_{-1/2}\sin^2\frac{1}{2}\theta_{BP} = P_{\frac{1}{2}-\frac{1}{2}}^{(\frac{1}{2})}(\theta_{BA})P_{-\frac{1}{2}\frac{1}{2}}^{(\frac{1}{2})}(\theta_{AP})\,I$. On the other hand, the intensity $I_{1/2}{}'$ observed with the analyzer B, without intervention of the analyzer A, is equal to $P_{\frac{1}{2}\frac{1}{2}}^{(\frac{1}{2})}(\theta_{BP})\,I$. The probabilities thus defined are related, according to (3), by the equation

$$P_{\frac{1}{2}\frac{1}{2}}^{(\frac{1}{2})}(\theta_{BP}) = P_{\frac{1}{2}\frac{1}{2}}^{(\frac{1}{2})}(\theta_{BA})\,P_{\frac{1}{2}\frac{1}{2}}^{(\frac{1}{2})}(\theta_{AP}) + P_{\frac{1}{2}-\frac{1}{2}}^{(\frac{1}{2})}(\theta_{BA})\,P_{-\frac{1}{2}\frac{1}{2}}^{(\frac{1}{2})}(\theta_{AP})$$

$$+ 2\sqrt{P_{\frac{1}{2}\frac{1}{2}}^{(\frac{1}{2})}(\theta_{BA})\,P_{\frac{1}{2}\frac{1}{2}}^{(\frac{1}{2})}(\theta_{AP})\,P_{\frac{1}{2}-\frac{1}{2}}^{(\frac{1}{2})}(\theta_{BA})\,P_{-\frac{1}{2}\frac{1}{2}}^{(\frac{1}{2})}(\theta_{AP})}\,\cos\delta. \quad (4)$$

The first term on the right of this equation represents the "compound probability" for a molecule from the polarizer beam (with $m = \frac{1}{2}$) to pass first through A emerging in the component $\bar{m} = \frac{1}{2}$ *and then* through B emerging in the component $\tilde{m} = \frac{1}{2}$. The second term on the right of

---

[6] Notice that the symbols relating to the later steps of analysis are placed on the left of those relating to the earlier ones. Mathematical symbols indicating successive steps of a process are usually ordered from the right to the left. Mathematics, like the English language, places the indications of operations and modifications before the indication of the object; one says "two times a" and one writes "2a" rather than "a2."

(4) represents the analogous probability for passage through A in the alternative component $\bar{m} = -\frac{1}{2}$ and then through B in the same final state $\bar{m} = \frac{1}{2}$. The last term of (4) represents the interference effect; it shows how the probability $P_{\frac{1}{2}\frac{1}{2}}^{(\frac{1}{2})}(\theta_{BP})$ of direct passage through B without intervention of A departs from the sum of probabilities of transmission *via* the alternative separate channels of A. As emphasized above, it is a fundamental feature of quantum physics that this departure exists and can be represented in the form indicated by (1), with a value of $\cos\delta$ between -1 and 1.

In the general case of molecular beams with $j \geq \frac{1}{2}$, one finds results quite analogous to those obtained with two-component beams. One may determine by direct observation with an analyzer B the probability $P_{\bar{m}m}^{(j)}(\theta_{BP})$ that a molecule prepared in the orientation state with quantum number m with respect to the direction $\mathbf{P}$ pass through B in the component with quantum number $\bar{m}$. Similarly, one may determine the compound probability

$$P_{\bar{m}\bar{m}}^{(j)}(\theta_{BA})P_{\bar{m}m}^{(j)}(\theta_{AP}) \tag{5}$$

of passage first through A, in the channel $\bar{m}$, and then through B. An interference effect is again observed, that is, the "direct" probability $P_{\bar{m}m}^{(j)}(\theta_{BP})$ differs from the sum of the probabilities (5) for all different channels of the intermediate analyzer A, that is, from the sum over all values of $\bar{m}$ from $-j$ to j. The departure is, however, subject to a restriction, analogous to that represented by Eq. 2 and by the diagram in Fig. 8.2. The rule can be illustrated graphically by representing, as in Fig. 8.4, each of the $2j + 1$ "channel" probabilities (5) as well as the "direct" probability $P_{\bar{m}m}^{(j)}(\theta_{BP})$ as the areas of squares; the squares can then always be combined to form a polygon with $2j + 1 + 1 = 2(j + 1)$ sides, analogous to the triangle of Fig. 8.2.

The angles between the "thin" sides of the polygon corresponding to the various probabilities (5) represent phase differences. There is one phase difference for each pair of channel probabilities; such a pair is identified by two values of $\bar{m}$, which we indicate as $\bar{m}$ and $\bar{m}'$, and the corresponding phase difference will be called $\delta_{\bar{m}'\bar{m}}$. The various phase differences are clearly not all independent, as shown by the fact that the mutual orientation of all parts of the polygon is fixed by the angles between adjacent sides; this condition is expressed by the formula

$$\delta_{\bar{m}''\bar{m}} = \delta_{\bar{m}''\bar{m}'} + \delta_{\bar{m}'\bar{m}}. \tag{6}$$

(In the example of beam analysis we are considering, the phase differences $\delta_{\bar{m}+1,\bar{m}}$ are either equal for different values of $\bar{m}$ or differ by 180°; in particular they are all equal to 0° or 180° if the directions $\mathbf{P}$, $\mathbf{A}$, and

B are coplanar, see Sect. 8.3.) The phase differences may be determined from a knowledge of the channel probabilities (5), and of the direct probability $P_{\bar{m}m}^{(j)}(\theta_{\mathbf{BP}})$, supplemented by more refined experiments that

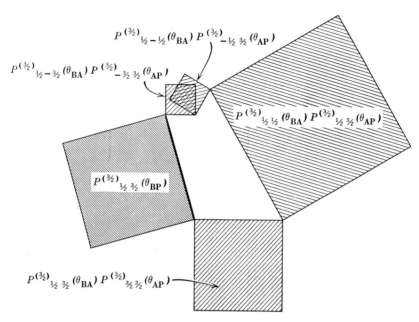

Fig. 8.4 Combination of channel probabilities in an ideal experiment on the magnetic analysis of a four-component molecular beam. The diagram corresponds to the following angles between the analyzer axes: $\theta_{\mathbf{AP}} = 60°$, $\theta_{\mathbf{BA}} = 120°$, angle between the planes **AP** and **BA** $= 60°$, $\theta_{\mathbf{BP}} = 128°40'$. The channel probabilities corresponding to the component eigenstates of **A** with $\bar{m} = \frac{3}{2}, \frac{1}{2}, -\frac{1}{2}, -\frac{3}{2}$ are, respectively, $\frac{243}{4096}, \frac{675}{4096}, \frac{27}{4096}, \frac{27}{4096}$; the phase differences of their interference are $\delta_{3/2\ 1/2} = \delta_{1/2\ -1/2} = 240°$, $\delta_{-1/2\ -3/2} = 60°$. The direct probability $P_{1/2\ 3/2}^{(3/2)}(\theta_{\mathbf{BP}})$ is $\frac{361}{4096}$.

will be described in Sect. 8.4. The mathematical formulation of the law obeyed by the probabilities is a generalization of (4), namely,[7]

$$P_{\bar{m}m}^{(j)}(\theta_{\mathbf{BP}}) = \Sigma_{\bar{m}=-j}^{j} P_{\bar{m}\bar{m}}^{(j)}(\theta_{\mathbf{BA}}) P_{\bar{m}m}^{(j)}(\theta_{\mathbf{AP}})$$

$$+ 2\Sigma_{\bar{m}=-j}^{j} \Sigma_{\bar{m}'=-j}^{\bar{m}-1} \sqrt{P_{\bar{m}\bar{m}'}^{(j)}(\theta_{\mathbf{BA}}) P_{\bar{m}'m}^{(j)}(\theta_{\mathbf{AP}}) P_{\bar{m}\bar{m}}^{(j)}(\theta_{\mathbf{BA}}) P_{\bar{m}m}^{(j)}(\theta_{\mathbf{AP}})} \cos\delta_{\bar{m}'\bar{m}}.$$

$$(7)$$

The first term on the right of this equation represents the sum of the channel probabilities (5) for a molecule from the polarizer beam to pass

---

[7] The last summation in (7) reduces to a single term when $j = \frac{1}{2}$, namely the term with $\bar{m} = \frac{1}{2}, \bar{m}' = -\frac{1}{2}$.

first through one of the alternative channels $\bar{m}$ of analyzer A and then through B emerging in the component $\tilde{m}$. The second term represents the sum of the effects of interference between all possible pairs $(\bar{m}, \bar{m}')$ of different channels of analyzer A.

Equation 7 constitutes a general relationship among quantum mechanical probabilities. However, its form is complicated and ill-suited to utilize the concept of superposition. An equivalent but more effective formula will be developed in the next section.

8.2   Mathematical Formulation of Superposition

Any given electromagnetic radiation can be represented as the combination, or "superposition," of a number of components with standard characteristics. For example, non-monochromatic light can be represented as a superposition of monochromatic components, and light of arbitrary polarization can be represented as a superposition of two components polarized linearly in different (usually orthogonal) directions. Mathematically, the superposition of radiation components is represented by simple addition of their electric and magnetic fields; the strength of the fields of each component is multiplied by a coefficient which represents the contribution of that component to the complete radiation field.

In the example of molecular beams, superposition means that the initial state of the molecules emerging from a polarizer may be regarded as a combination of the eigenstates $\bar{m}$ of an analyzer A even though these component eigenstates are not actually separated. According to Eq. 7, the probability of observations performed with the analyzer B on the molecules from the polarizer P can in fact be represented as a combination of the corresponding probabilities for molecules emerging from the analyzer A, but the combination does not consist of a simple summation. Equation 7 is analogous, in its structure, to the formula for the combination of radiation intensities; the intensities are proportional to the squared magnitudes of the fields and their combination depends on the phase differences between pairs of components. In the quantum physics of particles there are no directly observable quantities analogous to the electric and magnetic fields. Quantities suitable for the mathematical representation of superposition may, however, be defined indirectly in terms of observable quantities, much as a phase difference is defined by Eq. 3 even though it is not the difference of phases of oscillation.

Notice, as a clue to a convenient formulation of superposition, that, if the phase differences vanish, the right side of Eq. 7 is the square of a sum of terms and the equation is equivalent to

$$\sqrt{P_{\tilde{m}m}^{(j)}(\theta_{\mathbf{BP}})} = \Sigma_{\tilde{m}=-j}^{j}\sqrt{P_{\tilde{m}\tilde{m}}^{(j)}(\theta_{\mathbf{BA}})} \ \sqrt{P_{\tilde{m}m}^{(j)}(\theta_{\mathbf{AP}})}, \text{ when all } \delta = 0. \quad (8)$$

That is, in this special case, the square root of the "direct" probability equals the arithmetic sum of square roots of the channel probabilities (5). In the general case, the right side of (7) is formally identical with the square of a sum of n vectors $|\Sigma_{i=1}^{n}\mathbf{V}_i|^2 = \Sigma_{i=1}^{n}\mathbf{V}_i\cdot\mathbf{V}_i + 2\Sigma_{i=1}^{n}\Sigma_{j=1}^{i-1}\mathbf{V}_i\cdot\mathbf{V}_j = \Sigma_{i=1}^{n} V_i^2 + 2\Sigma_{i=1}^{n}\Sigma_{j=1}^{i-1} V_iV_j \cos\delta_{ij}$. In this formula δ_{ij} indicates the angle between the vectors $\mathbf{V}_i$ and $\mathbf{V}_j$ and corresponds to the phase differences that characterize the interference of different channels in Eq. 7. This formal identity underlies the construction of the diagram of Fig. 8.4: the thin sides of the polygon represent vectors of magnitude equal to the square roots of the channel probabilities, the angles between them represent the phase differences, and the thick side represents the "resultant" of the vector sum, equal in magnitude to the square root of the direct probability.[8]

Equation 8, which represents the square root of the direct probability as the sum of the square roots of the channel probabilities, corresponds to the special case in which all vectors are parallel and the angles between them vanish. This equation can be extended to the general case by replacing the arithmetic addition with a vector addition. To this end, each square root of a probability is replaced in Eq. 8 by a quantity called a "probability amplitude."[9] The probability amplitudes are defined by the requirements that their magnitudes equal the square roots of probabilities and their products are summed according to the rules of addition of vectors in a plane. These requirements imply that the probability amplitudes are not ordinary numbers but complex numbers, as shown below. A probability amplitude belongs to each pair of states, and it will be indicated by a two-part symbol into which are written letters or numbers that identify the two states. Thus the symbol

$$(\mathbf{B}\tilde{m} \,|\, \mathbf{P}m)$$

indicates the probability amplitude belonging to the eigenstate m of the polarizer with orientation $\mathbf{P}$ and to the eigenstate $\tilde{m}$ of the analyzer with orientation $\mathbf{B}$. Notice that the analyzer state in which the molecules are observed is indicated on the left of the initial state.[10] By means of

[8] The vectors of the diagram lie in a plane because the angles between them are not independent but obey the condition (6).

[9] The name "amplitude" originates from the description of wave phenomena, whose amplitude of oscillation (that is, the peak field strength in the case of macroscopic electromagnetism) is proportional to the square root of the intensity.

[10] See footnote 6 on page 106.

probability amplitudes we can then formulate a fundamental equation, which is equivalent to (7) and is more general than (8) in that it applies to $\delta \neq 0$, namely,

$$(\mathbf{B}\tilde{m} \mid \mathbf{P}m) = \Sigma^{j}_{\tilde{m}= -j} \, (\mathbf{B}\tilde{m} \mid \mathbf{A}\tilde{m})(\mathbf{A}\tilde{m} \mid \mathbf{P}m). \tag{9}$$

It is understood that the definition of probability amplitude must be completed in such a way that the sum is carried out according to the rules of vector addition. Equation 9 will be called in the following the "combination rule" of probability amplitudes.

The sum of a number of vectors, that is, their "resultant," has a magnitude which depends on the magnitude of the vectors and on the angles between them. In our problem, the quantities corresponding to the angles have been called "phase differences" and are represented by the angles in Figs. 8.2 and 8.4. In the diagram of Fig. 8.4 each side of the polygon has a definite orientation even though only the relative orientations have an influence on the magnitude of the resultant. Correspondingly, one may define the probability amplitudes so that each term of the summation in (9) has a *phase* of its own; the phase differences determined by experimental observations are then represented as "differences of phases." This procedure is followed because it facilitates the accounting of phase differences; however, it introduces in the mathematical representation elements (namely, the phases) which are *not* unique functions of experimentally observable quantities. Assigning a phase to each probability amplitude is equivalent to selecting a frame of reference for the orientation of analyzer axes, as will be illustrated in Sect. 8.3 and in Chapter 9.

If the probability amplitudes are so defined that each term in the summation (9) has a phase, that is, a numerical characteristic represented in Fig. 8.4 by a definite orientation, the probability amplitude on the left of (9) has also a phase. Therefore, in general, each probability amplitude has a magnitude and a phase.

The definition of probability amplitude is specified further by requiring that the phases of all factors $(\mathbf{B}\tilde{m} \mid \mathbf{A}\tilde{m})$ on the right of (9), and the phase of $(\mathbf{B}\tilde{m} \mid \mathbf{P}m)$ on its left, may be increased by an equal but arbitrary amount without changing the phase differences among the terms in the summation over $\tilde{m}$, which alone are unique functions of experimentally observable quantities. It follows that when two probability amplitudes are multiplied, the phase of the product must be the sum of the phases of the two factors.

The conditions specified above, regarding the combination of magnitudes and phases when probability amplitudes are multiplied or added, coincide with the specifications regarding magnitudes and phases of *complex numbers.* A complex number is indicated (see Appendix VI) in one of the equivalent forms

$$z = \rho e^{i\phi} = \rho(\cos\phi + i \sin\phi) = x + iy, \tag{10}$$

where ρ indicates the magnitude and ϕ the phase of the number,[11] where $e = 2.71828\cdots$ indicates the base of natural logarithms, $i = \sqrt{-1}$ is the imaginary unit, $x = \rho \cos\phi$ and $y = \rho \sin\phi$. The product of two complex numbers has a magnitude equal to the product of their magnitudes and a phase equal to the sum of their phases (see Appendix VI). The sum of two complex numbers has a magnitude and a phase given by the rules of vector addition. It is concluded that probability amplitudes are complex numbers.

Quantum mechanics describes phenomena and calculates the probabilities of their various outcomes by mathematical formulas constructed with probability amplitudes. These probability amplitudes are indicated by symbols of the type $(\mathbf{A}\bar{m}\,|\,\mathbf{P}m)$, with the indication of an eigenstate of the system on each side of the vertical bar. For example, the probability amplitude which relates a stationary state of a hydrogen atom characterized by an energy eigenvalue E and an eigenstate characterized by the eigenvalues x, y, z of the position coordinates of its electron is indicated by

$$(xyz\,|\,E). \tag{11}$$

The square of the magnitude of this amplitude, indicated by [12]

$$|\,(xyz\,|\,E)\,|^2, \tag{12}$$

represents the probability that the electron is at (xyz) if the atom is in the stationary state of energy E. The set of probability amplitudes belonging to one eigenstate of any variable and to all eigenstates of the position coordinates of a particle constitutes a function of these coordinates. As shown in the following chapters, this function is often oscillatory and is accordingly called a "wave function." A wave function is usually indicated by the letter ψ and one utilizes indifferently a function symbol or a probability amplitude symbol according to

$$\psi_a(xyz) = (xyz\,|\,a), \tag{13}$$

where a indicates an eigenstate of any variable. The name "wave function" is sometimes used more generally as a synomym of "probability amplitude."

---

[11] When the phase ϕ is entered in the exponent as in (10), it is usually expressed in radians rather than in degrees. One radian is the angle that subtends an arc of circle equal in length to the radius of the circle. Thus $360° = 2\pi$ radians.

[12] The sign $|\ |$ means "absolute value of," that is, "magnitude of."

Additional properties of probability amplitudes follow from the combination rule (9). When the polarizer and analyzer axes **P** and **B** are parallel, their sets of eigenstates coincide. Two states of this single set can be indicated with $\mathbf{P}m'$ and $\mathbf{P}m$. If $\mathbf{P}m'$ coincides with $\mathbf{P}m$ the probability amplitude is equal to one, because it belongs to two identical states and its squared magnitude represents the probability of detecting the molecule in the "retest" experiment of Fig. 7.6. Equation 9 becomes then [13]

$$(\mathbf{P}m \mid \mathbf{P}m) = \Sigma_{\bar{m}}(\mathbf{P}m \mid \mathbf{A}\bar{m})(\mathbf{A}\bar{m} \mid \mathbf{P}m) = 1. \tag{14}$$

If m' differs from m, $(\mathbf{P}m' \mid \mathbf{P}m)$ must vanish, because there is no probability of observing the molecule in a different (orthogonal) eigenstate in the retest experiment, and Eq. 9 becomes

$$(\mathbf{P}m' \mid \mathbf{P}m) = \Sigma_{\bar{m}}(\mathbf{P}m' \mid \mathbf{A}\bar{m})(\mathbf{A}\bar{m} \mid \mathbf{P}m) = 0 \qquad \text{for } m' \neq m. \tag{15}$$

Consider now that the probability of passing from the state $\mathbf{P}m$ to the state $\mathbf{A}\bar{m}$ is indicated by $|(\mathbf{A}\bar{m} \mid \mathbf{P}m)|^2$ and equals the probability $|(\mathbf{P}m \mid \mathbf{A}\bar{m})|^2$ of passing from $\mathbf{A}\bar{m}$ to $\mathbf{P}m$ in view of the reciprocity property discussed on page 96. Moreover, the sum of the probabilities of passing from the state $\mathbf{P}m$ to all states $\mathbf{A}\bar{m}$ must equal one, because the eigenstates $\mathbf{A}\bar{m}$ constitute a complete set. We have therefore

$$\Sigma_{\bar{m}} |(\mathbf{A}\bar{m} \mid \mathbf{P}m)|^2 = \Sigma_{\bar{m}} |(\mathbf{P}m \mid \mathbf{A}\bar{m})|^2$$
$$= \Sigma_{\bar{m}} |(\mathbf{P}m \mid \mathbf{A}\bar{m})| \, |(\mathbf{A}\bar{m} \mid \mathbf{P}m)| = 1. \tag{16}$$

Comparison of (14) with (16) suggests that the "reciprocal" probability amplitudes $(\mathbf{P}m \mid \mathbf{A}\bar{m})$ and $(\mathbf{A}\bar{m} \mid \mathbf{P}m)$ have *phases* equal in magnitude and of *opposite sign*. This surmise is confirmed by a mathematical proof. That is, the complex numbers $(\mathbf{P}m \mid \mathbf{A}\bar{m})$ and $(\mathbf{A}\bar{m} \mid \mathbf{P}m)$ differ, when expressed in the form (10), $\rho e^{i\phi}$, only in the sign of the exponent or, which is the same, only in the sign of the imaginary unit i. This property is expressed by writing

$$(\mathbf{P}m \mid \mathbf{A}\bar{m}) = (\mathbf{A}\bar{m} \mid \mathbf{P}m)^*, \tag{17}$$

where the asterisk (star) indicates "complex conjugation," that is, reversal of the sign of the imaginary unit i. In particular, reciprocal probability amplitudes are identical when their phases equal $0°$ or $180°$.

The probability amplitudes $(\mathbf{A}\bar{m} \mid \mathbf{P}m)$ pertaining to all eigenstates $\mathbf{P}m$ and to all eigenstates $\mathbf{A}\bar{m}$ can be laid out in a square array, in which each column contains all $(\mathbf{A}\bar{m} \mid \mathbf{P}m)$ with the same $\mathbf{A}\bar{m}$ and different $\mathbf{P}m$.

---

[13] The summation in this formula includes one term for each value of $\bar{m}$ from $\bar{m} = -j$ to $\bar{m} = j$, as in (9). However, the indication of the summation limits is omitted here and in the following, unless a misunderstanding seems likely.

(The array in Table 7.1 contains the experimental values of $|(\mathbf{A}\bar{m}|\mathbf{P}m)|^2$ only, without any indication of phases.)   This array is called a "matrix." The properties (14), (15), and (17) characterize the matrices of probability amplitudes as "unitary matrices."

The probability amplitudes pertaining to any two complete sets of orthogonal eigenstates have the properties (14) to (17).   In the example of the probability amplitudes (11), the Eqs. 14 and 15 become

$$(E'|E) = \Sigma_{xyz}(E'|xyz)(xyz|E) = \begin{cases} 1 \text{ for } E' = E \\ 0 \text{ for } E' \neq E. \end{cases} \tag{18}$$

The summation over x, y, and z is expressed more properly as an integration.   The integral form is utilized normally when $(xyz|E)$ is indicated in the form of a wave function according to (13).   Equation 18 is then written as

$$\iiint dx\, dy\, dz\, \psi_{E'}(x, y, z)^* \psi_E(x, y, z) = \begin{cases} 1 \text{ for } E' = E \\ 0 \text{ for } E' \neq E. \end{cases} \tag{19}$$

Equation 18 is complemented by the reciprocal equation

$$(x'y'z'|xyz) = \Sigma_E(x'y'z'|E)(E|xyz) = \begin{cases} 1 \text{ for } x' = x,\, y' = y,\, z' = z \\ 0 \text{ otherwise.} \end{cases} \tag{20}$$

8.3   Mathematical Expression of the Probability Amplitudes for Eigenstates of Atomic Orientation

The probability amplitudes associated with pairs of states of light polarization or of atomic current orientation represent data on successive operations of beam analysis.   The variables in these operations are the orientations of analyzers and the number of components into which a beam resolves when subjected to magnetic analysis.   The probability amplitude associated with an eigenstate of a given analyzer orientation and with an eigenstate of another orientation is a function only of the orientations and of the number of beam components.   The theoretical determination of this function, given the properties of probability amplitudes described in Sect. 8.2, constitutes a well-defined problem of geometry.   Quantitative results of beam experiments, such as the probabilities listed in Table 7.1, are *not* required for the solution of this problem but, on the contrary, are predicted theoretically by the solution.   The solution for the orientation states of atoms can be obtained by various mathematical procedures; a conceptually simple but lengthy derivation is carried out in Appendix VII.   In other problems of atomic physics an analyzer setting is identified by variables other than orientation of a magnetic field, such as the time of an observation or the strength of a field; the calculation of probability amplitudes rests then on some experimental law of atomic physics or on macroscopic laws otherwise known from theory or experiment, as will be seen in the following chapters and in Appendix VIII.

The mutual orientation of the directions **P** and **A** of the field in two Stern-Gerlach magnets is characterized primarily but not completely

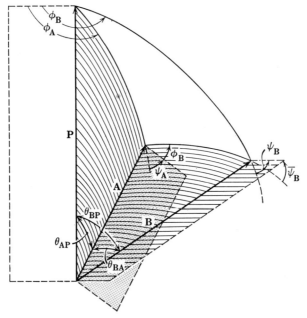

Fig. 8.5 Angles relating the orientations of the axes **P**, **A**, and **B** and of their respective reference planes.

by the angle θ_{AP} between these directions. Additional data are required to single out the plane containing the two directions **P** and **A** among all the planes that contain only the direction **P** or only the direction **A**. To specify all mutual orientations, one may attach to each analyzer axis an arbitrary reference plane, and identify any other plane through the same axis by the "azimuth" angle between that plane and the reference plane (see Fig. 8.5). The choice of an arbitrary reference plane is an analytic procedure unrelated to experimental variables; it is equivalent, as will be seen, to the arbitrary specification of the phases of probability amplitudes discussed in Sect. 8.2. On the other hand, azimuth *differences* are experimental variables, like phase differences; for example in Fig. 8.5

the azimuth difference between the planes **AP** and **BA** specifies the magnitude of the angle θ_{BP} once θ_{AP} and θ_{BA} are given.

Each probability amplitude is usually expressed, in our problem, as a function of three angles, called "Euler angles," one of which is the angle θ between two axes, whereas the other two are azimuth angles. For example, the probability amplitude $(\mathbf{A}\bar{m}\,|\,\mathbf{P}m)$ pertaining to the eigenstate m of the polarizer $\mathbf{P}$ and to the eigenstate $\bar{m}$ of the analyzer $\mathbf{A}$ is a function of: (a) the azimuth angle ϕ_A of the plane $\mathbf{AP}$ with respect to the reference plane attached to $\mathbf{P}$; (b) the angle θ_{AP} in the plane $\mathbf{AP}$; and (c) the azimuth angle ψ_A of the reference plane attached to $\mathbf{A}$ with respect to the plane $\mathbf{AP}$. (The reciprocal probability amplitude $(\mathbf{P}m\,|\,\mathbf{A}\bar{m})$ is then expressed as a function of the corresponding angles $\bar{\phi}_P = \pi - \psi_A$, $\theta_{PA} = \theta_{AP}$, and $\bar{\psi}_P = \pi - \phi_A$, as seen from Fig. 8.5.)

The magnitude of the probability amplitude $(\mathbf{A}\bar{m}\,|\,\mathbf{P}m)$ is the square root of the probability that a molecule pass through the component channel $\bar{m}$ of the analyzer $\mathbf{A}$ if it has been prefiltered through the channel m of the polarizer $\mathbf{P}$. This magnitude can accordingly depend only on

TABLE 8.1

PROBABILITY AMPLITUDES FOR TWO-, THREE-, AND FOUR-COMPONENT BEAM SPLITTING $(\psi = \phi = 0)$

$$\mathfrak{d}_{\bar{m}m}^{(1/2)}(\theta)$$

$\bar{m}$ \ m	$\frac{1}{2}$	$-\frac{1}{2}$
$\frac{1}{2}$	$\cos\frac{1}{2}\theta$	$\sin\frac{1}{2}\theta$
$-\frac{1}{2}$	$-\sin\frac{1}{2}\theta$	$\cos\frac{1}{2}\theta$

$$\mathfrak{d}_{\bar{m}m}^{(1)}(\theta)$$

$\bar{m}$ \ m	1	0	-1
1	$\cos^2\frac{1}{2}\theta$	$\sqrt{2}\sin\frac{1}{2}\theta\cos\frac{1}{2}\theta$	$\sin^2\frac{1}{2}\theta$
0	$-\sqrt{2}\sin\frac{1}{2}\theta\cos\frac{1}{2}\theta$	$\cos^2\frac{1}{2}\theta - \sin^2\frac{1}{2}\theta$	$\sqrt{2}\sin\frac{1}{2}\theta\cos\frac{1}{2}\theta$
-1	$\sin^2\frac{1}{2}\theta$	$-\sqrt{2}\sin\frac{1}{2}\theta\cos\frac{1}{2}\theta$	$\cos^2\frac{1}{2}\theta$

$$\mathfrak{d}_{\bar{m}m}^{(3/2)}(\theta)$$

$\bar{m}$ \ m	$\frac{3}{2}$	$\frac{1}{2}$	$-\frac{1}{2}$	$-\frac{3}{2}$
$\frac{3}{2}$	$\cos^3\frac{1}{2}\theta$	$\sqrt{3}\cos^2\frac{1}{2}\theta\sin\frac{1}{2}\theta$	$\sqrt{3}\cos\frac{1}{2}\theta\sin^2\frac{1}{2}\theta$	$\sin^3\frac{1}{2}\theta$
$\frac{1}{2}$	$-\sqrt{3}\cos^2\frac{1}{2}\theta\sin\frac{1}{2}\theta$	$\cos\frac{1}{2}\theta(1 - 3\sin^2\frac{1}{2}\theta)$	$\sin\frac{1}{2}\theta(3\cos^2\frac{1}{2}\theta - 1)$	$\sqrt{3}\cos\frac{1}{2}\theta\sin^2\frac{1}{2}\theta$
$-\frac{1}{2}$	$\sqrt{3}\cos\frac{1}{2}\theta\sin^2\frac{1}{2}\theta$	$\sin\frac{1}{2}\theta(1 - 3\cos^2\frac{1}{2}\theta)$	$\cos\frac{1}{2}\theta(1 - 3\sin^2\frac{1}{2}\theta)$	$\sqrt{3}\cos^2\frac{1}{2}\theta\sin\frac{1}{2}\theta$
$-\frac{3}{2}$	$-\sin^3\frac{1}{2}\theta$	$\sqrt{3}\cos\frac{1}{2}\theta\sin^2\frac{1}{2}\theta$	$-\sqrt{3}\cos^2\frac{1}{2}\theta\sin\frac{1}{2}\theta$	$\cos^3\frac{1}{2}\theta$

the angle θ_{AP}, whereas the phase of $(\mathbf{A}\bar{m}\,|\,\mathbf{P}m)$ may depend on the azimuth angles ϕ_A and ψ_A and thereby on the arbitrary choice of reference planes. This surmise is confirmed in Appendix VII by a proof that the functional dependence of $(\mathbf{A}\bar{m}\,|\,\mathbf{P}m)$ on the Euler angles θ_{AP}, ϕ_A, and ψ_A factors out into three functions of one angle each. The two functions of the azimuth angles have magnitude one, that is, consist only of a phase factor; the function of θ_{AP} can be real. The mathematical determination of the three functions in Appendix VII is rather laborious and yields

$$(\mathbf{A}\bar{m}\,|\,\mathbf{P}m) = e^{i\bar{m}\psi_A}\,\mathfrak{d}^{(j)}_{\bar{m}m}(\theta_{AP})\,e^{im\phi_A}, \tag{21}$$

where $\mathfrak{d}^{(j)}_{\bar{m}m}(\theta)$ can be expressed as a homogeneous polynomial of degree $2j$ in $\cos\frac{1}{2}\theta$ and $\sin\frac{1}{2}\theta$. Table 8.1 gives the explicit form of $\mathfrak{d}^{(j)}_{\bar{m}m}(\theta)$ for $j = \frac{1}{2}$, $j = 1$, and $j = \frac{3}{2}$. The squares of the expressions in this table coincide, as expected, with the expressions of the probabilities $P^{(j)}_{\bar{m}m}(\theta)$ given in Table 7.1.

As a final illustration, we consider now once more the combination laws of probability amplitudes and of probabilities, Eqs. 9 and 7, utilizing the expression (21) of the probability amplitudes. With reference to the angles indicated in Fig. 8.5, Eq. 9 is seen to be

$$(\mathbf{B}\tilde{m}\,|\,\mathbf{P}m) = e^{i\tilde{m}\psi_B}\,\mathfrak{d}^{(j)}_{\tilde{m}m}(\theta_{BP})\,e^{im\phi_B}$$

$$= e^{i\tilde{m}\bar{\psi}_B}\sum_{\bar{m}}\,\mathfrak{d}^{(j)}_{\tilde{m}\bar{m}}(\theta_{BA})\,e^{i\bar{m}\,\bar{\phi}_B}\,e^{i\bar{m}\psi_A}\,\mathfrak{d}^{(j)}_{\bar{m}m}(\theta_{AP})\,e^{im\phi_A}. \tag{22}$$

Most of the phase factors in this formula, in fact, all those that do not contain the quantum number $\bar{m}$, do not influence the magnitude of $(\mathbf{B}\tilde{m}\,|\,\mathbf{P}m)$ and drop out when one calculates the probability $P^{(j)}_{\tilde{m}m}(\theta_{BP})$, which is

$$P^{(j)}_{\tilde{m}m}(\theta_{BP}) = |(\mathbf{B}\tilde{m}\,|\,\mathbf{P}m)|^2 = \sum_{\bar{m}}\,[\mathfrak{d}^{(j)}_{\tilde{m}\bar{m}}(\theta_{BA})]^2\,[\mathfrak{d}^{(j)}_{\bar{m}m}(\theta_{AP})]^2$$

$$+ 2\sum_{\bar{m}}\,\sum_{\bar{m}'=-j}^{\bar{m}-1}\,\mathfrak{d}^{(j)}_{\tilde{m}\bar{m}}(\theta_{BA})\,\mathfrak{d}^{(j)}_{\bar{m}m}(\theta_{AP})\,\mathfrak{d}^{(j)}_{\tilde{m}\bar{m}'}(\theta_{BA})\,\mathfrak{d}^{(j)}_{\bar{m}'m}(\theta_{AP})\cos[(\bar{m}-\bar{m}')(\psi_A+\bar{\phi}_B)]. \tag{23}$$

Comparison of this equation with Eq. 7 shows how the functions $\mathfrak{d}^{(j)}$ represent the square roots of probabilities and how the phase difference $\delta_{\bar{m}\bar{m}'}$ equals the angle $\psi_A + \bar{\phi}_B$, between the planes $\mathbf{AP}$ and $\mathbf{BA}$, multiplied by the difference of quantum numbers $\bar{m} - \bar{m}'$.

8.4 Coherent and Incoherent Superposition

The superposition principle has been applied in Sect. 8.1 to treat light in an unknown state of polarization as the combination of light beams polarized linearly in two orthogonal directions. The description of phenomena in terms of superposition becomes more cogent when the component beams are first separated, then routed along different paths in space and finally recombined. Actually, the development of a phenomenon along separate paths, followed by recombination, constitutes a salient feature of most interference effects. (This chapter deals with interference effects upon the polarization of light beams or the orientation of intraatomic currents, but there are many other, more familiar examples of interference effects some of which will be considered in the next chapters.) Phenomena that develop along different paths point out aspects of interference and conditions governing it which have not emerged from the experiments discussed in Sect. 8.1.

Figure 8.6a shows the separation of linearly polarized components of a light beam in a Jamin interferometer. A first Iceland spar crystal A

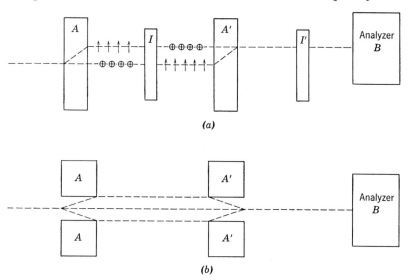

(a)

(b)

Fig. 8.6 (a) Light beam separation and recombination in a Jamin interferometer. (b) Idealized separation and recombination of a three-component molecular beam.

splits incident light into an ordinary and an extraordinary ray, which travel separately for a distance and then recombine when they traverse a second crystal A'. To even out the two paths there is inserted between A and A' an inverter crystal I which rotates each direction of polarization by 90°. Thereby each beam component traverses one spar as the ordinary ray and the other as the extraordinary ray. The action of the inverter I is compensated by a second inverter I' between A' and a final spar analyzer B. Figure 8.6b outlines an analogous schematic experiment with molecular beams, in which a first Stern-Gerlach magnet splits the beam components and focuses all of them along parallel paths, and a second magnet A' inverts the action of A. The beam emerging from A' is then observed with a final analyzer B.

The light intensities, which are called I_o', $I_o \cos^2\alpha$ and $I_e \sin^2\alpha$ in Sect. 8.1 and are determined by experiments with and without an initial spar crystal, can be observed with the arrangement of Fig. 8.6a without moving any crystal. The intensity I_o' is the intensity of the ordinary ray of B, because the arrangement of Fig. 8.6a is such that the spar and inverter actions cancel out. The intensity $I_o \cos^2\alpha$ is the intensity of the same ray when the upper component is intercepted between A and A' by a screen, $I_e \sin^2\alpha$ is the intensity when the lower component is intercepted. The interference effect consists, as in Sect. 8.1, of the fact that the intensity I_o' deviates from the sum of the component intensities $I_o \cos^2\alpha + I_e \sin^2\alpha$.

The molecular beam experiment, outlined in Fig. 8.6b, yields more detailed results than the analogous experiment of Sect. 8.1, when there are more than two components. In this case, one may let through, in turn, different pairs of component beams while intercepting the other ones. The intensity observed with B upon recombination of each pair determines separately the phase difference of the pair.

In both the optical and the molecular experiment of Fig. 8.6, the component beams may be influenced by various actions along their separate paths. For example, a glass plate may be inserted across one of the light beams, or the molecules may be subjected to a uniform magnetic field; the analyzer B reveals then a change respectively of polarization or of current circulation.

It is well-known in optics that interference effects occur only with beam components originating from the same source. For example, if the spar crystal A in Fig. 8.6a were removed and the upper and lower beams were piped-in with the same polarization as shown in the figure, but from different sources, the intensity measurement with B would yield

$$I_o' = I_o \cos^2\alpha + I_e \sin^2\alpha. \tag{24}$$

Analogous results are obtained with molecular beams. When recombination yields no interference effect, that is, no departure from (24), the component beams are said to be "incoherent."

The incoherent superposition of beams from different sources is a logical necessity. Emission of a photon by one source, followed by absorption in a counter behind the analyzer B, and emission by another source, followed by absorption in the same counter, constitute distinct, *mutually exclusive* events. In experiments at low intensity one can always check, at least in principle, in which source an atom has become de-excited in coincidence with the absorption of a photon in the counter. The total probability of occurrence of any two mutually exclusive events is equal to the sum of the probabilities of the separate events. This law of probability implies the corresponding law of combination (24) for the macroscopic intensities, because the macroscopic laws hold at all intensity levels, as noted in Chapter 5. The same probability argument applies to the travel of molecules from two different sources to a single counter.

This interpretation of incoherence emphasizes the contrasting property of the "coherent" superposition of component beams from the same source. The interference of component beams which are first separated and then recombined consists of the fact that the detection probability of a photon or particle in the recombined beam deviates from the sum of the probabilities in the separate beams. This phenomenon implies that alternative paths of travel from a source to a detector are *not* mutually exclusive. In general, coherent superposition implies that the component phenomena are not to be regarded as mutually exclusive, but as taking place concurrently, albeit at different points of space. Coherent superposition hinges on the circumstance that the detection of a photon or particle fails to indicate, even in principle, which among the combining alternative paths has been followed. Whenever the experimental conditions permit the passage of light or particles along alternative paths to leave any trace whatsoever, detectable even only in principle as is usual in macroscopic mechanics, the paths become associated to distinct, mutually exclusive events and interference disappears.

PROBLEMS

8.1 The analysis of light into polarization eigenstates can be represented in terms of probability amplitudes $(A\tilde{m}|Pm)$, where, for linear polarization, $\mathbf{P}$ and $\mathbf{A}$ are vectors perpendicular to the principal section of a spar analyzer and m equals 1 and 2, respectively, for the ordinary and extraordinary rays. With suitable conventions, one finds $(A1|P1) = (A2|P2) = \cos\alpha_{AP}$, $(A1|P2) = -(A2|P1) = \sin\alpha_{AP}$. Check that probability amplitudes with this mathematical form fulfill Eq. 9. (Take $m = \tilde{m} = 1$.)

8.2 Check that the functions in Table 8.1 fulfill Eq. 22, in the special case where the field directions $\mathbf{P}$, $\mathbf{A}$, and $\mathbf{B}$ in the analyzers are orthogonal, that is, where $\theta_{AP} = \theta_{BA} = \theta_{BP} = \frac{1}{2}\pi$. Take the plane AP as reference plane for $\mathbf{P}$ and $\mathbf{A}$, and the plane BA as reference for $\mathbf{B}$, so that $\phi_A = \psi_A = \bar{\psi}_B = 0$, $\phi_B = \bar{\phi}_B = \psi_B = \frac{1}{2}\pi$; take $j = \frac{1}{2}$ and $\tilde{m} = m = \frac{1}{2}$.

8.3 With reference to Fig. 8.6 and to Problem 8.1, consider light of 6000 A wavelength emerging as ordinary ray of a polarizer P and incident on a Jamin interferometer. Suppose that on the path of the extraordinary beam after the crystal A a device changes the refractive index of the air by 2 parts in 100,000 over a distance of 0.5 cm, with a resulting phase shift of $2 \times 10^{-5} \times 0.5/6 \times 10^{-5} = \frac{1}{6}$ of one wavelength $= \frac{1}{3}\pi$ radians. Calculate the intensity fraction f in the ordinary ray of analyzer B, as a function of the orientations of $\mathbf{P}$, $\mathbf{B}$, and $\mathbf{A}$.

Probability variations in the course of time

Macroscopic phenomena are described by stating the values of relevant variables at successive instants of time. In quantum physics each variable does not, in general, have a specific value. Therefore, quantum phenomena are described by stating the probability of the various eigenvalues of relevant variables at successive instants of time. For example, the emission of light by a hydrogen atom depends on internal currents, which are described by specifying how the probability distribution of electron positions varies in the course of time.

The time dependence of quantum mechanical probability distributions can be expressed by a simple law, utilizing the superposition principle. This dependence reflects, of course, variations of the state of the atom, or other system, with which one is concerned. The state itself is conveniently regarded as a combination of energy eigenstates, because these states remain stationary in the course of time. The time dependence of probability distributions can thus be derived from the time dependence of the probability amplitudes that identify the state as a combination of stationary states.

Moreover, it will be shown in this chapter that these probability amplitudes have themselves a constant magnitude. The time dependence is thereby confined to the phases of probability amplitudes. That is, the variation in the course of time of the probability of any eigenvalue may be represented as a variable effect of interference among the contributions of stationary states. In the example of light emission by a hydrogen atom, the state of the atom is made non-stationary by interaction with radiation; the probability distribution of electron positions oscillates in this non-stationary state and acts as a radiation source. The oscillations responsible for the emission of a given spectral line result from interference between the probability distributions of electron positions in the two stationary states between which the emission occurs.

Any variation of probability in the course of time can be represented as a combination of sinusoidal oscillations by the procedure of Fourier analysis (Appendix IV). In the analysis of the probabilities of atomic events, all component oscillations are found to have frequencies equal to differences between pairs of energy eigenvalues divided by Planck's constant h. It follows that any two stationary states, with energies E_i and E_k, interfere with a phase difference that varies in the course of time at the constant rate of $(E_i - E_k)/\hbar$ radians/sec, where $\hbar = h/2\pi$. (The symbol $\hbar$ is introduced to express conveniently rates of phase variations in radians/sec rather than in cycles/sec.) This general law is complemented by a convention regarding the assignment of a definite phase to each probability amplitude. The convention may be chosen as follows: when a state is identified by a variable $a(t)$ which varies in the course of time and is represented as a combination of stationary states with energies E_i by probability amplitudes $(E_i|a(t))$, the phase of $(E_i|a(t))$ decreases at the fixed rate of $-E_i/\hbar$ radians/sec.[1] This rule is represented by the formula

$$(E_i|a(t)) = e^{-i(E_i/\hbar)t}(E_i|a(0)), \tag{1a}$$

which is often written, for typographical convenience, as

$$(E_i|a(t)) = \exp\left(-i\frac{E_i}{\hbar}t\right)(E_i|a(0)). \tag{1b}$$

A simple example of oscillatory variation of probabilities is encountered in molecular beam analysis, when the molecules are subjected before the analysis to a uniform magnetic field for a variable length of time. This example is treated in Sect. 9.1. Section 9.2 outlines the evidence and the arguments which establish Eq. 1 as a fundamental law of quantum mechanics.

---

[1] Different conventions are often used, as pointed out in Sect. 9.2.

9.1   Variations of Intraatomic Current Orientation

Consider a beam of molecules, prefiltered by a Stern-Gerlach magnet with field orientation **P**, in an eigenstate with a given quantum number m. The polarizer is followed by a magnet which produces a *uniform* field with direction **A**, and then by a Stern-Gerlach analyzer with field orientation **B**, which separates components with various quantum numbers $\tilde{m}$. The intensity of the components is observed as a function of the time t spent by the molecule in the field of magnet **A** and of the field strength within this magnet. (The time spent within the field **A** equals the length l of the path through the magnet divided by the speed v of the molecules, and may be varied by changing l or v.)

The intensity of each beam component $\tilde{m}$ is found to be a periodic function of the time t spent by the molecules within the magnet **A** and of the field strength H within this magnet. More specifically, the intensity is a periodic function of the ratio $\mu H t/jh$, and resumes its value whenever this ratio increases by one (μ and j are the magnetic moment and the quantum number defined on page 90). The component intensities are proportional to the probabilities $P^{(j)}_{\tilde{m}m}(\theta)$ of Sect. 7.2, where θ is now a periodic function of $\mu H t/jh$. This indicates that the molecules incident on the analyzer are in an eigenstate of current circulation about an axis **Q** which no longer coincides with **P**, but forms with **B** an angle θ; the quantum number of this eigenstate is equal to m.

Measurement of the intensities of the beam components $\tilde{m}$ determines the angle θ but leaves the orientation of the axis **Q** still undetermined, as pointed out in Chapter 8 (see Fig. 8.1). Observations with the analyzer B in two different orientations are necessary to identify **Q**. Such observations show: (*a*) that the angle $\theta_{\textbf{AQ}}$ between **Q** and **A** remains unaffected by the passage of the molecules through the magnet A, (*b*) that **Q** turns around **A** at the constant speed $\mu H/j\hbar$ radians/sec, making one complete revolution in a time period T such that $\mu H T/j\hbar = 1$. This rotation of the axis of current circulation about the direction **A** of the uniform magnetic field is called "Larmor precession" and is due to a gyroscopic effect to be discussed in Chapter 15. The precession brings **Q** closer to **B** and then farther again at every turn, as shown by the periodic variation of θ.

The intensity variations of the beam components $\tilde{m}$ may be analyzed mathematically by regarding the variable state (**Q**$(t)m$) of the molecules as a combination of eigenstates (**A**$\tilde{m}$) of an analyzer with orientation **A**; these eigenstates are stationary states of molecules in a magnetic field with this orientation. (The component eigenstates with different quantum numbers $\tilde{m}$ may, in principle, be actually separated, by the device of Fig. 8.6b, then passed through the uniform field in the magnet A and finally recombined, without affecting the final result observed with the analyzer B.)

The probability of finding the molecule in the channel $\tilde{m}$ of the analyzer B is represented, according to Sect. 8.2, as the squared magnitude of the probability amplitude $(\mathbf{B}\tilde{m}\,|\,\mathbf{Q}(t)m)$. Further, the combination rule (9) of Sect. 8.2 represents $(\mathbf{B}\tilde{m}\,|\,\mathbf{Q}(t)m)$ as the sum of the contributions of the different component eigenstates of the orientation $\mathbf{A}$,

$$(\mathbf{B}\tilde{m}\,|\,\mathbf{Q}(t)m) = \Sigma_{\bar{m}}(\mathbf{B}\tilde{m}\,|\,\mathbf{A}\bar{m})(\mathbf{A}\bar{m}\,|\,\mathbf{Q}(t)m). \tag{2}$$

Since the angles between $\mathbf{Q}$ and $\mathbf{A}$ and between $\mathbf{A}$ and $\mathbf{B}$ remain constant in the course of time, the probability amplitudes $(\mathbf{B}\tilde{m}\,|\,\mathbf{A}\bar{m})$ and $(\mathbf{A}\bar{m}\,|\,\mathbf{Q}(t)m)$ have a constant magnitude. The variations of $(\mathbf{B}\tilde{m}\,|\,\mathbf{Q}(t)m)$ in the course of time are thereby represented as effects of *variable interference* between different terms of the summation (2).

The phase differences between these terms are proportional, as shown in Sect. 8.3, to the angle between the planes $\mathbf{QA}$ and $\mathbf{AB}$, which varies, owing to the rotation of $\mathbf{Q}$, with constant speed $\mu H/j\hbar$ radians/sec. The orientation of $\mathbf{P}$ with respect to $\mathbf{A}$ is identified, as shown in Fig. 8.5, by the angle $\psi_{\mathbf{A}}$ between the plane $\mathbf{PA}$ and the reference plane attached to $\mathbf{A}$. Similarly, since $\mathbf{Q}$ coincides with $\mathbf{P}$ at the time $t = 0$, the orientation of the variable axis $\mathbf{Q}$ is identified by the variable angle

$$\psi_{\mathbf{A}} + \frac{\mu H}{j\hbar}\, t, \tag{3}$$

between the plane $\mathbf{QA}$ and the reference plane attached to $\mathbf{A}$.

The result of any observation performed on the molecules after they emerge from the uniform field in the magnet A may be predicted in terms of the probability amplitudes $(\mathbf{A}\bar{m}\,|\,\mathbf{Q}(t)m)$. The mathematical expression of these probability amplitudes is derived from the expression of $(\mathbf{A}\bar{m}\,|\,\mathbf{P}m)$ given by (21) on page 117, by replacing the fixed angle $\psi_{\mathbf{A}}$ with the variable angle (3), and is

$$(\mathbf{A}\bar{m}\,|\,\mathbf{Q}(t)m) = \exp\left[i\bar{m}\left(\psi_{\mathbf{A}} + \frac{\mu H}{j\hbar}\, t\right)\right] \delta_{\bar{m}m}^{(j)}(\theta_{\mathbf{AP}})\,\exp(im\phi_{\mathbf{A}})$$

$$= \exp\left(i\bar{m}\,\frac{\mu H}{j\hbar}\, t\right)(\mathbf{A}\bar{m}\,|\,\mathbf{P}m) = \exp\left(i\bar{m}\,\frac{\mu H}{j\hbar}\, t\right)(\mathbf{A}\bar{m}\,|\,\mathbf{Q}(0)\,m). \tag{4}$$

Finally, according to (18) on page 93, the expression $-\bar{m}\mu H/j$ equals the magnetic energy $E_{\bar{m}}$ of a molecule in the stationary state $\bar{m}$ within the magnet A. Equation 4 may therefore be written in the form

$$(\mathbf{A}\bar{m}\,|\,\mathbf{Q}(t)m) \;=\; \exp\left(-\,i\,\frac{E_{\bar{m}}}{\hbar}\,t\right)(\mathbf{A}\bar{m}\,|\,\mathbf{Q}(0)m), \qquad (5)$$

which represents a special case of the general law (1).

In the derivation of (4) and (5) a convention has been made regarding the assignment of phases, namely, that the reference plane attached to the axis $\mathbf{A}$ remains constant in the course of time, while the axis $\mathbf{Q}$ precesses around $\mathbf{A}$.   A different convention is often made, or implied, namely, that the reference plane precesses itself around $\mathbf{A}$, together with $\mathbf{Q}$, at the constant rate of $\mu H/j\hbar$ radians/sec.   This alternative convention makes $(\mathbf{A}\bar{m}\,|\,\mathbf{Q}m)$ constant in the course of time.   It corresponds to the point of view that the probability amplitudes that identify a state as a combination of other states are constant in time.   From this point of view the stationary states are themselves variable in time, with regard to their phase, and in (2) one takes $(\mathbf{A}\bar{m}\,|\,\mathbf{Q}m)$ constant and $(\mathbf{B}\bar{m}\,|\,\mathbf{A}\bar{m})$ variable in time.

9.2   General Formulation

Given a system in a state identified by a variable parameter $a(t)$, the probability of finding it at the time t in an eigenstate x of a given analyzer may be expressed as the squared magnitude of the probability amplitude $|(x\,|\,a(t))|^2$.   The purpose of this chapter is to analyze the variations of this probability in the course of time, utilizing the superposition principle, that is, utilizing the combination rule (9) of Chapter 8, which gives

$$(x\,|\,a(t)) \;=\; \Sigma_i(x\,|\,E_i)(E_i\,|\,a(t)), \qquad (6)$$

where E_i is the eigenvalue that characterizes the ith energy eigenstate. (In the example of Sect. 9.1, $a(t)$ corresponds to $\mathbf{Q}(t)m$, x corresponds to $\mathbf{B}\bar{m}$, and the energy eigenvalue E_i is replaced with the pair of indices $\mathbf{A}\bar{m}$.

As stated before, the superposition principle should serve to describe the variations of arbitrary states in terms of simpler variations of special states; analysis into energy eigenstates is particularly useful because these states remain stationary.   The actual applicability of a superposition principle must, however, be established by experimental tests. Thus it is a non-trivial result of experiments that beam component intensities combine according to the polygon diagrams of Sect. 8.1.   The application of the superposition principle in this chapter rests on other non-trivial experimental verifications.

The evidence on the emission of radiation by atoms indicates that if, for example, a hydrogen atom is in a stationary state, the position of its electron has a probability distribution that remains constant in the course of time. In general, if a quantum mechanical system is in a stationary state with energy E_i, the probability that a certain variable has a particular value x, $|(x|E_i)|^2$, remains constant. This fundamental property of stationary states is surmised from the fact that atoms do not radiate while they remain in a stationary state. The surmise is supported by all evidence on quantum physics.

An atom, or other system, which is initially in a stationary state will, of course, remain in that state (unless external influences intervene to make the state no longer stationary). Moreover, if an atom has a certain probability $|(E_i|a(t))|^2$ of being in a stationary state with energy E_i, this probability is expected to remain constant in the course of time because transitions do not occur between stationary states (barring external influences). Indeed, spontaneous transitions between stationary states of an isolated system would violate the conservation of energy. That is, an atom which is *not* in a stationary state should have, nevertheless, a constant probability distribution of being found, by appropriate analysis, in its various energy eigenstates. This further surmise is confirmed in the phenomenon of Larmor precession (Sect. 9.1) by the fact that the axis **Q** forms a constant angle with **A**, so that the transition probability from an eigenstate **Q**$(t)m$ to an eigenstate **A**$\bar{m}$ is constant. The constancy of $|(E_i|a(t))|^2$ is verified to be a general law.

Once it is established that in Eq. 6 the magnitudes of the probability amplitudes $(x|E_i)$ and $(E_i|a(t))$ remain constant, the time dependence of the probability $|(x|a(t))|^2$ must result from variations in the interference, that is, in the mode of combination, of the different terms in the summation in (6). If the probability of the eigenvalue x is represented by the square of one side of a polygon, as in Fig. 8.4 or 9.1, with the other sides corresponding the various energy eigenvalues E_i, the length of the side corresponding to x varies in the course of time but the lengths of the other sides remain constant. That is, the variations of the side which corresponds to x (the resultant) reflect variations of the angles among the other sides.

The observed variations of any probability $|(x|a(t))|^2$ can be resolved into oscillations with frequencies equal to the differences between pairs of energy eigenvalues divided by h. More specifically, each probability amplitude can be represented in the form (6), and the phase difference between any two terms i and j of the summation varies in the course of time at the constant rate of $(E_i - E_j)/\hbar$ radians/sec. In the polygon diagram of Fig. 9.1, the variation of the resultant is determined by the rule that the angle $\delta_{i,i+1}$ between any two successive sides i and $i+1$ varies at the constant rate of $(E_i - E_{i+1})/\hbar$ radians/sec. These results

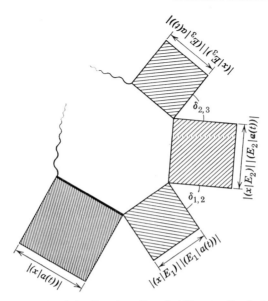

Fig. 9.1 The magnitude of the "resultant" probability amplitude $|(x|a(t))|$ varies in the course of time because of the variations of the angles δ, while the magnitudes of the components remain constant.

are formulated mathematically by expressing the probability $|(x|a(t))|^2$ according to Eq. 7 on page 108 as a combination of the "channel probabilities" $|(x|E_i)|^2|(E_i|a(t))|^2$ pertaining to the various energy eigenstates. One obtains the formula

$$|(x|a(t))|^2 = |\Sigma_i(x|E_i)(E_i|a(t))|^2$$

$$= \Sigma_i|(x|E_i)|^2|(E_i|a(t))|^2 \tag{7}$$

$$+ 2\Sigma_i\Sigma_j^{j=i-1}|(x|E_i)||(E_i|a(t))||(x|E_j)||(E_j|a(t))|\cos[\delta_{ij}(t)],$$

in which the channel probabilities and the phase differences obey the fundamental experimental laws

$$|(E_i|a(t))|^2 = \text{constant}, \tag{8}$$

$$\delta_{ij}(t) = \frac{E_i - E_j}{\hbar}t + \delta_{ij}(0). \tag{9}$$

The mathematical formulation can be made more specific by additional conventions. A standard convention corresponds to assigning a definite rate of rotation in the course of time to each side of the polygon in Fig. 9.1. (The rotation of the whole polygon is immaterial, as pointed out in Chapter 8.) The rate of rotation for the ith side is taken to be

$-E_i/\hbar$ radians/sec (notice the negative sign). This convention implies a corresponding convention about the sign of the angles between the sides of the polygon at the initial time $t = 0$, that is, a convention about the sign of the phase differences δ at $t = 0$; the implications will be considered as the occasions will arise.

Having thus assigned a phase variation $\exp[-i(E_i/\hbar)t]$ to each term of the summation in (6), one may still apportion this phase variation between the two probability amplitudes $(x|E_i)$ and $(E_i|a(t))$, by a further convention. Equation 1, which is adopted here as a general rule, corresponds to the convention that assigns the whole phase variation to $(E_i|a(t))$ and keeps constant the probability amplitudes $(x|E_i)$. As indicated at the end of Sect. 9.1, an opposite convention is often adopted, which assigns to each energy eigenstate a variable phase, so that $(x|E_i(t))$ varies, whereas $(E_i(t)|a(t))$ remains constant.

Notice that the probability amplitudes $(E_i|a(t))$, which vary in the course of time according to (1), are solutions of the differential equation

$$\frac{d}{dt}(E_i|a(t)) = -\frac{i}{\hbar}E_i(E_i|a(t)) \tag{10a}$$

or

$$-\frac{\hbar}{i}\frac{d}{dt}(E_i|a(t)) = E_i(E_i|a(t)). \tag{10b}$$

These equations belong to the class of *eigenvalue equations* which was mentioned on page 83. The energy eigenvalue E_i is an eigenvalue of Eq. 10b and the probability amplitude $(E_i|a(t))$ is the corresponding eigenfunction.

The general law (1) of time dependence may be applied to actual calculations to the extent that the probability amplitudes $(x|E_i)$ and $(E_i|a(0))$ are known, as they are in the example of Larmor precession of Sect. 9.1. The next application will be made at the end of the following chapter.

PROBLEMS

9.1 A Stern-Gerlach magnet **B** analyzes the effects of Larmor precession of nitrogen atoms (see Problem 7.1) in a uniform field **A**. The intensity I of any component separated by **B** varies as a function of the time t spent in the field **A** according to $I(t) = \Sigma_{n=0}^{3} A_n \cos 2\pi n\nu t$. Explain: (a) why the frequencies of the Fourier components of $I(t)$ are multiples of a single frequency; (b) why the highest frequency $n\nu$ has $n = 3$.

9.2 Calculate the Larmor precession of Ag atoms ($j = \frac{1}{2}$, $\mu = 9.0 \times 10^{-21}$ erg / gauss) in a uniform magnetic field of strength $H = 100$ gauss. Apply Eqs. 2 and 4, assuming the directions **P**, **A**, and **B**, to be orthogonal (as in Problem 8.2). Calculate the variations of the probabilities $|(\mathbf{B}\frac{1}{2}|Q(t)\frac{1}{2})|^2$ and $|(\mathbf{B}-\frac{1}{2}|Q(t)\frac{1}{2})|^2$ in the course of time.

chapter 10

Diffraction
and the motion
of free particles

The last few chapters have dealt with phenomena of light polarization and current orientation, which show with particular simplicity the relationships among quantum mechanical variables. The simplicity derives from the circumstance that the variables relevant to those phenomena have only a few eigenvalues. We come now to the more general problems in the mechanics of atomic particles which could not be analyzed successfully by "classical" methods, but are readily understood and analyzed mathematically utilizing the results of the preceding chapters.

Basic information regarding the motion of atomic particles is provided by "diffraction" phenomena. Briefly, when a beam of atomic particles (for example, electrons, neutrons, or even whole molecules) strikes an aggregate of atoms, be it a molecule or a crystal, the intensity scattered in various directions depends characteristically on the structure of the aggregate. The intensity distribution shows maxima and minima (Fig. 10.1) arranged in a "diffraction pattern"; there is, for example, a characteristic pattern of diffraction by cubic crystals of fixed orientation, one for powders of minute hexagonal crystals, one for diatomic molecules.

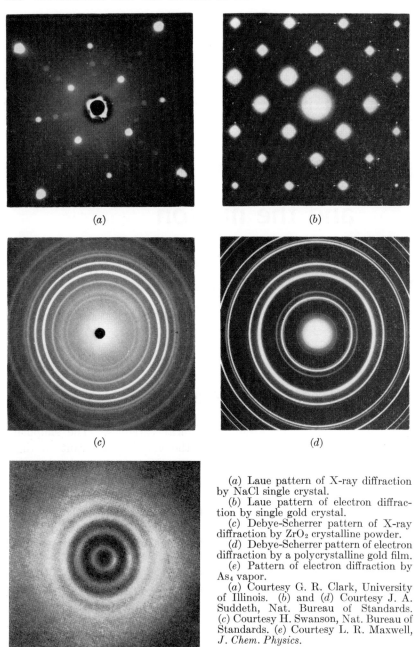

(a)

(b)

(c)

(d)

(e)

(a) Laue pattern of X-ray diffraction by NaCl single crystal.

(b) Laue pattern of electron diffraction by single gold crystal.

(c) Debye-Scherrer pattern of X-ray diffraction by ZrO_2 crystalline powder.

(d) Debye-Scherrer pattern of electron diffraction by a polycrystalline gold film.

(e) Pattern of electron diffraction by As_4 vapor.

(a) Courtesy G. R. Clark, University of Illinois. (b) and (d) Courtesy J. A. Suddeth, Nat. Bureau of Standards. (c) Courtesy H. Swanson, Nat. Bureau of Standards. (e) Courtesy L. R. Maxwell, *J. Chem. Physics.*

Fig. 10.1 Typical diffraction patterns.

The *relative* positions of maxima and minima constitute the pattern, which depends on the structure of the aggregate. The scale of the distribution, that is, the *absolute* value of the angular separation of maxima and minima, depends on the distance between the atoms of the aggregate and on the "momentum" (mass × velocity) of the incident particles. Different kinds of particles with equal momentum are scattered by the same material with probability distributions having maxima and minima in the same directions. Diffraction patterns with maxima and minima in the same directions are also observed when the incident beam of particles is replaced with a beam of electromagnetic radiation, provided the momentum of the radiation photons (see pages 76–77) is equal to the momentum of the particles. For example, X rays of frequency 2.4×10^{18} cycles/sec (photon energy 10,000 ev), electrons with 100 ev kinetic energy and neutrons with 0.054 ev kinetic energy have equal momenta of 5×10^{-19} g cm/sec and are diffracted by any given material with intensity maxima and minima in the same directions.

Macroscopic electromagnetism accounts for X-ray diffraction as the result of interference of the radiation scattered by different atoms, and similarly for the diffraction of light by "gratings," that is, by regularly ruled surfaces, as the result of interference of light scattered by different grooves (Sect. 10.1). Independently of macroscopic theory, the fact that the probability of combined scattering by the atoms of an aggregate differs sharply [1] from the sum of scattering probabilities by separate atoms constitutes a clear example of interference. The incident particles are characterized by a certain velocity in the direction of incidence, and their state is therefore an eigenstate of velocity and momentum. To regard diffraction as the result of combined scattering by the separate atoms of an aggregate implies an analysis of the eigenstate of incidence momentum as a coherent superposition of eigenstates characterized by positions of a particle within each separate scattering atom. The initial state must have components corresponding to positions in different atoms; otherwise no interference could occur. This conclusion is at variance with macroscopic mechanics which regards each particle as following a definite path even though the experimental conditions need not control which particular path a particle will follow (see Sect. 6.2 and footnote 11 on page 96). According to macroscopic mechanics, paths through different atoms would be mutually exclusive (see pages 119–120) and interference would be impossible.

The quantitative analysis of diffraction (Sect. 10.2), fashioned after

---

[1] The chemical combination of atoms in the aggregate can modify the scattering by each atom to some extent; this effect should be small, however, especially for the scattering of neutrons which interact only with atomic nuclei.

the macroscopic theory of radiation diffraction, shows that, when an eigenstate of momentum is analyzed into eigenstates of position, all components have equal probability and combine with phases that are linear functions of the momentum and of the positions coordinates. With suitable conventions, the probability amplitude of the eigenstate of momentum $\mathbf{p} = (p_x, p_y, p_z)$ and the eigenstate of position $\mathbf{r} = (x, y, z)$ is

$$(x,y,z \,|\, p_x,p_y,p_z) = \psi_{p_x p_y p_z}(x,y,z) = \exp\left(i\,\frac{p_x x + p_y y + p_z z}{\hbar} \right) \quad (1a)$$

or, with vector symbols,

$$(\mathbf{r} \,|\, \mathbf{p}) = \psi_{\mathbf{p}}(\mathbf{r}) = \exp\left(i\,\frac{\mathbf{p}}{\hbar} \cdot \mathbf{r} \right). \quad (1b)$$

In conclusion, the significance of particle diffraction may be outlined as follows: Diffraction occurs in classical physics whenever an oscillatory disturbance, be it an electromagnetic or elastic wave, is broken up by an obstacle. The diffraction pattern arises from the combination of the pattern of space distribution of the oscillatory quantity with the pattern of distribution of matter in the obstacle. (Hence diffraction may be called colloquially a "geometric" effect.) The quantum physics of particles involves no oscillating variable which is directly observable, but nevertheless it includes interference effects analogous to those of classical waves. The interference of particles is expressed in terms of phase differences of probability amplitudes. The periodic variation of these phases, from point to point of space, plays the same role in particle diffraction as the variation of the phases of oscillation of classical waves. For classical waves, the rates of variation of phases in space and time are represented, respectively, by the wave vector (page 82) and by the frequency. For probability amplitudes, the corresponding rates of variation are represented by the particle's momentum and energy divided by Planck's constant h. The Einstein equation between energy and frequency (page 39) and the corresponding equation between momentum and wave vector (page 83), which are established by the photoelectric effect, are thus seen to have very general significance. Because of the physical and mathematical analogy between the interference and diffraction of classical waves and of atomic particles, the quantum mechanics of particles is often called "wave mechanics."

The main mechanical properties of a single atomic particle are in essence consequences of the connection between the eigenstates of momentum and position, represented by Eq. 1. This connection provides the clue to explain the size and stability of atoms, as will be shown in Chapter 11.

In the present chapter, Sect. 10.1 deals with diffraction of electro-magnetic radiation and with simple interference phenomena which re-sult from pathlength differences. Section 10.2 describes the diffraction of particle beams and its theoretical analysis. Section 10.3 shows how the free motion of a particle with constant speed is represented by the interference of states with nearly equal energy and momentum.

10.1   Interference and Diffraction of Radiation Resulting from Pathlength Differences

The most familiar effects of optical interference occur, as mentioned previously, when a light beam is split into two or more components having the same polarization but following paths of different length prior to recombination. The diffraction of light and of X rays may be regarded as an interference effect of this class. Some of these phenomena will be considered here as an introduction to the diffraction of particle beams. Macroscopic theory serves again as a guide to formulate the experimental results suitably.

The *Michelson interferometer*, shown schematically in Fig. 10.2, con-sists in the main of a glass slide A, with a light metal coating which

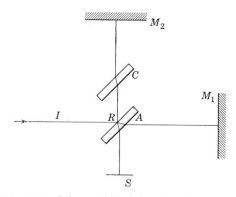

Fig. 10.2   Scheme of Michelson interferometer.

makes its surface semireflecting, and of two mirrors M_1 and M_2, all of which are rigidly attached to each other. The incident light beam I is split into two components by partial reflection at R. The transmitted component travels on from R to the mirror M_1, back to R, and is re-flected in part towards the screen S. The reflected component travels to the mirror M_2, back to R, and is transmitted in part onwards to S. (The slide C is introduced as a compensator, because the component reflected by M_1 traverses the slide A thrice and the component reflected by M_2 only once.) The light intensity on S results from the superposition of the two components which arrive *via* M_1 and M_2. These components have electromagnetic fields that oscillate in step (with equal phase) and combine to yield maximum intensity if the pathlengths RM_1RS and RM_2RS are identical or differ by a whole number of wavelengths; they yield minimum intensity if the pathlengths differ by a half-integer number of wavelengths. Because the wavelength is very small as compared to the size of the interferometer, the intensity observed at S depends very critically on the position and orientation of all parts of the interferometer.[2]

A still simpler interference effect which depends critically on the orientation of mirrors is observed with the *Fresnel mirror* arrangement (Fig. 10.3). Light from a source O may arrive on a screen S by reflection

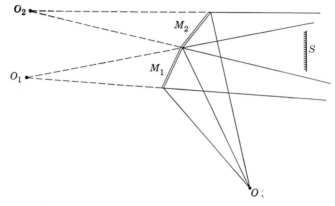

Fig. 10.3 Fresnel mirrors experiment.

on either of two mirrors M_1 and M_2. The light reflected by the mirrors appears to originate from virtual images of the source lying at O_1 and O_2. The light intensity at a point P of the screen results from the superposition of two components which appear to arrive from the virtual sources at O_1 and O_2. These components have electromagnetic fields that oscillate in step and combine to yield maximum intensity if the pathlengths O_1P and O_2P are identical or differ by a whole number of wavelengths, they yield minimum intensity if O_1P and O_2P differ by a half-integer number of wavelengths. The intensity at different points P across the screen therefore varies greatly, depending on the value of $O_1P - O_2P$. If the source images O_1 and O_2 are distant from the screen and not far from one another, the difference $O_1P - O_2P$ is a slowly varying function of the position of the point P on the screen. Therefore, regions of maximum and minimum intensity can be clearly distinguished across the screen; they are called "bright and dark fringes."

As an example of optical diffraction, we consider here the action of *ruled gratings* which constitutes one of the main tools of spectroscopy as noted before. A ruled grating is a reflecting surface on which evenly spaced grooves are scratched with a sharp point; the surface acquires thereby a periodically corrugated profile. The groove spacings are of the order of magnitude of 1 μ, that is, somewhat larger than the wavelengths of visible radiation. Light is usually directed on a grating in a direction oblique to its surface but perpendicular to the direction of the grooves (Fig. 10.4).

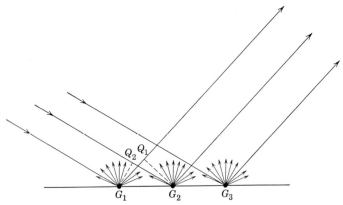

Fig. 10.4 Pathlength differences in diffraction by a ruled grating.

For purpose of qualitative analysis it is adequate to regard each groove as a sharply localized irregularity of the surface, which scatters light in all directions. A distant detector that "looks" at the surface from a certain direction receives light scattered by all grooves of the surface. The resulting intensity depends on the interference of the light components scattered by different grooves, that is, on the relative phase of oscillation of their electric and magnetic fields when they reach the detector.

We consider now the conditions of interference for a given direction of incidence, a given wavelength, and a given direction of detector. Compare in the diagram of Fig. 10.4 the light paths from a distant source to two adjacent grooves G_1 and G_2 and on from each groove to a distant detector. The radiation scattered by G_1 travels an extra pathlength G_1Q_1 to reach the detector. The radiation scattered by G_2 travels an extra pathlength Q_2G_2 from the source to the point of scattering. There-fore, the pathlength difference for the two scattered components is $G_1Q_1 - Q_2G_2$. If this difference equals a whole number of wavelengths, the same holds for the difference corresponding to scattering by any two grooves G_i and G_k, and all scattered light components reach the detector in step thus combining with "constructive interference" to yield a maxi-mum of intensity. (The special case of specular reflection corresponds to $G_1Q_1 = Q_2G_2$, that is, to a path difference of zero wavelengths.) On the other hand, if $G_1Q_1 - Q_2G_2$ differs from a whole number of wave-lengths, the light components scattered by G_1 and G_2 reach the detector with a certain phase difference δ, the components scattered by G_1 and G_3 with a difference 2δ, etc. The component scattered by the groove G_{n+1}, with $n \sim \pi/\delta$, reaches then the detector with a phase difference of $n\delta \sim \pi$ with respect to the component scattered by G_1. The fields of the light components scattered by different grooves thus cancel out in pairs, and the combined light intensity vanishes, at least approximately ("destruc-tive interference").

The condition for constructive interference is expressed mathemati-cally by

$$G_1Q_1 - Q_2G_2 = N\lambda \tag{2a}$$

or

$$\frac{G_1Q_1}{\lambda} - \frac{Q_2G_2}{\lambda} = N, \tag{2b}$$

where N is an integer and λ is the wavelength. For given directions of incidence and of the detector, (2) is fulfilled only by certain values of λ. The usefulness of ruled gratings lies in the fact that for a given value of λ and a given incidence they concentrate ("diffract") light in a number of directions corresponding to different values of the number N, which is called the "order" of the diffraction. Equation (2b) is expressed con-veniently with vectors because the pathlengths G_1Q_1 and Q_2G_2 are the projections of the groove spacing G_1G_2 in the directions of the detector and of the incident beam respectively. These directions may be repre-sented, together with the reciprocal wavelength $1/\lambda$, by wave vectors $\mathbf{k}'$ and $\mathbf{k}$ (see page 82), whose magnitudes are $1/\lambda$ and whose directions are the directions of propagation. The position coordinates of the grooves G_1 and G_2 may be indicated by vectors $\mathbf{r}_1 = (x_1,y_1,z_1)$ and $\mathbf{r}_2 = (x_2,y_2,z_2)$, so that $G_1G_2 = |\mathbf{r}_2 - \mathbf{r}_1|$. The product of the reciprocal wavelength $1/\lambda$ and of the projection G_1Q_1 of G_1G_2 along $\mathbf{k}'$ is then expressed as the scalar product of the vectors $\mathbf{k}'$ and $\mathbf{r}_2 - \mathbf{r}_1$. The condition of construc-tive interference (2b) takes the form

$$\mathbf{k}' \cdot (\mathbf{r}_2 - \mathbf{r}_1) - \mathbf{k} \cdot (\mathbf{r}_2 - \mathbf{r}_1) = (\mathbf{k}' - \mathbf{k}) \cdot (\mathbf{r}_2 - \mathbf{r}_1) = N. \tag{3}$$

That is, the scalar product of the groove separation $\mathbf{r}_2 - \mathbf{r}_1$ and of the difference $\mathbf{k'} - \mathbf{k}$, between the wave vectors of the diffracted and incident light, must equal a whole number. If this condition is fulfilled by the separation $\mathbf{r}_2 - \mathbf{r}_1$ of adjacent grooves, it is also fulfilled by its multiples $\mathbf{r}_3 - \mathbf{r}_1$, $\mathbf{r}_4 - \mathbf{r}_1$, etc.

Notice that, if $\frac{1}{2}\lambda$ exceeds the groove separation $|\mathbf{r}_2 - \mathbf{r}_1|$, k and k' are so small that $(\mathbf{k'} - \mathbf{k}) \cdot (\mathbf{r}_2 - \mathbf{r}_1)$ cannot be ever as large as ± 1, so that no diffraction can occur. On the other hand, if λ is far shorter than the separation, the condition (3) will be met by wave vectors $\mathbf{k'}$ of nearly equal directions, and there is a confuse multitude of diffracted beams.

The performance of a ruled grating as a spectral analyzer is limited by its size. As shown before, if the diffraction conditions are not fulfilled exactly and light components scattered by G_1 and G_2 reach the detector with a phase difference δ, the component scattered by G_{n+1} with $n \sim \pi/\delta$ interferes destructively with the component scattered by G_1. However, if δ is sufficiently small, π/δ may exceed the total number $\mathfrak{N}$ of grooves of the grating and there is no component of the scattered light which interferes destructively. It follows that light of a given wavelength is diffracted not in ideally defined directions but within bundles of directions covering an angle of the order of $1/\mathfrak{N}$ radians; destructive interference becomes effective only in directions outside those bundles.

X-ray diffraction by crystals is analogous to light diffraction by ruled gratings. A crystal may be regarded as a regular lattice of identical "cells," each of which contains one or more atoms. (For example, a cell of a NaCl crystal contains one Na^+ and one Cl^- ion.) A beam of X rays interacts with matter weakly and thus penetrates into crystals deeply, to be scattered to some extent by each cell; crystals diffract X rays but not light because their lattice spacing is comparable to X-ray wavelengths and much smaller than light wavelengths. We may treat the X rays scattered by each cell as though they originated from a single point within the cell, just as each groove is represented by a single point in Fig. 10.4. We consider therefore the combined scattering by a lattice of identical points, shown in cross section in Fig. 10.5.

For a given direction of incidence, a given wavelength and a given direction of detector, the conditions of interference of the X rays scattered by two cells, C_1 and C_2, may be examined with the diagram of Fig. 10.5. The X rays scattered by these cells follow paths whose lengths differ by the amount $Q_2C_1 + C_1Q_2'$. Interference is exactly constructive if this difference equals a whole number of wavelengths. This condition may be expressed in the same form (3) as for ruled gratings, where $\mathbf{r}_2 - \mathbf{r}_1$ indicates now the spacing of two crystal cells. Constructive interference of the X rays scattered by the whole crystal requires that the condition (3) be fulfilled for all pairs of cells.

Bragg has shown that this requirement can be analyzed conveniently as follows. Whenever the requirement is fully satisfied, there are sets of parallel planes of the lattice such that (3) is fulfilled with $N = 0$ by the spacing $\mathbf{r_1}' - \mathbf{r_1}$ of any two cells of a plane. (Each plane of the set is represented by a line of dots in Fig. 10.5.) The vector $\mathbf{k}' - \mathbf{k}$ is then

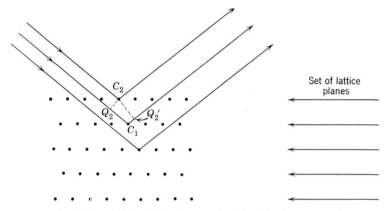

Fig. 10.5 Pathlength differences in diffraction by a crystal.

perpendicular to the set of lattice planes. It follows that the directions $\mathbf{k}'$ and $\mathbf{k}$ form equal angles with the planes, that is, that the constructive interference takes the aspect of combined specular reflection by the planes of the set. For this reason the occurrence of constructive interference by X rays scattered by crystal cells is called "Bragg reflection." Further, the X rays scattered by cells of different planes will interfere constructively provided only that (3) is fulfilled with $N \neq 0$ by the spacing $\mathbf{r_2} - \mathbf{r_1}$ of cells of adjacent planes.

The full condition for constructive interference is met for a given direction of incidence only by X rays of certain wavelengths, and for X rays of given wavelengths only by certain directions of incidence. Notice by contrast that diffraction by ruled gratings on a surface is not limited by any condition on the direction of $\mathbf{k}' - \mathbf{k}$, so that diffraction occurs in some direction for any combination of incidence and wavelength.

When a beam of non-monochromatic X rays falls upon a crystal with a given orientation, the conditions for Bragg reflection are fulfilled in general for each of various sets of lattice planes by particular monochromatic components of the incident beam. Each of these components is then diffracted in the direction corresponding to the particular orientation of the lattice planes. The set of directions so singled out constitutes the "Laue pattern" of the crystal.

When the incident beam is monochromatic, no Bragg reflection is observed in general with a crystal of given orientation, as noted above. However, if the beam falls upon a powder of crystals oriented at random, some of the crystals will be oriented just right for Bragg reflection on one of the various sets of lattice planes. Bragg reflection on any one set is

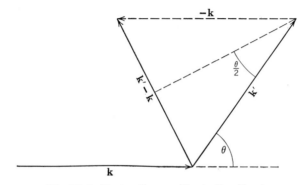

Fig. 10.6 Vector diagram illustrating Eq. 4.

characterized by a fixed magnitude of the wave vector difference $\mathbf{k}' - \mathbf{k}$ and of the diffraction angle θ. Fig. 10.6 shows that $|\mathbf{k}' - \mathbf{k}|$ and θ are related by

$$|\mathbf{k}' - \mathbf{k}| = 2k \sin\tfrac{1}{2}\theta. \tag{4}$$

X rays so reflected by a given set of lattice planes of crystals with different orientations travel in different directions all of which form the

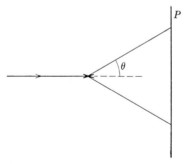

Fig. 10.7 Diffraction by crystal powder. The diagram shows two crystals with orientation required for Bragg reflection.

same angle θ with the incident beam. The scattered X rays form a ring on a photographic plate P placed as in Fig. 10.7. The sequence of rings corresponding to Bragg reflection on different sets of lattice planes constitute the "Debye-Scherrer pattern" of the powder.

10.2 Diffraction of Particle Beams

Diffraction by crystals. *Electrons* with kinetic energies of the order of 50 to 100 ev penetrate numerous layers of atoms into a crystal before being scattered back or losing their energy. Davisson and Germer in 1927 studied the electrons backscattered by a crystal without energy loss and observed in some cases, besides a diffuse backscattering, a peak of intensity in the direction of specular reflection. The peak appears when the direction of incidence and the velocity of the incident electrons satisfy a condition equivalent to the Bragg reflection condition for X rays. To express the conditions in the same form, the momenta $\mathbf{p}$ and $\mathbf{p}'$ of the incident and reflected electrons, divided by Planck's constant h, must be entered in Eq. 3 in place of $\mathbf{k}$ and $\mathbf{k}'$. The condition becomes

$$\left(\frac{\mathbf{p}'}{h} - \frac{\mathbf{p}}{h}\right) \cdot (\mathbf{r}_2 - \mathbf{r}_1) = N. \tag{3'}$$

Notice that this form of the equation applies to X rays also, because the wave vectors of X rays are related to the photon momenta by Eq. 6 on page 83, $\mathbf{p} = h\mathbf{k}$.

Concurrently with the discovery by Davisson and Germer, G. P. Thomson and collaborators observed Debye-Scherrer diffraction rings around beams of electrons that traverse thin layers of crystalline materials. The ring diameter is the same as expected for X-ray diffraction on the same materials, if the X-ray photons have the same momentum as the electrons. Laue patterns were also observed later with electron beams. Evidence accumulated in many experiments confirms that crystals diffract electrons and X rays into patterns with maxima and minima in the same positions if the electrons and photons have equal momentum.

The main difference between electron and X-ray diffraction stems from the circumstance that electrons are scattered by individual atoms to a much greater extent than X rays. Therefore, Bragg reflection of an electron beam is completed within a comparatively few layers of crystal cells and the diffraction patterns are unsharp, as in the case of light diffracted by a grating consisting of a few grooves only (see page 137).

Molecules incident on the surface of a crystal do not penetrate but generally bounce back. The crystal surface constitutes a two-dimensional lattice of identical cells with spacing of the order of a few Angstroms, and would diffract X rays if the X rays did not penetrate deep into the crystal. Stern and Estermann studied the back-scattering of molecular beams by crystal surfaces. Besides a diffuse scattering, they observed intensity peaks in the directions corresponding to specular reflection and to diffraction by the surface lattice (Fig. 10.8). Diffraction by a surface lattice requires that the condition (3′) be satisfied for the separations $r_1 - r_2$, $r_1 - r_3$, etc., of all pairs of adjacent cells. Notice that, for example, a molecule of oxygen traveling at 200 m/sec (thermal agitation velocity) has a momentum of magnitude $p = 10^{-18}$ g cm/sec, an equivalent wave number $p/h = 1.6 \times 10^8$ cm^{-1} and an equivalent wavelength h/p of 6×10^{-9} cm = 0.6 A, only a little smaller than the spacing of crystal cells. (The quantity h/p is called the "de Broglie wavelength" of a particle.) The quantitative relationships are accordingly just right to observe diffraction conveniently.

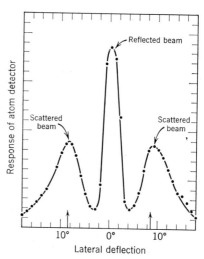

Fig. 10.8 Diffraction of He atoms by a LiF crystal. (Adapted from Estermann and Stern, *Z. Physik*, 1931.)

Neutrons penetrate crystals readily because they interact only with the nuclei of crystal atoms. All types of crystal diffraction (Bragg reflection, Laue patterns, and Debye-Scherrer patterns) have been observed with neutrons and studied extensively since sufficiently intense neutron beams have been provided by the development of nuclear reactors. In all experiments, diffraction occurs in the directions predicted by X-ray diffraction theory if the wave vectors are taken as equal to the neutron momenta divided by h. Neutron diffraction is sometimes proving even more valuable than X-ray diffraction as a tool to provide information on crystals.

Quantum mechanical analysis. The diffraction of electromagnetic radiation by ruled gratings and crystal lattices has been described in Sect. 10.1, according to macroscopic electromagnetism, as the result of interference of radiation components scattered by different grooves or, respectively, crystal cells. However, Sect. 8.1 has shown that interference need not be attributed to the combination of electromagnetic fields or of other measurable oscillating quantities. In quantum physics experimental results take the form of probability laws. The phenomenon of interference is described as a relationship among probabilities: When different components contribute to the probability of detection of a photon or particle, the combined probability departs, in general, from the sum of the probabilities of detection observed when each component acts separately. The departure of the combined probability from the sum of the separate probabilities can be expressed by means of phase differences of probability amplitudes.

From this standpoint, the probability of scattering of X rays towards a detector by a lattice of crystal cells is regarded as a combination of contributions from scattering by separate cells. The expression $(\mathbf{k}' - \mathbf{k}) \cdot (\mathbf{r}_2 - \mathbf{r}_1)$ on the left of Eq. 3 represents the phase difference in the combination of components from scattering by cells with relative positions indicated by $\mathbf{r}_2 - \mathbf{r}_1$. More precisely, $(\mathbf{k}' - \mathbf{k}) \cdot (\mathbf{r}_2 - \mathbf{r}_1)$, which equals a whole number in the event of fully constructive interference, represents the phase difference δ_{12} expressed in "cycles" and must be multiplied by 360° if the phase difference is to be expressed in degrees, or by 2π if it is to be expressed in radians.

This interpretation of radiation diffraction extends without any change to the diffraction of particle beams. For beam components arising from scatterers at $\mathbf{r}_i$ and $\mathbf{r}_k$ the expression of the phase difference in radians is obtained by replacing the wave vector $\mathbf{k}$ of electromagnetic theory with $2\pi\mathbf{p}/h = \mathbf{p}/\hbar$, and is therefore given by

$$\delta_{ik} = \left(\frac{\mathbf{p}'}{\hbar} - \frac{\mathbf{p}}{\hbar}\right) \cdot (\mathbf{r}_i - \mathbf{r}_k) \text{ radians.} \tag{5}$$

To analyze the interference mathematically according to the superposition principle, consider the probability amplitudes relating the state of the incident particles to the states of the scattered particles. The particles of the incident beam are in a state characterized by a momentum eigenvalue $\mathbf{p}$. This state is modified by interaction with a scatterer S which consists of the complete crystal. The state so modified is analyzed experimentally into momentum eigenstates with eigenvalues $\mathbf{p}'$. The probability amplitudes of these eigenstates is indicated by the symbol $(\mathbf{p}'|S|\mathbf{p})$. The squared magnitude $|(\mathbf{p}'|S|\mathbf{p})|^2$ represents the probability of detecting a particle in the direction of $\mathbf{p}'$.

The probability amplitude $(\mathbf{p}'|S|\mathbf{p})$ is to be expressed as the sum of contributions corresponding to the possibility of scattering by the various cells 1, 2, 3, $\cdots$ of a crystal, whose positions will be indicated by coordinate vectors $\mathbf{r}_i = (x_i, y_i, z_i)$. Each contribution consists of three factors. (a) The probability amplitude $(\mathbf{r}_i | \mathbf{p})$ that a particle of the incident beam, in a state identified by the momentum $\mathbf{p}$, be detected at the position $\mathbf{r}_i$ of the ith cell. (b) The probability amplitude $s_{\mathbf{p}'\mathbf{p}}$ that a particle be scattered from the direction of $\mathbf{p}$ to the direction of $\mathbf{p}'$ by collision with a single cell. (The amplitude $s_{\mathbf{p}'\mathbf{p}}$ is, of course, equal for all cells and its squared magnitude $|s_{\mathbf{p}'\mathbf{p}}|^2$ represents the cross section for scattering by the cell, as defined in Sect. 2.3. We regard this cross section as determined separately, for example, by an *ad hoc* experiment.) (c) The probability amplitude $(\mathbf{p}' | \mathbf{r}_i)$ that a particle scattered from a cell at $\mathbf{r}_i$ be detected in the beam of particles with momentum $\mathbf{p}'$ by a distant detector. The combination rule of probability amplitudes, Eq. 9, page 111, gives then

$$(\mathbf{p}' | S | \mathbf{p}) = s_{\mathbf{p}'\mathbf{p}} \, \Sigma_i (\mathbf{p}' | \mathbf{r}_i)(\mathbf{r}_i | \mathbf{p}). \tag{6}$$

This formula expresses the combined scattering probability $|(\mathbf{p}' | S | \mathbf{p})|^2$ in terms of the single-cell probability $|s_{\mathbf{p}'\mathbf{p}}|^2$ and of the probability amplitudes $(\mathbf{r}_i | \mathbf{p})$ and $(\mathbf{p}' | \mathbf{r}_i)$. We propose now to determine the values of these probability amplitudes utilizing experimental information on scattering by whole crystals. In particular, we utilize the conclusions drawn from the relationships between the diffraction patterns and crystal structure, namely, that the expression (5) represents the phase difference between pairs of terms of the summation in (6).

We consider first the magnitudes of $(\mathbf{r}_i | \mathbf{p})$ and $(\mathbf{p}' | \mathbf{r}_i)$, and then their phases. In discussing the diffraction of electromagnetic radiation according to macroscopic theory, we have implied that the incident and diffracted radiation beams are eigenstates of direction and photon momentum, represented by *plane waves* (see page 77, and 82 ff.). It had been pointed out that these states represent idealizations, in that plane waves extend over the whole space with uniform intensity. As a consequence, all scatterers are affected by the incident radiation with equal intensity, so that they also scatter with equal intensity. The indefinite extension of plane waves is an idealization, but in the macroscopic theory it is nevertheless essential that a very large number of scatterers actually receive the same radiation intensity. From the identity of results in diffraction experiments with X rays and with particles, we deduce that also in particle diffraction a very large number of scatterer cells have equal probability of receiving particles of the incident beam. It is also essential, of course, that scattering by different cells combines coherently, as noted on page 120. Furthermore, we surmise that eigenstates of particle momentum constitute, like eigenstates of photon momentum, idealizations and that particles in those eigenstates have a uniform probability of being detected at all points of space. This surmise is supported by all further evidence. We take, therefore, the magnitude $|(\mathbf{r}_i|\mathbf{p})|$ to be equal for all cell positions $\mathbf{r}_i$. The actual value of this magnitude is a matter of convention depending on the assumed particle density in the beam. One usually assigns to the magnitude the value one, corresponding to one particle per unit volume in the beam. The value of $|(\mathbf{p}'|\mathbf{r}_i)|$ is equal to $|(\mathbf{r}_i|\mathbf{p})|$ because $(\mathbf{p}'|\mathbf{r}_i)$ has the same magnitude as $(\mathbf{r}_i|\mathbf{p}')$ owing to reciprocity (pages 96 and 113) and because the probability of detecting a particle at $\mathbf{r}_i$ must be the same for momentum eigenstates of different directions $\mathbf{p}$ or $\mathbf{p}'$. We write accordingly

$$|(\mathbf{r}_i|\mathbf{p})| = |(\mathbf{p}'|\mathbf{r}_i)| = 1. \tag{7}$$

We come now to apportion the phase difference (5) among the terms of the summation in (6), that is, to assign a definite phase to each term. Since (5) consists of the difference of two terms, each of which depends on the position of one scatterer, it is an obvious convention to assign the phase $(\mathbf{p}/\hbar - \mathbf{p}'/\hbar)\cdot\mathbf{r}_i$ to the ith scatterer cell, and the phase $(\mathbf{p}/\hbar - \mathbf{p}'/\hbar)\cdot\mathbf{r}_k$ to the kth cell. Since our probability amplitudes have the magnitude one, we write

$$(\mathbf{p}'|\mathbf{r}_i)(\mathbf{r}_i|\mathbf{p}) = \exp\left[i\left(\frac{\mathbf{p}}{\hbar} - \frac{\mathbf{p}'}{\hbar}\right)\cdot\mathbf{r}_i\right]. \tag{8}$$

Finally, we apportion the phase of this product among its two factors. Here again the phase of (8) consists of two terms depending respectively on $\mathbf{p}$ and on $\mathbf{p}'$, which leads to the convention

$$(\mathbf{r}_i|\mathbf{p}) = \exp\left(i\frac{\mathbf{p}}{\hbar}\cdot\mathbf{r}_i\right), \qquad (\mathbf{p}'|\mathbf{r}_i) = \exp\left(-i\frac{\mathbf{p}'}{\hbar}\cdot\mathbf{r}_i\right). \tag{9}$$

equivalent to the general formulas (1a) and (1b). Notice that $(\mathbf{p}'|\mathbf{r}_i)$ has a phase equal but of opposite sign to that of $(\mathbf{r}_i|\mathbf{p}')$, in agreement with Eq. 17, on page 113.

The probability amplitudes (1) or (9) have phases which are linear functions of the position coordinates $\mathbf{r} = (x,y,z)$. These probability amplitudes are, therefore, sinusoidal functions of the coordinates $\mathbf{r}$, since $e^{i\phi} = \cos\phi + i\sin\phi$. Their mathematical expression is therefore analogous to the representation (5), page 82, of electromagnetic plane waves. Accordingly, the probability amplitudes (1) or (9) themselves are commonly called "plane waves." They are also often called "wave functions" or "momentum eigenfunctions" and indicated in the form (13), of page 112, as

$$\psi_{\mathbf{p}}(x,y,z) = \exp\left(i\frac{p_x x + p_y y + p_z z}{\hbar}\right) = \exp\left(i\frac{\mathbf{p}}{\hbar}\cdot\mathbf{r}\right). \tag{10}$$

Notice, finally, that these wave functions, like the electromagnetic plane waves, are eigenfunctions of the eigenvalue equations 7b, c, and d of page 83, with the eigenvalues $-(p_x/\hbar)^2$, $-(p_y/\hbar)^2$ and $-(p_z/\hbar)^2$, respectively. In addition, the plane waves (10) in the form of complex exponentials are eigenfunctions of the equations

$$\frac{\hbar}{i}\frac{\partial\psi}{\partial x} = p_x\psi, \qquad \frac{\hbar}{i}\frac{\partial\psi}{\partial y} = p_y\psi, \qquad \frac{\hbar}{i}\frac{\partial\psi}{\partial z} = p_z\psi, \tag{11}$$

with the eigenvalues p_x, p_y, and p_z. These three equations are represented together by the single vector equation

$$\frac{\hbar}{i}\operatorname{grad}\psi(\mathbf{r}) = \mathbf{p}\,\psi(r). \tag{12}$$

Diffraction by molecules. Diffraction effects are observed also in the scattering of X rays and of particles by gas molecules, owing to interference of the components scattered in any one direction by different atoms of a molecule. The diffraction patterns are characteristic for the arrangement of atoms in the molecules, even though the atoms may be of different kinds. As compared with crystals, molecules have a small number of atoms and a non-periodic structure; hence, the maxima and minima of their diffraction patterns are unsharp. Gas molecules have random orientation; hence, their diffraction patterns are of the Debye-Scherrer type.

As a simple example, we apply here the information obtained from crystal diffraction to calculate the pattern of diffraction of diatomic molecules with identical atoms, such as N_2 or O_2. In the expression (6) the summation consists now of two terms only,

$$(\mathbf{p}'|S|\mathbf{p}) = s_{\mathbf{p}'\mathbf{p}}[(\mathbf{p}'|\mathbf{r}_1)(\mathbf{r}_1|\mathbf{p}) + (\mathbf{p}'|\mathbf{r}_2)(\mathbf{r}_2|\mathbf{p})]$$

$$= s_{\mathbf{p}'\mathbf{p}}\left\{\exp\left[-i\left(\frac{\mathbf{p}'}{\hbar} - \frac{\mathbf{p}}{\hbar}\right)\cdot\mathbf{r}_1\right] + \exp\left[-i\left(\frac{\mathbf{p}'}{\hbar} - \frac{\mathbf{p}}{\hbar}\right)\cdot\mathbf{r}_2\right]\right\}, \tag{13}$$

where $\mathbf{r}_1$ and $\mathbf{r}_2$ indicate the positions of the centers of the two atoms. The combined probability of scattering in the direction $\mathbf{p}'$ is

$$|(\mathbf{p}'|S|\mathbf{p})|^2 = |s_{\mathbf{p}'\mathbf{p}}|^2\left\{1 + \exp\left[i\left(\frac{\mathbf{p}'}{\hbar} - \frac{\mathbf{p}}{\hbar}\right)\cdot(\mathbf{r}_1 - \mathbf{r}_2)\right]\right.$$

$$+ \exp\left[-i\left(\frac{\mathbf{p}'}{\hbar} - \frac{\mathbf{p}}{\hbar}\right)\cdot(\mathbf{r}_1 - \mathbf{r}_2)\right] + 1\bigg\}$$

$$= 2|s_{\mathbf{p}'\mathbf{p}}|^2\left\{1 + \cos\left[\left(\frac{\mathbf{p}'}{\hbar} - \frac{\mathbf{p}}{\hbar}\right)\cdot(\mathbf{r}_1 - \mathbf{r}_2)\right]\right\}. \tag{14}$$

We must now take the average value of this probability over all orientations of $\mathbf{r}_1 - \mathbf{r}_2$ with respect to $\mathbf{p}'/\hbar - \mathbf{p}/\hbar$. The value of the cosine of a product of vectors, $\cos(\mathbf{a} \cdot \mathbf{b})$, averaged over all mutual orientations of the vectors is a function only of the magnitudes of these vectors,

$$\langle \cos(\mathbf{a} \cdot \mathbf{b}) \rangle = \frac{1}{2} \int_{-1}^{1} dz \, \cos(abz) = \frac{\sin(ab)}{ab} \tag{15}$$

where z is the cosine of the angle between $\mathbf{a}$ and $\mathbf{b}$. In our case, the distance between the atoms, $|\mathbf{r}_1 - \mathbf{r}_2|$, may be called R, and according to (4) $|\mathbf{p}'/\hbar - \mathbf{p}/\hbar| = 2(p/\hbar) \sin\frac{1}{2}\theta$, where θ is the scattering angle. The probability of scattering by an angle θ is therefore

$$P(\theta) = 2|s_{\mathbf{p}'\mathbf{p}}|^2 \left\{ 1 + \frac{\sin[2(p/\hbar)R \sin\frac{1}{2}\theta]}{2(p/\hbar)R \sin\frac{1}{2}\theta} \right\}. \tag{16}$$

This probability may be regarded as the product of two factors, namely $2|s_{\mathbf{p}'\mathbf{p}}|^2$ (the sum of the scattering cross sections of two separate atoms)

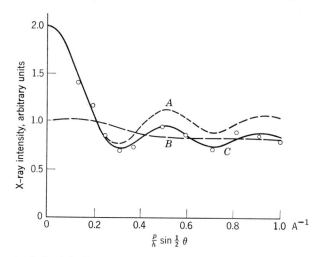

Fig. 10.9 Analysis of the X-ray intensities scattered in different directions by oxygen gas. Curve A represents the factor in braces in Eq. 16, curve B represents the factor $2|s_{\mathbf{p}'\mathbf{p}}|^2$ in the same equation, and curve C represents the product of A and B, equal $P(\theta)$. (Data by Wollan; figure and analysis after Compton and Allison, *X-Rays in Theory and Experiment*, D. Van Nostrand Co., New York, 1934, p. 163.)

and the oscillating factor in the braces which "modulates" the independent-atom cross section and represents the effect of diffraction. The maxima and minima of this oscillating factor occur at deflection angles that depend on the values of p, R and $\hbar$ in the combination

$(p/\hbar)R$. The oscillating factor depends only on the variables p and R and not at all on the nature of the particles, or electromagnetic radiation, or on the mechanism of interaction. Figure 10.9 illustrates how diffraction experiments serve to determine molecular dimensions. The experimental points show a diffraction maximum for a value of $(p/h) \sin\frac{1}{2}\theta = 0.51$ A^{-1}. In order that this maximum coincide with the maximum of the factor in the braces in Eq. 16 at $2(p/\hbar)R \sin\frac{1}{2}\theta = 5\pi/2$ radians, the interatomic distance R in the O_2 molecule must be equal to 1.09 A.

10.3   The Motion of Free Particles

When a particle moves freely, that is, without being subjected to forces, its energy depends only on its mass and velocity, or on the corresponding momentum,

$$E = \tfrac{1}{2}mv^2 = \tfrac{1}{2}m\left(\frac{p}{m}\right)^2 = \frac{p^2}{2m}. \tag{17}$$

To a definite value of the velocity, or of the momentum, corresponds a definite value of the energy since the mass is a constant. That is, the momentum eigenstates are also eigenstates of the energy (stationary states). These eigenstates are idealizations, as pointed out in the preceding section, because the probability distribution of the positions of particles in these states is uniform all over the space and stationary in time.

Any realistic quantum mechanical state of a free particle is nonstationary. Such a state may be represented as a superposition of momentum eigenstates. The probability distribution of particle positions is then uniform all over the space for each component eigenstate but vanishes for their combination outside a limited region, owing to destructive interference among the component distributions. In a nonstationary state the particle momentum is fairly well defined if component eigenstates with eigenvalues $\mathbf{p}$ very different from a mean value $\langle\mathbf{p}\rangle$ have negligible probability. The probability distributions of the momentum eigenvalues and of the particles positions are tied to one another by an important relationship to be described in the next chapter.

The quantum mechanical problem of the motion of a free particle can be stated as follows: Suppose that at an initial time $t = 0$ the particle is in a state identified as a given combination of position eigenstates $\mathbf{r}$. By which combination of the same position eigenstates will it be identified at a later time? In order that the mathematical symbols be similar to those used previously, we label the variable state of the particle with the symbol $a(t)$. The initial combination of position eigen-states is then specified by a set of probability amplitudes, which can also be indicated in the form of a wave function of the position eigen-values $\mathbf{r} = (x,y,z)$ according to (13), page 112,

$$(\mathbf{r}|a(0)) = \psi_a(\mathbf{r},0) = \psi_a(xyz,0). \tag{18}$$

The values of these probability amplitudes are assumed to be known. One must then calculate the state of the particle at a later time, as repre-sented by the wave function $(\mathbf{r}|a(t)) = \psi_a(\mathbf{r},t)$. Comparison of the probability distributions $|\psi_a(\mathbf{r},t)|^2$ and $|\psi_a(r,0)|^2$ will show how the particle has traveled during the time interval t.

The solution to this problem can be obtained by the method of Chapter 9 because we know that the momentum eigenstates are also energy eigenstates and because the probability amplitudes $(\mathbf{r}|\mathbf{p})$ of these eigenstates have been determined in the preceding section. To apply the method of Chapter 9 we represent then the state $a(t)$ as a super-position of momentum eigenstates

$$\psi_a(\mathbf{r},t) = (\mathbf{r}|a(t)) = \Sigma_\mathbf{p}(\mathbf{r}|\mathbf{p})(\mathbf{p}|a(t)) = \Sigma_\mathbf{p} \exp\left(i\frac{\mathbf{p}}{\hbar}\cdot\mathbf{r}\right)(\mathbf{p}|a(t)). \tag{19}$$

If $(\mathbf{r}|a(0))$ is given for all values of $\mathbf{r}$, the probability amplitudes $(\mathbf{p}|a(0))$ can be calculated by applying a combination formula reciprocal to (19), namely,[3]

$$(\mathbf{p}|a(0)) = \Sigma_\mathbf{r}(\mathbf{p}|\mathbf{r})(\mathbf{r}|a(0)) = \Sigma_\mathbf{r} \exp\left(-i\frac{\mathbf{p}}{\hbar}\cdot\mathbf{r}\right)(\mathbf{r}|a(0)). \tag{20}$$

Because the probability amplitudes $(\mathbf{r}|\mathbf{p}) = \exp[i(\mathbf{p}/\hbar)\cdot\mathbf{r}]$ are called plane waves, a superposition (19) which vanishes for positions $\mathbf{r}$ outside a limited region is often called a "wave packet."

The time variations of the probability amplitudes $(\mathbf{p}|a(t))$ is given by Eq. 1 of Chapter 9, considering that $(\mathbf{p}|a(t)) = (E|a(t))$ with $E = p^2/2m$ according to (17),

$$(\mathbf{p}|a(t)) = \exp\left(-i\frac{E}{\hbar}t\right)(\mathbf{p}|a(0)) = \exp\left(-i\frac{p^2}{2m\hbar}t\right)(\mathbf{p}|a(0)). \tag{21}$$

---

[3] Because the complex exponential wave function $(\mathbf{r}|\mathbf{p})$ can be expressed as a combination of a cosine and a sine function, the representation (19) of the wave function $(\mathbf{r}|a(0)) = \psi_a(\mathbf{r},0)$ constitutes mathematically a Fourier expansion (see Appendix IV), and Eq. 20 may be interpreted as the formula for the calculation of the coefficients of the expansion, Eq. 15 of Appendix IV.

It follows that

$$\psi_a(\mathbf{r},t) = (\mathbf{r} \,|\, a(t)) = \Sigma_\mathbf{p}(\mathbf{r}\,|\,\mathbf{p}) \exp\left(-i\,\frac{p^2}{2m\hbar}\,t\right)(\mathbf{p}\,|\,a(0))$$

$$= \Sigma_\mathbf{p} \exp\left[i\left(\frac{\mathbf{p}}{\hbar}\cdot\mathbf{r} - \frac{p^2}{2m\hbar}\,t\right)\right](\mathbf{p}\,|\,a(0)). \tag{22}$$

The time dependence of the probability distribution of particle positions, $|\psi_a(\mathbf{r},t)|^2$, results from changes in the interference of the plane wave components of the wave packet.

To obtain a more explicit form of $\psi_a(\mathbf{r},t)$, one must of course start from a specific analytical expression of $\psi_a(\mathbf{r},0)$. However, one can show in general that $\psi_a(\mathbf{r},t)$ actually represents a uniform motion of the particle, more properly, a progressive displacement of the probability distribution $|\psi_a(\mathbf{r},0)|^2$, *provided* the particle momentum departs but little from its mean value $\langle\mathbf{p}\rangle$. To this end, we express the particle energy in the form

$$\frac{p^2}{2m} = \frac{|\mathbf{p} - \langle\mathbf{p}\rangle|^2 + 2\,\mathbf{p}\cdot\langle\mathbf{p}\rangle - |\langle\mathbf{p}\rangle|^2}{2m}$$

$$\sim \mathbf{p}\cdot\langle\mathbf{v}\rangle - \frac{|\langle\mathbf{p}\rangle|^2}{2m}, \tag{23}$$

where the square deviation [4] $|\mathbf{p} - \langle\mathbf{p}\rangle|^2$ has been left out as negligible and $\langle\mathbf{p}\rangle/m$ has been indicated as the mean velocity $\langle\mathbf{v}\rangle$. When this expression of $p^2/2m$ is entered in (22), the term $-|\langle\mathbf{p}\rangle|^2/2m$ which is independent of $\mathbf{p}$ can be factored out of the summation. Equation 22 can then be written in the form

$$\psi_a(\mathbf{r},t) \sim \exp\left(i\,\frac{|\langle\mathbf{p}\rangle|^2}{2m\hbar}\,t\right)\Sigma_\mathbf{p} \exp\left(i\,\frac{\mathbf{p}}{\hbar}\cdot(\mathbf{r} - \langle\mathbf{v}\rangle t)\right)(\mathbf{p}\,|\,a(0)). \tag{24}$$

Notice now that the summation in this formula differs from the summation on the right of (19) only by the replacement of $\mathbf{r}$ with $\mathbf{r} - \langle\mathbf{v}\rangle t$. That is, the plane waves interfere at the point $\mathbf{r}$ at the time t with the same phase differences as at the point $\mathbf{r} - \langle\mathbf{v}\rangle t$ at $t = 0$. Therefore, (24) can be expressed in the form

$$\psi_a(\mathbf{r},t) \sim \exp\left(i\,\frac{|\langle\mathbf{p}\rangle|^2}{2m\hbar}\,t\right)\psi_a(\mathbf{r} - \langle\mathbf{v}\rangle t, 0) \tag{25}$$

and the probability distribution of the particle position is given by

$$|\psi_a(\mathbf{r},t)|^2 \sim |\psi_a(\mathbf{r} - \langle\mathbf{v}\rangle t, 0)|^2. \tag{26}$$

---

[4] See Appendix V.

The last formula shows that the probability distribution merely travels along, undisturbed, with the mean velocity $\langle \mathbf{v} \rangle$ of the particle, *in the approximation* where the squared deviations of the momentum, $|\mathbf{p} - \langle \mathbf{p} \rangle|^2$, are disregarded. Without this approximation, the phase factor in the summation of (24) should contain an additional term $(|\mathbf{p} - \langle \mathbf{p} \rangle|^2/2m\hbar)t$, which actually becomes substantially large after a sufficiently long time, no matter how small is $|\mathbf{p} - \langle \mathbf{p} \rangle|^2$. This factor alters the interference and thereby progressively changes the shape of the probability distribution $|\psi_a(\mathbf{r},t)|^2$, in accordance with the circumstance that the velocity of displacement of the wave packet is in fact not well defined.[5]

In the mathematical discussion of plane electromagnetic waves, on pages 82–84, the eigenvalue equations obeyed by plane waves are combined with the energy-momentum relationship for photons to yield the wave Eq. 9 of page 83. That equation is obeyed not only by plane waves but by any superpostion of plane waves, and relates the variations of the electric or magnetic field in space and in time. The same procedure may be applied to variations in space and in time of the wave function $\psi(\mathbf{r},t)$ of a free particle. As noted on page 145, the plane waves $\exp[i(\mathbf{p}/\hbar)\cdot\mathbf{r}]$ obey the Eqs. 7b, c, d, of page 83, with the eigenvalues $-(p_x/\hbar)^2$, etc. The sum of these equations, multiplied by $-\hbar^2/2m$, yields

$$-\frac{\hbar^2}{2m}\left(\frac{\partial^2\psi}{\partial x^2} + \frac{\partial^2\psi}{\partial y^2} + \frac{\partial^2\psi}{\partial z^2}\right) = \frac{1}{2m}(p_x^2 + p_y^2 + p_z^2)\psi = E\psi, \text{ for } \psi = \exp\left(i\frac{\mathbf{p}}{\hbar}\cdot\mathbf{r}\right),$$

(27)

according to the energy-momentum relationship (17), $E = (p_x^2 + p_y^2 + p_z^2)/2m$. Equation 27 is obeyed by each component of the wave packet (22). On the other hand, the probability amplitudes $(\mathbf{p}|a(t))$ in this wave packet obey the eigenvalue equation (10b) of page 128, $E(\mathbf{p}|a|(t)) = -(\hbar/i)\partial(\mathbf{p}|a(t))/\partial t$. It follows that the whole wave packet, that is, the wave function $\psi(\mathbf{r},t)$ of a free particle, obeys the wave equation

$$-\frac{\hbar^2}{2m}\left(\frac{\partial^2\psi}{\partial x^2} + \frac{\partial^2\psi}{\partial y^2} + \frac{\partial^2\psi}{\partial z^2}\right) = -\frac{\hbar}{i}\frac{\partial\psi}{\partial t}.$$

(28)

Example. Consider the application of Eqs. 19 ff. to the wave function defined by

$$(\mathbf{r}|a(0)) = (\sqrt{2\pi}\,d)^{-3/2}\exp(-r^2/4d^2 + i\,\mathbf{q}\cdot\mathbf{r}/\hbar).$$

(29)

The position of a particle in the state represented by this wave function is distributed symmetrically about the point $\mathbf{r} = 0$ with the gaussian probability law

$$|(\mathbf{r}|a(0))|^2 = (\sqrt{2\pi}\,d)^{-3}\exp(-r^2/2d^2).$$

(30)

[5] Notice the connection between the result obtained here and standard conventions which had been made regarding the phases of probability amplitudes. The phase of the probability amplitude (22) decreases in the course of time for constant $\mathbf{r}$ and increases for constant time if $\mathbf{r}$ moves in the direction of $\mathbf{p}$, as a consequence of conventions made in arriving at the Eqs. 1 of Chapters 9 and 10. These conventions were not independent of one another as they seemed to be; otherwise (26) might have yielded a displacement in the wrong direction.

The phase variation of $(\mathbf{r}\,|\,a(0))$ from point to point is represented by the factor $\exp\,(i\mathbf{q}\cdot\mathbf{r}/\hbar)$ which is the same as for a momentum eigenstate with momentum $\mathbf{q}$. The wave function (29), as well as the probability distribution (30) and the analogous functions given below, can be written as the product of three identical functions of x, y, and z (or p_x, p_y, p_z),

$$(\mathbf{r}\,|\,a(0)) = f(x)f(y)f(z), \text{ with } f(x) = (\sqrt{2\pi}\,d)^{-\frac{1}{2}}\exp(-x^2/4d^2 + iq_x x/\hbar). \quad (29')$$

The probability amplitudes $(\mathbf{p}\,|\,a(0))$ are obtained from (20), considering that the symbol $\Sigma_{\mathbf{r}}$ is understood to mean integration over x, y, and z from $-\infty$ to ∞; the result must be divided by $h^{3/2}$ in order that $\Sigma_{\mathbf{p}}|(\mathbf{p}\,|\,a(0))|^2 = 1$. Equation 20 becomes now

$$(\mathbf{p}\,|\,a(0)) = h^{-3/2}\int_{-\infty}^{\infty}dx\int_{-\infty}^{\infty}dy\int_{-\infty}^{\infty}dz\,\exp(-i\mathbf{p}\cdot\mathbf{r}/\hbar)(\mathbf{r}\,|\,a(0)). \quad (31)$$

After substitution of (29) in this integral, the integrations over x, y, and z are carried out separately, owing to (29'), and yield

$$(\mathbf{p}\,|\,a(0)) = (\sqrt{2\pi}\,\hbar/2d)^{-3/2}\exp[-|\mathbf{p}-\mathbf{q}|^2/4(\hbar/2d)^2]. \quad (31')$$

The momentum of the particle is, accordingly, distributed symmetrically about $\mathbf{p} = \mathbf{q}$ with the gaussian probability law

$$|(\mathbf{p}\,|\,a(0))|^2 = (\sqrt{2\pi}\,\hbar/2d)^{-3}\exp[-|\mathbf{p}-\mathbf{q}|^2/2(\hbar/2d)^2]. \quad (32)$$

The wave function at a later time t is then obtained from (22), considering that $\Sigma_{\mathbf{p}}$ is understood to mean integration over p_x, p_y, and p_z and division by $h^{3/2}$, as above,

$$(\mathbf{r}\,|\,a(t)) = h^{-3/2}\int_{-\infty}^{\infty}dp_x\int_{-\infty}^{\infty}dp_y\int_{-\infty}^{\infty}dp_z\,\exp[i(\mathbf{p}\cdot\mathbf{r}-p^2t/2m)/\hbar]\,(\mathbf{p}\,|\,a(0)). \quad (33)$$

The integrations over p_x, p_y, and p_z can again be carried out separately and are analogous to those in (31), but require more complicated algebraic manipulations. They yield

$$(\mathbf{r}\,|\,a(t)) = (\sqrt{2\pi}\,d\sqrt{1+t^2/\tau^2}\,)^{-3/2}\exp[-|\mathbf{r}-\mathbf{q}t/m|^2/4d^2(1+t^2/\tau^2)$$
$$+ i(\mathbf{q}\cdot\mathbf{r}-q^2t/2m)/\hbar + i\tfrac{3}{2}\arctan(t/\tau)$$
$$+ i(t/\tau)\,|\mathbf{r}-\mathbf{q}t/m|^2/4d^2(1+t^2/\tau^2)], \quad (33')$$

where $\tau = 2d^2m/\hbar$. The position of the particle at the time t is accordingly distributed symmetrically about the point $\mathbf{r} = \mathbf{q}t/m$ (which is reached from $\mathbf{r} = 0$ traveling with velocity $\mathbf{q}/m$) with the gaussian probability law

$$|(\mathbf{r}\,|\,a(t))|^2 = (\sqrt{2\pi}\,d\sqrt{1+t^2/\tau^2}\,)^{-3}\exp[-|\mathbf{r}-\mathbf{q}t/m|^2/2d^2(1+t^2/\tau^2)]. \quad (34)$$

The width of this distribution increases in the course of time in proportion to $\sqrt{1+t^2/\tau^2}$. The second term in the exponential of (33') coincides with the phase of the wave function of a particle in a momentum eigenstate with momentum $\mathbf{q}$.

PROBLEMS

10.1   A crystal has a set of lattice planes with spacing $d = 2.1$ A. It is desired to observe Bragg reflection on this set of planes. (a) Calculate the maximum wavelength of X rays which can be so reflected and specify the orientation of the X-ray beam with respect to the lattice planes which corresponds to the maximum wavelength. (b) Calculate the minimum energies of electrons and neutrons which can be reflected by the same set of planes.

10.2   A beam of slow neutrons ($v = 2000$ m/sec) is scattered coherently by a pair of identical scattering centers P and Q. The vector $\mathbf{d}$ joining P to Q is perpendicular to the beam and is $2A$ long. If only one scatterer were present, the neutron intensity received by a detector at a distance r in a direction $\mathbf{D}$ could be indicated by $I = s^2/r^2$ and would be independent of $\mathbf{D}$. Calculate the intensity $I(\theta)$ received from the pair of scatterers when $\mathbf{D}$ lies in the plane of P and Q and of the beam direction, and forms an angle θ with this direction.

10.3   Calculate and plot the cross section $\sigma(\theta)$ for scattering of slow neutrons ($v = 2900$ m/sec) by CO_2 molecules. The cross sections for scattering by single atoms of C and O are independent of the scattering angle and can be indicated by s_C^2 and s_O^2, with $s_C = 6.4 \times 10^{-13}$ cm and $s_O = 5.8 \times 10^{-13}$ cm. The CO_2 molecule has the linear structure $O = C = O$ with a spacing $d_{CO} = 1.13$ A between adjacent atoms.

Complementarity
and the size of atoms

Particles and X rays obey the same diffraction law, as seen in the last chapter. In general, atomic particles exhibit many properties that are known in macroscopic physics as wave properties. For example, electromagnetic radiation or sound waves confined to a narrow region of space are bound to have a short wavelength and a high pitch. This chapter deals with the analogous property of atomic particles: Any particle confined to a narrow region of space is bound to have a high momentum and a high kinetic energy. This link determines the stability and the size of atoms. Analogous relations exist between other variables.

When a particle has a definite momentum **p**, the probability distribution of its position is uniform all over the space, just like the intensity of a plane sinusoidal radiation wave. If the position of a particle is restricted to a region of given size, its state may nevertheless be represented as a combination of momentum eigenstates with different eigenvalues **p**, the probability of finding the particle at a position outside the given region being canceled by destructive interference. The transition from constructive interference inside the region to destructive interference outside of it depends on the change of the phase differences in the combination of eigenstates. The phase difference of two eigenstates with momenta $\mathbf{p}$ and $\mathbf{p}'$ varies from point to point at the rate of $\mathbf{p}/\hbar - \mathbf{p}'/\hbar = 2\pi(\mathbf{k} - \mathbf{k}')$ radians/cm. (See Eq. 5, page 142.) Therefore, if a set of momentum eigenstates interferes constructively at one point, the interference can become destructive only at a distance of the order of the reciprocal of the largest wave vector difference $|\mathbf{k} - \mathbf{k}'|$ within the set. Conversely, if constructive interference is confined to a region of space with a diameter of the order a, the range of wave vectors in the combination ("band width") must be of the order of magnitude of $1/a$ and the corresponding range of momenta of the order of $\hbar/a$. Even though the range may include vanishingly small momenta, the combination must include momenta *at least as large as* $\sim \hbar/a$. This link between the values of the position and momentum of a particle is called "complementarity relation."

The complementarity relation is treated in Sect. 11.1. Its mathematical formulation may be derived from the general theory of the combination of sinusoidal functions, that is, of the Fourier analysis sketched in Appendix IV. The size of the region to which a particle or radiation is confined and the range of momenta or wave vectors of component eigenstates can be expressed as statistical estimates of the uncertainties about the values of position and momentum variables. Accordingly, the link between position and momentum was called by Heisenberg an "uncertainty relation."

Complementarity is not directly noticeable in macroscopic phenomena, so that position and momentum are properly regarded in classical physics as independently measurable variables. The discovery, in 1926, of the previously unsuspected uncertainty relations caused considerable surprise. Heisenberg accompanied the mathematical proof of his result with an analysis of conceivable experimental procedures directed to show that simultaneous measurements of position and momentum, beyond the limits of accuracy fixed by the uncertainty relation, are, in fact, incompatible. This analysis was developed further and extended by Bohr into a general point of view, called the "principle of complementarity," whose essentials are contained in the concepts of incompatibility and randomness, introduced in Chapters 6 and 7.

The complementarity of the position and momentum of a particle implies the "tendency to expand" which was surmised in Sect. 3.4 as the basis of the stability of atoms. If an atomic electron is held by electrostatic attraction within a distance a from the nucleus, its mean squared momentum must be at least of the order of $\hbar^2/a^2$ and its mean kinetic energy of the order of $\hbar^2/2ma^2$. If a is of the order of atomic radii, that is, 1 A $= 10^{-8}$ cm, and $m \sim 10^{-27}$ g, $\hbar^2/2ma^2$ is of the order of 10 ev and therefore comparable to the potential energy e^2/a due to the attraction of a hydrogen nucleus. The nuclear attraction strives to draw in the electron, but a decrease of a forces up the kinetic energy. If a should decrease by a factor of ten, the mean kinetic energy would rise hundredfold; this increase could not be provided for by the increase of potential energy, which would be only tenfold. Actually, the size of the hydrogen atom stabilizes at an approximate radius somewhat smaller than 1 A, as will be shown in Sect. 11.2.

The treatment of the complementarity of position and momentum given in this chapter rests on the relation between the eigenstates of these variables which was derived, in turn, from the analysis of diffraction. In fact, the diffraction experiments need not be regarded as independent experimental evidence in our treatment. Appendix VIII shows how the relation between the eigenstates of position and momentum follows from the concepts and laws introduced in Chapters 4 to 9 only. The mathematical formulation of quantum theory, outlined in Appendix VIII, provides a general procedure for identifying pairs of complementary variables. In particular, the strength of the magnetic field of a monochromatic radiation is shown to be complementary to the electric field strength. (Notice that the electric field is proportional to the rate of change of the magnetic field in the course of time, much as the momentum of a particle is proportional to the rate of change of its position.) The quantum properties of radiation follow from the complementarity of the electric and magnetic fields.

11.1 Uncertainty Relations

Complementarity between a pair of variables is a special case of incompatibility. Incompatibility was introduced in Chapter 7 with regard to the analysis of radiation and particle beams and will be reviewed here.

In macroscopic electromagnetism it is trivial that a disturbance may have alternative characteristics such that, when one is present, the other one is missing altogether. Circular and linear polarization afford a typical example in that circularly polarized light has no trace of linear polarization, and vice versa. Similarly, a plane sinusoidal wave, whose variation in space is specified by a wave vector, spreads uniformly all over space and thus has no localization at all, whereas a disturbance sharply localized at one point has no definite wave vector at all. There is, of course, light of intermediate types which partakes of two opposite characteristics; thus elliptical polarization partakes of linear and circular characteristics.

This situation is unfamiliar in the classical mechanics of particles and rigid bodies. For example, if a magnetic needle has a given orientation, the component of its magnetic moment in any direction of space has a definite value. Similarly, if an assembly of macroscopic bodies is prepared with a procedure that exerts maximum control on all their variables, the energy of each body has a definite value, predictable in advance for each position of the body and at any time. However, we know that these macroscopic expectations do not hold at the atomic level. Molecules made homogeneous by filtration through a Stern-Gerlach magnet behave inhomogeneously when analyzed with a magnet of different orientation. Ions which emerge in the same excited state from the source of a canal ray beam release their energy by emission of light photons at different points along their tracks (page 60) and thus become inhomogeneous with respect to excitation energy; that is, each ion is in a state which varies in the course of time and is accordingly nonstationary, so that its energy does not have a definite, predictable value.

The experimental evidence on quantum phenomena shows that a definite value of any variable exists only for systems in an eigenstate of that variable, that is, for systems prepared by suitable experimental procedures. Two variables may have simultaneously definite values only if the system possesses an eigenstate common to the two variables. If the experimental procedures for preparing eigenstates of the two variables are incompatible, there are no joint eigenstates and no joint eigenvalues and the variables themselves are called incompatible.

Incompatibility hinges on the fundamental statistical aspects of quantum phenomena discussed in Chapter 6. When a system is in an eigenstate of one variable, there is an inherent statistical uncertainty regarding the values of incompatible variables. This uncertainty is negligible in macroscopic mechanics so that incompatibility goes unnoticed. When Heisenberg and Bohr emphasized the intrinsic connection between eigenvalues and experimental procedures, the statistical aspects of quantum phenomena had not yet been fully recognized. In that period, many striking quantum phenomena were interpreted theoretically within a very short time by different workers. Each theory attracted immediately much attention before a unified understanding had emerged from the fragmentary development. Different aspects appeared disconnected and sometimes paradoxical, so that while the mathematical logic of each successful theoretical procedure was clear, an intuitive interpretation of the phenomena seemed hard to achieve.

The incompatibility of position and momentum may be established through the following sequence of steps. From the standpoint of macroscopic electromagnetism, the incompatibility of position and wave vector of a disturbance is trivial, as noted above. The observations on the photoelectric effect reveal the existence of photon momentum and its proportionality to the wave vector. They also show an inherent randomness in the position of a photon absorption and in the magnitude and direction of the absorbed momentum. The macroscopic incompatibility of position and wave vector is thereby translated into quantum mechanical incompatibility of position and momentum of photon absorption. Finally, the identical behavior of radiation and particles in diffraction phenomena shows that position and momentum are incompatible for particles as well as for photon absorptions. Alternatively, one may argue directly from particle diffraction experiments that particles with a well-defined direction and velocity have a uniform probability of colliding with atoms spaced widely apart within a crystal. Because scattering by different cells combines *coherently* to yield diffraction, the randomness of collision positions is an inherent property of each incident particle rather than the result of failure to control its track. That is, homogeneity in the direction of flight of particles entails a dispersion in their points of impact. Conversely, if the particles were focussed to collide with only a few atoms of a crystal, the diffraction pattern would be smeared, and one would argue from this result an unsharpness of the direction of incidence.

Complementarity between two variables implies, besides incompatibility, some quantitative relationship between the ranges of statistical variation of the variables in any one state of the system. Momentum eigenstates of a particle are idealizations, as pointed out in Chapter 10, and so are also position eigenstates. In a realistic state, the values of both these variables are subject to statistical uncertainties, that is, if either variable were measured, one would find in different experimental runs random variations about a mean. Accordingly, complementarity will be expressed as a relation between random deviations of the two variables.

The mean square deviation (See Appendix V) serves as a convenient index of the magnitude of the statistical uncertainty. One defines, therefore, the mean value of the position coordinate x of a particle in a state a as

$$\langle x \rangle = \Sigma_{xyz}\, x \mid (xyz \mid a) \mid^2, \tag{1a}$$

where $\mid (xyz \mid a) \mid^2$ indicates the probability of finding the particle at the position xyz, and the mean square deviation as

$$\Delta x^2 = \langle (x - \langle x \rangle)^2 \rangle = \Sigma_{xyz}(x - \langle x \rangle)^2 \mid (xyz \mid a) \mid^2. \tag{2a}$$

Similarly, one defines $\langle y \rangle$, $\langle z \rangle$, and Δy^2 and Δz^2, and, with vector symbols,

$$\langle \mathbf{r} \rangle = \Sigma_\mathbf{r} \, \mathbf{r} \, | (\mathbf{r} | a) |^2 \tag{1b}$$

$$\Delta \mathbf{r}^2 = \Delta x^2 + \Delta y^2 + \Delta z^2 = \langle | \mathbf{r} - \langle \mathbf{r} \rangle |^2 \rangle = \Sigma_\mathbf{r} | \mathbf{r} - \langle \mathbf{r} \rangle |^2 | (\mathbf{r} | a) |^2. \tag{2b}$$

With regard to the probability distribution of momentum, one takes likewise

$$\langle p_x \rangle = \Sigma_{p_x p_y p_z} \, p_x \, | (p_x p_y p_z | a) |^2. \tag{3a}$$

$$\Delta p_x{}^2 = \langle (p_x - \langle p_x \rangle)^2 \rangle = \Sigma_{p_x p_y p_z} (p_x - \langle p_x \rangle)^2 | (p_x p_y p_z | a) |^2. \tag{4a}$$

$$\langle \mathbf{p} \rangle = \Sigma_\mathbf{p} \, \mathbf{p} \, | (\mathbf{p} | a) |^2. \tag{3b}$$

$$\Delta \mathbf{p}^2 = \Delta p_x{}^2 + \Delta p_y{}^2 + \Delta p_z{}^2 = \langle | \mathbf{p} - \langle \mathbf{p} \rangle |^2 \rangle = \Sigma_\mathbf{p} \, | \mathbf{p} - \langle \mathbf{p} \rangle |^2 | (\mathbf{p} | a) |^2. \tag{4b}$$

Since to each momentum $\mathbf{p}$ corresponds a wave vector $\mathbf{k} = \mathbf{p}/h$, one may define, in analogy to (3) and (4), $\langle k_x \rangle = \langle p_x \rangle / h$ and $\Delta k_x{}^2 = \Delta p_x{}^2 / h^2$.

Notice that mean values and mean square deviations of position and wave vector may be defined not only in connection with quantum mechanical probability distributions but also with regard to macroscopic distributions of light intensity, field strengths, etc. For example, given the values of the electric field $\mathbf{E}(xyz)$ of a localized disturbance, one may define the mean value of x averaged over the squared field strength as

$$\langle x \rangle = \Sigma_{xyz} \, x \, | \mathbf{E}(xyz) |^2. \tag{5}$$

The point of coordinates $\langle x \rangle$, $\langle y \rangle$, $\langle z \rangle$ may be regarded as the center of the localized disturbance. If the field strength is represented by Fourier analysis (Appendix IV) as a combination of sinusoidal plane waves, with wave vectors $\mathbf{k}$ and amplitudes $\mathbf{E}(\mathbf{k})$, one may define the mean value of a wave vector component

$$\langle k_x \rangle = \Sigma_{k_x k_y k_z} \, k_x \, | \mathbf{E}(k_x k_y k_z) |^2. \tag{6}$$

Mean square deviations Δx^2, Δy^2, Δz^2, $\Delta k_x{}^2$, $\Delta k_y{}^2$, $\Delta k_z{}^2$ are similarly defined.

The qualitative argument on page 154 indicates that the root mean square deviation Δk_x (that is, the square root of the mean square deviation $\Delta k_x{}^2$), must be at least of the order of magnitude of the reciprocal of Δx. Complementarity is formulated by a mathematical law which places a lower limit on the product of root mean square deviations $\Delta x \, \Delta k_x$.

This law, called the Heisenberg uncertainty relation, is

$$\Delta x \, \Delta k_x \geq \frac{1}{4\pi}, \tag{7}$$

or, replacing the wave vector with the momentum,

$$\Delta x \, \Delta p_x \geq \tfrac{1}{2}\hbar. \tag{8}$$

The same limitations hold for $\Delta y \, \Delta k_y$, $\Delta y \, \Delta p_y$, etc. The uncertainty relations hold equally for averages, like (1) to (4), taken over the quantum mechanical probability distributions of a particle and for averages taken, like (5) and (6), over the distribution of macroscopic variables. One verifies that the equality sign in (7) and (8), corresponding to minimum uncertainty, obtains when the probability distribution of a particle position, $|(\mathbf{r}\,|\,a)|^2$, is represented by a Gaussian function, for example, $\exp(-r^2/a^2)/\pi^{3/2}a^3$.

In macroscopic statistics, one can formulate an uncertainty relation analogous to (7) or (8). As outlined in Appendix V, the product of the mean square deviations Δn^2 and Δm^2 of two macroscopic random variables cannot be smaller than the squared mean product of their deviations, $(\Delta nm)^2$ (otherwise the correlation of n and m would be larger than 1). In quantum mechanics the mean product Δnm has a definite meaning only if n and m have joint eigenstates. It will be shown here that the quantum mechanical uncertainty relation is established in terms of a suitably defined analog of the mean product Δnm.

The uncertainty relation (8) will be established in three steps. First, the expression (4a) of $\Delta p_x{}^2$ will be transformed so as to be expressed, like Δx^2, as a summation over position eigenvalues $\mathbf{r}$. Then a mathematical analog of the relationship $\Delta n^2 \Delta m^2 \geq (\Delta nm)^2$ of macroscopic statistics will be established. Finally, the analog of $(\Delta nm)^2$ will be discussed and evaluated.

Equation 4a may be written in the form

$$\Delta p_x{}^2 = \Sigma_{\mathbf{p}} \, (a\,|\,\mathbf{p})(p_x - \langle p_x\rangle)(p_x - \langle p_x\rangle)(\mathbf{p}\,|\,a). \tag{9}$$

The conditions (14) and (15, page 113 on probability amplitudes require that $\Sigma_{\mathbf{r}}(\mathbf{p}'\,|\,\mathbf{r})(\mathbf{r}\,|\,\mathbf{p})$ equal 1 when $\mathbf{p} = \mathbf{p}'$ and 0 otherwise. Therefore (9) can be written once more in the form [1]

$$\Delta p_x{}^2 = \Sigma_{\mathbf{p}'}\Sigma_{\mathbf{p}} \, (a\,|\,\mathbf{p}')(p_x' - \langle p_x\rangle) \, [\Sigma_{\mathbf{r}}(\mathbf{p}'\,|\,\mathbf{r})(\mathbf{r}\,|\,\mathbf{p})] \, (p_x - \langle p_x\rangle)(\mathbf{p}\,|\,a)$$
$$= \Sigma_{\mathbf{r}} \, [\Sigma_{\mathbf{p}'}(a\,|\,\mathbf{p}')(p_x' - \langle p_x\rangle)(\mathbf{p}'\,|\,\mathbf{r})] \, [\Sigma_{\mathbf{p}}(\mathbf{r}\,|\,\mathbf{p})(p_x - \langle p_x\rangle)(\mathbf{p}\,|\,a)]. \tag{10}$$

We call the expression in the second brackets in the last line $g(\mathbf{r})$ and utilize the fact that the probability amplitudes $(\mathbf{r}\,|\,\mathbf{p})$ obey the eigenvalue equations (11) of page 145, which gives

$$g(\mathbf{r}) = \Sigma_{\mathbf{p}}(\mathbf{r}\,|\,\mathbf{p})(p_x - \langle p_x\rangle)(\mathbf{p}\,|\,a) = \Sigma_{\mathbf{p}} \left[\frac{\hbar}{i}\frac{\partial(\mathbf{r}\,|\,\mathbf{p})}{\partial x} - \langle p_x\rangle(\mathbf{r}\,|\,\mathbf{p})\right] (\mathbf{p}\,|\,a). \tag{11}$$

---

[1] The summation over $\mathbf{p}'$ may be introduced and $\mathbf{p}$ changed into $\mathbf{p}'$ as convenient because the sum over $\mathbf{r}$ vanishes unless $\mathbf{p} = \mathbf{p}'$.

Now that $\mathbf{p}$ appears only in the probability amplitudes $(\mathbf{r}|\mathbf{p})$ and $(\mathbf{p}|a)$, these amplitudes can be combined into $(\mathbf{r}|a) = \psi_a(\mathbf{r})$ and (11) becomes

$$g(\mathbf{r}) = \frac{\hbar}{i}\frac{\partial(\mathbf{r}|a)}{\partial x} - \langle p_x \rangle(\mathbf{r}|a) = \frac{\hbar}{i}\frac{\partial \psi}{\partial x} - \langle p_x \rangle \psi, \tag{12}$$

where, as in the following, $\psi_a(\mathbf{r})$ is abbreviated to ψ. The first bracket in the last line of (10) is the complex conjugate of the second one, owing to the reciprocity property of probability amplitudes indicated by Eq. 17 of page 113. Therefore, we write (10) in the form

$$\Delta p_x{}^2 = \Sigma_{\mathbf{r}}\, g^*(\mathbf{r})\, g(\mathbf{r}) = \int |g(\mathbf{r})|^2\, dx\, dy\, dz = \langle |g|^2 \rangle, \tag{13}$$

where the symbol $\langle |g|^2 \rangle$ has been introduced as a compact representation of the preceding integral. The mean square deviation of x may be expressed similarly, defining

$$f(\mathbf{r}) = (x - \langle x \rangle)(\mathbf{r}|a) = (x - \langle x \rangle)\psi, \tag{14}$$

so that $(2a)$ takes the form

$$\Delta x^2 = \Sigma_{\mathbf{r}}|f(\mathbf{r})|^2 = \int |f(\mathbf{r})|^2\, dx\, dy\, dz = \langle |f|^2 \rangle. \tag{15}$$

As a next step we state and prove the inequality

$$\Delta x^2\, \Delta p_x{}^2 = \langle |f|^2 \rangle \langle |g|^2 \rangle \geq |\langle f^*\, g \rangle|^2, \tag{16}$$

which holds for any pair of well-behaved functions $f(\mathbf{r})$, $g(\mathbf{r})$. Consider the expression $|\langle |g|^2 \rangle f - \langle fg^* \rangle g|^2$, which is the square of a magnitude and therefore certainly non-negative. The integral of this expression over all points of space is also certainly non-negative, and therefore we write [2]

$$0 \leq \int |\langle |g|^2 \rangle f - \langle fg^* \rangle g|^2\, d\mathbf{r}$$

$$= \langle |g|^2 \rangle^2 \langle |f|^2 \rangle - \langle |g|^2 \rangle \langle fg^* \rangle \langle f^*g \rangle - \langle |g|^2 \rangle \langle f^*g \rangle \langle fg^* \rangle + |\langle fg^* \rangle|^2 \langle |g|^2 \rangle$$

$$= \langle |g|^2 \rangle \{ \langle |f|^2 \rangle \langle |g|^2 \rangle - |\langle f^*g \rangle|^2 \}. \tag{17}$$

The factor $\langle |g|^2 \rangle$ is certainly non-negative, and therefore the same must hold for the factor in braces, which proves the inequality (16).

Equation 16 would be equivalent to the relation $\Delta n^2\, \Delta m^2 \geq (\Delta nm)^2$ of macroscopic statistics if the functions f and g were real. Actually, $\langle f^*g \rangle$ is complex and therefore does not represent the mean value of a physical variable. However, the squared magnitude $|\langle f^*g \rangle|^2$ may be expressed as the sum of two squared real quantities, each of which may in turn represent the mean value of a physical variable,[3]

$$|\langle f^*g \rangle|^2 = |\langle \tfrac{1}{2}(f^*g + fg^*) \rangle + i\langle \tfrac{1}{2}(f^*g - fg^*)/i \rangle|^2$$

$$= \langle \tfrac{1}{2}(f^*g + fg^*) \rangle^2 + \langle \tfrac{1}{2}(f^*g - fg^*)/i \rangle^2. \tag{18}$$

---

[2] Equation 17 utilizes the complex number identity $|a - b|^2 = (a^* - b^*)(a - b) = |a|^2 - a^*b - ab^* + |b|^2$.

[3] See Eq. 4 of Appendix VI.

To perform this separation, we write out the expression of $\langle f^*g \rangle$ according to the definitions (12) and (14),

$$\langle f^*g \rangle = \int f^*(\mathbf{r}) \, g(\mathbf{r}) \, d\mathbf{r} = \int (x - \langle x \rangle) \, \psi^* \left(\frac{\hbar}{i} \frac{\partial \psi}{\partial x} - \langle p_x \rangle \psi \right) d\mathbf{r}. \tag{19a}$$

In this formula $\langle p_x \rangle$ multiplies the expression for the mean of the deviation $x - \langle x \rangle$, which vanishes, of course; therefore, the term with $\langle p_x \rangle$ may be stricken off,

$$\langle f^*g \rangle = \int (x - \langle x \rangle) \psi^* \frac{\hbar}{i} \frac{\partial \psi}{\partial x} \, d\mathbf{r}. \tag{19b}$$

Transformation of (19b) by partial integration, considering that for any realistic state the probability amplitude ψ vanishes at infinitely distant points, yields [4]

$$\langle f^*g \rangle = - \int (x - \langle x \rangle) \frac{\partial \psi^*}{\partial x} \frac{\hbar}{i} \psi \, d\mathbf{r} - \int \frac{\partial(x - \langle x \rangle)}{\partial x} \psi^* \frac{\hbar}{i} \psi \, d\mathbf{r}$$

$$= \int (x - \langle x \rangle) \psi \left(-\frac{\hbar}{i} \frac{\partial \psi^*}{\partial x} \right) d\mathbf{r} - \frac{\hbar}{i} \int |\psi|^2 \, d\mathbf{r} = \langle fg^* \rangle + i\hbar. \tag{20}$$

It follows that $\langle f^*g \rangle - \langle fg^* \rangle = i\hbar$, whatever be the wave function ψ, and also that $\langle f^*g \rangle - \frac{1}{2} i\hbar = \langle fg^* \rangle + \frac{1}{2} i\hbar$ and is accordingly real and equal to $\frac{1}{2} \langle f^*g + fg^* \rangle$. Combining (16) and (18), we have finally

$$\Delta x^2 \, \Delta p_x{}^2 \geq \left\{ \int (x - \langle x \rangle) \frac{1}{2} \left(\psi^* \frac{\hbar}{i} \frac{\partial \psi}{\partial x} - \frac{\hbar}{i} \frac{\partial \psi^*}{\partial x} \psi \right) d\mathbf{r} \right\}^2 + (\tfrac{1}{2}\hbar)^2. \tag{21}$$

The first term on the right represents the quantum mechanical equivalent of the squared mean product of deviations $(\Delta x p_x)^2$; it may vanish, as it does, for example, when ψ is real, indicating a lack of macroscopic correlation. The second term has a fixed value and stems from the quantum mechanical incompatibility of the variables x and p_x. The uncertainty relation (8) follows from (21) by disregarding the first term on the right of (21) which is certainly non-negative.

The derivation of the uncertainty relation given above rests on the fact that the probability amplitudes $(\mathbf{r}\,|\,\mathbf{p})$ are plane waves, that is, have a constant magnitude and are sinusoidal functions of the position coordinates x,y,z and of the momentum components p_x,p_y,p_z. All other steps of the derivation are purely mathematical; considerations of statistical correlations, etc., have been presented only to illustrate the mathematical arguments by physical interpretations. One may conclude, therefore, that two variables α and β are complementary whenever they are connected by probability amplitudes or other relationships having the functional form $\exp(i\alpha\beta)$. A general uncertainty relation is given in Appendix VIII.

---

[4] We utilize the formula $\int uv(dw/dx) \, dx = - \int u(dv/dx)w \, dx - \int (du/dx)vw \, dx$, and also $\partial(x - \langle x \rangle)/\partial x = 1$ and $\int |\psi|^2 \, d\mathbf{r} = 1$, (Eq. 14, page 113).

Notice in particular the complementarity between time and frequency or energy. Consider the probability of a certain event, for example, of detecting a particle at a point $\mathbf{r}$ as a function of the time t of observation. If the probability of detection varies in the course of time, the state of the particle is not stationary, because all probabilities are constant in any stationary state. We label this state $a(t)$ and indicate the probability of detection by $P(t) = |(\mathbf{r}|a(t))|^2$. The probability variation may be represented as a combination of sinusoidal oscillations with frequency ν, by Fourier analysis of the function $P(t)$, according to Appendix IV, if $P(t)$ is given in any form whatsoever. If the state $a(t)$ is represented as a superposition of stationary states with known probability amplitudes, then the Fourier analysis is ready-made and is given by Eq. 7 of Chapter 9, namely,

$$P(t) = |\Sigma_E(\mathbf{r}|E)(E|a(t))|^2 = \left|\Sigma_E(\mathbf{r}|E)\exp\left(-i\frac{E}{\hbar}t\right)(E|a(0))\right|^2$$

$$= \Sigma_E|(\mathbf{r}|E)|^2|(E|a(0))|^2 + 2\Sigma_E\Sigma_{E'}^{E'<E}\left\{|(\mathbf{r}|E)||(E|a(0))|\right.$$

$$\left.\times |(\mathbf{r}|E')||(E'|a(0))|\cos\left[\frac{E-E'}{\hbar}t + \delta_{EE'}(0)\right]\right\}. \quad (22)$$

The variations of $P(t)$ are represented in this formula as effects of variable interference between components stationary states. In particular, the interference of two states with energies E and E' yields component oscillations with frequency $(E - E')/h$.

One defines, in analogy with (1) to (6) a mean time of detection and its mean square deviation

$$\langle t \rangle = \int_{-\infty}^{\infty} t\, P(t)\, dt; \qquad \Delta t^2 = \int_{-\infty}^{\infty} (t - \langle t \rangle)^2 P(t)\, dt. \quad (23)$$

The mean energy and its mean square deviation are

$$\langle E \rangle = \Sigma_E E|(E|a(0))|^2; \qquad \Delta E^2 = \Sigma_E(E - \langle E \rangle)^2|(E|a(0))|^2. \quad (24)$$

Finally, one may define for the frequency of oscillation a root mean square deviation

$$\Delta\nu = \Delta E/h. \quad (25)$$

The mean square deviations defined here obey uncertainty relations quite analogous to (7) and (8), namely

$$\Delta t\, \Delta\nu \geq \frac{1}{4\pi} \quad (26)$$

$$\Delta t\, \Delta E \geq \tfrac{1}{2}\hbar. \quad (27)$$

The root mean square deviation $\Delta\nu$ is often called the "frequency band width" of the function of time $P(t)$.

11.2   The Size of the Hydrogen Atom

If an electron belongs to an atom, the probability of finding it at positions distant from the nucleus of that atom must be vanishingly small.   This fact alone provides essential information regarding the motion of the electron within the atom, owing to the uncertainty relations.

Call a a distance yet to be determined which indicates the approximate radius of a hydrogen atom, and let us label with that symbol the unknown stationary state of the electron in this atom.   We indicate any possible position of the electron with a vector $\mathbf{r} = (x,y,z)$, such that $\mathbf{r} = 0$ represents the position of the nucleus and $r = \sqrt{x^2 + y^2 + z^2}$ the distance of the electron from the nucleus.   The probability of finding the electron at a position $\mathbf{r}$ is indicated by $|(\mathbf{r}|a)|^2$ or $|\psi_a(\mathbf{r})|^2$ and must be negligible for $\mathbf{r}$ much larger than a.

If the wave function $\psi_a(\mathbf{r})$ were known, one could calculate the probability of each momentum eigenvalue.   The probability amplitudes $(\mathbf{p}|a)$ are given, as in (20), page 148 by

$$(\mathbf{p}|a) = \Sigma_{\mathbf{r}}(\mathbf{p}|\mathbf{r})(\mathbf{r}|a) = \Sigma_{\mathbf{r}} \exp\left(- i\frac{\mathbf{p}}{\hbar} \cdot \mathbf{r}\right)(\mathbf{r}|a). \tag{28a}$$

The symbol $\Sigma_{\mathbf{r}}$ represents in fact an integral, the same as in Eq. (31), page 151, and therefore

$$(\mathbf{p}|a) = h^{-3/2} \int_{-\infty}^{\infty} dx \int_{-\infty}^{\infty} dy \int_{-\infty}^{\infty} dz \exp\left(- \frac{i}{\hbar}(p_x x + p_y y + p_z z)\right)\psi_a(xyz). \tag{28b}$$

The probability of the momentum eigenvalue $\mathbf{p}$ is $|(\mathbf{p}|a)|^2$.   The kinetic energy of the atomic electron, $K = p^2/2m$ is the same as the total energy of a free electron (see Eq. 17, p. 147).   The total energy of an atomic electron includes, besides K, a potential energy V due to the attraction by the nucleus.   The mean value of K is

$$\langle K \rangle = \frac{1}{2m}\langle p^2 \rangle = \frac{1}{2m}\Sigma_{\mathbf{p}}\, p^2 |(\mathbf{p}|a)|^2 \tag{29a}$$

that is, in analogy with (33), page 151,

$$\langle K \rangle = h^{-3/2} \int_{-\infty}^{\infty} dp_x \int_{-\infty}^{\infty} dp_y \int_{-\infty}^{\infty} dp_z \frac{1}{2m}(p_x^2 + p_y^2 + p_z^2)|(p_x p_y p_z|a)|^2. \tag{29b}$$

Even though the wave function $\psi_a(\mathbf{r})$ is unknown and (28) and (29) cannot be calculated explicitly, the uncertainty relation (8) provides a minimum estimate of the value of $\langle K \rangle$, based only on the information that $|\psi_a(\mathbf{r})|^2$ is negligible for $r \gg a$. This condition implies that the mean square distance of the electron from the nucleus, namely,

$$\langle r^2 \rangle = \langle x^2 \rangle + \langle y^2 \rangle + \langle z^2 \rangle = \Sigma_r \, r^2 |\psi_a(\mathbf{r})|^2, \tag{30}$$

is of the order of magnitude of a^2. It follows that each of the mean square deviations $\Delta x^2 = \langle (x - \langle x \rangle)^2 \rangle = \langle x^2 \rangle - \langle x \rangle^2$, Δy^2 and Δz^2, is itself of the order of magnitude of a^2 (if not smaller). The uncertainty relation (8) gives then

$$\langle p_x^2 \rangle = \langle p_x \rangle^2 + \Delta p_x^2 \geq \Delta p_x^2 \gtrsim \frac{1}{4} \frac{\hbar^2}{a^2}, \tag{31}$$

and similar relations for $\langle p_y^2 \rangle$ and $\langle p_z^2 \rangle$. We conclude that the mean kinetic energy (29) is itself subject to the limitation

$$\langle K \rangle \gtrsim \frac{1}{2m} \frac{\hbar^2}{a^2}. \tag{32}$$

This result means that the electron, by the very fact of being held within the atom, cannot be at rest. The probability distribution of its momentum components must be such that values of each component p_x of magnitude $\sim \hbar/a$ are quite likely. The smaller is a, the larger is $\langle p_x^2 \rangle$. This fact represents the inherent tendency to expand that was anticipated in Chapter 3 from the qualitative evidence on the stability of atoms.[5]

The atomic electron does not escape from the atom, despite the tendency to expand, because it is held back by the nuclear attraction. As outlined in Sect. 3.4, the size of hydrogen atoms is fixed by a condition of equilibrium between the tendency to expand and the nuclear attraction. The tendency to expand is represented by a decrease of the mean kinetic energy (32) as the atomic "radius" a increases. The nuclear attraction is represented by a decrease of the mean potential energy of the electron when a decreases. Equilibrium results for a value a which minimizes the total energy (kinetic plus potential).

---

[5] The same tendency to expand is noticed in the motion of a free particle, represented by a traveling wave packet in Sect. 10.3. The term $(|\mathbf{p} - \langle \mathbf{p} \rangle|^2/2m\hbar)t$, which was omitted in the phase of the plane wave combination (24) page 149, becomes important within a time of the order $2ma^2/\hbar$, where a indicates a "radius" of the wave packet. After this time, the shape of the probability distribution $|\psi_a(\mathbf{r},t)|^2$ changes substantially, that is, the wave packet dissolves.

The electric potential at a distance r from the positive charge e of a hydrogen nucleus is e/r. The potential energy of an electron with charge $-e$, at this distance, is $V = -e(e/r) = -e^2/r$. If the distance of the electron from the nucleus is of the order of magnitude a, the mean value of V will be

$$\langle V \rangle \sim -e^2/a. \tag{33}$$

Assuming that the kinetic energy remains close to its minimum possible value, we express the mean total energy in the form

$$\langle E \rangle = \langle K \rangle + \langle V \rangle = C \frac{\hbar^2}{2ma^2} - C' \frac{e^2}{a}, \tag{34}$$

where C and C' indicate unknown numerical constants of the order of 1.

For purpose of orientation we also calculate the values of $\langle K \rangle$, $\langle V \rangle$, and $\langle E \rangle$ which correspond to a hypothetical but specific analytical form of $\psi_a(\mathbf{r})$ that does not depend on the direction of $\mathbf{r}$ but only on its magnitude $r = \sqrt{x^2 + y^2 + z^2}$,

$$(\mathbf{r}\,|\,a) = \psi_a(\mathbf{r}) = \frac{1}{\sqrt{\pi a^3}} e^{-r/a}. \tag{35}$$

This exponential function decreases rapidly when r is much larger than a. The constant $1/\sqrt{\pi a^3}$ is chosen so that $(\mathbf{r}\,|\,a)$ meets the general requirement $\Sigma_{\mathbf{r}}\,|(\mathbf{r}\,|\,a)|^2 = 1$, introduced in Eq. 14 on page 113. (The expression (35) happens to represent the correct wave function for the ground state of the hydrogen atom, as will be shown in Chapter 14.) The integrals in (28b) and (29b) can be calculated analytically in succession, introducing in (28b) the function $\psi_a(\mathbf{r})$ as given by (35). The results are [6]

$$(\mathbf{p}\,|\,a) = \frac{8\sqrt{\pi a^3/\hbar^3}}{(1 + p^2 a^2/\hbar^2)^2}, \tag{36}$$

$$\langle K \rangle = \frac{\hbar^2}{2ma^2}. \tag{37}$$

Moreover, one finds

$$\langle V \rangle = \int_{-\infty}^{\infty} dx \int_{-\infty}^{\infty} dy \int_{-\infty}^{\infty} dz \left(-\frac{e^2}{r} \right) \frac{1}{\pi a^3} e^{-2r/a} = -\frac{e^2}{a}. \tag{38}$$

Therefore, in this example, (34) holds with $C = C' = 1$.

---

[6] The integral in (28b) is carried out conveniently replacing (x,y,z) with polar coordinates (r,θ,ϕ), with the axis $\theta = 0$ in the direction of $\mathbf{p}$. The integration over ϕ is trivial, that over θ is equivalent to Eq. 15, on page 146.

Figure 11.1 shows plots of $\langle K \rangle$ and $\langle V \rangle$ as functions of a, for $C = C' = 1$. Because $\langle K \rangle$ is inversely proportional to a^2, and $\langle V \rangle$ to a, we have $-\langle V \rangle > \langle K \rangle$ for large a, and $-\langle V \rangle < \langle K \rangle$ for small a. That is, the attraction predominates for large a and the expansive tendency for small a. Therefore the sum $\langle K \rangle + \langle V \rangle$, also shown in the Figure, has a minimum.

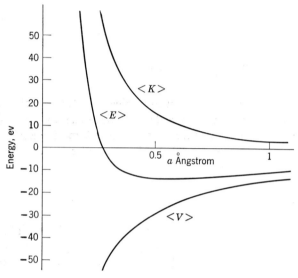

Fig. 11.1 Dependence of the kinetic, potential and total energy upon the atomic "radius" a. (From Eqs. 37, 38.)

The minimum lies at the value of a at which the plots of $\langle K \rangle$ and $\langle V \rangle$ have slopes of equal magnitude and opposite sign. The slopes represent the expansive and attractive forces respectively. From (34) one calculates the slopes

$$\frac{d\langle K \rangle}{da} = -C\,2\,\frac{\hbar^2}{2ma^3}\;; \qquad \frac{d\langle V \rangle}{da} = C'\,\frac{e^2}{a^2}. \tag{39}$$

These slopes are of equal magnitude and opposite sign when the ratio

$$-\frac{d\langle K \rangle/da}{d\langle V \rangle/da} = \frac{C}{C'}\,\frac{\hbar^2}{ma^3}\,\frac{a^2}{e^2} = \frac{C}{C'}\,\frac{\hbar^2}{me^2}\,\frac{1}{a} = 1, \tag{40}$$

that is, when

$$a = \frac{C}{C'}\,\frac{\hbar^2}{me^2}. \tag{41}$$

Entering in this expression the numerical values $\hbar = h/2\pi = 1.05 \times 10^{-27}$ erg sec, $e = 4.80 \times 10^{-10}$ esu and $m = 9.0 \times 10^{-28}$ g, one finds

$$a = \frac{C}{C'} 0.53 \text{ A}, \tag{42}$$

which is of the right order of magnitude. (Actually $a = \hbar^2/me^2$ is the correct value to be entered in the wave function (35) which represents the solution of the complete quantum mechanical problem; this value of a had also been predicted by Bohr by the procedure given in Sect. 4.4.)

The minimum value of the mean energy $\langle E \rangle$, obtained by entering the expression (41) in (34) is

$$\langle E \rangle = C \left(\frac{C'}{C}\right)^2 \frac{me^4}{2\hbar^2} - C' \frac{C'}{C} \frac{me^4}{\hbar^2} = -\frac{C''^2}{C} \frac{me^4}{2\hbar^2} = -\frac{C''^2}{C} 13.6 \text{ ev}. \tag{43}$$

This is the correct value of the electron energy in the ground state of the hydrogen atom, if one takes $C = C' = 1$. It also coincides with the value (20), page 52, calculated by Bohr, for $n = Z = 1$.

These results extend directly to the treatment of the H-like ions, He^+, Li^{++}, $Be^{+++} \cdots$, which differ from H only in their higher nuclear charge, Ze instead of e. It is sufficient to replace e^2 with Ze^2 in (33) and in all the following formulas. Thereby the values (41) and (42) of a are reduced by a factor Z and the value (43) of $\langle E \rangle$ is increased by a factor Z^2, in agreement with the experimental evidence.

PROBLEMS

11.1   Calculate for the state $a(t)$ with the wave function (33′) on page 151 the mean values and the root mean square deviations of the coordinates x, y, z, and of the momentum components p_x, p_y, p_z, as functions of time. Check that the uncertainty relation (8) is fulfilled. (Factorize the probability distributions in analogy with (29′), page 151, and utilize the formulas $2 \int_{-\infty}^{\infty} \xi^2 \exp(-\xi^2) d\xi = \int_{-\infty}^{\infty} \exp(-\xi^2) d\xi = \sqrt{\pi}$, $\int_{-\infty}^{\infty} \xi \exp(-\xi^2) d\xi = 0$.

11.2   Consider an electron whose state is represented by the wave function $(\pi a^3)^{-1/2} \exp(-r/a)$. Calculate the probability $P(R)$ that the electron lies within a sphere of radius R about the origin of coordinates. Find the value $R_{1/2}$ such that $P(R_{1/2}) = \frac{1}{2}$.

The Schroedinger equation

The energy and size of a hydrogen atom in its ground state, estimated in Chapter 11 by qualitative arguments of complementarity, can be determined by a quantitative mathematical procedure. For the ground state as for every stationary state of the hydrogen atom, one can calculate: (*a*) the energy eigenvalue, and (*b*) the set of probability amplitudes (wave function) which represents the state as a combination of eigenstates of the electron position and thereby describes the probability distribution of this position throughout the atom.

This chapter formulates the equation, established by Schroedinger, which determines the energy eigenvalues and the wave functions for the stationary states of any particle subject to forces. An analogous equation can be formulated to determine the eigenvalues of any variable in any quantum mechanical system and to identify the corresponding eigenstates as combination of eigenstates of other variables. One obtains thus a quantum analog to the relations among macroscopic variables (see Appendix VIII).

As basic data on a particle subject to forces we consider the following: (a) the kinetic energy of the particle is a known function of its momentum **p**, $K = p^2/2m$, where m is the mass of the particle, (b) the potential energy is a known function of the position of the particle, for example, $V(\mathbf{r}) = -e^2/r$ for the electron of a hydrogen atom, (c) the eigenvalues of each component, p_x, p_y, p_z of the momentum and of each position coordinate x, y, z of the particle range with continuity from $-\infty$ to $+\infty$ and the probability amplitudes relating the eigenstates of momentum and position are $(\mathbf{r} | \mathbf{p}) = \exp[i(\mathbf{p}/\hbar) \cdot \mathbf{r}]$ (page 132). Since the momentum and position of a particle have no common eigenstates, an eigenvalue of the total energy is not simply the sum of eigenvalues of K and V as in macroscopic problems (page 75). The macroscopic formula $E = K + V$ must be replaced with a relationship among mean values

$$\langle E \rangle = \langle K \rangle + \langle V \rangle \tag{1}$$

One regards then the macroscopic equation as an approximation of (1), applicable when the statistical uncertainties due to incompatibility are negligible and the distinction between eigenvalues and mean values becomes irrelevant. Equation 1 has already been utilized to estimate the size of the hydrogen atom (Sect. 11.2) with $\langle K \rangle$ and $\langle V \rangle$ given in terms of the wave function which identifies a state as a superposition of position eigenstates.

The main step in the formulation of the Schroedinger equation (Sect. 12.1) consists of identifying a property which characterizes mathematically the eigenstates of the energy, or of any other variable. One may consider, in particular, how the mean value of the energy $\langle E \rangle$ depends on the state of a particle and, more specifically, on the probability amplitudes which represent the state as a combination of position eigenstates. A small variation ϵ of one of these probability amplitudes yields in general a variation of $\langle E \rangle$ proportional to ϵ; however, for stationary states the variation of $\langle E \rangle$ is proportional to ϵ^2. This mathematical characterization by means of a "variational principle" has familiar analogs throughout classical physics; for example, the equilibrium position of a marble at the bottom of a bowl may be identified by the requirement that a displacement ϵ of the marble yield a change of its potential energy proportional to ϵ^2. Mathematical properties of this type may be expressed in terms of the rates of variation of the quantity of interest, in our case the mean energy, as a function of the quantity that is varied, in our case the probability amplitude.

The second step in establishing the Schroedinger equation (Sect. 12.2) consists of formulating the characteristic property of eigenstates when the mean energy of a particle is expressed according to (1). The mean kinetic energy in Eq. 1 can be expressed in terms of derivatives of the wave function of a particle subject to forces, as was done for free particles on page 150. The potential energy is also expressed in terms of the same wave function. Thereby the characteristic property of eigenstates takes the form of an equation, the Schroedinger equation, among the unknown wave function $(\mathbf{r}\,|\,E_n)$ of an energy eigenstate, its derivatives, the potential energy $V(\mathbf{r})$, and the unknown energy eigenvalue E_n:

$$-\frac{\hbar^2}{2m}\left[\frac{\partial^2(\mathbf{r}\,|\,E_n)}{\partial x^2} + \frac{\partial^2(\mathbf{r}\,|\,E_n)}{\partial y^2} + \frac{\partial^2(\mathbf{r}\,|\,E_n)}{\partial z^2}\right] + V(\mathbf{r})(\mathbf{r}\,|\,E_n) = (\mathbf{r}\,|\,E_n)E_n.$$

$$(2)$$

12.1 The Characteristic Property of Eigenstates

To calculate the properties of a particle in an energy eigenstate, one must establish a criterion to determine whether any given state of the particle is an energy eigenstate. As pointed out on page 97, a quantum mechanical state can be identified, in principle, by the setting of an instrument which prepares the system in that state. This fundamental procedure is often unpractical, and one identifies the state by the probability amplitudes which represent it as a combination of eigenstates of a suitable variable, such as particle position.

Let us return to the example of molecular beams, whose states of current orientation are identified by the settings of a polarizer magnet (Sect. 7.2). In order that the beam prepared by a given polarizer be in an eigenstate of a given analyzer, the polarizer must be set parallel to the analyzer. Suppose that the orientation of the analyzer is hidden and one can read only some characteristic response on a dial. For example, the dial may indicate the mean deflection of all molecules, that is, their mean energy $\langle E \rangle$ in a magnetic field of given strength. The response varies as a function of the polarizer orientation but remains temporarily stationary when the polarizer passes through a position parallel to the analyzer. This happens because for parallel orientation the analyzer performs no splitting of the beam. If the orientations differ by a small angle ϵ, the analyzer lets through one main component and weak ones with intensities proportional to ϵ^2 (see Table 7.1, page 92).[1] The rate of variation of the mean deflection is thus proportional to ϵ and vanishes at $\epsilon = 0$. Thus the zero-point of the rate of variation singles out which states of the molecules prepared by the polarizer are eigenstates of the analyzer.

---

[1] The intensities of the various components are given by the entries in one column of the table, with $\theta = \epsilon$; the intense component corresponds to the entry on the main diagonal of the table.

A state of the electron in a hydrogen atom is not conveniently identified by a setting of a preparing instrument, but by the probability amplitudes which represent it as a superposition of position eigenstates. The behavior of the mean energy $\langle E \rangle$ as a function of the probability amplitudes serves to single out the energy eigenstates.

A variation of probability amplitudes, corresponding to the variation of an instrument setting, must be such that the sum of their squares, that is, the total probability of finding the particle anywhere in space, remains equal to one (Eq. 14, page 113). The mathematical analysis, however, is simplified by considering unrestricted variations of the probability amplitudes. This corresponds, in the example of molecular beams, to considering changes of the initial beam intensity, besides changes of polarizer orientation; the response to be observed is then the product of the mean deflection and of the beam intensity. When the polarizer and analyzer are parallel, an unrestricted change of state causes a change of response which must stem entirely from the change of intensity and be equal to this change multiplied by the beam deflection (in this case, the beam is not split). For an electron in a stationary state, an unrestricted change of probability amplitudes must similarly change the mathematical expression of the mean energy by the product of the energy eigenvalue and of the change of total probability, as verified by the following calculation.

If the energy eigenvalues $E_1, E_2, \cdots E_i, \cdots$ of a particle were known, and the state of the particle were identified by the set of probability amplitudes $(E_1 \mid a), (E_2 \mid a), \cdots (E_i \mid a) \cdots$, the mean energy would be

$$\langle E \rangle = E_1 \mid (E_1 \mid a) \mid^2 + E_2 \mid (E_2 \mid a) \mid^2 + \cdots + E_i \mid (E_i \mid a) \mid^2 + \cdots$$

$$= \Sigma_i E_i \mid (E_i \mid a) \mid^2. \tag{3}$$

We shall have to consider the mean energy $\langle E \rangle$ as a function of the probability amplitudes $(E_i \mid a)$ and of their complex conjugates $(a \mid E_i)$, regarded as separate variables. Accordingly, we write (3) in the equivalent form

$$\langle E \rangle = (a \, E_1) E_1 (E_1 \mid a) + (a \mid E_2) E_2 (E_2 \mid a) + \cdots + (a \mid E_i) E_i (E_i \mid a) + \cdots$$

$$= \Sigma_i (a \mid E_i) E_i (E_i \mid a). \tag{4}$$

To formulate the Schroedinger equation, we shall consider the dependence of the mean energy on the probability amplitudes $(a \mid \mathbf{r})$ or $(\mathbf{r} \mid a)$ which represent the state a as a combination of position eigenstates. We need to consider the dependence on $(a \mid \mathbf{r})$ only; the dependence on $(\mathbf{r} \mid a)$ yields an equivalent equation, because these reciprocal probability amplitudes are complex conjugate to each other (see page 113).   The probability amplitude $(a|E_i)$ in Eq. 4 can be expressed as a function of $(a|\mathbf{r})$ by the combination formula

$$(a|E_i) = \Sigma_{\mathbf{r}}(a|\mathbf{r})(\mathbf{r}|E_i). \tag{5}$$

(Notice that the set of probability amplitudes $(\mathbf{r}|E_i)$ for all positions $\mathbf{r}$ constitutes the wave function of the ith stationary state, whose determination is our eventual goal.)   We replace, then, in Eq. 4 the probability amplitude $(a|E_i)$ with its expression (5), and write

$$\langle E \rangle = \Sigma_i[\Sigma_{\mathbf{r}}(a|\mathbf{r})(\mathbf{r}|E_i)]E_i(E_i|a)$$
$$= \Sigma_{\mathbf{r}}(a|\mathbf{r})\{\Sigma_i(\mathbf{r}|E_i)E_i(E_i|a)\}. \tag{6}$$

This formula shows the mean energy to be a linear function of the probability amplitude $(a|\mathbf{r})$, with the coefficient given be the expression in the braces.   Therefore, the variation of $\langle E \rangle$ as a function of $(a|\mathbf{r})$ is characterized by the proportionality rate.[2]

$$\frac{\partial \langle E \rangle}{\partial(a|\mathbf{r})} = \Sigma_i(\mathbf{r}|E_i)E_i(E_i|a). \tag{7}$$

This general law of variation provides the criterion to single out eigenstates: when the state is an energy eigenstate with eigenvalue E_n, every probability amplitude $(E_i|a)$ vanishes for $i \neq n$, while $(E_n|a) = 1$. Equation 7 then reduces to

$$\left(\frac{\partial \langle E \rangle}{\partial(a|\mathbf{r})}\right)_{a=E_n} = (\mathbf{r}|E_n)E_n. \tag{8}$$

The unknown wave functions $(\mathbf{r}|E_n)$ and eigenvalues E_n of energy eigenstates are determined by the requirement that they fulfill Eq. 8 when $\langle E \rangle$ is expressed as $\langle K \rangle + \langle V \rangle$ according to (1).   The discussion of unrestricted changes of probability amplitudes anticipated that the rate of variation of $\langle E \rangle$ should be the product of the energy eigenvalue E_n and of the rate of variation of the total probability, when the state is an energy eigenstate.   The total probability is $\Sigma_{\mathbf{r}}(a|\mathbf{r})(\mathbf{r}|a)$; its derivative, when $a = E_n$, is $\{\partial[\Sigma_{\mathbf{r}}(a|\mathbf{r})(\mathbf{r}|a)]/\partial(a|\mathbf{r})\}_{a=E_n} = \{(\mathbf{r}|a)\}_{a=E_n}$, and the expression on the right of (8) is actually the product of this derivative and of E_n.

Notice that the whole treatment in this section is adaptable to the determination of eigenstates of variables other than the energy.

---

[2] When a quantity depends on more than one variable, its derivative with respect to one of the variables is indicated by the sign ∂ instead of d.

When a particle is in a state which is not stationary but is a function of time, $a(t)$, Eq. 7 holds at every instant of time. The product $E_i(E_i | a)$ in this equation may be expressed in terms of the time derivative of $(E_i | a)$ according to the time variation law (10b), page 128. When this is done, the eigenvalues E_i enter the equation only in the combination formula $\Sigma_i(\mathbf{r} | E_i) \partial(E_i | a) / \partial t$, which is equal to $\partial(\mathbf{r} | a) / \partial t$. Therefore, Eq. 7 takes the form

$$\frac{\partial \langle E \rangle}{\partial (a(t) | \mathbf{r})} = \Sigma_i \, (\mathbf{r} | E_i) \left(- \frac{\hbar}{i} \frac{\partial (E_i | a(t))}{\partial t} \right) = - \frac{\hbar}{i} \frac{\partial (\mathbf{r} | a(t))}{\partial t}. \tag{9}$$

12.2   Formulation of the Schroedinger Equation

We give here a convenient expression of $\langle E \rangle = \langle K \rangle + \langle V \rangle$ to be entered in Eq. 8. The mean kinetic energy may be expressed initially in the same general form as in (29), page 163,

$$\langle K \rangle = \frac{1}{2m} \langle p^2 \rangle = \frac{1}{2m} \Sigma_\mathbf{p} \, p^2 \, | \, (\mathbf{p} | a) \, |^2 = \frac{1}{2m} \Sigma_\mathbf{p} \, (a | \mathbf{p}) p^2 (\mathbf{p} | a). \tag{10}$$

Since we are interested in the dependence of $\langle E \rangle$ on the probability amplitude $(a | \mathbf{r})$, we replace $(a | \mathbf{p})$ with the combination $\Sigma_\mathbf{r}(a | \mathbf{r})(\mathbf{r} | \mathbf{p})$ and get

$$\langle K \rangle = \frac{1}{2m} \Sigma_\mathbf{p} \, \Sigma_\mathbf{r} (a | \mathbf{r})(\mathbf{r} | \mathbf{p}) p^2 (\mathbf{p} | a). \tag{11}$$

At this point we can utilize the knowledge of the mathematical form of the probability amplitudes $(\mathbf{r} | \mathbf{p})$ and in particular the fact that $(\mathbf{r} | \mathbf{p})$ obeys Eq. 27, on page 150, namely,

$$(\mathbf{r} | \mathbf{p}) \frac{p^2}{2m} = \frac{1}{2m} (\mathbf{r} | \mathbf{p})(p_x^2 + p_y^2 + p_z^2)$$

$$= - \frac{\hbar^2}{2m} \left[\frac{\partial^2 (\mathbf{r} | \mathbf{p})}{\partial x^2} + \frac{\partial^2 (\mathbf{r} | \mathbf{p})}{\partial y^2} + \frac{\partial^2 (\mathbf{r} | \mathbf{p})}{\partial z^2} \right]. \tag{12}$$

When this expression of $(\mathbf{r} | \mathbf{p}) p^2 / 2m$ is entered into (11), the momentum $\mathbf{p}$ appears only in combinations like $\Sigma_\mathbf{p} \partial^2 (\mathbf{r} | \mathbf{p})(\mathbf{p} | a) / \partial x^2$, which is equal to $\partial^2 (\mathbf{r} | a) / \partial x^2$. Thereby the momentum is eliminated from the explicit calculation of $\langle K \rangle$, as it was eliminated from the calculation of Δp_x^2 on pages 159–160, and we have

$$\langle K \rangle = - \frac{\hbar^2}{2m} \Sigma_\mathbf{r} \, (a | \mathbf{r}) \left[\frac{\partial^2 (\mathbf{r} | a)}{\partial x^2} + \frac{\partial^2 (\mathbf{r} | a)}{\partial y^2} + \frac{\partial^2 (\mathbf{r} | a)}{\partial z^2} \right]. \tag{13}$$

The potential energy of a particle is a function of the particle position $V(\mathbf{r})$, whose value depends on the force which acts on the particle at each point of space.[3] Since the eigenstates of the position of a particle are also eigenstates of its potential energy, the mean potential energy is expressed directly as a function of the probability amplitudes $(a \mid \mathbf{r})$ and $(\mathbf{r} \mid a)$,

$$\langle V \rangle = \Sigma_{\mathbf{r}}(a \mid \mathbf{r}) V(\mathbf{r})(\mathbf{r} \mid a). \tag{14}$$

We have then

$$\langle E \rangle = -\frac{\hbar^2}{2m} \Sigma_{\mathbf{r}}(a \mid \mathbf{r}) \left[\frac{\partial^2(\mathbf{r} \mid a)}{\partial x^2} + \frac{\partial^2(\mathbf{r} \mid a)}{\partial y^2} + \frac{\partial^2(\mathbf{r} \mid a)}{\partial z^2} \right] + \Sigma_{\mathbf{r}}(a \mid \mathbf{r}) V(\mathbf{r})(\mathbf{r} \mid a), \tag{15}$$

and, proceeding as on page 172,

$$\frac{\partial \langle E \rangle}{\partial(a \mid \mathbf{r})} = -\frac{\hbar^2}{2m} \left[\frac{\partial^2(\mathbf{r} \mid a)}{\partial x^2} + \frac{\partial^2(\mathbf{r} \mid a)}{\partial y^2} + \frac{\partial^2(\mathbf{r} \mid a)}{\partial z^2} \right] + V(\mathbf{r})(\mathbf{r} \mid a). \tag{16}$$

This expression of the rate of variation of the mean energy, combined with Eq. 8, $[\partial \langle E \rangle / \partial(a \mid \mathbf{r})]_{a=E_n} = (\mathbf{r} \mid E_n) E_n$, yields

$$-\frac{\hbar^2}{2m} \left[\frac{\partial^2(\mathbf{r} \mid E_n)}{\partial x^2} + \frac{\partial^2(\mathbf{r} \mid E_n)}{\partial y^2} + \frac{\partial^2(\mathbf{r} \mid E_n)}{\partial z^2} \right] + V(\mathbf{r})(\mathbf{r} \mid E_n) = (\mathbf{r} \mid E_n) E_n. \tag{17}$$

This is the Schroedinger equation and serves to determine the eigenvalues E_n and the corresponding probability amplitudes $(\mathbf{r} \mid E_n)$ for the stationary states of a particle subject to forces represented by the potential energy $V(\mathbf{r})$. Given the function $V(\mathbf{r})$ [4] and the mass m of the particle, the solution of Eq. 17 constitutes a well-defined mathematical problem, which will be treated for a number of special cases in the following chapters. Equations analogous to (17) may be established to determine the eigenvalues of variables other than the energy and the probability amplitudes which identify the corresponding eigenstates.

---

[3] The force is the negative gradient of the potential energy, $\mathbf{F} = -\operatorname{grad} V(\mathbf{r})$, that is, the force components along the coordinate axes, F_x, F_y, F_z, are the negative rates of variation $-\partial V/\partial x$, $-\partial V/\partial y$, $-\partial V/\partial z$. We consider here only forces, like the electrostatic attraction or repulsion, which can be represented by the gradient of a potential energy. With this assumption, a knowledge of the force is sufficient to determine the difference between the potential energies of the particle at any given point and at an arbitrary reference position. Only the difference matters, as shown in footnote 4.

[4] As mentioned above in footnote 3, the values of the potential energy $V(\mathbf{r})$ at all points are defined with reference to the value at a particular point, which is fixed as an arbitrary standard. For instance, for the electron of a hydrogen atom, V is usually taken to vanish when the electron is at infinite distance from the nucleus. A change of the arbitrary standard by an amount V_0 brings about an equal increase of $V(\mathbf{r})$ at all points of space, and thereby an increase of every energy eigenvalue E_n by V_0; it represents therefore a shift in the zero-point of the scale of energies.

The general procedure for formulating such equations is indicated in Appendix VIII. In particular, Eq. 17 is readily generalized to apply to the whole system of electrons of an atom other than hydrogen.

Equation 17 belongs to the mathematical class of eigenvalue equations (see pages 82–84) which require a function, after being transformed in a specified manner, to remain proportional to the function itself. The proportionality factor is the eigenvalue E_n. Equations of this class may have solutions corresponding to an arbitrary choice of the eigenvalue, or else solutions may exist only for special values of that parameter. It will be seen later that the eigenvalues E_n of Eq. 17 range with continuity up to infinity when the particle is not confined by forces within a limited region of space, but that only a discrete set of eigenvalues exists when a particle is confined.

The probability amplitudes $(\mathbf{r}\,|\,a(t))$, which identify a non-stationary state of a particle, obey the equation obtained by entering the expression (16) of $\partial\langle E\rangle/\partial(\mathbf{r}\,|\,a)$ into (9),

$$-\frac{\hbar^2}{2m}\left[\frac{\partial^2(\mathbf{r}\,|\,a(t))}{\partial x^2} + \frac{\partial^2(\mathbf{r}\,|\,a(t))}{\partial y^2} + \frac{\partial^2(\mathbf{r}\,|\,a(t))}{\partial z^2}\right] + V(\mathbf{r})(\mathbf{r}\,|\,a(t)) = -\frac{\hbar}{i}\frac{\partial(\mathbf{r}\,|\,a(t))}{\partial t}. \quad (18)$$

This equation is called the "time dependent Schroedinger equation." It is clearly a generalization of Eq. 28, page 150, to which it reduces when $V(\mathbf{r}) = 0$, that is, when the particle is free from the action of forces. Equation 18 relates the rates of variation in space and in time of the wave function $(\mathbf{r}\,|\,a(t)) = \psi_a(\mathbf{r},t)$ and belongs accordingly to the mathematical class of "wave equations." The considerations which illustrate the wave equation of free particles on page 150 apply to Eq. 18 as well.

The quantum mechanics of the motion of particles consists of studying the solutions of the wave equation 18 whenever all external influences upon the particles are represented adequately by a potential energy. It relates to macroscopic mechanics in the following manner. If a particle in motion has a rather large mass, its momentum is correspondingly large and its effective wavelength short; that is, the wave function varies steeply from point to point in space. When the variations of the wave function are much larger than those of the potential energy $V(\mathbf{r})$, the wave equation 18 has approximate solutions having the form of "wave packets" (page 148) which remain rather well concentrated in space for a great length of time. Such packets move in space according to the law of motion of macroscopic particles $m(d\mathbf{r}/dt) = -\mathrm{grad}\,V(\mathbf{r})$. These approximate solutions of the quantum mechanical wave equation are analogous to the approximate solutions of the electromagnetic wave equation which exist when the refractive index varies but little over a wavelength and which follow the laws of geometrical optics. In fact, the wave equation 18 was first established as an analog of the wave equation of physical optics, with the requirement that it have as approximate solutions wave packets traveling in space according to the laws of macroscopic mechanics.

chapter 13

Interference
in the motion
of confined particles

The stationary states of the electron of a hydrogen atom, and those of any particle whose motion is restricted by forces, are characterized by patterns of peaks in the probability distribution of the particle position. The peaks and valleys may be called "interference fringes." We have not yet encountered such interference effects when dealing with free particles, so we shall consider first how and under what circumstances they arise. Second, we shall see how the patterns of the probability distributions relate to the motion of particles. Finally, the fitting of interference patterns in confined spaces restricts the type and energy of the stationary states of bound particles and thus accounts for the occurrence of discrete energy levels in atomic spectra.

To a given energy eigenvalue of the Schroedinger equation corresponds, in some instances, a single wave function, and thus a single state with uniquely defined properties. In other instances, stationary states with different characteristics exist with the same energy eigenvalue, much like different polarizations—indeed different, incompatible types of polarization—exist for light of given frequency. In this event, an eigenvalue of the energy no longer suffices to identify a stationary state of a particle; the eigenvalue of another variable, such as, for instance, the direction of motion, must also be given. With regard to free particles, we have considered thus far stationary states which are also eigenstates of the momentum and represent a steady particle flow in the direction of momentum. There exist also stationary states of free particles without any flow, which may be regarded as combinations of two states with momenta of equal magnitude and opposite direction. The interference between these component states varies from point to point, yielding an alternation of maximum and vanishing probability of finding the particle, that is, a sequence of bright and dark fringes (Sect. 13.1).

Confinement of a particle prevents, in general, a stationary flow, so that stationary states of confined particles are normally characterized by interference fringes and by the absence of any net flow. Stationary states with a net flow, for example, with a steady current of electrons around an axis, exist only under special circumstances. It will also be shown, in Sect. 13.1, that in the absence of a net flow the phases of the wave function at different points differ by either 0° or 180° and therefore the *probability* distribution of the position suffices to describe a state completely.

Variations of the probability of particle position may be described as effects of interference among component eigenstates of momentum, even when the particle is bound and the momentum eigenstates are not themselves stationary. Peaks and valleys in the plot of the probability distribution along any one direction are accordingly called interference fringes. The curvature of the plot relates mathematically to the second derivatives of the wave function in the Schroedinger equation and physically to the mean squared momentum component in the direction one considers. Narrow interference fringes correspond to a high curvature, to a short wave length, and to a high mean squared momentum. Remember, in this connection, that the mean square of a momentum component may differ from zero and thus contribute to the kinetic energy even though the mean of that same momentum component vanishes and there is no net flow in that direction. (The internal consistency of these properties hinges, of course, on their statistical nature, see page 64.) In the following, we shall say that a particle is "in motion" along a certain direction of space, provided only that the corresponding mean *squared* momentum component differs from zero, whereas macroscopically the motion is expressed by the velocity, or momentum, and thus implies a net flow. The probability distribution provides a complete picture of the quantum-mechanical motion when there is no net flow, that is, when there is no motion of the familiar macroscopic type.

The motion of a particle depends on the symmetry, if any, of the forces that confine it. The symmetry thereby shapes the geometrical pattern of the probability distribution of the particle position. In the hydrogen atom, the attraction toward the nucleus has spherical symmetry; this fact alone determines the geometrical characteristics of possible stationary states, as will be seen in the next chapter. This chapter illustrates interference effects in schematic problems where the patterns are still simpler than in the hydrogen atom. In these problems, the potential energy is the sum of terms, each of which depends only on one cartesian coordinate of the particle, $V(\mathbf{r}) = V_1(x) + V_2(y) + V_3(z)$; that is, each component, F_x, F_y, F_z, of the force acting on the particle depends on one coordinate only, $F_x = F_x(x)$, $F_y = F_y(y)$, $F_z = F_z(z)$. Since the kinetic energy is the sum of separate components, $p_x{}^2/2m$, $p_y{}^2/2m$, $p_z{}^2/2m$, separation of the potential energy causes the total energy to be resolved into three contributions, $E_x + E_y + E_z$, whose eigenvalues are determined by separate Schroedinger equations (Sect. 13.2). Further schematizations will be considered which permit an analytic solution of the Schroedinger equation, by assuming variations of the potential energy either much steeper or much flatter than those of the wave function. The general conclusions drawn from the mathematical study of examples are summarized in the following paragraphs.

When a particle is prevented from traveling indefinitely in one direction, for example, toward positive x, by an opposing force and is thereby "reflected," the probability distribution in a stationary state exhibits a sequence of bright and dark fringes along the x axis. The sequence terminates near the farthest point the particle would be expected to reach in the x direction before its kinetic energy is spent in overcoming the opposing force and the particle is turned back or "reflected." However, the point of farthest penetration is not sharply defined in quantum mechanics. Analogous phenomena are observed in the reflection of light or radio waves, where the radiation intensity exhibits interference fringes parallel to the reflecting surface and where the reflection takes place not at an idealized "surface" but over a depth of material of the order of one wavelength.

When a particle cannot travel indefinitely in either of two opposite directions, owing to forces that confine it within a central region, there arises in this region an interference pattern which must meet reflection conditions at both ends. Each stationary state is then characterized by a number of bright fringes in that region and by the number of dark fringes which separate them. Any increase in the number of fringes entails a non-infinitesimal increase of the energy eigenvalue. The discrete character of the spectra of atomic energy levels results from this circumstance. The existence of a ground state with non-vanishing kinetic energy results from the circumstance that at least one bright interference fringe must fit within the atom.

As long as particles are confined only in two opposite directions, for example, of positive and negative x, there may be a net flow in directions perpendicular to the x axis, and stationary states exist in which each interference fringe, whether dark or bright, extends indefinitely in the y and z directions. When the motion is confined on all sides, the bright fringes reduce to islands separated by a network of dark fringe surfaces. In the simple case when the confinement arises from separate forces in the directions of the x, y, and z axes, the dark fringes run parallel to the coordinate planes yz, zx, and xy. The characteristic oscillations of electromagnetic waves in a rectangular cavity resonator are similarly characterized by a network of orthogonal dark fringe planes.

13.1   Stationary States and Particle Flow

To illustrate different types of stationary states and the relationships among them, we begin by considering a pair of momentum eigenstates with momenta of equal magnitude p and of opposite direction along the x axis. These states are eigenstates of the momentum component p_x with eigenvalues, respectively, p and $-p$, and of the components p_y and p_z with eigenvalues zero. They are represented by the wave functions:

$$\exp\left(i\frac{p}{\hbar}x\right) \quad (1a); \qquad\qquad \exp\left(i\frac{-p}{\hbar}x\right), \quad (1b)$$

and involve a particle flow in the direction, respectively, of positive and negative x. If the particle is not subject to forces, these states are also stationary states with equal energy eigenvalues $p^2/2m$. Any superposition of these states is then also a stationary state with the same energy eigenvalue. In particular, superpositions with probability amplitudes of equal magnitude correspond to equal probability of flow in the two opposite directions and therefore to no net flow. A pair of such states is represented by the wave functions:

$$\frac{1}{\sqrt{2}}\exp\left(i\frac{p}{\hbar}x\right) + \frac{1}{\sqrt{2}}\exp\left(i\frac{-p}{\hbar}x\right) = \sqrt{2}\cos\left(\frac{p}{\hbar}x\right), \quad (2a)$$

$$\frac{1}{\sqrt{2}\,i}\exp\left(i\frac{p}{\hbar}x\right) - \frac{1}{\sqrt{2}\,i}\exp\left(i\frac{-p}{\hbar}x\right) = \sqrt{2}\sin\left(\frac{p}{\hbar}x\right). \quad (2b)$$

Both of these states are eigenstates of the squared momentum component p_x^2 with the same eigenvalue p^2, but they are *not* eigenstates of p_x.

Notice that either of the wave functions (1) or any combination of them may be obtained from the superpositions of the wave functions (2a) and (2b); the wave functions (2) may thus be regarded as a "base set" alternative to the set (1).

The wave functions (1) yield probability distributions of the particle position equal to one per unit volume at all points and have phases that vary with continuity from point to point. The wave function (2a) yields a probability distribution that oscillates from point to point, namely,

$$2 \cos^2 \left(\frac{p}{\hbar} x \right) = 1 + \cos \left(2 \frac{p}{\hbar} x \right), \tag{3}$$

and has a phase equal to either 0 or π (Fig. 13.1). The occurrence of these oscillations (bright and dark fringes) may be regarded as the effect

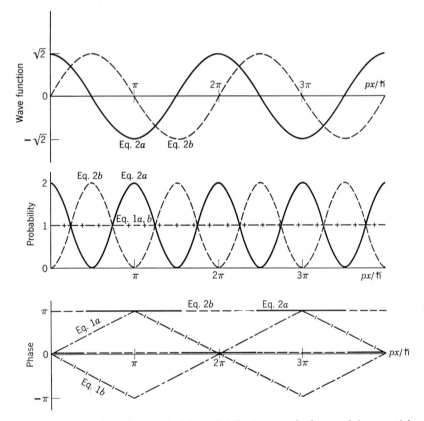

Fig. 13.1 Wave functions, probability distributions, and phases of free particle states represented by Eqs. 1 and 2. The wave functions (1) are not represented because they are complex.

of interference between the possibility of motion in two opposite directions with the same kinetic energy. The state with the wave function (2a) is characterized by the occurrence of a bright fringe centered at $x = 0$; the state with the wave function(2b) by a dark fringe at $x = 0$. The two states have the same eigenvalue of $p_x{}^2$ and their bright and dark fringes interchanged. The magnitude of the kinetic energy determines the value of p in the wave functions (1) and thereby the rate of variation of their phase differences and the width of each fringe, which is $\frac{1}{4}\lambda = \frac{1}{4}h/p$. We see here that a given kinetic energy may be associated with either a variation of phase or a variation of amplitude of the wave function, but a net particle flow is certainly associated with a variation of phase.

This conclusion holds whether one deals with confined or with free particles. The net particle flow at a given point of space $\mathbf{r}$ is a vector $\langle\mathbf{\Phi}(\mathbf{r})\rangle$ whose components may be defined as follows. Consider a small ideal particle counter placed at a given point with its sensitive surface perpendicular to the x axis, and rigged so as to score a positive count when traversed in the direction of positive x and a negative count when traversed in the opposite direction. The mean count scored per unit time and per unit sensitive area of the counter is the value of $\langle\Phi_x(\mathbf{r})\rangle$. For a particle in a general state represented by a wave function $(\mathbf{r}\,|\,a)$, the net flow component $\langle\Phi_x(\mathbf{r})\rangle$ is given by the rate of change of the phase of $(\mathbf{r}\,|\,a)$ from point to point in the x direction, multiplied by $\hbar/m$ and by the probability $|(\mathbf{r}\,|\,a)|^2$.[1] Therefore, the net flow vanishes whenever the wave function $(\mathbf{r}\,|\,a)$ is real, that is, whenever its phase is either 0 or π, and jumps from one to the other value only at the points $\mathbf{r}$ where $(\mathbf{r}\,|\,a)$ vanishes.

Because neither the kinetic nor the potential energy of a particle de-

---

[1] An alternative form of this result is

$$\langle\Phi_x(\mathbf{r})\rangle = \frac{\hbar}{2im}\left[(a\,|\,\mathbf{r})\frac{\partial(\mathbf{r}\,|\,a)}{\partial x} - \frac{\partial(a\,|\,\mathbf{r})}{\partial x}(\mathbf{r}\,|\,a)\right], \tag{4a}$$

or, with vector symbols

$$\langle\mathbf{\Phi}(\mathbf{r})\rangle = \frac{\hbar}{2im}\{(a\,|\,\mathbf{r})[\text{grad}(\mathbf{r}\,|\,a)] - [\text{grad}(a\,|\,\mathbf{r})](\mathbf{r}\,|\,a)\}. \tag{4b}$$

To obtain this result one considers the rate of change in time of the probability $|(\mathbf{r}\,|\,a(t))|^2$ in a non-stationary state, which must reflect a convergence (or divergence) of the net flow $\langle\mathbf{\Phi}(\mathbf{r})\rangle$ toward $\mathbf{r}$. The rate of change $\partial|(\mathbf{r}\,|\,a(t))|^2/\partial t$ can be expressed in terms of the variations of $(\mathbf{r}\,|\,a(t))$ from point to point utilizing the Schroedinger time-dependent equation 18 on page 175. Equation 4 follows by inspection of the resulting expression. In the special case of the momentum eigenstates (1) the result is verified directly.

pends on its direction of motion,[2] a particle which has a stationary state with a non-vanishing net flow must also have another stationary state with flow in opposite direction and with the same energy eigenvalue. Mathematically, the Schroedinger equation 17, on page 174, involves no complex number except possibly the wave function $(\mathbf{r}\,|\,E)$ itself; if it has a complex solution $(\mathbf{r}\,|\,E)$, the complex conjugate wave function $(\mathbf{r}\,|\,E)^*$ must also be a solution with the same eigenvalue but with flow in opposite direction. Superpositions of two such eigenstates with wave functions analogous to $(2a)$ and $(2b)$ represent then another pair of eigenstates with the same energy eigenvalue, with real wave functions and without any net flow. On the other hand, the Schroedinger equation with a given energy eigenvalue may well have only a single solution, which must then be real and represent an eigenstate without any net flow. Therefore, the state of a particle can always be represented as the combination of stationary states without any net flow but, in general, there is no complete set of stationary states having a net flow.

13.2   Separate Motion in Different Directions.   Examples

We consider here schematic problems in which the potential energy of a particle is the sum of separate contributions,

$$V(\mathbf{r}) = V(x,y,z) = V_1(x) + V_2(y) + V_3(z), \tag{5}$$

each of which depends on a single cartesian coordinate of the particle position. The Schroedinger equation 17 on page 174 takes then the form

$$-\frac{\hbar^2}{2m}\left[\frac{\partial^2(\mathbf{r}\,|\,E)}{\partial x^2} + \frac{\partial^2(\mathbf{r}\,|\,E)}{\partial y^2} + \frac{\partial^2(\mathbf{r}\,|\,E)}{\partial z^2}\right]$$
$$+ [V_1(x) + V_2(y) + V_3(z)](\mathbf{r}\,|\,E) = (\mathbf{r}\,|\,E)E, \tag{6}$$

where, for simplicity, E_n is replaced with E. Because on the left of this equation separate terms depend on the coordinates x,y,z, the equation can be solved completely by representing each eigenvalue as the sum of three terms,

$$E = E_x + E_y + E_z \tag{7}$$

and each eigenfunction as a product of three factors

$$(\mathbf{r}\,|\,E) = (x,y,z\,|\,E_x + E_y + E_z) = (x\,|\,E_x)(y\,|\,E_y)(z\,|\,E_z). \tag{8}$$

---

[2] The energy of a particle in a magnetic field depends on the particle direction of motion and cannot be regarded as the sum of kinetic and potential energies. The conclusions stated in this paragraph do not hold for particles subjected to magnetic forces.

This form of the wave function corresponds to statistical independence of the motions in the directions x, y, and z since it yields a probability $|(\mathbf{r}\,|\,E)|^2$ of finding the particle at the point $\mathbf{r} = (x,y,z)$ which is the product of the separate probabilities $|(x\,|\,E_x)|^2$ etc. Notice that the probability amplitudes $(x,y,z\,|\,p_x,p_y,p_z)$ of the stationary states of a free particle, as given by Eq. 1, page 132, have the form (8). The Schroedinger equation 6 is satisfied by the wave function (8) if the probability amplitudes $(x\,|\,E_x)$, $(y\,|\,E_y)$, and $(z\,|\,E_z)$ obey the separate equations

$$-\frac{\hbar^2}{2m}\frac{\partial^2(x\,|\,E_x)}{\partial x^2} + V_1(x)(x\,|\,E_x) = (x\,|\,E_x)E_x. \tag{9a}$$

$$-\frac{\hbar^2}{2m}\frac{\partial^2(y\,|\,E_y)}{\partial y^2} + V_2(y)(y\,|\,E_y) = (y\,|\,E_y)E_y. \tag{9b}$$

$$-\frac{\hbar^2}{2m}\frac{\partial^2(z\,|\,E_z)}{\partial z^2} + V_3(z)(z\,|\,E_z) = (z\,|\,E_z)E_z. \tag{9c}$$

Interference fringes form a simple pattern in states whose wave function factors out according to (8). The probability $|(\mathbf{r}\,|\,E)|^2$ of finding the particle at $\mathbf{r}$ vanishes whenever any one of the three factors, $(x\,|\,E_x)$, $(y\,|\,E_y)$, or $(z\,|\,E_z)$ vanishes. The points where the wave function vanishes are called its "points of zero," or "nodes." In our problem, the nodes constitute three sets of planes defined by equations $x = $ const., $y = $ const., or $z = $ const., respectively. That is, the complete wave function $(\mathbf{r}\,|\,E)$ has three mutually orthogonal sets of "nodal planes." Each of these planes constitutes the center of a dark fringe of the probability distribution $|(\mathbf{r}\,|\,E)|^2$. These dark fringes cut up the probability distribution into separate islands which are the bright fringes.

The potential energy of the electron of a hydrogen atom depends only on one coordinate of the electron, namely, its distance r from the nucleus. The motion of this electron may also be resolved into three components: a "radial" component (motion along radii of the atom) which is influenced directly by the nuclear attraction, and two rotational components which are free from the influence of this force. The separation into radial and rotational motions is, however, more complicated than the separation carried out here, as will be seen in the next chapter.

(a) Reflection at a potential step. (Figure 13.2.) Consider a particle which is prevented from traveling in the direction of positive x, for example, by electric repulsion from a grid perpendicular to the x axis. For mathematical simplicity in solving the problem we assume that the potential energy is given by

$$V_1(x) = 0 \quad \text{for } x < 0, \qquad V_1(x) = V_0 \quad \text{for } x > 0,$$

$$V_2(y) = V_3(z) = 0. \tag{10}$$

This schematization limits the repulsion to an infinitely thin layer along the plane $x = 0$, such as the gap between two grids at different electric potentials which are brought close to one another to the point of coinciding with the plane $x = 0$. The magnitude of V_0 is the product of the charge of the particle and of the potential difference of the grids.

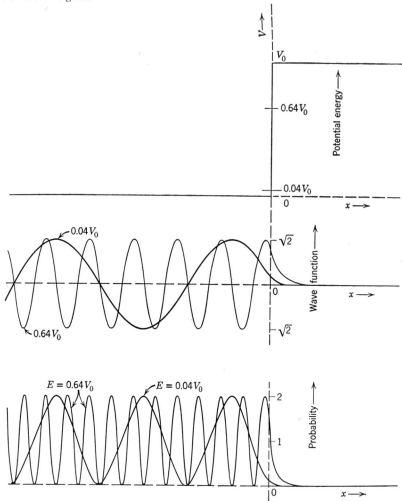

Fig. 13.2 Potential energy step, wave functions, and probability distributions for eigenstates with energies $E_x = 0.04\ V_0$ and $E_x = 0.64\ V_0$.

The motion in the directions y and z is free and its stationary states are represented by any of the types of wave function considered in Sect. 13.1, with arbitrary energy eigenvalues E_y and E_z. We consider in particular stationary states of motion in the x direction, with eigenvalues $E_x < V_0$, so that the particle is not expected to travel beyond the grids in the direction of positive x. Since the potential energy vanishes for $x < 0$, the particle moves freely in that region and the solution of the Schroedinger equation 9a for $x < 0$ may have any of the forms considered in Sect. 13.1 with $p_x{}^2$ related to E_x by $E_x = p_x{}^2/2m$, that is,

$$p_x{}^2 = 2mE_x. \tag{11}$$

In view of the limitation to the particle flow in stationary states, discussed on page 182, we consider stationary states without any net particle flow, that is, states represented by one of the wave functions (2), or by a superposition thereof, with real probability amplitudes. This yields

$$(x \,|\, E_x) = \sqrt{2} \cos \left[\sqrt{\frac{2mE_x}{\hbar^2}}\, x + \delta \right], \qquad \text{for } x < 0, \tag{12}$$

where δ is a phase constant which indicates the position of the bright and dark fringes along the x axis.

For $x > 0$, it is expected on the basis of macroscopic mechanics, but not proved *a priori*, that the probability $|(x \,|\, E_x)|^2$ of finding the particle must vanish. In fact, the Schroedinger equation 9a, with $V_1(x) = V_0$ and $E_x < V_0$, has solutions of the general form

$$(x \,|\, E_x) = A \exp \left[\frac{\sqrt{2m(V_0 - E_x)}}{\hbar}\, x \right] + B \exp \left[-\frac{\sqrt{2m(V_0 - E_x)}}{\hbar}\, x \right] \qquad \text{for } x > 0, \tag{13a}$$

where A and B are undetermined constants. Notice that for $E_x > V_0$ the particle could move freely at $x > 0$ and the solution of the Schroedinger equation would be a combination of wave functions of momentum eigenstates with kinetic energy $p_x{}^2/2m = E_x - V_0$, that is with momenta $p_x = \pm\sqrt{2m(E_x - V_0)}$, namely,

$$(x \,|\, E_x) = A \exp \left[i\frac{\sqrt{2m(E_x - V_0)}}{\hbar}\, x \right] + B \exp \left[-i\frac{\sqrt{2m(E_x - V_0)}}{\hbar}\, x \right]$$

$$\text{for } x > 0. \tag{13b}$$

The Eqs. (13a) and (13b) are mathematically equivalent, since the imaginary unit i compensates for the difference of sign under the square root. The first term on the right of (13a) becomes infinitely large as x increases, which is inadmissible because the probability $|(x \,|\, E_x)|^2$ must remain finite by definition; therefore, the constant A must be equal to zero. The second term vanishes rapidly as x increases, which is consistent with the macroscopic fact that the particle does not go beyond $x = 0$; by macroscopic standards $\hbar$ is small and $\sqrt{2m(E_x - V_0)}/\hbar$ large, so that the probability $|(x \,|\, E_x)|^2$ approaches zero very rapidly for $x > 0$. On the atomic scale, the probability $|(x \,|\, E_x)|^2$ does not vanish altogether, but only gradually, for $x > 0$.

Consider now the Schroedinger equation 9a at $x = 0$. The circumstance that the value of $V_1(x)$ jumps discontinuously at $x = 0$ causes the second derivative $\partial^2(x \,|\, E_x)/\partial x^2$, that is, the curvature of the wave function, to change discontinuously at that point, but the wave function itself and its slope $\partial(x \,|\, E_x)/\partial x$ remain continuous.

This condition fixes the values of the constants δ and B, which are still undetermined, through the equations

$$\sqrt{2}\cos\delta = B, \tag{14a}$$

$$-\sqrt{\frac{2mE_x}{\hbar^2}}\sqrt{2}\sin\delta = -\sqrt{\frac{2m(V_0 - E_x)}{\hbar^2}}\,B. \tag{14b}$$

Solving these equations, one concludes that any value of the energy E_x between 0 and V_0 is an eigenvalue and that to this eigenvalue corresponds a single stationary state whose wave function is given by (12) and (13a) with $\delta = \arccos\sqrt{E_x/V_0}$, $A = 0$, $B = \sqrt{2E_x/V_0}$.

The Schroedinger equation with the steplike potential energy (10) has therefore a continuous range of eigenvalues

$$0 \leq E_x \leq V_0 \tag{15a}$$

and eigenstates represented by the wave functions

$$(x\,|\,E_x) = \sqrt{2}\cos\left[\frac{\sqrt{2mE_x}}{\hbar}x + \arccos\sqrt{\frac{E_x}{V_0}}\right] \quad \text{for } x \leq 0 \tag{15b}$$

$$(x\,|\,E_x) = \sqrt{2}\sqrt{\frac{E_x}{V_0}}\exp\left[-\frac{\sqrt{2m(V_0 - E_x)}}{\hbar}x\right] \quad \text{for } x \geq 0. \tag{15c}$$

Notice that for $E_x \ll V_0$ we have $\delta \sim \pi/2$ and $B \sim 0$, that is, the potential step is nearly in the middle of a dark fringe and the wave function fails to penetrate beyond the step. On the other hand, as E_x increases toward V_0, the first bright fringe moves closer to $x = 0$ and the penetration beyond the step increases.

(b) Reflection by a weak force (smoothly varying potential). Whereas in the preceding example the potential energy was assumed to have a very sharp variation, for the sake of mathematical simplicity, we make here the opposite assumption, namely, that the potential energy $V_1(x)$ in the Schroedinger equation 9a varies slowly from point to point. An approximate solution of (9a) can then be obtained by a procedure, called the "Wentzel-Kramers-Brillouin method," in which the rate of variation dV_1/dx is disregarded. A slow variation of $V_1(x)$ implies that the particle moves along x in the proximity of any point much as though it were free with a kinetic energy $E_x - V_1(x)$. At points where $E_x - V_1(x) > 0$, the wave function has then the approximate form (12), with E_x replaced with $E_x - V_1(x)$. As $V_1(x)$ varies as a function of x, $(x\,|\,E_x)$ will be an approximate sinusoidal function, with variable wavelength. At points where $E_x - V_1(x) < 0$, the wave function will be similarly an approximate exponential, analogous to (13) with A or B equal to zero.

If $V_1(x)$ rises steadily as x increases, that is, if the force $F = -dV_1(x)/dx$ pulls the particle always toward negative x, there is a single value x_0 of x at which $E_x = V_1(x_0)$. This is the farthest point toward $x = \infty$ which a particle with energy E_x could reach according to classical mechanics. For $x > x_0$, the wave function $(x\,|\,E_x)$ decreases exponentially; for $x < x_0$, it oscillates. If $V_1(x)$ were constant, the number of oscillations between the abscissas x_a and x_b would be $\sqrt{2m(E_x - V_1)/\hbar^2}\,(x_a - x_b)$, at a rate of $\sqrt{2m(E_x - V_1)/\hbar^2}$ oscillations per unit distance. The variations of $V_1(x)$ cause the rate of oscillation per unit distance to vary, and the number of oscillations in a finite range of abscissas is given by an integral, namely $\int_{x_a}^{x_b}\sqrt{2m[E_x - V_1(x)]/\hbar^2}\,dx$.

The approximate solution of (9a) is

$$(x\,|\,E_x) \sim \frac{C}{[E_x - V_1(x)]^{\frac14}} \cos \left\{ \int_x^{x_0} \frac{\sqrt{2m[E_x - V_1(x)]}}{\hbar}\, dx + \frac14 \pi \right\} \qquad \text{for } x < x_0, \quad (16a)$$

$$(x\,|\,E_x) \sim \frac{C}{[V_1(x) - E_x]^{\frac14}} \exp \left\{ -\int_{x_0}^x \frac{\sqrt{2m[V_1(x) - E_x]}}{\hbar}\, dx \right\}, \qquad \text{for } x > x_0, \quad (16b)$$

where C is left undetermined in our treatment. Notice that the factor $[E_x - V_1(x)]^{\frac14}$ in (16a) makes the probability of finding the particle at x inversely proportional to $\sqrt{E_x - V_1(x)} = \sqrt{p^2/2m} = \sqrt{m/2}\, v$, which was to be expected since the faster the particle moves through a point, the less likely it is to be observed there. The constant δ of (12) has here the specific value $\frac14 \pi$; this value is determined by a more accurate calculation of $(x\,|\,E_x)$ in the proximity of x_0, where the approximation (16) becomes very poor.

(c) **Leakage through a potential barrier.** Suppose that the potential energy $V_1(x)$ is smaller than E_x at $x < x_0$, then becomes larger than E_x for $x > x_0$ as in the preceding example, but finally recedes below E_x at $x > x_0' > x_0$. If one calculates, as in the preceding example, the reflection due to the force which pulls in the negative direction in the region around $x = x_0$, the wave function $(x\,|\,E_x)$ decreases exponentially in the region of high potential energy between x_0 and x_0', according to (16b), but is not exactly zero at $x = x_0'$. Thereafter, for $x > x_0'$, $E_x - V_1(x)$ becomes positive once more and the wave function is again of the type (16a), that is, it oscillates, albeit with very low amplitude. Therefore, reflection is not complete, but a particle starting at $x < x_0$ with energy E_x has some probability of leaking through the region of high potential energy between x_0 and x_0'. This would not be expected to occur according to macroscopic mechanics.

A number of phenomena of this type are observed in quantum physics, among them the escape of α particles from atomic nuclei and the escape of electrons from metals in the effect of "cold emission." Cold emission occurs when two metal surfaces at greatly different potentials are brought very close to one another, separated by a narrow gap of empty space. An electron in the metal M_- at negative potential is attracted toward the other methal M_+ but the attraction by the positive charges within the atoms of M_- pulls back any electron that might leave the metal. This pull is represented by a very rapid rise of the potential energy V_1 of the electron at the surface of M_-. This rise amounts to a few electron volts within a distance of the order of $1\ A = 10^{-8}$ cm; thereafter, V_1 decreases in the direction of M_+ with a slope which may be of the order of 10^6 ev/cm. A passage of electrons from M_- to M_+ through the vacuum is observed under these conditions.

Analogous phenomena are known in radiation physics. For example, if a hollow pipe is too narrow to allow the free propagation of microwaves of a given frequency, some of this radiation nevertheless leaks through any finite length of the pipe. In the phenomenon of "total reflection" of light at a glass-air interface, some light leaks through an air gap if another glass surface is brought close to the totally reflecting surface.

(d) **Particle confined between two potential steps (potential well).** (Figure 13.3.) Consider now the motion of a particle in the x direction confined between two potential steps. Suppose specifically that $V_1(x)$ vanishes for x between $\pm \frac12 a$ and equals V_0 outside this limited region. In problem (a), for a given value of the energy E_x the wave function has the form (15b) for $x < 0$, which yields a sequence of bright fringes centered at points where $(\sqrt{2mE_x}/\hbar)x + \arccos\sqrt{E_x/V_0}$ is a multiple of π. These points lie at a distance from the potential step equal to

$$\frac{\hbar}{\sqrt{2mE_x}}\left(n\pi + \arccos\sqrt{\frac{E_x}{V_0}}\right), \qquad n = 0, 1, 2, \cdots. \tag{17}$$

In our problem, the wave function in the region between $\pm\frac{1}{2}a$ must also have the form $\cos[(\sqrt{2mE_x}/\hbar)x + \delta]$, but the position of each bright fringe must now fulfill

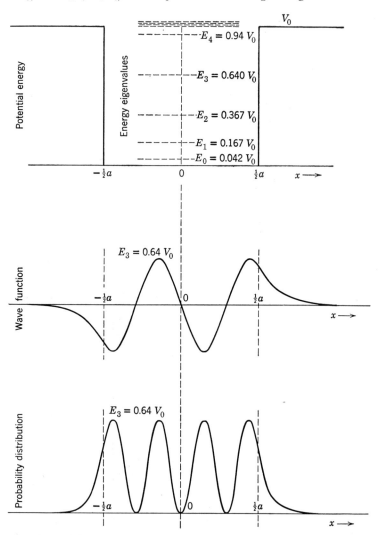

Fig. 13.3 Potential well with energy eigenvalues and a typical wave function and probability distribution. The height and width of the well and the particle's mass are related by $\sqrt{2mV_0}a/\hbar = 13.138$.

two similar conditions: its distance from each of the two potential steps at $x = \pm\frac{1}{2}a$ must be given by (17). These two requirements are consistent only if the total distance a between the two potential steps fulfills the condition

that is,

$$\frac{\hbar}{\sqrt{2mE_x}}\left(n\pi + 2\arccos\sqrt{\frac{E_x}{V_0}}\right) = a, \qquad n = 0, 1, 2, \cdots. \tag{18}$$

or also

$$\frac{\sqrt{2mE_x}}{\hbar} a - n\pi + 2\arccos\sqrt{\frac{E_x}{V_0}}, \tag{19}$$

$$E_x = \frac{\hbar^2}{2ma^2}\left(n\pi + 2\arccos\sqrt{\frac{E_x}{V_0}}\right)^2. \tag{20}$$

Thus the eigenvalues E_x smaller than V_0 form a discrete sequence in correspondence to the successive values of the number n. The number of bright fringes is $n + 1$, the number of dark fringes which separate the bright ones is just n. Compare this exact result obtained for a schematic problem with the estimate of the minimum kinetic energy of a particle confined within a region of size a, which was given in Chapter 11, Eq. 32, namely, $\langle K \rangle = \hbar^2/2ma^2$.

(e) Particle confined by weak forces. Consider now a particle confined to a limited region in the x direction by weak forces, represented by a potential energy $V_1(x)$ which varies slowly and falls below a given level E_x only within a limited range $x_1 < x < x_2$. The condition for the existence of a stationary state with the energy E_x can be cast in a form similar to (19) by the approximation method of problem (b). Combining the approximate treatment of reflection in problem (b) with the considerations of the position of fringes in problem (d), one finds that E_x must fulfill the condition

that is,

$$\int_{x_1}^{x_2} \sqrt{2m[E_x - V_1(x)]/\hbar^2}\, dx = n\pi + \tfrac{1}{2}\pi, \tag{21}$$

$$2\int_{x_1}^{x_2} \sqrt{2m[E_x - V_1(x)]}\, dx = (n + \tfrac{1}{2})h. \tag{22}$$

An approximate form of this condition (with nh instead of $(n + \tfrac{1}{2})h$ on the right side) had been established prior to the development of quantum mechanics by semi-empirical arguments derived from Bohr's treatment of the hydrogen atom (Sect. 4.4). It was called the "Sommerfeld quantum condition."

PROBLEMS

13.1 A particle approaches the potential step of Sect. 13.2a traveling in the direction of positive x with kinetic energy $E > V_0$. Calculate the probability $R(E/V_0)$ that it be reflected. (Express the wave function in the form $(x\,|\,E) = \exp(iKx) + A\exp(-iKx)$ for $x \leq 0$ and $(x\,|\,E) = B\exp(iK'x)$ for $x > 0$, where $K = \sqrt{2mE}/\hbar$ and $K' = \sqrt{2m(E - V_0)}/\hbar$; determine A and B from the conditions of continuity of $(x\,|\,E)$ and $d(x\,|\,E)/dx$ at $x = 0$, as in Sect. 13.2a; the probability $R(E/V_0)$ is $|A|^2$.)

13.2 A particle traveling in the direction of positive x with energy E approaches a potential barrier, or well, represented by $V(x) = 0$ for $x < 0$ and $x > a$, $V(x) =$

V_0 for $0 < x < a$. Calculate the probability that it be reflected. (Express the wave function in the form $(x|E) = \exp(iKx) + A \exp(-iKx)$ for $x \leq 0$, $(x|E) = B \exp(iK'x) + C \exp(-iK'x)$ for $0 \leq x \leq a$, $(x|E) = D \exp(iKx)$ for $x \geq a$, where $K = \sqrt{2mE}/\hbar$ and $K' = \sqrt{2m(E - V_0)}/\hbar$, K' being real for $V_0 < E$ and imaginary for $V_0 > E$. The continuity of $(x|E)$ and of $d(x|E)/dx$ at $x = 0$ and $x = a$ yields four equations among A, B, C, and D. Solve for A; the probability of reflection is $|A|^2$ and is conveniently expressed as a function of E/V_0 and of $\sin^2 K'a = 1/(1 + \cot^2 K'a)$.) Plot the probability of reflection as a function of V_0 for a particle of the electron's mass, of energy $E = 2$ ev and for $a = 10$ A.

13.3 Consider the potential well problem of Sect. 13.2d in the limit of $V_0 = \infty$. Give formulas for the energy eigenvalues and for the corresponding wave functions.

13.4 Consider a particle held in the vicinity of $x = 0$ by an elastic force $f = -kx$, to which corresponds the potential energy $V_x(x) = \frac{1}{2}kx^2$. The Schroedinger equation (9a) with this potential energy has the eigenfunctions

$$(x|N) = (2^N N! a\sqrt{\pi})^{-\frac{1}{2}} \exp(-\tfrac{1}{2}x^2/a^2) H_N(x/a),$$

where $N = 0, 1, 2, \cdots$, $a = (\hbar^2/km)^{\frac{1}{4}}$, and H_N is a Hermite polynomial given, for $N = 0, 1, 2$, and 3, by

$$H_0 = 1, \ H_1 = 2x/a, \ H_2 = 4x^2/a^2 - 2, \ H_3 = 8x^3/a^3 - 12x/a.$$

Calculate the energy eigenvalue E_N by means of the Schroedinger equation and calculate the mean potential energy $\langle V_x \rangle$ for the first few values of N. Compare $\langle V_x \rangle$ with the energy eigenvalue and obtain the mean kinetic energy. Utilize the formulas $\int_{-\infty}^{\infty} \xi^{2n} \exp(\xi^2)\,d\xi = \sqrt{\pi}\,\frac{1}{2}\cdot\frac{3}{2}\cdot\frac{5}{2}\cdots(n-\frac{1}{2})$, and $\int_{-\infty}^{\infty} \xi^{2n+1} \exp(-\xi^2)\,d\xi = 0$.

13.5 A particle is moving within a conduit of rectangular cross section and infinite length represented by the potential energy functions

$$V_x(x) = 0 \quad \text{for } -\tfrac{1}{2}a \leq x \leq \tfrac{1}{2}a, \qquad V_x(x) = \infty \quad \text{for } x \leq \tfrac{1}{2}a \text{ and } x \geq \tfrac{1}{2}a,$$

$$V_y(y) = 0 \quad \text{for } -\tfrac{1}{2}b \leq y \leq \tfrac{1}{2}b, \qquad V_y(y) = \infty \quad \text{for } y \leq \tfrac{1}{2}b \text{ and } y \geq \tfrac{1}{2}b,$$

$$V_z(z) = 0.$$

Consider energy eigenstates in which the motion in the x and y direction is characterized, respectively, by n_x and n_y bright fringes, and the motion along the z direction is characterized by an eigenvalue of the momentum component p_z. Utilizing the results of Problem 13.3, give formulas for the energy and the wave function of these eigenstates. Make a map of the probability distribution $|(x|n_x)(y|n_y)|^2$ of the particle position over a cross section of the conduit, for $n_x = 2$, $n_y = 3$, and for $a = 3$ A and $b = 6$ A.

13.6 A particle in the potential well of Problem 13.3 is in a non-stationary state $b(t)$ which is represented at the time $t = 0$ by the probability amplitudes $(n|b(0)) = \sqrt{\frac{1}{2}}$ for $n = 2$ and $n = 3$, $(n|b(0)) = 0$ for n other than 2 or 3. Calculate, as functions of t: (a) the wave function $(x|b(t))$, (b) the probability distribution $|(x|b(t))|^2$, (c) the mean position $\langle x \rangle = \int_{-\frac{1}{2}a}^{\frac{1}{2}a} x |(x|b(t))|^2\,dx$. Plot $|(x|b(t))|^2$ against x for $t = 0$ $t = 4ma^2/5\hbar$, $t = 8ma^2/5\hbar$.

The stationary states
of the hydrogen atom

The main properties of the ground state of the electron in the hydrogen atom are determined readily by qualitative analysis. It is sufficient to consider that the electron is confined within the atom by a force which points always in the direction of the nucleus. The motion of confined particles is analyzed conveniently, as shown in the preceding chapter, by disregarding initially the possibility of net particle flow; each stationary state is then characterized by its pattern of interference fringes.

In the ground state, the probability distribution of the position of a confined particle consists of a single bright interference fringe. In the hydrogen atom, the symmetry of the force about the nucleus dictates that the interference fringe is centered at the nucleus and distributed uniformly in all directions. Furthermore, the probability of finding the electron at large distances from the nucleus tapers off, as the electron is "reflected" back toward the nucleus by the attractive force. At very large distances, the force becomes vanishingly weak as it does beyond the potential edge in the example of Fig. 13.1; the probability must then taper off exponentially. Owing to the symmetry of the fringe, the probability distribution varies only in radial directions; accordingly, the mean squared momentum has only one non-vanishing component directed radially. The electron motion is therefore entirely radial, instead of rotational as was suggested by the early planetary model.

The requirements indicated above are fulfilled by the wave function considered tentatively in Chapter 11,

$$(\mathbf{r}\,|\,E_1) = \frac{1}{\sqrt{\pi a^3}}\, e^{-r/a}, \tag{1}$$

where $\mathbf{r}$ indicates the position of the electron with respect to the nucleus, r is the distance from the nucleus irrespective of direction, and [1]

$$a = \frac{\hbar^2}{m_e e^2} = 0.53 \text{ A} \tag{2}$$

indicates an average value of the distance from the nucleus, called the "Bohr radius." One verifies that the wave function (1) is a solution of the Schroedinger equation 2 on page 170, with $m = m_e$, $V(\mathbf{r}) = -e^2/r$ and [2]

$$E_1 = -\frac{1}{2}\frac{m_e e^4}{\hbar^2} = -\frac{1}{2}\frac{e^2}{a} = -13.6 \text{ ev.} \tag{3}$$

A more detailed discussion of this solution of the Schroedinger equation is given in Sect. 14.2.

Stationary states with particle flow exist only when different arrangements of interference fringes are consistent with the same energy eigenvalue. There is no such possibility for the ground state of the hydrogen atom whose fringe characteristics are uniquely defined. This ground state is, however, unique only insofar as the electron is regarded as a pointlike particle whose states are described fully by wave functions of its position coordinates. On this basis one accounts for the gross properties of the hydrogen atom in its various stationary states. Finer, though important, features of the electron motion will be taken up in the next chapter.

The excited stationary states are treated at some length in this chapter to account for the spectral energy levels and other properties of the hydrogen atom, and especially because their systematics underlies the analysis of the structure and chemical properties of other atoms. For

---

[1] The electron mass will be indicated here by m_e to avoid confusion with a different symbol m.

[2] As pointed out on page 51, the energy levels of the stationary states of atoms are normally negative because they are expressed in a scale where $E = 0$ indicates the energy of the atom after dissociation.

each excited energy level of the hydrogen atom there exist different stationary states. These states may be classified according to one or another suitable characteristic, like, for example, the symmetry of the probability distribution of the electron position or the presence or absence of a net flow of the electron. A systematic classification singles out a set of energy eigenstates which is "complete," that is, such that any other state can be represented as a combination of states of that set.

Sections 14.1 and 14.2 describe a complete set of states, characterized by the absence of net flow and by interference fringes arranged symmetrically about the nucleus and about an axis through the nucleus. This set is obtained by dealing separately with the electron motion in radial directions, which is influenced by the nuclear attraction, and with the motion in directions perpendicular to the radii, that is, along spherical surfaces centered at the nucleus. The "rotational" motion along spherical surfaces is free from the action of forces.

In the schematic problems of Sect. 13.2 the forces were such as to leave the components of the motion along three coordinate axes wholly independent of one another; each stationary state is then identified by three separate energy eigenvalues of motion along the different axes. In the problem of the hydrogen atom, the rotational motion is not independent of the radial motion. It is common experience that any whirling body slows down when the radius of its path increases. The characteristic of a free rotational motion which remains constant independently of its radius is not its kinetic energy or its momentum, but the product of the momentum and of the radius of the path. This product is called the "moment of momentum" or "orbital angular momentum." For a given orbital angular momentum, the kinetic energy of the rotational motion is a function of the radius; the effect of this dependence on the radial motion is the centrifugal force (Sect. 14.1(a)).

The orbital angular momentum is defined as a vector, the vector product of the radius vector and of the momentum

$$\mathbf{l} = \mathbf{r} \times \mathbf{p}, \tag{4}$$

shown in Fig. 14.1. In Chapter 13, the stationary states of free particles without net flow are characterized by interference fringes whose width corresponds to the magnitude of the squared momentum components. Similarly, stationary states of rotational motion without net flow are characterized by patterns of interference fringes whose size and number relates to the values of the squared angular momentum $\mathbf{l}^2$ and of its components (see footnote 1, page 80).

The stationary states of the hydrogen atom, described in Sect. 14.1 and 14.2, are classified first according to a number of interference fringes arranged symmetrically about a coordinate axis (usually the z axis); this number corresponds to an eigenvalue of the squared angular momentum component $l_z{}^2$. For a given value of $l_z{}^2$ there are different states of rotational motion with different possible eigenvalues of $\mathbf{l}^2$, and a corresponding number of dark fringes that crisscross every spherical surface. For a given value of $\mathbf{l}^2$ there are different states of radial motion characterized by a number of spherical dark fringes and by an eigenvalue of the total energy of the atom.

The spectrum of energy eigenvalues which one obtains agrees very well with the experimental results mentioned in Chapter 4. The number

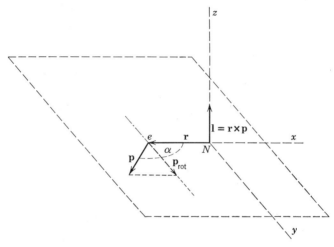

Fig. 14.1 Diagram of orbital angular momentum $\mathbf{l} = \mathbf{r} \times \mathbf{p}$. The magnitude of $\mathbf{l}$ is $rp_{\mathrm{rot}} = rp \sin \alpha$.

of states of the set for each energy eigenvalue is a main factor determining the period length in Mendeleev's system of chemical elements (see Chapter 18).

There are also stationary states of the hydrogen atom with a net flow of electron about an axis. These are eigenstates of the angular momentum component about that axis and may be represented as superpositions of states with no flow. Section 14.3 describes a standard set of stationary states with flow around the z axis that are eigenstates of l_z and of $\mathbf{l}^2$.

Whereas the stationary states which are eigenstates of $\mathbf{l}^2$ have their interference fringes arranged symmetrically about the nucleus, there are other stationary states with no flow, in which the probability distribution of the electron position is off center with respect to the nucleus.

Section 14.4 describes some of these states which are important for the formation of chemical bonds.

A correct treatment of the hydrogen atom takes into account that the nucleus is not a fixed point, but is itself set into motion by the attraction toward the electron. A correction for this effect is introduced simply into fixed-nucleus calculations by replacing the electron mass m_e with a "reduced mass" μ, as in the Bohr semi-classical theory of Sect. 4.4. The correction brings the energy eigenvalues into better agreement with the experimental data obtained with hydrogen isotopes of different mass (Sect. 14.5). The results are also extended to hydrogen-like ions by replacing the product e^2 of the electron and nuclear charges with Ze^2, again as was done in Sects. 4.4 and 11.2.

14.1 A Basic Set of Stationary States

(*a*) *Separation of the motion in different directions.* The velocity **v** of the electron in a hydrogen atom may be regarded as the sum of two components, one $\mathbf{v}_{\mathrm{rad}}$ directed along the radius from the nucleus to the electron, and one $\mathbf{v}_{\mathrm{rot}}$ which represents the rotation of the electron around the nucleus and is therefore perpendicular to $\mathbf{v}_{\mathrm{rad}}$. The total energy of the electron can accordingly be expressed in the form

$$E = K + V = \frac{1}{2}m_e v^2 - \frac{e^2}{r} = \left[\frac{1}{2}m_e v_{\mathrm{rad}}^2 - \frac{e^2}{r}\right] + \frac{1}{2}m_e v_{\mathrm{rot}}^2. \tag{5}$$

The total energy is thus split into two parts, one pertaining to the radial motion, including the potential energy, and one pertaining to the rotational motion.

The energy of rotation is not constant in the course of motion whether on the macroscopic or atomic scale, even though there is no force along $\mathbf{v}_{\mathrm{rot}}$. The diagram in Fig. 14.2 shows that, even though the total velocity **v** remain fixed, its decomposition into $\mathbf{v}_{\mathrm{rad}}$ and $\mathbf{v}_{\mathrm{rot}}$ depends on the position of the electron in the atom. On the other hand, the product of the distance from the nucleus and of the rotational speed, $r v_{\mathrm{rot}}$, remains constant and so does the magnitude of the orbital angular momentum $l = m_e r v_{\mathrm{rot}}$. The total energy E is therefore conveniently expressed in the form

$$E = \left(\frac{1}{2}m_e v_{\mathrm{rad}}^2 - \frac{e^2}{r}\right) + \frac{1}{2}m_e \frac{(r v_{\mathrm{rot}})^2}{r^2} = \left(\frac{p_{\mathrm{rad}}^2}{2m_e} - \frac{e^2}{r}\right) + \frac{l^2}{2m_e r^2}. \tag{6}$$

There are stationary states of the electron which are eigenstates of the squared orbital momentum $\mathbf{l}^2$. For a given eigenvalue of $\mathbf{l}^2$, the kinetic energy term $\mathbf{l}^2/2m_e r^2$ in (6) is a definite function of r. The whole energy E may then be regarded as energy of radial motion, with $\mathbf{l}^2/2m_e r^2$ interpreted as an additional potential energy. The force corresponding

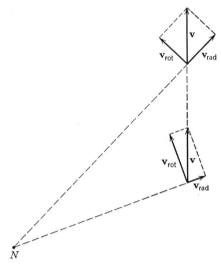

Fig. 14.2 The components $\mathbf{v}_{\text{rot}}$ and $\mathbf{v}_{\text{rad}}$ of the same velocity $\mathbf{v}$ depend upon the position of the electron in the atom.

to this potential energy is the centrifugal force due to the rotational motion since it is directed radially and its strength

$$-\frac{d(\mathbf{l}^2/2m_e r^2)}{dr} = \frac{\mathbf{l}^2}{m_e r^3} = \frac{(m_e r v_{\text{rot}})^2}{m_e r^3} = \frac{m_e v_{\text{rot}}^2}{r} \tag{7}$$

coincides with the ordinary expression of the centrifugal force.

To determine the eigenvalues of $\mathbf{l}^2$, one resolves further the velocity $\mathbf{v}_{\text{rot}}$ and $\mathbf{l}^2$ itself, into components. The position $\mathbf{r}$ of the electron with respect to the nucleus is represented in a system of polar coordinates (see Fig. 14.3), namely, the distance r from the nucleus, a latitude angle θ, which varies between $0°$ and $180°$, and a longitude angle ϕ which varies between $0°$ and $360°$. The "polar axis" identified by $\theta = 0$ is usually taken to coincide with the z axis of cartesian coordinates.[3] We have then $\mathbf{v}_{\text{rot}} = \mathbf{v}_\theta + \mathbf{v}_\phi$(see Fig. 14.3), $v_{\text{rot}}^2 = v_\theta^2 + v_\phi^2$ and $\mathbf{l}^2 = (m_e r v_\theta)^2 + (m_e r v_\phi)^2$. These two components of $\mathbf{l}^2$ are not constant in the course of a free rotational motion, even though $\mathbf{l}^2$ is constant. How-

[3] The relations between polar and cartesian coordinates are $r = \sqrt{x^2 + y^2 + z^2}$, $\cos\theta = z/r$, $\tan\phi = y/x$. One should call θ a "colatitude" since latitudes usually run from $+90°$ to $-90°$.

ever, the product of the distance $r \sin\theta$ of the electron from the polar axis and of the speed along a parallel circle, namely, $r \sin\theta \, v_\phi$, remains constant and so does the component of the orbital angular momentum

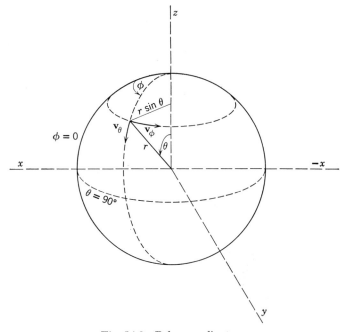

Fig. 14.3   Polar coordinates.

$l_z = m_e r \sin\theta \, v_\phi$. The squared angular momentum l^2 is therefore conveniently expressed as

$$l^2 = (m_e r v_\theta)^2 + (m_e r v_\phi)^2$$

$$= (m_e r v_\theta)^2 + \frac{(m_e r \sin\theta \, v_\phi)^2}{\sin^2\theta} = (m_e r v_\theta)^2 + \frac{l_z{}^2}{\sin^2\theta}. \tag{8}$$

There are stationary states of the electron which are eigenstates of $l_z{}^2$. For a given eigenvalue of $l_z{}^2$, the contribution $l_z{}^2/\sin^2\theta$ to the squared angular momentum is a definite function of θ. The whole kinetic energy of rotational motion $l^2/2m_e r^2$ may then be regarded as energy of motion along θ, with $(l_z{}^2/\sin^2\theta)/2m_e r^2$ interpreted as a potential energy. For $l_z{}^2 \neq 0$, this potential energy is lowest at the equator, where $\sin\theta$ has a maximum, and infinite at the poles, where $\sin\theta = 0$. This energy represents a centrifugal force which draws the electron toward the equatorial plane. (A whirling sling is similarly drawn to move in a plane.)

In view of the interdependence of the different components of the electron motion, the stationary states of the hydrogen atom will be analyzed as follows: The motion along parallel circles (ϕ coordinate) is considered first and the eigenstates of l_z^2 are singled out. Secondly, for a given eigenvalue of l_z^2 we consider the motion along meridian circles (θ coordinate) and single out the eigenstates of l^2. Finally, for a given eigenvalue of l^2, we study the radial motion and single out the eigenstates of the total energy as represented by Eq. 6.

(**b**) *Motion along parallel circles.* Stationary states of motion along parallel circles without any net flow are marked by a number **m** = 0, 1, 2, $\cdots$ of nodal surfaces of constant longitude (meridian

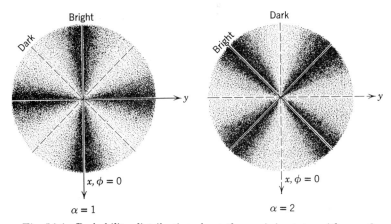

Fig. 14.4 Probability distribution about the z axis in states with **m** = 2.

planes). Because the conditions are uniform along each parallel circle, that is, because there is symmetry about the axis of polar coordinates, the nodal planes are evenly spaced (see Fig. 14.4). These planes and the dark fringes about them separate the probability distribution of the electron's ϕ coordinate into 2**m** bright fringes.

The larger the number **m**, the narrower is each fringe and the higher is the eigenvalue of l_z^2 and the corresponding value of the kinetic energy of this motion. The calculation in the next section shows that the eigenvalues of l_z^2 equal $\mathbf{m}^2\hbar^2$. Each interference fringe is, of course, narrower near the coordinate axis than at larger radii, as seen in Fig. 14.4, and the kinetic energy corresponding to each value of **m** is inversely proportional to the squared distance from the axis, $(r\sin\theta)^2$, as expected from (6) and (8). For **m** = 0 there is no nodal surface and no fringe, only a uniformly distributed probability of the electron's longitude; this is a state of no motion along the parallel circles, with $l_z{}^2 = 0$ and no corresponding contribution to the kinetic energy.

For a given value of $\mathbf{m} \neq 0$ one may choose a set of two orthogonal states, with the positions of the dark and bright fringes interchanged (see Fig. 14.4). Any other eigenstate of $l_z{}^2$ with the same eigenvalue may be regarded as a superposition of two such states. We label the states of such a base set by $(\mathbf{m}\alpha)$, where $\alpha = 1$ when a bright fringe centers at zero longitude and $\alpha = 2$ when a dark fringe centers there.[4]

(c) *Motion along meridian circles.* This motion is always confined, in effect, because the latitude coordinate θ runs only from 0 to π radians, from one pole to the other; (proceeding beyond one of the poles

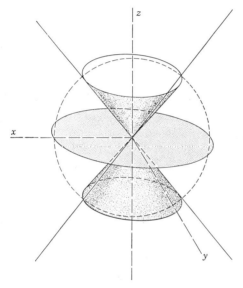

Fig. 14.5 The nodal surfaces of the probability distribution of the electron in a state with $l = 3$, $\mathbf{m} = 0$.

in continuation of a meridian circle, one encounters a reverse variation of latitude and a jump of π in the longitude coordinate). There is accordingly no stationary state with a net flow along meridian circles. Each stationary state is marked by a number of nodal surfaces of constant latitude; these surfaces are cones (see Fig. 14.5) and intersect all meridian planes and all spherical surfaces at right angles. (A nodal

---

[4] Two stationary states with a net flow along the parallel circles and with the same eigenvalue of $l_z{}^2$ are usually considered (see Sect. 14.3) and each is labeled with a single index $m = \pm\mathbf{m}$, instead of the pair of indices $(\mathbf{m}\alpha)$.

cone with aperture $\theta = \frac{1}{2}\pi$ is the equatorial plane and occurs whenever the number of cones is odd.)

The motion along meridians depends on the motion along parallels, as pointed out in (a) above. For an eigenstate of no motion along ϕ (that is, with eigenvalue $l_z{}^2 = 0$ and $\mathbf{m} = 0$) the motion along meridians is free. In this event there is a stationary state of no motion along meridians, in which the probability of the particle position is distributed uniformly over spherical surfaces of any radius; this state has the eigenvalue $\mathbf{l}^2 = 0$ of the squared angular momentum and no kinetic energy of rotational motion. For $\mathbf{m} = 0$ there are also stationary excited states of rotational motion, with a number l of nodal cones. Each of these states has a bright fringe centered at each pole (otherwise the wave function would have a discontinuity of value or slope at the poles). The larger the number of nodal cones, the narrower are the fringes and the larger are the squared angular momentum $\mathbf{l}^2$ and the kinetic energy of the motion along meridians. It will be shown in the next section that the eigenvalues of $\mathbf{l}^2$ are obtained by solving a differential equation; they are $l(l + 1)\hbar^2$. The corresponding values of the kinetic energy of rotational motion are $l(l + 1)\hbar^2/2m_e r^2$, according to (6), being larger near the nucleus where all fringes are narrower.

For $\mathbf{m} \neq 0$, the centrifugal effect of the motion along parallels confines the motion along meridians toward the equator, as noted at the end of (a) above. Owing to this confinement, the motion along meridians yields a non-vanishing contribution to $\mathbf{l}^2$ and to the kinetic energy, even in the state with no nodal cones; this minimum contribution increases with increasing $\mathbf{m}$ and increasing confinement.[5] Each stationary state of excited motion along meridians is characterized by a number of nodal cones, for $\mathbf{m} \neq 0$ as for $\mathbf{m} = 0$. The squared angular momentum $\mathbf{l}^2$ depends, however, only on the total number of nodal surfaces, meridian planes plus cones, and not on the separate numbers of the two types of surfaces. This total number may therefore be indicated by the same symbol l as in the special case of $\mathbf{m} = 0$. The number l is called "orbital angular momentum quantum number" or "azimuthal quantum number." There are, therefore, different states and different probability distributions of the electron position with the same eigenvalue of $\mathbf{l}^2 = l(l + 1)\hbar^2$ and the same kinetic energy $l(l + 1)\hbar^2/2m_e r^2$, but with different $\mathbf{m} \leq l$ (see Fig. 14.6).

---

[5] The existence of this minimum energy is an effect of complementarity which was not noticed in the early development of quantum physics, and emerged as an unexpected result from the solution of the Schroedinger equation.

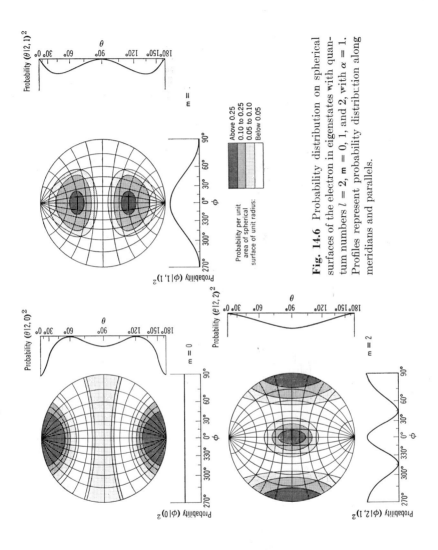

Fig. 14.6 Probability distribution on spherical surfaces of the electron in eigenstates with quantum numbers $l = 2$, $m = 0$, 1, and 2, with $\alpha = 1$. Profiles represent probability distribution along meridians and parallels.

States with different eigenvalues of l_z^2 but with the same $\mathbf{l}^2$ correspond to different breakdowns of $\mathbf{l}^2 = l(l + 1)\hbar^2$ into its components $l_z^2 = \mathsf{m}^2\hbar^2$ and $(l_x^2 + l_y^2) = [l(l + 1) - \mathsf{m}^2]\hbar^2$. Notice that the eigenstates of l_z^2 are not, in general, eigenstates of the separate cartesian components l_x^2 and l_y^2.[6] Eigenstates of each of these components can be singled out by the same procedure followed for l_z^2, starting with a system of polar coordinates of different orientation, for example, with the axis $\theta = 0$ in the x or y direction. For a given $\mathbf{l}^2$, each eigenstate of l_x^2, or of l_y^2, can be regarded as a superposition of eigenstates of l_z^2 with different eigenvalues $\mathsf{m}^2\hbar^2$. The requirement that eigenstates of $\mathbf{l}^2$ with any one eigenvalue can be described identically in coordinate systems with different polar axes underlies the existence of eigenstates with equal $\mathbf{l}^2$ and different l_z^2. Superpositions of these eigenstates with real probability amplitudes yield new eigenstates of $\mathbf{l}^2$ with equal number l of nodal surfaces of different orientation or shape.

An eigenstate of $\mathbf{l}^2$ may be labeled by $(l\mathsf{m}\alpha)$, the index α being irrelevant for $\mathsf{m} = 0$. For a given l there are $2l + 1$ such states, namely, $(l,0)$, $(l,1,1)$, $(l,1,2)$, $\cdots$ $(l,l,1)$, $(l,l,2)$. Eigenstates of $\mathbf{l}^2$ are often called by standard code letters rather than by the corresponding values of l, as follows:

l value:	0	1	2	3	4	5
code name:	s	p	d	f	g	h.

States with $l = 1$ labeled by $(1,1,1)$, $(1,1,2)$, and $(1,0)$ are often called respectively, p_x, p_y, and p_z; the subscript indicates the coordinate axis perpendicular to the single nodal plane.

(*d*) **Radial motion.** The radial motion is confined if the total energy E of the electron lies below its potential energy at infinite distance from the nucleus $V(\infty)$, that is, if $E < 0$ when $V(\infty)$ is taken as zero. Any value of $E > 0$ is an eigenvalue corresponding to ionized states of the atom, which will not be considered here. We consider in this section stationary states of confined motion ("bound states") each of which is characterized first as an eigenstate of $\mathbf{l}^2$ and then by a number n_r of spherical nodal surfaces, called the "radial quantum number."

In states with no rotational motion ($l = 0$), the radial motion of the electron is confined only by the nuclear attraction. Any stationary state has then a bright fringe centered at the position of the nucleus, and distributed uniformly in all directions. The ground state of the

---

[6] Prior to the development of quantum mechanics it was not realized that a state need not be an eigenstate of every variable, and the occurrence of different values of l_z^2 or of l_z for a given $\mathbf{l}^2$ was visualized as reflecting different orientations of the vector $\mathbf{l}$. The symbol l was adopted for the azimuthal quantum number in the belief that this quantum number represented the magnitude of the angular momentum $\mathbf{l}$ divided by $\hbar$. Here, to avoid confusion between the symbols representing the quantum number and the magnitude of the angular momentum we use the symbol $\mathbf{l}^2$ for the squared magnitude of the angular momentum, instead of l^2.

atom, represented by the wave function (1), has just this one central fringe. Each excited state with $l = 0$ has n_r spherical dark fringes. The mathematical form of the wave functions of these states will be discussed in the next section. The energy eigenvalues are

$$E_n = \frac{E_1}{n^2} = -\frac{1}{2}\frac{m_e e^4}{n^2 \hbar^2} = -\frac{1}{n^2} 13.6 \text{ ev}, \tag{9}$$

with $n = n_r + 1$.

Successive eigenstates of increasing energy differ from one another by a substantial increase of the mean distance of the electron from the nucleus. As the electron's energy increases, the electron meets a de-

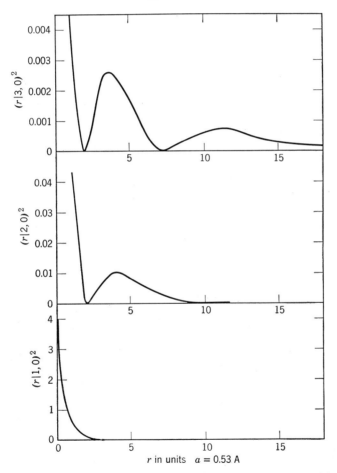

Fig. 14.7 Radial probability distributions in the absence of centrifugal force, for $n = 1, l = 0; n = 2, l = 0; n = 3, l = 0$.

creasing attraction in the farthest region it can reach. Successive eigenstates differ primarily by the occurrence of additional bright fringes of rapidly increasing radii (see Fig. 14.7); the radius of the outermost fringe of each eigenstate is roughly proportional to the squared number of fringes. The energy difference between successive eigenstates decreases rapidly, $E_{n+1} - E_n = E_1(2n + 1)/n^2(n + 1)^2 \sim E_1 2/n^3$; thereby an infinite sequence of eigenvalues lies in the limited range between $E_1 = -13.6$ ev and zero.[7] The stationary states with very large radii can

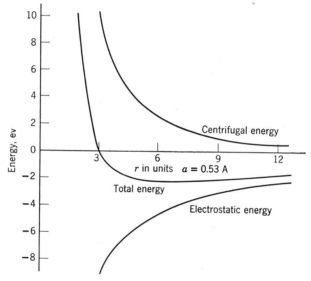

Fig. 14.8　Dependence on the radius r of the electrostatic, centrifugal, and total potential energy for a hydrogen atom in a state with $l = 2$.

exist undisturbed only in an extremely rarefied gas, where the atoms are sufficiently far apart from one another. There is, however, spectroscopic evidence for the existence of long sequences of stationary states with increasing radii.

When the electron has a rotational motion with $l \neq 0$, the centrifugal force keeps it away from the nucleus. This force is represented in Eq. 6 by an effective potential energy $l^2/2m_e r^2$. The combined potential energy, centrifugal and electrostatic, has the trend shown in Fig. 14.8, with a minimum at $r = l(l + 1)\hbar^2/m_e e^2 = l(l + 1)a$, where a is the Bohr radius (2). The predominance of the centrifugal force at

---

[7] This situation is opposite to the one encountered in the problem of confinement between sharp potential barriers (Sect. 13.2d); in the example of Fig. 13.3, there are only five bound stationary states.

$r < l(l + 1)$ has roughly the effect of wiping out the l innermost fringes
that one would observe for $l = 0$ (Fig. 14.9).   On the other hand, for
$r > l(l + 1)a$, the nuclear attraction predominates and the radial motion
is approximately independent of l.   It turns out that the total energy
of the electron depends only on the total number of nodal surfaces

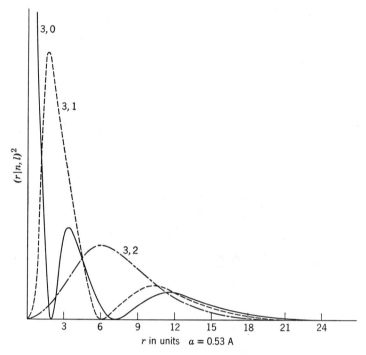

Fig. 14.9 Radial probability distribution for $n = 3$, $l = 0$, $l = 1$, and $l = 2$.

$n_r + l$, and not on the separate values of n_r and l.[8]   That is, all energy
eigenvalues are given by (9), in agreement with experimental evidence,
where n, the "principal quantum number" is now defined as $n = n_r + l + 1$.   Probability distributions in the xz plane across the atom
are shown for a number of states in Fig. 14.10.

A complete set of stationary states is fully identified by the quantum
numbers $(n,l,\mathbf{m},\alpha)$.   As seen at the end of (c) above, the set includes
$2l + 1$ states for a given l.   For a given n, the quantum number l may be

---

[8] This result follows from the fact that the Schroedinger equation for the hydrogen
atom can be expressed as the equation for the free motion of a particle on a "sphere"
of a four-dimensional space.   This additional mathematical symmetry is much less
apparent than the spherical symmetry of the nuclear attraction which causes the
eigenvalues of l^2 to be independent of $\mathbf{m}$.

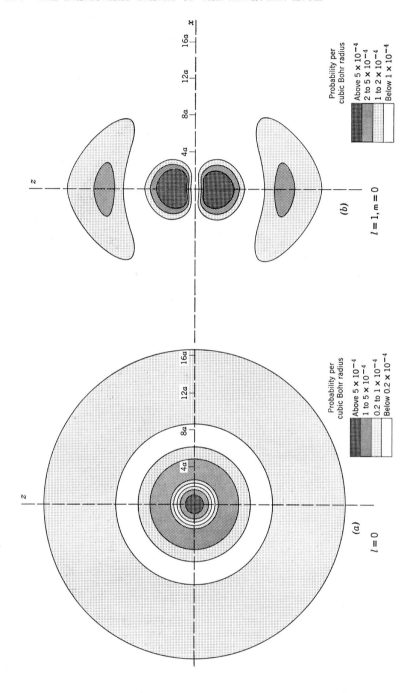

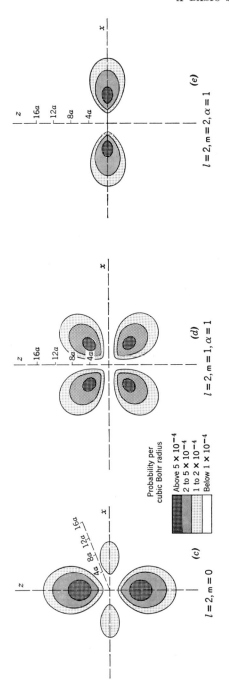

Fig. 14.10 Probability distributions on the xz plane of the electron in eigenstates with quantum number $n = 3$ and (a) $l = 0$; (b) $l = 1$, $m = 0$; (c) $l = 2$, $m = 0$; (d) $l = 2$, $m = 1$, $\alpha = 1$; and (e) $l = 2$, $m = 2$, $\alpha = 1$. Contour lines represent levels of equal probability per $10^{-4} a^3$, that is per 1.5×10^{-5} A³.

$l = 2$, $m = 2$, $\alpha = 1$ (e)

$l = 2$, $m = 1$, $\alpha = 1$ (d)

$l = 2$, $m = 0$ (c)

Probability per
cubic Bohr radius

Above 5×10^{-4}
2 to 5×10^{-4}
1 to 2×10^{-4}
Below 1×10^{-4}

any integer from 0 to $n - 1$, and therefore the number of states is

$$1 + 3 + 5 + \cdots + [2(n - 1) + 1] = n^2, \tag{10}$$

for each energy eigenvalue E_n. This result has fundamental consequences for the chemical properties of atoms, as will be shown in Chapter 18. Stationary states with given quantum numbers n and l are often indicated with a numerical prefix equal to n, combined with the code letter indicated at the end of (c) above; for example "$3p$" means $n = 3$, $l = 1$.

14.2   Solution of the Schroedinger Equation

The Schroedinger equation for the electron of a hydrogen atom is a special case of the equation (2) on page 170, in which the particle's mass has the value m_e and the potential energy is $V(\mathbf{r}) = -e^2/r$, as on page 165,

$$-\frac{\hbar^2}{2m_e}\left[\frac{\partial^2(\mathbf{r}|E_n)}{\partial x^2} + \frac{\partial^2(\mathbf{r}|E_n)}{\partial y^2} + \frac{\partial^2(\mathbf{r}|E_n)}{\partial z^2}\right] - \frac{e^2}{r}(\mathbf{r}|E_n) = (\mathbf{r}|E_n)E_n. \tag{11}$$

The qualitative analysis in the preceding section suggests that the solutions of this equation be represented in polar coordinates. To this end, the derivatives with respect to the cartesian coordinates may be replaced with derivatives with respect to polar coordinates by a mathematical transformation which changes Eq. 11 into [9]

$$-\frac{\hbar^2}{2m_e}\left\{\left[\frac{\partial^2(\mathbf{r}|E_n)}{\partial r^2} + \frac{2}{r}\frac{\partial(\mathbf{r}|E_n)}{\partial r}\right] + \frac{1}{r^2}\left[\frac{\partial^2(\mathbf{r}|E_n)}{\partial\theta^2} + \cotan\theta\,\frac{\partial(\mathbf{r}|E_n)}{\partial\theta}\right]\right.$$

$$\left. + \frac{1}{r^2\sin^2\theta}\frac{\partial^2(\mathbf{r}|E_n)}{\partial\phi^2}\right\} - \frac{e^2}{r}(\mathbf{r}|E_n) = (\mathbf{r}|E_n)E_n. \tag{12}$$

Further, we seek to identify stationary states whose wave functions are products of a function of r, of a function of θ, and of a function of ϕ,

---

[9] An example of the formulas utilized in the transformation is

$$\frac{\partial f(\mathbf{r})}{\partial x} = \frac{\partial f(r,\theta,\phi)}{\partial x} = \frac{\partial r}{\partial x}\frac{\partial f}{\partial r} + \frac{\partial\theta}{\partial x}\frac{\partial f}{\partial\theta} + \frac{\partial\phi}{\partial x}\frac{\partial f}{\partial\phi}$$

$$= \sin\theta\,\cos\phi\,\frac{\partial f}{\partial r} + \cos\theta\,\cos\phi\,\frac{1}{r}\frac{\partial f}{\partial\theta} - \frac{\sin\phi}{\sin\theta}\frac{1}{r}\frac{\partial f}{\partial\phi},$$

which follows from the formulas in footnote 3 on page 196.

in analogy with the separation carried out in Sect. 13.2. We indicate such a wave function by

$$(\mathbf{r}\,|\,E_n) = (r,\theta,\phi\,|\,E_n) = (r,\theta,\phi\,|\,n,l,\mathbf{m},\alpha)$$
$$= (r\,|\,n,l)(\theta\,|\,l,\mathbf{m})(\phi\,|\,\mathbf{m},\alpha). \tag{13}$$

This wave function is a solution of the full Schroedinger equation, provided that its factors fulfill the separate equations

$$-\frac{\partial^2(\phi\,|\,\mathbf{m},\alpha)}{\partial\phi^2} = \mathbf{m}^2(\phi\,|\,\mathbf{m},\alpha), \tag{14a}$$

$$-\left[\frac{\partial^2(\theta\,|\,l,\mathbf{m})}{\partial\theta^2} + \cot\theta\,\frac{\partial(\theta\,|\,l,\mathbf{m})}{\partial\theta}\right] + \frac{\mathbf{m}^2}{\sin^2\theta}(\theta\,|\,l,\mathbf{m}) = (\theta\,|\,l,\mathbf{m})\,l\,(l+1), \tag{14b}$$

$$-\frac{\hbar^2}{2m_e}\left[\frac{\partial^2(r\,|\,n,l)}{\partial r^2} + \frac{2}{r}\frac{\partial(r\,|\,n,l)}{\partial r}\right] + \left[\frac{\hbar^2 l(l+1)}{2m_e r^2} - \frac{e^2}{r}\right](r\,|\,n,l) = (r\,|\,n,l)E_n. \tag{14c}$$

These equations pertain, respectively, to the motion along parallels, meridians, and radii of polar coordinates within the atom. The Eqs. 14 of separate motions in polar coordinates are not wholly independent of one another, at variance from the corresponding separate equations in cartesian coordinates (Eq. 9, page 183), in that (14b) and (14c) depend, respectively, on the eigenvalues of (14a) and (14b).

Equation 14a is the Schroedinger equation that determines the eigenvalues and eigenstates of the squared angular momentum component $l_z{}^2$, or rather of $l_z{}^2/\hbar^2$. It can be established directly, rather than by separating (12), by applying the method of Chapter 12 and considering that $\langle l_z{}^2\rangle = \langle(xp_y - yp_x)^2\rangle$. Similarly, Eq. 14b is the Schroedinger equation which determines the eigenvalues of the squared angular momentum $\mathbf{l}^2$, or rather of $\mathbf{l}^2/\hbar^2$, consistent with the eigenvalue $l_z{}^2 = \mathbf{m}^2\hbar^2$. Equations 14a and 14b apply to the rotational motion of a particle whose potential energy is any function of the distance from a center. Equation 14a has solutions that are continuous functions of ϕ, only if $\mathbf{m}$ is an integer. A complete set of solutions is

$$\text{for } \mathbf{m} = 0: \qquad (\phi\,|\,\mathbf{m}) = \frac{1}{\sqrt{2\pi}},$$

$$\text{for } \mathbf{m} \neq 0: \qquad (\phi\,|\,\mathbf{m},1) = \frac{1}{\sqrt{\pi}}\cos\mathbf{m}\phi, \tag{15}$$

$$(\phi\,|\,\mathbf{m},2) = \frac{1}{\sqrt{\pi}}\sin\mathbf{m}\phi.$$

The probability distribution of the ϕ coordinate is given by $|(\phi|m,\alpha)|^2$ and consists of m equal bright fringes, one of them centered at $\phi = 0$ when $\alpha = 1$, as shown in Fig. 14.4. The magnitude of each wave function is such that the total probability $\Sigma_\phi |(\phi|m,\alpha)|^2 = 1$.

Equation 14b has solutions that are continuous functions of θ, with acceptable properties at $\theta = 0$ and $\theta = \pi$, only if the quantum number l is an integer no smaller than m. Its solutions, $(\theta|l,m)$, are called "associated Legendre functions" and are, for $l \leq 2$,

$$(\theta|0,0) = \sqrt{\tfrac{1}{2}},$$

$$(\theta|1,0) = \sqrt{\tfrac{2}{3}} \cos\theta, \qquad (\theta|1,1) = \sqrt{\tfrac{3}{4}} \sin\theta, \tag{16}$$

$$(\theta|2,0) = \sqrt{\tfrac{5}{8}} (3 \cos^2\theta - 1), \qquad (\theta|2,1) = \sqrt{\tfrac{15}{4}} \sin\theta \cos\theta,$$

$$(\theta|2,2) = \sqrt{\tfrac{15}{16}} \sin^2\theta.$$

Notice that each function $(\theta|l,m)$ has a factor $(\sin\theta)^m$ which vanishes at the poles and results from the centrifugal action of the motion along parallels. Besides this factor, which vanishes only at the poles, each function contains a polynomial in $\cos\theta$ with $l - m$ nodes, a behavior anticipated in Sect. 14.1c.

Equation 14c has solutions which remain finite at $r = 0$ and $r = \infty$, only if the eigenvalue E_n either equals $-\tfrac{1}{2}m_e e^4/n^2\hbar^2$, with n integral and larger than l, or else is positive. Its solutions are, for $n \leq 3$,

$$(r|1,0) = \frac{2}{\sqrt{a^3}} e^{-r/a}, \text{ (the ground state function)},$$

$$(r|2,0) = \frac{2}{\sqrt{(2a)^3}} e^{-r/2a} \left(\frac{r}{2a} - 1\right), \qquad (r|2,1) = \frac{2}{\sqrt{3(2a)^3}} e^{-r/2a} \frac{r}{2a},$$

$$(r|3,0) = \frac{2}{\sqrt{(3a)^3}} e^{-r/3a} \left[\frac{2}{3}\left(\frac{r}{3a}\right)^2 - 2\frac{r}{3a} + 1\right],$$

$$(r|3,1) = \frac{4}{3} \sqrt{\frac{2}{(3a)^3}} e^{-r/3a} \frac{r}{3a} \left(\frac{1}{2}\frac{r}{3a} - 1\right),$$

$$(r|3,2) = \frac{4}{3\sqrt{10(3a)^3}} e^{-r/3a} \left(\frac{r}{3a}\right)^2, \tag{17}$$

where $a = \hbar^2/m_e e^2 = 0.53$ A is the Bohr radius of the hydrogen atom in its ground state. Each of these functions consists of the following factors: (a) an exponential $e^{-r/na}$ which characterizes the trend of the wave function far away from the nucleus, depends on the energy eigenvalue, and is analogous to the decreasing exponential in Eq. 13, page 185; (b) a factor r^l which characterizes the trend of the wave function near the nucleus and depends only on the centrifugal force; (c) a polynomial of degree $n - l - 1 = n_r$ which is an oscillating function of r with n_r nodes, of a type called "associated Laguerre polynomial"; and (d) a numerical factor which depends on the size of the outermost interference fringe and is such that the total probability of all electron positions equals one.

14.3 Stationary States with Electron Flow

Stationary states with a net flow around an axis exist and can be represented by the superposition of two states with no flow. The axis can be chosen as the axis of polar coordinates, and the component states with no flow have then the same quantum numbers n, l, and m, and the different positions of the fringes indicated by $\alpha = 1$ or $\alpha = 2$. A pair of states with flow in opposite directions about the z axis is indicated by the quantum numbers (n,l,m), where m is called the "magnetic quantum number" and has the values $\pm m$. These states relate to the states (n,l,m,α) with $\alpha = 1$ or $\alpha = 2$ in the same way as the momentum eigenstates represented by Eq. 1, page 179, relate to the states with no flow and with interference fringes represented by the wave functions (2), page 179. In each state (n,l,m), the probability of the electron position is uniform along each parallel circle, that is, independent of ϕ. The wave functions of these states are

$$(r,\theta,\phi \,|\, n,l,m) = (r \,|\, n,l)(\theta \,|\, l,m)(\phi \,|\, m) \tag{18}$$

with

$$(\phi \,|\, m) = \left[\frac{1}{\sqrt{2}}(\phi \,|\, m,1) + \frac{i}{\sqrt{2}}(\phi \,|\, m,2) \right] = \frac{1}{\sqrt{2\pi}}(\cos m\phi + i\,\sin m\phi)$$

$$= \frac{1}{\sqrt{2\pi}}e^{im\phi} = \frac{1}{\sqrt{2\pi}}e^{im\phi} \qquad \text{for } m = m \neq 0, \tag{19a}$$

$$(\phi \,|\, m) = \left[\frac{1}{\sqrt{2}}(\phi \,|\, m,1) - \frac{i}{\sqrt{2}}(\phi \,|\, m,2) \right] = \frac{1}{\sqrt{2\pi}}e^{-im\phi} = \frac{1}{\sqrt{2\pi}}e^{im\phi}$$

$$\qquad\qquad \text{for } m = -m \neq 0, \tag{19b}$$

$$(\phi \,|\, m) = (\phi \,|\, m) = \frac{1}{\sqrt{2\pi}} \qquad \text{for } m = m = 0, \tag{19c}$$

and with

$$(\theta \,|\, l,m) = (-1)^m(\theta \,|\, l,m) \qquad \text{for } m = m, \tag{20a}$$

$$(\theta \,|\, l,m) = (\theta \,|\, l,m) \qquad \text{for } m = -m. \tag{20b}$$

The formulas (19) are summarized by the single formula

$$(\phi \,|\, m) \;=\; \frac{1}{\sqrt{2\pi}}\, e^{im\phi} \qquad \text{for all } m. \tag{21}$$

The factor $(-1)^m$ in (20a) is introduced for convenient standardization.

One may consider as a complete set of stationary bound states of the hydrogen atom the states with the wave functions (18), where m takes all the $2l + 1$ integral values between $-l$ and l, l takes all the integral values between 0 and $n - 1$, and n takes all integral values larger than zero. This set is an alternate to the set of states represented by the wave functions (13). The states of this new set are eigenstates of the angular momentum component l_z, with the eigenvalues $m\hbar$.

In the wave function (21) one may indicate the quantum number m as $l_z/\hbar$ and write

$$(\phi \,|\, l_z) \;=\; \frac{1}{\sqrt{2\pi}}\, \exp\left(i\,\frac{l_z}{\hbar}\,\phi\right). \tag{21'}$$

The angular momentum component l_z is thus seen to be related to the longitude coordinate ϕ of the electron position by probability amplitudes with the same mathematical form as $(x \,|\, p_x)$. The eigenvalues of l_z and the probability amplitudes $(\phi \,|\, l_z)$, which describe the eigenstates as combinations of position eigenstates, can be determined directly by formulating and solving the pertinent Schroedinger equation. Starting from an expression of $\langle l_z \rangle = \langle x p_y - y p_x \rangle$, the procedure of Chapter 12 yields the equation

$$\frac{\hbar}{i}\,\frac{\partial(\phi \,|\, l_z)}{\partial\phi} \;=\; (\phi \,|\, l_z) l_z. \tag{22}$$

This equation has the eigenvalues $l_z = m\hbar$, with m integer, and the eigenfunctions (21'). Notice the similarity of this equation to Eq. 11, page 145, which is the Schroedinger equation of momentum eigenstates.

14.4 Off-center Electron Distributions

The stationary states of the hydrogen atom considered thus far are eigenstates of the squared angular momentum $\mathbf{l}^2$. Their interference fringes are distributed about the nucleus with such symmetry that the mean position of the electron lies at the nucleus. Because stationary states with equal n and different l have the same energy and different eigenvalues of $\mathbf{l}^2$, the hydrogen atom has also stationary states which are not eigenstates of $\mathbf{l}^2$, and may be described as superpositions of states with equal n and different l. The mean position of the electron differs, in general, from the position of the nucleus in any state which is not an eigenstate of $\mathbf{l}^2$. An off-center probability distribution of the electron position is favorable for the formation of chemical bonds, as will be seen in Chapter 20.

The simplest and most important examples of stationary states with off-center distribution arise from the superposition of states of the type $2s$ and $2p$, that is, $n = 2$, $l = 0$, and $n = 2$, $l = 1$ (see the code names on page 202). Superposition of $2s$ and $2p_z$ with equal amplitudes yields, according to (13), (15), (16), and (17),

$$\frac{1}{\sqrt{2}}\,(r,\theta,\phi\,|\,2,0,0) + \frac{1}{\sqrt{2}}\,(r,\theta,\phi\,|\,2,1,0)$$

$$= \frac{1}{\sqrt{2}}\,\frac{1}{\sqrt{2\pi}}\,\frac{1}{\sqrt{2}}\,\frac{2}{\sqrt{(2a)^3}}\,e^{-r/2a}\left(\frac{r}{2a} - 1\right) + \frac{1}{\sqrt{2}}\,\frac{1}{\sqrt{2\pi}}\,\sqrt{\tfrac{3}{2}}\,\cos\theta\,\frac{2}{\sqrt{3(2a)^3}}\,e^{-r/2a}\,\frac{r}{2a}$$

$$= \frac{1}{2}\,\frac{1}{\sqrt{4\pi a^3}}\,e^{-r/2a}\left(\frac{r + z}{2a} - 1\right), \tag{23}$$

where $z = r\cos\theta$, see footnote 3, page 196. This wave function has a single nodal surface represented by the equation $r + z = 2a$, that is $z = a - (x^2 + y^2)/4a$, which is a paraboloid with the axis z as axis of symmetry. The bright fringe outside this paraboloid includes a higher total probability then the inner one (see Fig. 14.11).

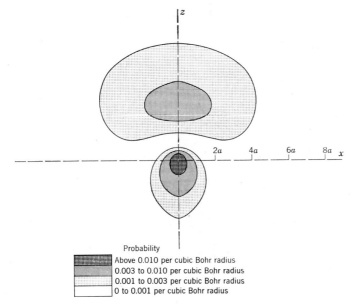

Probability
Above 0.010 per cubic Bohr radius
0.003 to 0.010 per cubic Bohr radius
0.001 to 0.003 per cubic Bohr radius
0 to 0.001 per cubic Bohr radius

Fig. 14.11 Off-center probability distribution of the electron position in a hydrogen atom. This stationary state is a superposition of states $(n = 2, l = 0)$, and $(n = 2, l = 1)$, with equal probability amplitudes.

Because the probability distribution is symmetrical about the z axis, in this state the mean position of the electron lies on that axis at the coordinate

$$\langle z \rangle = \Sigma_{\mathbf{r}}\, z\left[\frac{1}{2}\,\frac{1}{\sqrt{4\pi a^3}}\,e^{-r/2a}\left(\frac{r + z}{2a} - 1\right)\right]^2$$

$$= \int_{-\infty}^{\infty} dx \int_{-\infty}^{\infty} dy \int_{-\infty}^{\infty} dz\, z\,\frac{1}{64\pi a^5}\,e^{-r/a}\,(\sqrt{x^2 + y^2 + z^2} + z - 2a)^2 = 3a. \tag{24}$$

The state with the wave function

$$\frac{1}{\sqrt{2}}\,(r,\theta,\phi\,|\,2,0,0) \;-\; \frac{1}{\sqrt{2}}\,(r,\theta,\phi\,|\,2,1,0) \;=\; \frac{1}{2}\,\frac{1}{\sqrt{4\pi a^3}}\,e^{-r/2a}\left(\frac{r-z}{2a}-1\right) \qquad (25)$$

is equivalent to (23) but has opposite orientation along the z axis. It is orthogonal to (23). The pair of states represented by (23) and (25) constitutes a set alternative to the pair $2s$, $2p_z$.

Superposition of $2s$ and $2p_z$ with amplitudes in a ratio $1:\sqrt{2}$ yields a state with the wave function

$$\sqrt{\tfrac{1}{3}}\,(r,\theta,\phi\,|\,2,0,0) \;+\; \sqrt{\tfrac{2}{3}}\,(r,\theta,\phi\,|\,2,1,0) \;=\; \frac{1}{\sqrt{6}}\,\frac{1}{\sqrt{4\pi a^3}}\,e^{-r/2a}\left(\frac{r+\sqrt{2}\,z}{2a}-1\right). \qquad (26)$$

The single nodal surface of this wave function is a paraboloid somewhat wider than that of (23) and with the same axis of symmetry, namely, the z axis. The mean position of the electron in this state lies at $\langle z\rangle = 2\sqrt{2}\,a = 2.83a$. Two stationary states orthogonal to (26) are obtained from the superposition of $2s$, $2p_z$, and $2p_x$; their wave functions are

$$\sqrt{\tfrac{1}{3}}\,(r,\theta,\phi\,|\,2,0,0) \;-\; \sqrt{\tfrac{1}{6}}\,(r,\theta,\phi,\,|\,2,1,0) \;\pm\; \sqrt{\tfrac{1}{2}}\,(r,\theta,\phi\,|\,2,1,1,1). \qquad (27)$$

These two states (with $+$ or $-$ sign) differ from (26) in that their axis of symmetry lies in one of the two directions within the xz plane which form an angle of 120° with the z axis. The three states represented by (26) and (27) constitute a set alternative to the set of three states $2s$, $2p_x$, and $2p_z$. A pair of wave functions orthogonal to (26), with their axes in the yz plane, is obtained by replacing in (27) the p_x function $(r,\theta,\phi\,|\,2,1,1,1)$ with the p_y function $(r,\theta,\phi\,|\,2,1,1,2)$.

Finally, superposition of $2s$ and $2p_z$ with amplitudes in a ratio $1:\sqrt{3}$ yields a state with the wave function

$$\frac{1}{2}\,(r,\theta,\phi\,|\,2,0,0) \;+\; \frac{\sqrt{3}}{2}\,(r,\theta,\phi\,|\,2,1,0) \;=\; \frac{1}{\sqrt{8}}\,\frac{1}{\sqrt{4\pi a^3}}\,e^{-r/2a}\left(\frac{r+\sqrt{3}\,z}{2a}-1\right). \qquad (28)$$

This wave function has a nodal paraboloid surface still wider than (26) and the same symmetry about the z axis. The mean position of the electron lies at $\langle z\rangle = \tfrac{3}{2}\sqrt{3}\,a = 2.60a$. Three stationary states orthogonal to (28) are obtained from the superposition of $2s$, $2p_z$, $2p_x$, and $2p_y$; their wave functions are

$$\frac{1}{2}\,(r,\theta,\phi\,|\,2,0,0) \;-\; \frac{1}{2\sqrt{3}}\,(r,\theta,\phi\,|\,2,1,0) \;+\; \sqrt{\tfrac{2}{3}}\,(r,\theta,\phi\,|\,2,1,1,1),$$

$$\frac{1}{2}\,(r,\theta,\phi\,|\,2,0,0) \;-\; \frac{1}{2\sqrt{3}}\,(r,\theta,\phi\,|\,2,1,0) \;-\; \sqrt{\tfrac{1}{6}}\,(r,\theta,\phi\,|\,2,1,1,1) \;\pm\; \sqrt{\tfrac{1}{2}}\,(r,\theta,\phi\,|\,2,1,1,2).$$

$$(29)$$

The four states (28) and (29) have axes of symmetry that point towards the vertices of a tetrahedron with its center at the origin of coordinates. They constitute a set of states alternative to the set $2s$, $2p_x$, $2p_y$, and $2p_z$.

14.5   Effect of Nuclear Motion

The Schroedinger equation we have considered thus far pertains to the motion of an electron under the influence of a force whose strength and direction depend only on the position of the electron. The force acting on the electron of a hydrogen atom does not quite fit this specification. It depends on the position of the nucleus and the nucleus is itself in motion subject to the attraction by the electron. However, the nucleus, being much heavier than the electron, moves much more slowly and hence was correctly regarded as fixed in a first approximation.

To formulate the Schroedinger equation, taking into account the nuclear motion, one may write the total kinetic energy of the nucleus and electron in the form

$$K = \frac{1}{2} m_N v_N{}^2 + \frac{1}{2} m_e v_e{}^2 = \frac{p_N{}^2}{2m_N} + \frac{p_e{}^2}{2m_e}, \tag{30}$$

and then calculate its mean value in a state represented by the probability amplitudes $(\mathbf{r}_N, \mathbf{r}_e \mid a)$ of finding the nucleus at $\mathbf{r}_N$ and the electron at $\mathbf{r}_e$. Proceeding as in Sect. 12.2, one finds, instead of Eq. 13, page 173,

$$\langle K \rangle = \Sigma_{\mathbf{r}_N} \Sigma_{\mathbf{r}_e} (a \mid \mathbf{r}_N, \mathbf{r}_e) \left\{ -\frac{\hbar^2}{2m_N} \left[\frac{\partial^2 (\mathbf{r}_N, \mathbf{r}_e \mid a)}{\partial x_N{}^2} + \frac{\partial^2 (\mathbf{r}_N, \mathbf{r}_e \mid a)}{\partial y_N{}^2} + \frac{\partial^2 (\mathbf{r}_N, \mathbf{r}_e \mid a)}{\partial z_N{}^2} \right] \right.$$
$$\left. -\frac{\hbar^2}{2m_e} \left[\frac{\partial^2 (\mathbf{r}_N, \mathbf{r}_e \mid a)}{\partial x_e{}^2} + \frac{\partial^2 (\mathbf{r}_N, \mathbf{r}_e \mid a)}{\partial y_e{}^2} + \frac{\partial^2 (\mathbf{r}_N, \mathbf{r}_e \mid a)}{\partial z_e{}^2} \right] \right\}, \tag{31}$$

and the Schroedinger equation becomes, instead of (2), page 170,

$$-\frac{\hbar^2}{2m_N} \left[\frac{\partial^2 (\mathbf{r}_N, \mathbf{r}_e \mid E)}{\partial x_N{}^2} + \frac{\partial^2 (\mathbf{r}_N, \mathbf{r}_e \mid E)}{\partial y_N{}^2} + \frac{\partial^2 (\mathbf{r}_N, \mathbf{r}_e \mid E)}{\partial z_N{}^2} \right]$$
$$-\frac{\hbar^2}{2m_e} \left[\frac{\partial^2 (\mathbf{r}_N, \mathbf{r}_e \mid E)}{\partial x_e{}^2} + \frac{\partial^2 (\mathbf{r}_N, \mathbf{r}_e \mid E)}{\partial y_e{}^2} + \frac{\partial^2 (\mathbf{r}_N, \mathbf{r}_e \mid E)}{\partial z_e{}^2} \right] + V(\mathbf{r})(\mathbf{r}_N, \mathbf{r}_e \mid E) = (\mathbf{r}_N, \mathbf{r}_e \mid E) E \cdot \tag{32}$$

In this equation, the potential energy depends, of course, on the relative position of the two particles $\mathbf{r} = \mathbf{r}_e - \mathbf{r}_N$, and the eigenvalue E represents the total energy of the two particles.

Because the force depends only on the relative position of the two particles, one wants to treat separately their relative motion and their collective motion. The collective motion may be regarded (see Appendix III) as a motion of the total mass

$$M = m_N + m_e, \tag{33}$$

as though it were concentrated at the center of mass

$$\mathbf{R} = \frac{m_N}{M} \mathbf{r}_N + \frac{m_e}{M} \mathbf{r}_e. \tag{34}$$

To this end, the total kinetic energy may be expressed as in Eq. 19, Appendix III,

$$K = \frac{1}{2} M V^2 + \frac{1}{2} \mu v^2 = \frac{P^2}{2M} + \frac{p^2}{2\mu}, \tag{35}$$

where

$$\mu = \frac{m_e m_N}{m_e + m_N} \sim m_e \left(1 - \frac{m_e}{m_N} \right) \tag{36}$$

indicates the reduced mass. (The approximate expression on the right holds insofar as $m_e \ll m_N$.) The mean value of the kinetic energy in this form can be calculated in terms of a wave function $(\mathbf{R},\mathbf{r}\,|\,a)$ by arguing that the wave functions $(\mathbf{R}\,|\,\mathbf{P})$ and $(\mathbf{r}\,|\,\mathbf{p})$ have the same mathematical form as $(\mathbf{r}_e\,|\,\mathbf{p}_e)$. Alternatively, one may proceed as in the formulation of the equation in polar coordinates (Sect. 14.2) by transforming the coordinates in (31) and (32) from $(\mathbf{r}_N,\mathbf{r}_e)$ to $(\mathbf{R},\mathbf{r})$. The Schroedinger equation becomes

$$-\frac{\hbar^2}{2M}\left[\frac{\partial^2(\mathbf{R},\mathbf{r}\,|\,E)}{\partial X^2} + \frac{\partial^2(\mathbf{R},\mathbf{r}\,|\,E)}{\partial Y^2} + \frac{\partial^2(\mathbf{R},\mathbf{r}\,|\,E)}{\partial Z^2}\right]$$

$$-\frac{\hbar^2}{2\mu}\left[\frac{\partial^2(\mathbf{R},\mathbf{r}\,|\,E)}{\partial x^2} + \frac{\partial^2(\mathbf{R},\mathbf{r}\,|\,E)}{\partial y^2} + \frac{\partial^2(\mathbf{R},\mathbf{r}\,|\,E)}{\partial z^2}\right] + V(\mathbf{r})(\mathbf{R},\mathbf{r}\,|\,E) = (\mathbf{R},\mathbf{r}\,|\,E)E. \quad (37)$$

Here, as in Sect. 13.2, separate terms on the left side depend on the separate variables $\mathbf{R}$ and $\mathbf{r}$, and one may also regard the energy eigenvalue as the sum of two terms

$$E = K_M + E_n, \quad (38)$$

of which the first one represents the kinetic energy of the collective motion of the whole atom, with mass M, and the second term represents an eigenvalue of the internal energy of the atom. The collective and relative motions are then independent and one may factor the probability amplitude, again as in Sect. 13.2,

$$(\mathbf{R},\mathbf{r}\,|\,E) = (\mathbf{R}\,|\,K_M)(\mathbf{r}\,|\,E_n) \quad (39)$$

The wave function $(\mathbf{R}\,|\,K_M)$ obeys the Schroedinger equation for a free particle of mass M, and the wave function $(\mathbf{r}\,|\,E_n)$ obeys the equation

$$-\frac{\hbar^2}{2\mu}\left[\frac{\partial^2(\mathbf{r}\,|\,E_n)}{\partial x^2} + \frac{\partial^2(\mathbf{r}\,|\,E_n)}{\partial y^2} + \frac{\partial^2(\mathbf{r}\,|\,E_n)}{\partial z^2}\right] + V(\mathbf{r})(\mathbf{r}\,|\,E_n) = (\mathbf{r}\,|\,E_n)E_n, \quad (40)$$

which has the standard form utilized in the earlier applications. The only difference is that the reduced mass μ of the electron and of the nucleus enters in (40) instead of the electron mass m_e, and that the coordinates (x,y,z) are coordinates of the electron in a moving frame of reference attached to the nucleus.

The results in the preceding sections need therefore only to be reinterpreted slightly, and to be corrected by replacing m_e with μ in the expression (2) of the Bohr radius a and in the expressions (3) and (9) of the energy eigenvalues E_n. According to (36), this correction amounts to a fraction $\sim m_e/m_N$, which is less than one part in one thousand. As pointed out at the end of Chapter 4, this correction is different for hydrogen isotopes with different masses m_N and greatly improves the agreement with experimental results.

PROBLEMS

14.1 Following the impact of an electron, a hydrogen atom is in a nonstationary state $b(t)$ identified, at the time $t = 0$, as a superposition of states (n,l,m) by the following set of probability amplitudes: $(1,0,0\,|\,b(0)) = \sqrt{\frac{1}{2}}$, $(2,1,0\,|\,b(0)) = \frac{1}{2}$, $(3,2,0\,|\,b(0)) = \frac{1}{2}$, all other $(n,l,m\,|\,b(0)) = 0$. Calculate, as functions of t: (a) the wave function

$(\mathbf{r}\,|\,b(t))$, (b) the probability distribution of the electron position $|(\mathbf{r}\,|\,b(t))\,|^2$, (c) the mean position $\langle\mathbf{r}\rangle = (\langle x\rangle, \langle y\rangle, \langle z\rangle)$.

14.2 Calculate the mean potential energy $\langle -e^2/r\rangle$ of the electron of a hydrogen atom in stationary states with quantum number $n = 1, 2, 3 \cdots$. (Utilize the wave functions from Sect. 14.2 and the formula $\int_0^\infty \xi^n \exp(-\xi)\, d\xi = n!$.) Compare this mean value with the energy eigenvalue, thus obtaining the mean kinetic energy for the various stationary states.

chapter 15

The electron spin

The hydrogen atom has stationary states with a net electron flow, described in Sect. 14.3, which are eigenstates of a component l_z of the orbital angular momentum. The electron flow constitutes a current circulating about the z axis, such as one detects through the magnetic experiments described in Sect. 7.2, namely, molecular beam deflection and modification of optical spectra by a magnetic field (Zeeman effect). One can readily predict the magnitude of the magnetic effects of the electron flow within atoms, which is called an "orbital current." This flow must yield an effective magnetic moment proportional to its orbital angular momentum. The proportionality factor, called "gyromagnetic ratio," depends only on the charge-to-mass ratio of the electrons and equals $-\frac{1}{2}e/m_ec$, where c is the light velocity (Sect. 15.1c).

These predictions are not fully borne out by the magnetic experiments with hydrogen atoms, whose results are more complicated than expected on the basis of orbital currents. As a preliminary to the analysis of these results, it is shown in Sect. 15.1 how magnetic experiments determine the angular momenta of circulating currents. A magnetic field exerts a torque upon any current circulating within an atom; the effect of the torque is a change of angular momentum of the atom, demonstrated by a change of current orientation. The angular momentum can thus be defined without any reference to the flow of electrons. Magnetic experiments determine the eigenvalues of the angular momentum and the gyromagnetic ratio which relates it to the magnetic moment. The gyromagnetic ratio so defined does not coincide, in general, with the value expected for electron orbital currents.

A beam of hydrogen atoms in their ground state splits into *two* components when traversing a Stern-Gerlach magnet; whereas in this state there is no orbital current (see pages 191 and 192) and therefore there should be no splitting. The field in the Stern-Gerlach magnet resolves the ground state into two stationary states whose angular momentum in the direction of the magnet axis is $\pm\frac{1}{2}\hbar$ and whose gyromagnetic ratio is $-e/m_e c$ (instead of $-\frac{1}{2}e/m_e c$). This angular momentum and gyromagnetic ratio belong to a circulating current which is a property of the electron, independent of the orbital motion. Experiments on hydrogen atoms in their excited states, and on other atoms, consistently show the coexistence of two types of currents, the orbital current, and a "spin current" which appears to circulate within the electron (Sect. 15.2).

The interaction of the electron spin current with orbital currents and with the fields of magnets will be discussed in the next chapter. Even though these interactions are weak, the electron spin has a major influence on the structure of atoms and molecules by the very fact that it has two alternative states of orientation with respect to any field or current. The number of mutually exclusive, that is, orthogonal, states of the electron is thereby doubled.

15.1 Current Circulation and Angular Momentum

(*a*) *Mechanics of Larmor precession.* This section shows how one may define and determine the angular momentum of atomic particles by means of magnetic experiments, in particular by an analysis of the Larmor precession phenomenon, which was described in Sect. 9.1. The Larmor precession results from the action of a uniform magnetic field upon intramolecular currents and consists of a change of orientation of the currents. It provides information on the angular momentum because the uniform field exerts a torque on circulating currents (see page 87), and the effect of a torque may be expressed as a variation of angular momentum.

The angular momentum **j** of a macroscopic body remains constant as long as no torque acts on the body. In the presence of a torque, the angular momentum varies in the course of time at a rate dj/dt equal to the torque **M**. (Similarly, the momentum **p** of a body varies at a rate equal to the force acting on it.) The macroscopic equation between angular momentum and torque is interpreted in quantum mechanics as an equation between the mean values of these quantities,

$$\frac{d\langle \mathbf{j} \rangle}{dt} = \langle \mathbf{M} \rangle. \tag{1}$$

The torque exerted by a magnetic field upon a macroscopic current loop is represented by the vector product of the magnetic moment of the loop, **μ**, and of the field, **H**, namely by $\mathbf{M} = \mathbf{\mu} \times \mathbf{H}$. The magnetic moment **μ** of a flat current loop has a direction perpendicular to the loop and a magnitude equal to the current intensity i times the area A of the loop.

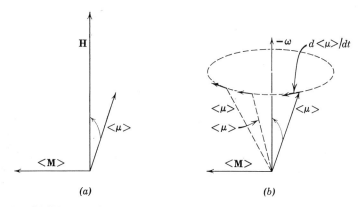

(a) $\qquad\qquad\qquad$ (b)

Fig. 15.1 (a) Diagram showing the direction of the mean torque $\langle \mathbf{M} \rangle$. (b) Diagram showing the Larmor precession of $\langle \mathbf{\mu} \rangle$, with $\dfrac{d\langle \mathbf{\mu} \rangle}{dt}$ parallel to $\langle \mathbf{M} \rangle$.

The action of a field on atomic currents may be similarly represented by a mean torque $\langle \mathbf{M} \rangle = \langle \mathbf{\mu} \rangle \times \mathbf{H}$ (Fig. 15.1), where the mean magnetic moment $\langle \mathbf{\mu} \rangle$ is defined by the characteristics of the atoms and by the method of preparation as follows. Given a beam of atoms, for example in their ground state but with unspecified current orientation, analysis by filtration through a Stern-Gerlach magnet [1] oriented in the z direction resolves the beam in a number of eigenstates of current orientation. Each eigenstate is identified by a deflection of the molecules proportional to the eigenvalue of the effective magnetic moment μ_z in the z direction.

---

[1] In a magnet of this type the field is not uniform and exerts a deflecting force on the molecules; the effect of filtration is due to this force rather than to a torque, see page 87.

The eigenvalues of μ_z (called μ_{eff} in Chapter 7) are equally spaced and are represented by the formula (17), page 90, $\mu_z = \mu m/j$. In this formula, μ indicates the largest of the eigenvalues of μ_z, μ/j is the constant difference between successive eigenvalues, $2j + 1$ is the number of eigenvalues, and the quantum number [2] m, which runs in integral steps from $-j$ to j, identifies a particular eigenvalue. The mean deflection of all molecules of a beam, as they emerge from the Stern-Gerlach magnet, determines the mean value $\langle \mu_z \rangle$. Independent analysis with the magnet oriented along other coordinate axes determines the mean values $\langle \mu_x \rangle$ and $\langle \mu_y \rangle$. The mean vector $\langle \boldsymbol{\mu} \rangle$ is defined as the vector with components $\langle \mu_x \rangle$, $\langle \mu_y \rangle$, and $\langle \mu_z \rangle$. The atoms of a beam prepared by filtration through a polarizer magnet have their mean magnetic moment $\langle \boldsymbol{\mu} \rangle$ parallel to the polarizer axis.[3]

The effect of the mean torque $\langle \boldsymbol{\mu} \rangle \times \mathbf{H}$ upon the atomic currents is demonstrated by the Larmor precession experiment described in Sect. 9.1. The mean torque drives the axis of current circulation, represented by the direction of $\langle \boldsymbol{\mu} \rangle$, around the direction of $\mathbf{H}$. The rate of precession of $\langle \boldsymbol{\mu} \rangle$ around $\mathbf{H}$ can be represented by a vector, namely an angular velocity $\boldsymbol{\omega}$, directed along the axis of precession and of magnitude proportional to H. The negative ratio $-\omega/H$ is called the "gyromagnetic ratio" γ. Its magnitude is found experimentally to be equal to the difference μ/j between successive eigenvalues of μ_z, divided by the Planck constant $\hbar$,

$$-\frac{\omega}{H} = \gamma = \frac{\mu}{j\hbar}. \tag{2}$$

The law of variation of $\langle \boldsymbol{\mu} \rangle$ in the Larmor precession experiment is represented, in terms of $\boldsymbol{\omega}$ or of γ and $\mathbf{H}$, by the equation

$$\frac{d\langle \boldsymbol{\mu} \rangle}{dt} = \boldsymbol{\omega} \times \langle \boldsymbol{\mu} \rangle = -\gamma \mathbf{H} \times \langle \boldsymbol{\mu} \rangle, \tag{3}$$

which is illustrated in Fig. 15.1b. Since the vector product $-\mathbf{H} \times \langle \boldsymbol{\mu} \rangle = \langle \boldsymbol{\mu} \rangle \times \mathbf{H}$ in this equation is the mean torque $\langle \mathbf{M} \rangle$, the experimental law (3) may be combined with the mechanical law (1) to yield

$$\frac{d\langle \boldsymbol{\mu} \rangle}{dt} = \gamma \langle \mathbf{M} \rangle = \gamma \frac{d\langle \mathbf{j} \rangle}{dt}. \tag{4}$$

---

[2] As will be seen, the number m may, but need not, coincide with the quantum number m which characterizes in Sect. 14.3 the eigenstates of an orbital angular momentum component l_z.

[3] Two analyzers perpendicular to the polarizer but opposite to one another must yield equal mean deflections, because they form equal angles with the polarizer (Sect. 7.2b), but deflections of opposite sign since their directions are opposite. Therefore, any component of $\langle \boldsymbol{\mu} \rangle$ perpendicular to the polarizer must vanish.

Further evidence on the angular momentum is provided by the fact that the torque causes the direction of $\langle\mu\rangle$ to precess around the direction of **H** without approaching it. The action of a torque, like that of a force, is opposed by the inertia of the body to which it is applied. A body which is pulled toward a fixed point or twisted toward a fixed axis may be prevented by its inertia from yielding respectively to the pull of the force or to the twist of the torque. Thus a planet moving on a circular orbit never gets closer to the sun, despite the gravitational attraction

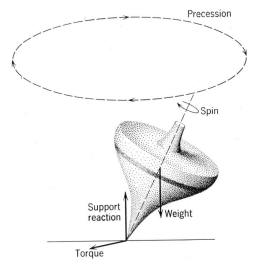

Fig. 15.2 Gyroscopic precession.

which is just sufficient to deflect the planet's momentum along the curved orbit; the inertia is represented by a centrifugal force that balances the attraction. Similarly, a top with a skew axis spinning on its tip is pulled by its weight to fall sideways; (the combination of the weight and of the support on the tip constitutes a torque, as shown in Fig. 15.2). It is well known that the top does not actually fall as long as it spins rapidly, but precesses around the vertical direction through the tip. This change proceeds at a rate equal in magnitude and direction to the torque exerted by the weight, much as the rate of change of the planet's momentum is equal to the gravitational force. The Larmor precession of intraatomic currents is quite analogous to the precession of a top and is accordingly called a "gyroscopic" motion. The failure of the torque to bring $\langle\mu\rangle$ closer to **H** shows that the mean angular momentum $\langle\mathbf{j}\rangle$ has such a magnitude and direction that its precession balances the torque.

If the mean angular momentum $\langle\mathbf{j}\rangle$ precesses together with the mean magnetic moment $\langle \mu \rangle$ with the angular velocity ω, the resulting rate of variation of $\langle j \rangle$ is given by a formula equivalent to (3), namely, $d\langle j \rangle / dt = \omega \times \langle j \rangle = -\gamma H \times \langle j \rangle$. This rate of variation equals the mean torque $\langle M \rangle = -H \times \langle \mu \rangle$, provided that $\langle j \rangle$ and $\langle \mu \rangle$ are proportional to one another at all times according to

$$\langle \mu \rangle = \gamma \langle j \rangle. \tag{5}$$

Equation 4 ensures that this formula will hold at all times provided only that it holds initially.

The proportionality of $\langle \mu \rangle$ and $\langle j \rangle$ permits an experimental determination of the angular momentum of atomic particles by magnetic experiments.

(b) Eigenvalues of the angular momentum. The experimental value of the gyromagnetic ratio γ is the same for all states of current orientation of the particles of a beam. The vector equation (5) means then that all components of $\langle \mu \rangle$ and $\langle j \rangle$ are in the same fixed ratio $\gamma = \langle \mu_x \rangle / \langle j_x \rangle = \langle \mu_y \rangle / \langle j_y \rangle = \langle \mu_z \rangle / \langle j_z \rangle$. Any two quantities whose mean values are in a fixed ratio must have common eigenstates and eigenvalues in that ratio. Particles that are in an eigenstate of current circulation about a z axis with eigenvalue μ_z of the magnetic moment are, therefore, in an eigenstate of angular momentum about the z axis with eigenvalue $j_z = \mu_z / \gamma$. The eigenvalues of j_z turn out to depend only on the number of components into which a given beam splits upon filtration by a Stern-Gerlach magnet.

Since successive eigenvalues of μ_z differ by μ/j, and since $\gamma = \mu/j\hbar$ (Eq. 2), successive eigenvalues of j_z differ by $(\mu/j)/\gamma = (\mu/j)/(\mu/j\hbar)$ $= \hbar$. This requirement is fulfilled by the eigenvalues of the component of orbital angular momentum, $l_z = m\hbar$, with integral m, which were calculated on page 212. Moreover, the factor μ of the gyromagnetic ratio represents the largest eigenvalue of μ_z; therefore the corresponding eigenvalue of j_z is $\mu/(\mu/j\hbar) = j\hbar$. This requirement is also fulfilled by the eigenvalues of l_z, but only when j is an integer and coincides with the orbital angular momentum quantum number l of Chapter 14. On the other hand, the quantum number j determined by molecular beam experiments may have half-integral values; this happens for beams which split into an even number of components (page 90). Thus the angular momentum of some atomic systems, as defined by their behavior in magnetic fields, has sets of eigenvalues in excess to those of the orbital angular momentum of a particle's motion with respect to a center of coordinates. Summarizing, a component μ_z of the magnetic moment μ has the eigenvalues indicated in Eq. 17 page 90, namely, $\mu m/j$, where

m is a number that varies in steps of one from $-j$ to j; the value $\mu/j\hbar$ of the gyromagnetic ratio requires a component j_z of $\mathbf{j}$ to have the eigenvalues

$$j_z = m\hbar, \tag{6}$$

with the same limitations on m.

As mentioned on page 221, molecular beam particles which are in an eigenstate of μ_z have their mean magnetic moment $\langle\boldsymbol{\mu}\rangle$ directed along the z axis, so that $\langle\mu_x\rangle = \langle\mu_y\rangle = 0$. It follows that the mean components of the angular momentum $\langle j_x\rangle$ and $\langle j_y\rangle$ vanish for any particle in an eigenstate of j_z. On the other hand, the mean squared values $\langle\mu_x{}^2\rangle$, $\langle\mu_y{}^2\rangle$, and $\langle j_x{}^2\rangle$, $\langle j_y{}^2\rangle$, do not vanish, in general, for particles in an eigenstate of μ_z and j_z. These mean square values can be calculated, since the probability of each eigenvalue $\bar{m}\hbar$ of j_x or j_y is known for particles in an eigenstate of j_z. This probability can be taken from the Table on page 92 with $\theta = 90°$. It is particularly important that each eigenstate of j_z proves to be an eigenstate of $j_x{}^2 + j_y{}^2$ [4] with the eigenvalues

$$j_x{}^2 + j_y{}^2 = [j(j+1) - m^2]\hbar^2. \tag{7}$$

Therefore, all eigenstates of j_z are also eigenstates of the squared angular momentum $\mathbf{j}^2 = j_x{}^2 + j_y{}^2 + j_z{}^2$, for molecular beams that split into a simple pattern as assumed in Chapter 7. Even though the eigenvalues $j_z = m\hbar$ depend on m, the eigenvalues of $\mathbf{j}^2$ depend only on j, since

$$\mathbf{j}^2 = j_x{}^2 + j_y{}^2 + j_z{}^2 = [j(j+1) - m^2]\hbar^2 + m^2\hbar^2 = j(j+1)\hbar^2. \tag{8}$$

These eigenvalues coincide with the eigenvalues of the squared orbital angular momentum $\mathbf{l}^2$ (page 200) when j is an integer and coincides with l. Any molecular beam whose particles are homogeneous except for current orientation and that splits into $2j + 1$ components in a Stern-Gerlach experiment can be regarded as a combination of eigenstates of j_z and is therefore in an eigenstate of $\mathbf{j}^2$ with the eigenvalue (8). That is, the squared angular momentum of atomic particles is determined by the number of states of orientation of their internal currents separated by a Stern-Gerlach magnet.

(c) Gyromagnetic ratio of orbital currents. Experimental measurements of the gyromagnetic ratio γ serve to test assumptions about the mechanism of current circulation within atoms by comparing

---

[4] To prove this, one must show that the mean value of $(j_x{}^2 + j_y{}^2)^2$ is just the square of the mean value of $j_x{}^2 + j_y{}^2$; the proof requires not only the probabilities given in the Table on page 92 but also the corresponding probability amplitudes in the Table on page 116. The proof can also be given by equivalent but more direct mathematical procedures.

experimental and calculated values. The calculation of γ is simple when the current consists of a charge transport by pointlike particles in any state of motion with a net flow along closed loops. Given a uniform magnetic field of strength H in the z direction, the energy of any current loop is $-iA_zH$, where i is the current intensity (in electromagnetic units) and A_z the area enclosed by the loop projected on a plane perpendicular to z (see also page 87). The product iA_z is the magnetic moment component μ_z of the loop. If the current consists of a charge q which revolves around the loop n times per second, we have $iA_z = qnA_z$. The product nA_z equals the component l_z of the orbital angular momentum of the particle divided by twice its mass. The proof of this statement is simplest for a circular loop: calling r the radius of the loop, v the velocity of the particle and m its mass, we have $nA_z = (v/2\pi r)(\pi r^2) = \frac{1}{2}vr = \frac{1}{2}(mvr)/m = \frac{1}{2}l_z/m$. The gyromagnetic ratio is therefore

$$\gamma = \frac{\mu_z}{l_z} = \frac{q(\frac{1}{2}l_z/m)}{l_z} = \frac{1}{2}\frac{q}{m}. \tag{9}$$

That is, the gyromagnetic ratio depends only on the specific charge of the carrier particles. For an electron the charge q, in electromagnetic units, is $-e/c$ (c = light velocity) and $m = m_e$, so that the gyromagnetic ratio of any electron flow along closed loops is

$$\gamma = -\frac{1}{2}\frac{e}{m_ec}. \tag{10}$$

It will be seen that the experimental values of the gyromagnetic ratio of atoms do not agree, in general, with the calculated value (10). Therefore, internal atomic currents do not consist entirely of a flow of electrons.

15.2   Evidence on the Electron Spin

(a) Nature of experimental information. Evidence on intraatomic currents is provided by molecular beam experiments and by observation of the Zeeman effect, that is, of the optical spectra of atoms in a magnetic field. The interpretation of molecular beam experiments is very direct, but these experiments are performed mainly on atoms in their ground state. On the other hand, the determination of atomic energy levels from the Zeeman effect has very extensive applications, but requires a detailed analysis of the observed wavelengths of spectral lines, taking into account their relative intensities. Both types of experiments determine in last resort energy eigenvalues of atoms in a uniform magnetic field.

The number of different energy eigenvalues increases in the presence of a magnetic field because the energy of an atom includes a magnetic term which depends on the orientation of internal currents with respect to the field. If the field direction is taken as the z axis, the magnetic energy is $-\mu_z H$ (Eq. 18, page 93); one may express μ_z as the product of the angular momentum component j_z and of the gyromagnetic ratio (2), $\gamma = \mu/j\hbar$, and write

$$E_{\mathrm{magn}} = -\mu_z H = -\gamma j_z H = -\gamma m\hbar H. \tag{11}$$

When a group of energy levels is separated by the action of a magnetic field, the number of levels identifies, in general, the angular momentum quantum number j, and the spacing $\gamma\hbar H$ between levels with successive values of m measures the gyromagnetic ratio γ. For the excited states of the hydrogen atom, however, the analysis is complicated by the unusual circumstance that in the absence of a magnetic field states of different squared angular momentum $\mathbf{l}^2$ have the same energy, in the approximation of Chapter 14. Relativistic corrections, due to the fact that the electron's velocity is not altogether negligible with respect to the light velocity, make the energy dependent on $\mathbf{l}^2$, but only by a very small amount, comparable to the level separation by a magnetic field. The combination of comparable effects complicates the analysis.

Valuable and clear-cut evidence is provided by experiments with elements other than hydrogen, particularly with the alkaline metals. An alkali atom may be regarded in good approximation (see Chapter 18) as a combination of a single electron and of a positive ion which acts as a center of attraction. The classification of stationary states is then quite similar to that of the hydrogen atom, but states with equal n and different l have different energies.[5, 6]

Additional evidence on intraatomic currents and their magnetic effects is provided by the "fine structure" of atomic spectra, that is, by the occurrence of tight groups of energy levels in the absence of an external magnetic field. The well-known "doublet" of the sodium spectrum, consisting of two yellow lines with wavelengths of 5890 and 5896 A, is due to transitions originating from two closely spaced energy levels. The interpretation of the fine structure will be given in the next chapter.

---

[5] The energy levels of the hydrogen atom are independent of l owing to a special property of the attraction by a pointlike nucleus, see footnote 8, page 205.

[6] The azimuthal quantum number l of energy levels was determined empirically by spectral analysis even before its mechanical significance was established. The classification of l values rests on the fact that light is emitted or absorbed with great intensity only in transitions in which an electron gains or loses one unit of angular momentum (see Appendix IX).

(**b**) *Results.* The following qualitative results on intraatomic currents cannot be interpreted entirely on the basis of a flow of electrons of the type considered in Chapter 14.

(1) Beams of hydrogen atoms in their ground state split into two components upon analysis with a Stern-Gerlach magnet, whereas no electron flow exists in this state, according to the qualitative and mathematical analysis of the electron motion. That is, magnetic analysis reveals the existence of two ground states whose energies coincide in the absence of a field. A number of energy levels *double* that expected from the study of electron motion is observed by magnetic analysis of all systems with a single electron, notably in the spectrum of hydrogen and of the alkalies. The occurrence of fine structure doublets in the alkali spectra is similarly unexpected on the basis of electron motion.

(2) The observed gyromagnetic ratios depart, in general, from the value $-\frac{1}{2}e/m_e c$, which is expected according to Eq. 10 for currents consisting of an electron flow. The circulating currents detected by magnetic analysis in the ground states of hydrogen, of the alkalies, and of other atoms, for example, Ag, have a gyromagnetic ratio, $-e/m_e c$, double that of orbital currents.

(3) The splitting of ground states into two components, and, in general, the splitting of any energy level in an *even* number of components, is incompatible with the assumption that the squared angular momentum $\mathbf{j}^2$ of the level arises entirely from the rotational motion of electrons. (The squared orbital angular momentum $\mathbf{l}^2$ of the rotational motion has the eigenvalues $l(l + 1)\hbar^2$, with l integer, and it has an *odd* number, $2l + 1$, of eigenstates for each eigenvalue.) In other words, the experimental occurrence of states of current circulation with *half-integer* quantum numbers m and j is not accounted for by the orbital motion of the electrons. Even numbers of components and half-integer quantum numbers are observed for all levels of atoms with an odd number of electrons and never for atoms with an even number of electrons.

These results can be sorted out empirically in terms of two types of circulating currents, one of which consists of an electron flow, as expected from the earlier treatment of the electron motion, and another one, called the "spin current" which requires further definition. From this standpoint one may state that:

(4) Stationary states with no orbital motion, that is, with $l = 0$, and without any electron flow exhibit spin currents with gyromagnetic ratio $-e/m_e c$.

(5) Stationary states with $l \neq 0$, which are expected to exhibit an orbital current, exhibit in general circulating currents whose gyromag-

netic ratio is neither $-\frac{1}{2}e/m_ec$ nor $-e/m_ec$. This result indicates a coexistence of orbital and spin currents and is associated with the occurrence of the fine structure in the spectra.

(6) In atoms with an even number of electrons, some of the energy levels have no fine structure. The stationary states of these levels exhibit circulating currents attributable entirely to electron flow with a gyromagnetic ratio $-\frac{1}{2}e/m_ec$.

(c) *Conclusions.* Even though the experimental observations on circulating currents are not accounted for by the treatment of electron motion outlined in Chapter 14, that treatment proves quite successful in many respects. Not only does it yield the correct gross spectrum of energy levels and the size of the hydrogen atom but also many other correct results, for example, the intensity of spectral lines and the energy eigenvalues of the atom when subjected to an electric field. Besides these successes, one must consider that currents consisting of electron flow appear to be present, as predicted in Chapter 14, even though accompanied by other currents. The treatment of Chapter 14 appears thus to be incomplete rather than erroneous.

Let us recall that the objective in Chapter 14 was to represent a complete set of energy eigenstates as combination of position eigenstates of the electron. It can be verified that the problem so formulated was solved completely, that is, without overlooking any combination of position eigenstates.[7] The detection by magnetic experiments of twice as many stationary states as predicted in Chapter 14 means that stationary states are not described fully in terms of the position of the electron. The electron must then have another variable with just two eigenvalues, no more, no less; otherwise the number of stationary states would not be just doubled. This variable must be independent of the position coordinates and compatible with them, that is, either of its eigenvalues is consistent with any eigenvalue of the electron position. It also interacts very weakly with other characteristics of the electron motion, as shown by the small separation of the energy levels in the fine structure.

The additional variable is represented by a quantum number which identifies the eigenstates of spin current circulation about an arbitrary axis. Stationary states that exhibit only spin currents, such as the ground state of hydrogen (item (4) above), are identified by eigenvalues of the angular momentum component in the direction of the magnetic field, $j_z = m\hbar = \pm\frac{1}{2}\hbar$. One takes the magnetic quantum number

---

[7] The set of states classified in Sect. 14.1 is "complete" in the sense indicated on page 97 when extended to include ionized states. That is, any state of an electron which is represented as a combination of position eigenstates by probability amplitudes $(\mathbf{r}|a)$, can also be represented as a combination of stationary states, $(\mathbf{r}|a) = \Sigma_{Elm\alpha}(\mathbf{r}|Elm\alpha)(Elm\alpha|a)$.

$m = \pm\frac{1}{2}$ in this formula as the spin current variable, with two eigenvalues, $\frac{1}{2}$ and $-\frac{1}{2}$. To indicate that this quantum number pertains to the spin current, a subscript s is added to the general symbol m. The spin variable is then

$$m_s = \pm\tfrac{1}{2}. \tag{12}$$

This variable describes adequately the relevant information about the spin current, since this current is detected and defined only by its angular momentum and magnetic moment. The spin angular momentum is usually indicated by the symbol $\mathbf{s}$ whose component along the z axis has the eigenvalues

$$s_z = m_s\hbar = \pm\tfrac{1}{2}\hbar. \tag{13}$$

The squared spin angular momentum is indicated by $\mathbf{s}^2$ and has a single eigenvalue characterized, in analogy with other angular momenta, by a quantum number s with the single value $\frac{1}{2}$. The eigenvalue of $\mathbf{s}^2$ is therefore

$$\mathbf{s}^2 = s(s+1)\hbar^2 = \tfrac{1}{2}(\tfrac{1}{2}+1)\hbar^2 = \tfrac{3}{4}\hbar^2. \tag{14}$$

The spin magnetic moment has the eigenvalues

$$\mu_z = -\frac{e}{m_e c}s_z = -m_s\frac{e}{m_e c}\hbar = \pm\frac{e\hbar}{2m_e c}. \tag{15}$$

The magnitude of these eigenvalues,

$$\frac{e\hbar}{2m_e c} = 9.0 \times 10^{-21}\frac{\text{erg}}{\text{gauss}} = 5.6 \times 10^{-9}\frac{\text{ev}}{\text{gauss}}, \tag{16}$$

is a convenient unit of atomic magnetic moments, called the "Bohr magneton." For comparison, notice that the magnetic moment of an orbital current is, according to (10), $\mu_z = -\frac{1}{2}(e/m_e c)l_z = -\frac{1}{2}(e/m_e c)m\hbar = -(e\hbar/2m_e c)m$, that is, a multiple of the Bohr magneton.

The spin current and angular momentum considered here must be a property of electrons because all stationary states of an odd number of atomic electrons have half-integral values of the angular momentum quantum number j; the value of j is integral when the number of electrons is even (end of item (3)). The occurrence of this current and angular momentum is regarded as a basic property of electrons, called "electron spin." [8]

---

[8] Dirac has shown that the electron spin emerges automatically from a treatment of electron quantum mechanics which is consistent from the start with the requirements of relativity theory. The treatment in this book extends to quantum physics the laws of ordinary, non-relativistic, macroscopic physics. Dirac's theory relates the spin to a persistent fluctuating motion of the electron's charge and mass about an average position coordinate.

The next chapter outlines how the spin current combines with orbital currents through a weak magnetic interaction to yield the fine structure of alkali atoms and their observed Zeeman effect.   It also indicates how the spin currents of different electrons may combine with one another and particularly cancel out in pairs, in some instances, so as to leave the electron flow undisturbed.

PROBLEMS

15.1   Analysis by a Stern-Gerlach magnet splits a beam of nitrogen atoms into four components and determines that these atoms have a magnetic moment $\mu = 2.7 \times 10^{-20}$ erg/gauss (see Problems 7.1 and 7.2).   Calculate from these data the gyromagnetic ratio of the atoms and thereby determine whether their magnetic moment stems from orbital or spin currents.

15.2   The spectral line of mercury at 1849 A splits, under the influence of a magnetic field of 1000 gauss, into three components separated by 0.0016 A intervals.   Determine whether this Zeeman effect is normal or anomalous, and thereby determine the orbital or spin character of the current affected by the field.

Magnetic interactions and the combination of angular momenta

Orbital and spin currents exert magnetic forces on one another and are also influenced by external magnets. These magnetic forces are weak but influence greatly the type of stationary states and the spectrum of energy levels. Weak disturbances have a major effect when different stationary states have the same energy; for example, if there are states with the same energy but with different eigenvalues of an angular momentum component, an infinitesimal torque may change one of these states into another one. This chapter deals with the effect of magnetic forces on the orbital and spin currents of a single electron, and particularly on the electron's energy levels. Emphasis is laid, however, on features of the treatment which occur in numerous problems of atomic and molecular physics.

The first step of the procedure consists of singling out groups of states that would have the same energy if magnetic forces did not exist, namely, states that differ only in the orientation of their orbital and spin currents. When the magnetic disturbance is introduced, there will be new stationary states which can be represented as combinations of the old ones.

Primarily, a weak disturbance combines states with the same, or nearly the same, energy; states with greatly different energy enter the combination with negligible probability amplitudes. The treatment of weak disturbances relies on the approximation of disregarding combinations of states whose energy difference greatly exceeds the energy of the disturbance. In our problem, each combination includes only a group of states with exactly the same energy, because energy differences between groups are much larger than the magnetic interaction energy. It is helpful that each group consists only of a limited number of states.

The second step consists of identifying some predictable characteristic of the eigenstates of the total energy inclusive of magnetic interactions. Thus, in the absence of any strong magnetic field, the total energy eigenstates are shown to be eigenstates of the squared total (orbital + spin) angular momentum $\mathbf{j}^2$ and of one of its components j_z (Sect. 16.1).

The next step of the procedure determines the eigenvalues of $\mathbf{j}^2$ and j_z for states represented as combinations of an initial group of states. Since the initial group consists of eigenstates of the squared orbital and spin angular momenta, $\mathbf{l}^2$ and $\mathbf{s}^2$, and since $\mathbf{j} = \mathbf{l} + \mathbf{s}$, this problem is called the "addition of angular momenta." It is a problem that occurs often in atomic physics. With the eigenvalues of $\mathbf{j}^2$, $\mathbf{l}^2$, and $\mathbf{s}^2$ expressed in the form $j(j + 1)\hbar^2$, $l(l + 1)\hbar^2$, and $s(s + 1)\hbar^2$, it is shown that, for given l and s, the possible values of j range in steps of one between the sum and difference of l and s, that is, are [1]

$$j = l + s, \qquad l + s - 1, \cdots, \qquad |l - s| + 1, \qquad |l - s|. \qquad (1)$$

Since $s = \frac{1}{2}$ for the spin angular momentum, j takes only the two values $l \pm \frac{1}{2}$, which accounts for the *doublet* fine structure of the alkali spectra (Sect. 16.2).

Equation 1 also gives the rule for the combination of spin angular momenta in atoms and molecules with more than one electron. Combination of any pair of spins with $s_1 = s_2 = \frac{1}{2}$ yields only two possible eigenvalues of their squared resultant angular momentum, with $j = s_1 + s_2 = 1$ and $j = s_1 - s_2 = 0$. The spin currents and spin angular momenta of electron pairs thus cancel out exactly when their combined state has $j = 0$, as anticipated on page 230. Any magnetic effect depends, then, only on orbital currents.

Once the eigenvalues of $\mathbf{j}^2$ are thus identified, the problem of magnetic interaction is already solved to a considerable extent. The eigenstates of $\mathbf{j}^2$ are just the energy eigenstates inclusive of interaction energy in the absence of an external field. The joint eigenstates of $\mathbf{j}^2$ and j_z are also approximately stationary states in the presence of a weak magnetic

---

[1] The symbol $|l - s|$ indicates $l - s$ or $s - l$, whichever is non-negative.

field in the z direction.   Details of the magnetic interactions need not even be calculated for the purpose of a qualitative investigation.   Without any further detail, one can enumerate and classify the closely spaced energy levels which constitute the "fine structure" of energy spectra. For each level one can also determine the gyromagnetic ratio of the combined orbital and spin currents, which is the main characteristic of the anomalous Zeeman effect.   On the other hand, when there is a strong external magnetic field, the orbital and spin currents interact with it more strongly than with one another, and the initial groups of states turn out to be approximately stationary (Sect. 16.3).

16.1   Qualitative Analysis

States of the hydrogen atom with a definite circulation of orbital current about the z axis have been described in Sect. 14.3.   A state of this type is identified by the set of quantum numbers (n,l,m) and is represented as a combination of position eigenstates by a wave function $(r,\theta,\phi \,|\, n,l,m)$ (Eq. 18, page 211).   A definite circulation of spin current about a direction parallel to the z axis is specified by the quantum number $m_s = \pm \frac{1}{2}$.   A state with a definite orientation of each separate current with respect to the z axis is therefore specified by the set of *four* quantum numbers

$$(n,l,m,m_s). \tag{2}$$

These numbers indicate that the state is an eigenstate of the following quantities: (*a*) spin angular momentum component s_z with eigenvalue $m_s \hbar$; (*b*) orbital angular momentum component l_z with eigenvalue $m\hbar$; (*c*) squared orbital angular momentum $\mathbf{l}^2$ with eigenvalue $l(l+1)\hbar^2$; and (*d*) radial motion with $n - l - 1$ dark interference fringes.   An alkali atom, regarded as a combination of a single electron with a positive ion, has states identified by the same set of quantum numbers (2) as the hydrogen atom.

States identified by the quantum numbers (n,l,m,m_s) are *not*, in general, stationary states, because of the interaction ("coupling") of the orbital and spin currents.   Each of these currents generates a magnetic field which causes the other current to precess, much as in the Larmor phenomenon.   However, the magnetic energy of the spin-orbit coupling is negligible as compared to the differences between the energy levels of an electron which are found by the methods of Chapter 14.   Therefore, one achieves a very good approximation by representing each stationary state of the total energy, inclusive of magnetic interactions, as a combination of a group of states (n,l,m,m_s) with the same non-magnetic energy.

The treatment of the hydrogen atom meets a special difficulty at this point. Stationary states with equal n and different l have the same energy, according to Chapter 14, but then the energy is modified by effects of relativity (see page 226) to an extent which depends on l. The modifications are comparable to the energy of spin-orbit coupling and therefore both effects must be considered simultaneously in a realistic treatment. To avoid this complication, the treatment in this chapter is intended to apply to the single outer electron of an alkali atom rather than to hydrogen.

The non-magnetic energy is then dependent on both quantum numbers n and l, and will be indicated as E_{nl}. For given values of n and l, the total energy has eigenvalues close to E_{nl} and eigenstates represented by combinations of states (n,l,m,m_s) with equal (n,l) and different (m,m_s), that is, with different orientations of the orbital and spin currents. There are $2l + 1$ values of m for the given l and two values of m_s, namely, $\pm\frac{1}{2}$; therefore, we are considering a group of $2(2l + 1)$ states.

To determine the total energy eigenvalues and the corresponding eigenstates, one might follow here the general procedures indicated in Chapter 12 or in Appendix VIII. One would express the mean value of the total energy of the electron in a state represented as a combination of our group of $2(2l + 1)$ states with arbitrary probability amplitudes. The dependence of the mean energy on these probability amplitudes would then single out exactly $2(2l + 1)$ combinations which represent energy eigenstates. However, one may proceed more rapidly by noticing that in our problem the total energy eigenstates have a number of characteristics sufficient to identify them.

The magnetic coupling between orbital and spin currents within an atom exerts no torque on the atom as a whole. Therefore, the coupling leaves unaffected the total angular momentum of the atom, which may be indicated as the vector sum of the orbital and spin angular momenta

$$\mathbf{j} = \mathbf{l} + \mathbf{s}. \tag{3}$$

Spin-orbit coupling leaves, therefore, the mean angular momentum $\langle \mathbf{j} \rangle$ constant. It follows that the stationary states in the presence of spin-orbit coupling can be eigenstates of $\mathbf{j}^2$ and of one component of $\mathbf{j}$, for example, of $j_z = l_z + s_z$. It will be shown in the next section that there are exactly $2(2l + 1)$ eigenstates of $\mathbf{j}^2$ and j_z with different eigenvalues of these variables. Therefore, specification of these eigenvalues is sufficient to identify an eigenstate of the spin-orbit coupling energy.

Prior to the development of quantum mechanics, it was not realized that components of the angular momentum in different directions have no common eigenstate (except when $\mathbf{j}^2 = 0$), and that, therefore, $\mathbf{j}$ has no definite direction. The effect of spin-orbit coupling was then illustrated by the diagram of Fig. 16.1 and by the statement that **j** remains fixed, whereas the coupling causes **l** and **s** to precess about **j**.

Eigenstates of $\mathbf{j}^2$ and j_z with the same eigenvalue of $\mathbf{j}^2$ and different eigenvalues of j_z must have the same energy of spin-orbit coupling, because the component j_z of the angular momentum relates to an arbitrary coordinate axis which is irrelevant to the spin-orbit coupling. Therefore, the spin-orbit energy can have only as many different eigenvalues as there are different eigenvalues of $\mathbf{j}^2$. There are only two of these eigenvalues consistent with a given eigenvalue of $\mathbf{l}^2$, as will be shown in the next section.

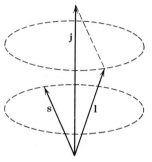

Consider now the total energy in the presence of a magnetic field in the z direction. The energy consists of the non-magnetic energy E_{nl}, of the spin-orbit coupling energy, and of the interaction energy with the field. In the first place, the energy depends now on the value of j_z, so that each energy level of spin-orbit coupling splits into as many levels

Fig. 16.1 Vector model of the addition and precession of angular momenta.

as there are eigenvalues of j_z; this number is $2j + 1$ for states with $\mathbf{j}^2 = j(j + 1)\hbar^2$. Second, the magnetic field exerts a torque on the orbital and spin currents and the energy eigenstates are no longer, in general, eigenstates of $\mathbf{j}^2$, but only eigenstates of j_z because the torque has no component in the z direction. However, eigenstates of $\mathbf{j}^2$ and j_z remain approximately eigenstates of the energy, as long as the energy of interaction with the external field remains much smaller than the energy of spin-orbit coupling. A detailed calculation is necessary to identify the eigenstates when the coupling with the external field is comparable to the spin-orbit coupling. When the coupling with the external field predominates, it is sufficient to consider that the energy of this coupling depends only on the separate orientations of the orbital and spin currents with respect to the field. Therefore, the initial states with quantum numbers (n,l,m,m_s) are the approximate energy eigenstates.

An additional magnetic interaction exists between the spin and orbital currents of atomic electrons and internal currents within the nuclei of atoms. Atomic nuclei have angular momenta, called "nuclear spins," with the same eigenvalues as electron angular momenta. However, their gyromagnetic ratios are smaller by factors of the order of 1000, corresponding to the much higher mass to be entered in the gyromagnetic ratio (9), page 225, for a flow of protons (hydrogen nuclei). The coupling of the electron currents and nuclear spins brings about an additional multiplicity of energy levels, called "hyperfine structure." The level separation in the hyperfine structure is small in proportion to the smallness of the nuclear gyromagnetic ratio. Like the spin-orbit coupling, the coupling of electrons and nuclei also complicates the energy levels of atoms in magnetic fields. However, one can often find a range of magnetic field strengths such that the interaction with the field is much stronger than the electron-nuclear coupling and weaker than the spin-orbit coupling. The complications of the coupling are then minimized.

16.2   The Addition of Angular Momenta

We wish to determine the eigenvalues of $\mathbf{j}^2 = (\mathbf{l} + \mathbf{s})^2$ and of $j_z = l_z + s_z$, whose joint eigenstates can be represented as combinations of the initial states (n,l,m,m_s). The states (n,l,m,m_s) are themselves eigenstates of l_z and s_z with eigenvalues $m\hbar$ and $m_s\hbar$, as noted on page 233. If l_z and s_z have a definite value, so has their sum j_z. Therefore, each initial state is an eigenstate of j_z, with the eigenvalue

$$j_z = l_z + s_z = (m + m_s)\hbar. \tag{4}$$

The problem is thereby greatly reduced, since we shall have to consider only combinations of states (n,l,m,m_s) with different (m,m_s) but with the same sum $m + m_s$.

Classification of the initial states as eigenstates of j_z permits the determination of the possible eigenvalues of $\mathbf{j}^2$, as may be seen through the following example. Consider the case of $l = 2$. We have here $2(2l + 1) = 10$ initial states (n,l,m,m_s) whose combinations of quantum numbers are listed in Table 16.1. The table shows one state with each of the eigenvalues $j_z = \frac{5}{2}\hbar$, $-\frac{5}{2}\hbar$, and two states with each of the eigenvalues $\frac{3}{2}\hbar$, $\frac{1}{2}\hbar$, $-\frac{1}{2}\hbar$, $-\frac{3}{2}\hbar$. Since there is only one state with $m + m_s = \frac{5}{2}$, namely $(2,\frac{1}{2})$, this state must be itself an eigenstate of $\mathbf{j}^2$, whereas, for example, for $m + m_s = \frac{3}{2}$ an eigenstate of $\mathbf{j}^2$ is a combination of the states $(2,-\frac{1}{2})$ and $(1,\frac{1}{2})$. By the same token, the state $(-2,-\frac{1}{2})$ is also an eigenstate of $\mathbf{j}^2$. For the two states $(2,\frac{1}{2})$ and $(-2,-\frac{1}{2})$ the eigenvalue of $\mathbf{j}^2$ must be $j(j + 1)\hbar^2$, with $j = \frac{5}{2}$. Any smaller value of j would be inconsistent with $j_z = \pm\frac{5}{2}\hbar$. Any larger value of j would imply the existence of eigenstates of j_z with eigenvalues larger than $\frac{5}{2}\hbar$, because for any $\mathbf{j}^2 = j(j + 1)\hbar^2$ there are states with all eigenvalues of j_z from $-j\hbar$ to $j\hbar$.[2] The same argument shows that, since there are eigenstates of $\mathbf{j}^2$

---

[2] In this problem, all directions of space are equivalent and therefore all components of $\mathbf{j}$ must have eigenstates with the same eigenvalues. Any eigenstate of j_z and of $\mathbf{j}^2$, with the eigenvalue $\mathbf{j}^2 = j(j + 1)\hbar^2$ splits out into $2j + 1$ eigenstates when analyzed according to the component of $\mathbf{j}$ in a direction different from z. Therefore, every component must have every one of its possible eigenvalues.

TABLE 16.1

Eigenstates of	l_z	s_z	j_z	$\mathbf{j}^2$
Quantum Numbers	m	m_s	$m + m_s$	j

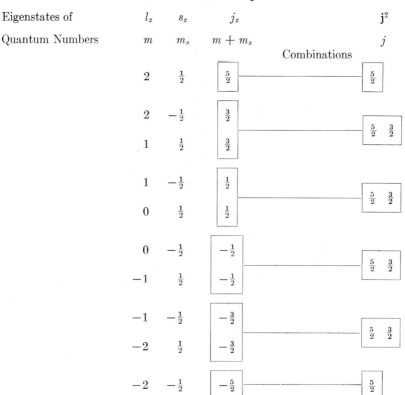

Combinations

with $j = \frac{5}{2}$ and $j_z = \pm\frac{5}{2}\hbar$, there must be four more eigenstates of $\mathbf{j}^2$ with $j = \frac{5}{2}$ and with eigenvalues of j_z equal to $\frac{3}{2}\hbar$, $\frac{1}{2}\hbar$, $-\frac{1}{2}\hbar$ and $-\frac{3}{2}\hbar$. Each of these states must be a combination of the two states with $m + m_s$ equal $\frac{3}{2}$, $\frac{1}{2}$, $-\frac{1}{2}$, and $-\frac{3}{2}$, respectively.

Once a combination of any two states is singled out, in our case as an eigenstate of $\mathbf{j}^2$ with eigenvalue $j = \frac{5}{2}$, there is only one other combination mutually exclusive with it. Therefore, there still remain four combinations, one for each of the four eigenvalues of j_z from $\frac{3}{2}\hbar$ to $-\frac{3}{2}\hbar$. These combinations constitute a set of eigenstates of $\mathbf{j}^2$ with $j = \frac{3}{2}$, as indicated in Table 16.1.

The analysis is thereby concluded. The ten initial states (n,l,m,m_s) combine into two new sets consisting respectively of 6 and 4 eigenstates of $\mathbf{j}^2$, with two values of the quantum number j, namely, $\frac{5}{2}$ and $\frac{3}{2}$. This

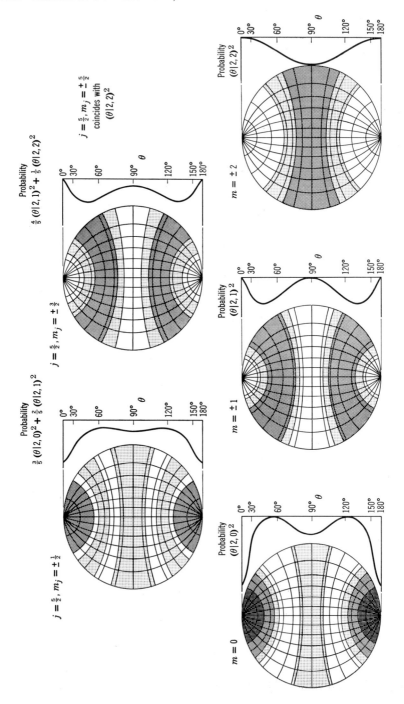

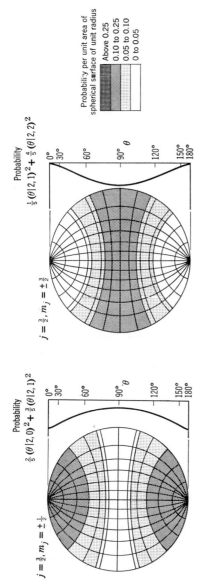

Fig. 16.2 Probability distribution on spherical surfaces of the electron in eigenstates (n,l,j,m_j) and (n,l,m) with $l = 2$, and $j = \frac{5}{2}, j = \frac{3}{2}$. Profiles represent probability distribution along meridians. Top row: (r,l,j,m_j) with $j = \frac{5}{2}$; middle row: (n,l,m); bottom row: (n,l,j,m_j) with $j = \frac{3}{2}$.

result has been obtained simply by scoring the possible combinations without any need for determining the probability amplitudes of each combination. Each of the eigenstates of $\mathbf{j}^2$ may be identified by a set of four quantum numbers. Two quantum numbers are the same n and l which label the initial states; one is the total angular momentum quantum number j, and the fourth one indicates the value of $m + m_s$ and is called for brevity m_j,

$$(n,l,j,m_j). \tag{5}$$

Two generalizations of the preceding example are readily obtained. Firstly, if l has any value other than zero, the possible values of j are

$$j = l + \tfrac{1}{2}, \qquad j = l - \tfrac{1}{2}. \tag{6}$$

For $l = 0$ there is no orbital current and the problem does not arise; j coincides with the spin quantum number $s = \tfrac{1}{2}$. The two eigenvalues (6) are said, somewhat loosely, to result, respectively, from parallel and opposite orientations of the orbital and spin currents and angular momenta. The doublet structure of alkali energy levels is explained by the result (6). The two levels of the doublet are identified by the two different values of j with the same value of n and l. The yellow doublet lines of the sodium spectrum arise from transitions between the levels of a doublet, with $l = 1$ and $j = \tfrac{3}{2}$ and $\tfrac{1}{2}$, and the ground state with $l = 0$ and $j = \tfrac{1}{2}$.

Second, one may regard $\mathbf{l}$ and $\mathbf{s}$ as representing any two angular momenta, not necessarily orbital and spin, so that the quantum number s need not be $\tfrac{1}{2}$ and l need not even be an integer. Table 16.1 becomes then more extensive and its analysis more laborious, but no different principle is involved. The possible values of j are found to be

$$j = l + s, l + s - 1, l + s - 2, \cdots |l - s| + 1, |l - s|. \tag{7}$$

This result, already noted on page 232, is called the "triangular condition," because of its analogy with the macroscopic problem of vector addition indicated in Fig. 16.1. The construction of a triangle whose sides are represented by vectors $\mathbf{a}$, $\mathbf{b}$, and $\mathbf{c} = \mathbf{a} + \mathbf{b}$ requires that c be no larger that the sum of a and b and no smaller than their difference.

The probability amplitudes which serve to represent the states (n,l,j,m_j) as combinations of states (n,l,m,m_s), and also to represent reciprocally the (n,l,m,m_s) as combinations of (n,l,j,m_j) may be indicated by $(m,m_s|j,m_j)$. They are algebraic functions of the quantum numbers l,s,j,m,m_s and $m_j = m + m_s$, called "Wigner coefficients." Knowledge of these coefficients is required to calculate the probability distribution of electron positions in states (n,l,j,m_j). The probability distribution in states (n,l,m,m_s) is given by the wave functions $(r,\theta,\phi|n,l,m)$ of Sect.

14.3, which are not altered by the presence of the spin current, indicated by m_s, since in our initial states the precession of orbit and spin currents is not taken into account. However, the precession, represented by the combination of states with different m and m_s, has the effect of smearing out the probability distribution. An example of this effect is illustrated in Fig. 16.2.

16.3   Energy Eigenvalues

The energy of spin-orbit coupling, that is, the magnetic interaction energy of the orbital and spin currents, may be expressed as energy of the spin current in the magnetic field generated by the orbital motion. The spin current must be considered in a coordinate system attached to the electron. In this system, the electron's charge is at rest and does not generate any magnetic field, but the nucleus of the atom appears to be in motion and to generate a magnetic field. This field is proportional to the orbital angular momentum and depends on the strength of the nuclear electric attraction upon the electron. The coupling energy is found to be given by

$$E_{\text{coup}} = \left\langle \frac{Z}{r^3} \right\rangle_{nl} \frac{1}{2} \left(\frac{e}{m_e c} \right)^2 \mathbf{l} \cdot \mathbf{s}. \tag{8}$$

In this formula $\langle Z/r^3 \rangle_{nl}$ indicates the mean value of the effective nuclear charge [3] in units of e divided by the cubed distance of the electron from the nucleus and averaged over the probability distribution of this distance for a state with the given quantum numbers (n,l); $\frac{1}{2}(e/m_e c)^2$ is the product of the gyromagnetic ratios of the orbital and spin currents.

Even though there are no eigenstates of the directions of $\mathbf{l}$ and $\mathbf{s}$, and of the angle between them, there are eigenstates of the product $\mathbf{l} \cdot \mathbf{s}$, because this product can be expressed as a function of the squared angular momenta $\mathbf{l}^2$, $\mathbf{s}^2$, and $\mathbf{j}^2$. A set of eigenvalues of $\mathbf{j}^2$, $\mathbf{l}^2$, and $\mathbf{s}^2$ defines in effect the mutual orientation of the orbital and spin currents, as indicated by the diagram in Fig. 16.1. The product $\mathbf{l} \cdot \mathbf{s}$ is obtained from the relation $\mathbf{j} = \mathbf{l} + \mathbf{s}$ through the formula $\mathbf{j}^2 = (\mathbf{l} + \mathbf{s})^2 = \mathbf{l}^2 + \mathbf{s}^2 + 2\,\mathbf{l} \cdot \mathbf{s}$, which gives

$$E_{\text{coup}} = \left\langle \frac{Z}{r^3} \right\rangle_{nl} \frac{1}{2} \left(\frac{e}{m_e c} \right)^2 \mathbf{l} \cdot \mathbf{s} = \left\langle \frac{Z}{r^3} \right\rangle_{nl} \frac{1}{4} \left(\frac{e}{m_e c} \right)^2 (\mathbf{j}^2 - \mathbf{l}^2 - \mathbf{s}^2). \tag{9}$$

---

[3] In atoms other than hydrogen, the net attraction experienced by an electron at a distance r from the nucleus results from the combination of the nuclear attraction and of the repulsion by the other electrons. The net attraction may be expressed as the attraction by a single particle with an "effective charge" Ze where Z depends on the distance r from the nucleus.

Here the eigenvalue of $\mathbf{l}^2$ is $l(l+1)\hbar^2$ for each group of levels with the same (n,l); $\mathbf{s}^2$ has the single eigenvalue $s(s+1)\hbar^2 = \frac{3}{4}\hbar^2$ according to Eq. 14, page 229, and $\mathbf{j}^2 = j(j+1)\hbar^2$ with the two eigenvalues $j = l \pm \frac{1}{2}$ given by Eq. 6. The two eigenvalues of E_{coup} are therefore

$$E_{\text{coup}} = \left\langle \frac{Z}{r^3} \right\rangle_{nl} \frac{1}{4} \left(\frac{e}{m_e c} \right)^2 [j(j+1) - l(l+1) - s(s+1)]\hbar^2$$

$$= \begin{cases} \left\langle \dfrac{Z}{r^3} \right\rangle_{nl} \left(\dfrac{e\hbar}{2m_e c} \right)^2 \left[\left(l + \dfrac{1}{2}\right)\left(l + \dfrac{1}{2} + 1\right) - l(l+1) - \dfrac{3}{4} \right] \\[2mm] \qquad = \left\langle \dfrac{Z}{r^3} \right\rangle_{nl} \left(\dfrac{e\hbar}{2m_e c} \right)^2 l, \\[4mm] \left\langle \dfrac{Z}{r^3} \right\rangle_{nl} \left(\dfrac{e\hbar}{2m_e c} \right)^2 \left[\left(l - \dfrac{1}{2}\right)\left(l - \dfrac{1}{2} + 1\right) - l(l+1) - \dfrac{3}{4} \right] \\[2mm] \qquad = -\left\langle \dfrac{Z}{r^3} \right\rangle_{nl} \left(\dfrac{e\hbar}{2m_e c} \right)^2 (l+1). \end{cases} \tag{10}$$

For each stationary state (n,l,j,m_j), the eigenvalue (10) of E_{coup} must be added to the non-magnetic energy eigenvalue E_{nl}.

In the presence of an external magnetic field, the combined energy of all magnetic interactions is the sum of the energy E_{coup} and of the energy of the orbital and spin currents in the magnetic field. The energy of a circulating current in a magnetic field of strength H along the z axis is $-\mu_z H$ (see Eq. (18), page 93), where μ_z is the effective moment of the current circulating about the z axis. Utilizing the expressions of the orbital and spin moments given by Eqs. 9, 10, page 225 and 15, page 229, the combined magnetic energy is given by

$$\left\langle \frac{Z}{r^3} \right\rangle_{nl} \frac{1}{2} \left(\frac{e}{m_e c} \right)^2 \mathbf{l} \cdot \mathbf{s} - (\mu_{\text{orbit}})_z H - (\mu_{\text{spin}})_z H$$

$$= \left\langle \frac{Z}{r^3} \right\rangle_{nl} \frac{1}{2} \left(\frac{e}{m_e c} \right)^2 \mathbf{l} \cdot \mathbf{s} + \left(\frac{1}{2} \frac{e}{m_e c} l_z + \frac{e}{m_e c} s_z \right) H$$

$$= \left\langle \frac{Z}{r^3} \right\rangle_{nl} \left(\frac{1}{2} \frac{e}{m_e c} \right)^2 \left(\mathbf{j}^2 - \mathbf{l}^2 - \mathbf{s}^2 \right) + \frac{1}{2} \frac{e}{m_e c} \left(j_z + s_z \right) H. \tag{11}$$

The determination of the eigenstates and eigenvalues of this energy is not immediate, in general, because $\mathbf{j}^2$ and s_z have no common eigenstate, as pointed out in the qualitative analysis. On the other hand, there is no difficulty with $\mathbf{l}^2$, $\mathbf{s}^2$, and j_z, which have common eigenstates with either $\mathbf{j}^2$ or s_z. When the magnetic field strength H is sufficiently low, the stationary states of the electron are approximately eigenstates of $\mathbf{j}^2$.[4] One may then replace in (11) $\mathbf{j}^2$ with its eigenvalue $j(j+1)\hbar^2$ and s_z with its mean value calculated for an eigenstate of $\mathbf{j}^2$. For the calculation of this mean value the eigenstates of $\mathbf{j}^2$ need not be expressed as combinations of states (n,l,m,m_s), because one can show that $\langle s_z \rangle = (\mathbf{s}\cdot\mathbf{j}/\mathbf{j}^2)\,j_z$, with $j_z = m_j\hbar$; it is also seen, in analogy to (9), that $\mathbf{s}\cdot\mathbf{j} = \frac{1}{2}(\mathbf{j}^2 + \mathbf{s}^2 - \mathbf{l}^2)$. We have therefore

$$\langle s_z \rangle = \frac{\mathbf{s}\cdot\mathbf{j}}{\mathbf{j}^2}\,j_z = \frac{1}{2}\frac{j(j+1)+s(s+1)-l(l+1)}{j(j+1)}j_z, \tag{12}$$

and

$$(\mu_{\mathrm{orb}})_z + (\mu_{\mathrm{spin}})_z = -\frac{1}{2}\frac{e}{m_e c}(j_z + \langle s_z \rangle)$$

$$= -\frac{1}{2}\frac{e}{m_e c}\left[1 + \frac{1}{2}\frac{j(j+1)+s(s+1)-l(l+1)}{j(j+1)}\right]j_z$$

$$= -\frac{1}{2}\frac{e}{m_e c}\,g\,j_z. \tag{13}$$

In this formula, the coefficient g, called the "Lande' factor," serves to convert the gyromagnetic ratio $-\frac{1}{2}e/m_e c$ of orbital currents into a combined gyromagnetic ratio of the spin and orbital currents in an eigenstate of $\mathbf{j}^2$. Notice that g is larger or smaller than one depending on whether $j = l \pm \frac{1}{2}$, that is, on whether the spin and orbital currents have parallel or opposite directions.

The combined magnetic energy (11) becomes now

$$\left\langle \frac{Z}{r^3} \right\rangle_{nl}\left(\frac{1}{2}\frac{e}{m_e c}\right)^2 (\mathbf{j}^2 - \mathbf{l}^2 - \mathbf{s}^2) + \frac{1}{2}\frac{e}{m_e c}gHj_z$$

$$= \left\langle \frac{Z}{r^3} \right\rangle_{nl}\left(\frac{e\hbar}{2m_e c}\right)^2 [j(j+1) - l(l+1) - s(s+1)] + \frac{e\hbar}{2m_e c}gHm_j. \tag{14}$$

Thus the energy levels of stationary states separate out in a weak magnetic field by amounts proportional to the magnetic field strength H. This separation, observed as a splitting of spectral lines, is called the

---

[4] The remarks on page 170 are important in this connection. A small error ϵ in the probability amplitudes which should identify a stationary state as a combination of states (n,l,m,m_s) yields an error of smaller order ϵ^2 in the resulting estimate of the energy eigenvalue.

"Zeeman effect." The Zeeman effect is "normal" when there is no effective spin current and successive levels differ by $(e\hbar/2m_ec)H$, that is, when $g = 1$, it is "anomalous" when the level separation is modified by the presence of spin currents, according to Eqs. 13 and 14.

As the magnetic field strength H increases, the stationary states depart increasingly from being eigenstates of $\mathbf{j}^2$. The magnetic field exerts separate torques upon the orbital current and the spin current and strives to make them precess at different rates, owing to their different gyromagnetic ratios, while the spin-orbit coupling strives to keep their mutual orientation constant. To determine the energy eigenvalues one must then derive a Schroedinger equation by the general methods of Chapter 12 or of Appendix VIII; however, the procedure is neither complicated nor laborious as each stationary state is a combination of only two initial states (n,l,m,m_s). In fact, the Schroedinger equation reduces to a system of two first degree algebraic equations. In this case the separation of energy levels is no longer proportional to the field strength.

For very strong fields the spin-orbit coupling has only a very minor effect and the stationary states are approximately states of independent orientation of the orbital and spin currents, that is, they coincide approximately with the initial states (n,l,m,m_s). In the expression (11) of the total magnetic energy one may then replace l_z and s_z with their eigenvalues $m\hbar$ and $m_s\hbar$, and $\mathbf{l}\cdot\mathbf{s}$ with its mean value calculated for a state (n,l,m,m_s). In a state of this type the components of $\mathbf{l}$ and $\mathbf{s}$ perpendicular to the z axis have mean value zero, so that $\langle\mathbf{l}\cdot\mathbf{s}\rangle = \langle l_x s_x\rangle + \langle l_y s_y\rangle + \langle l_z s_z\rangle$ reduces to $\langle l_z\rangle\langle s_z\rangle$, the product of the eigenvalues $m\hbar$ and $m_s\hbar$. Equation 11 becomes then

$$\left\langle\frac{Z}{r^3}\right\rangle_{nl} \frac{1}{2}\left(\frac{e}{m_ec}\right)^2 \langle\mathbf{l}\cdot\mathbf{s}\rangle + \left(\frac{1}{2}\frac{e}{m_ec}l_z + \frac{e}{m_ec}s_z\right)H$$

$$= \left\langle\frac{Z}{r^3}\right\rangle_{nl} 2\left(\frac{e\hbar}{2m_ec}\right)^2 mm_s + \left(\frac{e\hbar}{2m_ec}\right)H(m + 2m_s). \quad (15)$$

Under these conditions the level separations are again proportional to the magnetic field strength. Because the magnetic field controls the spin orientation to a much greater extent than the spin-orbit coupling, the orbital motion can readily change from one to another stationary state without any change of spin orientation. Emission and absorption of light occurs then usually without any change of the quantum number m_s. The splitting of spectral lines observed in a very strong field derives only from level separations $(e\hbar/2m_ec)H$ and thus constitutes a normal Zeeman effect.

PROBLEMS

16.1   Apply the general procedure for the analysis of weak disturbances to discuss and evaluate the effect of an electric field of 1000 volts/cm on the group of states of the H atom with quantum number $n = 2$.   Disregard the effect of the electron spin.

16.2   Calculate the gyromagnetic ratio of the H atom in states with the following values of the quantum numbers l and j: $(0, \frac{1}{2})$, $(1, \frac{1}{2})$, $(1, \frac{3}{2})$, $(2, \frac{3}{2})$, $(2, \frac{5}{2})$.

16.3   The doublet lines of the sodium spectrum at 5890 and 5896 A are due to transitions to the ground state $(l = 0, j = \frac{1}{2})$ from the two excited states with $l = 1$ and with $j = \frac{1}{2}$ and $j = \frac{3}{2}$.   Estimate the magnetic field strength required to disturb significantly the spin-orbit coupling, taking as a criterion of significance that the energy difference between the states $(l = 1, j = \frac{3}{2}, m_j = \frac{1}{2})$ and $(l = 1, j = \frac{1}{2}, m_j = \frac{1}{2})$ be changed by the field by $\frac{1}{100}$ of its value in the absence of field.

chapter 17

The Pauli
exclusion principle

The volume of a macroscopic amount of condensed matter shrinks only slightly under external pressure. This property of matter is not adequately accounted for by the structural stability of single atoms, that is, by the fact that the electrons of an atom withstand the electric attraction by the nucleus without collapsing on it. The stability of macroscopic matter also implies that atoms have the property of withstanding interpenetration. Moreover, the resistance to interpenetration must operate not only between atoms but also between different electrons of an atom; otherwise the increasing nuclear charge of successive atoms along the periodic system of elements would draw in their electrons into decreasing volumes, contrary to evidence.

The stability of atoms against collapse under the nuclear attraction has been formulated in Chapter 11 as an effect of the reaction of electrons to confinement. The stability against interpenetration derives from another property of electrons, which was discovered by Pauli in 1925 and is called the "exclusion principle." This property expresses a characteristic of any system of two or more electrons, or of any identical

particles, (for example, protons) with the same spin properties as electrons. Experimental evidence shows that no two such particles are ever
confined within the same region of space, to the extent permitted by
complementarity, unless their spin currents are opposite. Therefore,
once an electron is confined within a certain region, it "excludes" from
it any other electron whose spin current is not opposite to its own.

The stability of a physical system against a disturbance implies that
the disturbance would force up the internal energy of the system. The
stability of bulk matter against external pressure is regarded macroscopically as deriving from an increase of "elastic" energy which ac-
companies a reduction in volume. Atomistically, it hinges on the stability of atomic electrons against both the nuclear attraction and interpenetration. The stability of an electron against nuclear attraction
derives from the increase of *kinetic energy* which would result from confinement into a narrower volume. The stability against interpenetration
will also be shown to derive from an increase in kinetic energy which
occurs when a number of electrons are forced into the same region of
space.

Examination of the properties of light atoms in their ground state
leads to an elementary formulation of the exclusion principle: In an
approximation where the motion of each electron of an atomic system is
characterized by a complete set of quantum numbers, for example, by
the set (n,l,m,m_s), which applies to the hydrogen atom, *no two electrons
have the same quantum numbers* (Sect. 17.1). This formulation constitutes only a particular case of a more general property of any system
of identical particles. It is, however, adequate to interpret most features of the ground states of atoms and molecules, which are the subject
of the following chapters.

The general formulation of the exclusion principle may be derived from
the study of phenomena, like the collision of two electrons, which involve
only two identical particles, without the complication of an atomic
nucleus. If we call L the azimuthal quantum number of the rotation of
two identical particles about their center of mass and S their total spin
angular momentum quantum number, the sum $L + S$ is experimentally
observed to be always even. In particular, two electrons with parallel
spins, $(S = 1)$, must have L odd and therefore different from zero;
thereby their rotational motion about their center of mass has a non-
vanishing angular momentum and yields a centrifugal force which keeps
the electrons apart (Sect. 17.2).

A convenient formulation of this result is commonly given by representing states of two electrons initially *as though* the electrons were different and therefore identifiable by indices. If two electrons are at

positions r_1 and r_2, it is inherently undefined which of them is at r_1 and which at r_2. Nevertheless, one usually considers states identified as $(r_1, m_{s1}; r_2, m_{s2})$, meaning that electron 1 is at r_1 with spin orientation quantum number m_{s1}, and electron 2 is at r_2 with orientation m_{s2}. The state in which electron 1 is at r_2 with orientation m_{s2} and electron 2 is at r_1 with orientation m_{s1} is regarded formally as different from $(r_1, m_{s1}; r_2, m_{s2})$ and may be identified by $P(r_1, m_{s1}; r_2, m_{s2})$, where P means permutation, or interchange, of the particles. Neither of these states exists in fact, but an actual state may be represented formally as a superposition of pairs of states $(r_1, m_{s1}; r_2, m_{s2})$ and $P(r_1, m_{s1}; r_2, m_{s2})$. The exclusion principle is then formulated by stating that the probability amplitudes of the states of such a pair differ by a factor -1. The elementary formulation follows from this property (Sect. 17.3).

This general formulation of the exclusion principle has a typical application in the treatment of the optical spectrum of the helium atom. The energy of each spectral level of this atom depends strongly on whether its two electrons have parallel or opposite spin currents, whereas the magnetic interaction between these currents has only a minor effect. The exclusion principle makes the motion of the electrons strongly dependent upon their spin orientation and explains the observed spectrum in considerable detail (Sect. 17.4).

17.1 Evidence from Light Atoms

Evidence on the exclusion property of electrons is provided by the trend of properties of atoms along the periodic system. It is sufficient to consider the ground state of atoms of the first five or six elements, and specifically their radii, their ionization potentials, and their magnetic properties. The radii and the ionization potentials are inversely related to one another, as it is to be expected since a small radius implies a tight binding of the electrons.

As compared to hydrogen, the helium atom has a small radius and a high ionization potential, 24.6 volts as compared to 13.6 volts. This property results clearly from the stronger attraction by the nucleus; the attraction is opposed by the electrostatic repulsion between the electrons, which, however, has a small influence as could be easily predicted. A beam of helium atoms in their ground state remains undeflected in molecular beam experiments, showing that the spin currents of the two electrons are so oriented as to cancel one another's magnetic moment and angular momentum. Mutual cancellation is one of the two possible results of the addition of two spin angular momenta, as explained on page 232. The sum of two angular momenta with quantum number

$s = \frac{1}{2}$ may yield a total angular momentum with a quantum number S [1] equal to either $\frac{1}{2} + \frac{1}{2} = 1$ or $\frac{1}{2} - \frac{1}{2} = 0$. No state of helium with parallel spins ($S = 1$) exists whose binding energy and radius are comparable to those of the ground state; the lowest level with $S = 1$ has a binding energy of 4.8 ev as compared to 24.6 ev for the ground state. This result shows that two electrons can be confined to the extent permitted by complementarity only if their resultant spin angular momentum vanishes.

The three-electron atom, namely Li, is larger than He and also larger than H and has a lower ionization potential, 5.4 volts. It behaves in molecular beam experiments exactly like hydrogen, showing that the magnetic properties of its ground state stem from the spin of a single electron with no circulating orbital current. It appears thus that three electrons cannot be packed within as narrow a space as two electrons, and that two out of the three electron spin currents cancel out in the atom. Notice that the Li^+ ion with two electrons is quite analogous to the He atom, only smaller.

The successive atoms in the periodic system, from Li through Ne, get progressively smaller, until Ne is nearly as small as He with an ionization potential of 21.6 volts. (The next atom after Ne, namely Na, is again much larger.) The four-electron atom which follows Li, namely Be, is, like He, undeflected in molecular beam experiments, and therefore has a zero resultant angular momentum. A beam of B atoms (five electrons) is resolved into two components, like a beam of H or Li. However, the gyromagnetic ratio of the ground state of B is much smaller than the value $e/m_e c$ which pertains to an electron spin uncoupled to any orbital current. It has the value pertaining to a spin current coupled with an orbital current of azimuthal quantum number $l = 1$.

All these properties of light atoms are readily formulated in an "independent-electron" approximation, in which each electron is initially considered as subject to an average force due to the nuclear attraction and to repulsion by the other electrons. Each electron has then stationary states that may be characterized by the set of quantum numbers (n,l,m,m_s) which apply to the electron of the hydrogen atom. In this approximation, each electron has two possible ground states, with $n = 1$, $l = m = 0$ and $m_s = \pm\frac{1}{2}$. The He atom appears to have one of its two electrons in each of these ground states. (If both electrons had the same value of m_s, the resultant S value would be one, contrary to the molecular beam evidence.) The larger radius of Li implies that

---

[1] Capital letters are commonly used to indicate variables and quantum numbers pertaining to a system of two or more particles.

one of its electrons has kinetic energy higher than the minimum corresponding to the ground state of a single electron and must therefore be in a state with $n > 1$, presumably with $n = 2$. The absence of orbital currents shows that $l = 0$ and therefore also $m = 0$ (see Sect. 14.3). The similarity of the Li^+ ion to the He atom indicates that two of the electrons of Li are in the same states as the electrons of He. For Be, the Be^+ ion resembles the Li atom, while the Be^{++} ion resembles He. The third and fourth electrons of Be must have opposite spin orientation and appear to be in the two states with $n = 2$, $l = 0$ and $m_s = \pm\frac{1}{2}$. In B, four electrons are in the same states as the Be electrons, while the fifth one has an orbital angular momentum with quantum number $l = 1$.

This analysis can be extended to all atoms of the periodic system, but the data considered thus far suffice to show that no two atomic electrons have the same set of quantum numbers (n,l,m,m_s). Similar evidence can be gathered from other systems with several electrons, in particular from molecules (see Part II). Whatever complete set of quantum numbers characterizes the states of individual electrons, no two electrons of a system are ever in the same state.

17.2   States of Two Identical Particles

The exclusion properties of two identical particles are best studied in phenomena where the particles are isolated, that is, not subjected to external forces like the attraction by a nucleus. Identical particles with an electric charge, for example, electrons or protons, or He nuclei (α particles), repel each other; therefore, they do not form by themselves stable combinations, but their motion with respect to one another is studied in collision processes. These processes are observed through experimental arrangements shown schematically in Fig. 17.1 and analogous to the Rutherford scattering experiment. A beam of particles is scattered by particles of the same kind contained in the thin layer of matter which serves as a target. The scattering of any incident particle is accompanied by recoil of the target particle with which the collision has taken place. Two particles emerge, therefore, from the target. Both of them can be observed simultaneously but, if they are identical, it remains inherently undefined which of them is the "scattered" and which the "recoil" particle. The results of experiments or theory must therefore give the probability of observing two particles emerging at angles θ and θ' with respect to the direction of incidence, rather than the probability of deflection θ of the incident particle. Actually, the angles θ and θ' are not independent because, when two identical particles collide and one was initially at rest, they emerge from the collision traveling in directions perpendicular to one another, that is, with $\theta + \theta' = 90°$.[2] The result of a collision is therefore identified by a single angle θ which ranges from $0°$ to $90°$ (a value of $\theta > 90°$ would be inconsistent with the

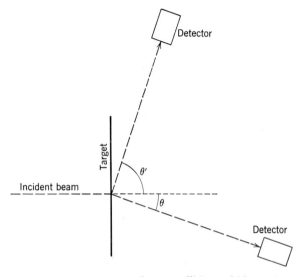

Incident beam

Target

Fig. 17.1 Schematic arrangement to observe collisions of identical particles. The detectors score simultaneously only if their directions are perpendicular and coplanar with the direction of the incident beam.

conservation of momentum in an elastic collision between identical particles). Since $\theta' = 90° - \theta$, particle counters placed at the angles θ and $90° - \theta$ must score at equal rates. That is, the plot of the cross

---

[2] For two particles of the same mass, the conservation of momentum requires that the transverse components of the velocities **V** and **V'** be opposite,

$$V \sin\theta - V' \sin\theta' = 0 \qquad (a)$$

and that the sum of the longitudinal components equal the velocity v of the incident particle,

$$V \cos\theta + V' \cos\theta' = v. \qquad (b)$$

The conservation of energy requires that

$$V^2 + V'^2 = v^2. \qquad (c)$$

The square of (a) added to the square of (b) yields

$$V^2 + V'^2 + 2VV'(\cos\theta \cos\theta' - \sin\theta \sin\theta') = v^2,$$

which, combined with (c), reduces to

$$2VV' \cos(\theta + \theta') = 0, \text{ that is } \theta + \theta' = 90°.$$

section is symmetric with respect to $\theta = 45°$, in contrast to the Rutherford formula.

Experiments bear out these conclusions, showing that the cross section for collisions between identical particles departs substantially from that observed with different particles under otherwise similar conditions. Thus the scattering of α particles on helium gas consisting of the normal isotope of mass 4 departs from the Rutherford formula, but the Rutherford formula holds when the α particles of mass 4 are replaced with nuclei of the helium isotope of mass 3. Similarly, the scattering of protons on hydrogen depends on the isotopic composition of the hydrogen. Electron-electron scattering also departs from the Rutherford formula. The departure is not simply due to different detection procedures, because the cross section for collision of identical particles with emergence of one particle at an angle θ is not the average of the Rutherford cross sections for deflections θ and $90° - \theta$. The departure derives from differences in the interference effects, which are considered below.

In the theoretical analysis of a collision between two particles, it is sufficient to consider the motion of the particles with respect to one another, separately from the uniform motion of their center of mass. (See Appendix III and the treatment of the hydrogen atom in Sect. 14.5.) It is also sufficient to consider a stationary state of the relative motion, that is, a steady flow of particles (see page 181) approaching one another in the direction of incidence and scattered out in various directions by their mutual repulsion. The scattering cross section is determined by the ratio of the flow outgoing in any one direction to the incident flow. The stationary state is represented by a wave function that obeys a Schroedinger equation analogous to that of the hydrogen atom. The stationary state is not an eigenstate of the squared orbital angular momentum, but can be regarded as a combination of such eigenstates; it is in this sense analogous to the states of hydrogen with off-center probability distributions, described in Sect. 14.4.

The quantum mechanical calculation of the collision between *different* charged particles yields the same results as the classical Rutherford calculation of Chapter 3. Characteristic differences between the states of identical and different particles are pointed up by the analysis of these states in eigenstates of the orbital angular momentum **L** of the two particles with respect to their center of mass. In either case, the state of the colliding particles is an eigenstate of the component L_z of **L** in the direction of incidence with eigenvalue $L_z = 0$, because **L**, the moment of momentum, has no component in the direction of incidence. In the quantum mechanical calculation, the state of the colliding particles can be represented as a superposition of eigenstates of the squared orbital angular momentum $\mathbf{L}^2 = L(L + 1)\hbar^2$. In each of these eigenstates the direction of the relative position of the two particles (see Fig. 17.2) has the same probability of forming an angle Θ or $180° - \Theta$ with the z axis. (This symmetry is the same as that of the proton-electron direction in the H atom, which is symmetrical with respect to the equatorial plane;

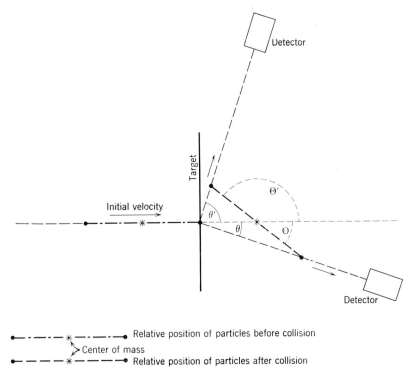

Fig. 17.2 Relative positions of particles at equal times before and after collision in the arrangement of Fig. 17.1.

see Fig. 14.6, etc.) In the eigenstates of $\mathbf{L}^2$ and of $L_z = 0$, the probability distribution of the direction joining the two particles has a bright or a dark fringe centered on the equatorial plane $\Theta = 90°$, depending on whether the quantum number L is even or odd. The interference among states with a bright fringe centered at $\Theta = 90°$ preserves the symmetry of the probability distribution, and so does the interference among states with a dark fringe centered at $\Theta = 90°$. On the other hand, the cross interference of states with dark and bright fringes destroys the symmetry. In the quantum-mechanical calculation of the Rutherford cross section, the asymmetry of the result with respect to $\Theta = 90°$ stems from the cross interference. In collisions of identical particles the symmetry with respect to $\theta = 45°$ in Fig. 17.1 is equivalent to symmetry with respect to $\Theta = 90°$ in Fig. 17.2. This *symmetry excludes cross interference* between component eigenstates with even and odd L.

The exclusion of cross interference in the collision of identical particles follows from symmetry consideration only. More detailed information is to be drawn from analysis of experimental data. The results apply to pairs of particles with spin quantum numbers s equal to any half-integer or integer; for example, $s = 0$ for α particles, and $s = \frac{1}{2}$ for electrons or protons. For any such pair, an eigenvalue of the squared resultant spin angular momentum is indicated by $\mathbf{S}^2 = S(S + 1)\hbar^2$, where the quantum number S has integral values between zero and $2s$; for example, $S = 0$ or 1 for a pair of electrons with opposite or parallel spins. Analysis of the collision experiments shows that all states of identical particles result from the superposition of eigenstates of $\mathbf{L}^2$ with even values of L if S is even and with odd values of L if S is odd. That is, all states of identical particles which are eigenstates of $\mathbf{L}^2$ and of $\mathbf{S}^2$ obey the rule

$$L + S = \text{even.} \tag{1}$$

This rule, confirmed by all relevant experiments, constitutes one of the basic formulations of the exclusion principle, when applied to particles with half-integer spin quantum number s. It states, in particular, that any pair of electrons with parallel spins, that is, with $S = 1$, cannot have a vanishing orbital angular momentum, that is, $L = 0$. The non-vanishing rotational motion gives rise to a centrifugal force which keeps the electrons apart from one another.

States of identical colliding particles that are eigenstates of $\mathbf{L}^2$ and of $\mathbf{S}^2$ have not been isolated for direct experimental study. However, isolation of such states and direct verification of rule (1) are possible when the particles are bound together by some external agent which does not otherwise disturb them. Such is the case for the pair of protons bound together as nuclei of a normal hydrogen molecule (H_2). The structure of this molecule will be discussed in Chapter 19; here it suffices to consider that the presence of the electrons confines the distance of the two nuclei to an approximately fixed value, but does not influence their rotational motion about their center of mass or the orientation of the nuclear spins. Stationary states of this rotation are eigenstates of $\mathbf{L}^2$ and $\mathbf{S}^2$. Molecular beam experiments separate out molecules in different eigenstates and measure the eigenvalues of $\mathbf{L}^2$ and $\mathbf{S}^2$. Equivalent information is provided by the low temperature thermodynamics and infrared spectroscopy of hydrogen, which behaves as a mixture of two substances, called para- and orthohydrogen. The two substances change into one another only very slowly. They differ by having their nuclear spins respectively opposite and parallel to one another, that is, by being in eigenstates of $\mathbf{S}^2 = S(S + 1)\hbar^2$ with $S = 0$ and $S = 1$. The stationary states of molecular rotation about the center of mass of the nuclei are eigenstates of $\mathbf{L}^2 = L(L + 1)\hbar^2$ with L even for parahydrogen and odd for orthohydrogen, in agreement with (1). The ground state of the rotation has $L = 0$ and therefore belongs to parahydrogen. The energy difference between the lower stationary states of rotation exceeds the energy of thermal agitation at temperatures of the order of $50°K$ ($-220°C$). At these temperatures, all molecules of orthohydrogen drop first into their lowest energy level, with $L = 1$, and then are slowly converted into parahydrogen, thereby dropping to the ground state with $L = 0$.

17.3   Formulation in Terms of Probability Amplitudes

For a pair of identical particles, the limitations to the eigenvalues of $\mathbf{L}^2$ and $\mathbf{S}^2$ expressed by (1) constitutes a formulation of the exclusion principle in terms of observable quantities. An equivalent but more flexible formulation can be given in terms of the probability amplitudes which identify a general state of two or more identical particles as a superposition of eigenstates of any variables of the separate particles. It is convenient and usual to express these probability amplitudes in a form that would be appropriate if the particles were not quite identical, that is, *as though* one could identify one specific particle as 1, another one as particle 2, etc. The effects of this unrealistic assumption are subsequently compensated by a restriction applied to the probability amplitudes.

Given two particles, 1 and 2, with spin quantum numbers $s = \frac{1}{2}$, a complete set of states of the pair is indicated by position coordinates and spin orientation quantum numbers $(\mathbf{r}_1, m_{s1}; \mathbf{r}_2, m_{s2})$. Since the relative motion of the particles is independent of the motion of their center of mass, the coordinates $\mathbf{r}_1$ and $\mathbf{r}_2$ are conveniently replaced, as on page 215, with

$$\mathbf{R} = \tfrac{1}{2}(\mathbf{r}_1 + \mathbf{r}_2), \qquad \mathbf{r} = r\boldsymbol{\omega} = \mathbf{r}_1 - \mathbf{r}_2, \qquad (2)$$

where $\mathbf{R}$ is the position of the center of mass and $\boldsymbol{\omega}$ is a unit vector pointing from $\mathbf{r}_2$ toward $\mathbf{r}_1$. The set of states may then be indicated by $(\mathbf{R}, r, \boldsymbol{\omega}, m_{s1}, m_{s2})$. Since the two particles are identical, a state of this set is physically identical with the state $P(\mathbf{R}, r, \boldsymbol{\omega}, m_{s1}, m_{s2})$ that differs from it by an interchange of the particle positions (that is, reversal of $\boldsymbol{\omega}$) and spin orientations. Therefore, any actual state a of the two particles must be represented as a superposition of the pairs of states $(\mathbf{R}, r, \boldsymbol{\omega}, m_{s1}, m_{s2})$

and $P(\mathbf{R},r,\boldsymbol{\omega},m_{s1},m_{s2})$, with probability amplitudes

$$(\mathbf{R},r,\boldsymbol{\omega},m_{s1},m_{s2}\,|\,a) \tag{3a}$$

and

$$P(\mathbf{R},r,\boldsymbol{\omega},m_{s1},m_{s2}\,|\,a) \tag{3b}$$

respectively. Consider now how the probability amplitudes (3a) and (3b) differ when the state a is an eigenstate of $\mathbf{L}^2$, L_z, $\mathbf{S}^2$, and of the component S_z of $\mathbf{S}$ whose eigenvalues will be called $M_S\hbar$. The state a is identified by the quantum numbers L,M,S,M_S, by an additional index α which characterizes the relative radial motion of the particles along $\boldsymbol{\omega}$ and might be, for example, an energy, and by a momentum $\mathbf{P}$ which specifies the state of free motion of the center of mass. The probability amplitude (3) factors then out in the form

$$(\mathbf{R},r,\boldsymbol{\omega},m_{s1},m_{s2}\,|\,\mathbf{P},\alpha,L,M,S,M_S)$$
$$= (\mathbf{R}\,|\,\mathbf{P})(r\,|\,\alpha,L,M)(\boldsymbol{\omega}\,|\,L,M)(m_{s1},m_{s2}\,|\,S,M_S). \tag{4}$$

Here $(\boldsymbol{\omega}\,|\,L,M)$ is the same as $(\theta\,|\,l,m)(\phi\,|\,m)$ on page 211, if θ and ϕ are polar coordinates of $\boldsymbol{\omega}$, and $(m_{s1},m_{s2}\,|\,S,M_S)$ is determined by the procedure of addition of angular momenta of Sect. 16.2.

Interchange of the electron positions leaves the factors $(\mathbf{R}\,|\,\mathbf{P})$ and $(r\,|\,\alpha,L,M)$ unaffected, and reverses the direction of $\boldsymbol{\omega}$ in $(\boldsymbol{\omega}\,|\,L,M)$. According to Chapter 14, this reversal leaves $(\boldsymbol{\omega}\,|\,L,M)$ unaffected or changes its sign depending on whether L is even or odd,

$$P(\boldsymbol{\omega}\,|\,L,M) = (-\boldsymbol{\omega}\,|\,L,M) = (-1)^L(\boldsymbol{\omega}\,|\,L,M). \tag{5}$$

Interchange of the spin orientation quantum numbers leaves the last factor of (4), $(m_{s1},m_{s2}\,|\,S,M_S)$, unchanged when the electrons have parallel spin orientations, that is, when $S = 1$, whereas the interchange reverses the sign of this factor when $S = 0$.[3] This result is represented by

$$P(m_{s1},m_{s2}\,|\,S,M_S) = (-1)^{S+1}(m_{s1},m_{s2}\,|\,S,M_S). \tag{6}$$

In conclusion we have

$$P(\mathbf{R},r,\boldsymbol{\omega},m_{s1},m_{s2}\,|\,\mathbf{P},\alpha,L,M,S,M_S)$$
$$= (-1)^{L+S+1}(\mathbf{R},r,\boldsymbol{\omega},m_{s1},m_{s2}\,|\,\mathbf{P},\alpha,L,M,S,M_S). \tag{7}$$

---

[3] The quantum numbers, $S = 1$, $M_S = 1$, imply $m_{s1} = m_{s2} = \frac{1}{2}$, in which case the interchange clearly has no effect; the same holds for $S = 1$, $M_S = -1$. The result extends to $(S = 1, M_S = 0)$ because the value of M_S depends on an irrelevant choice of coordinate orientation. The state $S = 1$, $M_S = 0$ is then a superposition of $(m_{s1} = \frac{1}{2}, m_{s2} = -\frac{1}{2})$ and $(m_{s1} = -\frac{1}{2}, m_{s2} = \frac{1}{2})$ with equal probability amplitudes. The state $(S = 0, M_S = 0)$ is a superposition of the same states orthogonal to $(S = 1, M_S = 0)$ and therefore with probability amplitudes of equal magnitude and opposite sign.

The restriction established by experimental observation and expressed by the formulation (1) of the exclusion principle comes to bear at this point. Since $L + S$ is always even, the factor $(-1)^{L+S+1}$ equals -1 and Eq. 7 reduces to

$$P(\mathbf{R},r,\boldsymbol{\omega},m_{s1},m_{s2}\,|\,\mathbf{P},\alpha,L,M,S,M_S)$$
$$= -(\mathbf{R},r,\boldsymbol{\omega},m_{s1},m_{s2}\,|\,\mathbf{P},\alpha,L,M,S,M_S). \quad (8)$$

This equation embodies the formulation (1) of the exclusion principle, but its form is independent of the values of the quantum numbers L and S. Therefore, it holds for any combination of the eigenstates of $\mathbf{L}^2$ and $\mathbf{S}^2$ represented by (4), that is, it holds for a general state a,

$$P(\mathbf{R},r,\boldsymbol{\omega},m_{s1},m_{s2}\,|\,a) = -(\mathbf{R},r,\boldsymbol{\omega},m_{s1},m_{s2}\,|\,a). \quad (9)$$

Returning to separate position coordinates of the two particles, we may also write
$$P(\mathbf{r}_1,m_{s1}\,;\mathbf{r}_2,m_{s2}\,|\,a) = -(\mathbf{r}_1,m_{s1}\,;\mathbf{r}_2,m_{s2}\,|\,a). \quad (10)$$

That is, any state of two electrons, or of any two identical particles with $s = \frac{1}{2}$, can be represented as a superposition of states $(\mathbf{r}_1,m_{s1}\,;\mathbf{r}_2,m_{s2})$ labeled as though the particles were not identical, but the probability amplitudes of the components $(\mathbf{r}_1,m_{s1}\,;\mathbf{r}_2,m_{s2})$ and $P(\mathbf{r}_1,m_{s1}\,;\mathbf{r}_2,m_{s2})$ must differ exactly by a factor -1.

In atoms and molecules one deals usually with states of two electrons in which their center of mass does not move freely and which are not eigenstates of $\mathbf{L}^2$ but are eigenstates of $\mathbf{S}^2$ because the interaction between spin and orbital currents is negligible. These states are identified by quantum numbers S, M_S while the state of orbital motion may remain unspecified at this point and indicated with the letter β. These states are represented as superpositions of eigenstates of position and spin orientation of the individual electrons by probability amplitudes that factor out in the form

$$(\mathbf{r}_1,m_{s1}\,;\mathbf{r}_2,m_{s2}\,|\,\beta,S,M_S) = (\mathbf{r}_1,\mathbf{r}_2\,|\,\beta,S)(m_{s1},m_{s2}\,|\,S,M_S). \quad (11)$$

The complete probability amplitude must obey Eq. 10 and the factor $(m_{s1},m_{s2}\,|\,S,M_S)$ must obey Eq. 6. The probability amplitude $(\mathbf{r}_1,\mathbf{r}_2\,|\,\beta,S)$ of the position coordinates must then have the property

$$P(\mathbf{r}_1,\mathbf{r}_2\,|\,\beta,S) = (-1)^S\,(\mathbf{r}_1,\mathbf{r}_2\,|\,\beta,S). \quad (12)$$

That is, any state of orbital motion of two electrons can be represented as a superposition of position eigenstates $(\mathbf{r}_1,\mathbf{r}_2)$ labeled as though the two electrons were different, but the probability amplitudes of the components $(\mathbf{r}_1,\mathbf{r}_2)$ and $P(\mathbf{r}_1,\mathbf{r}_2)$ must be identical or differ by a factor -1, depending on whether the spins are opposite or parallel.

Equation 12 implies that in states with parallel spins ($S = 1$) the probability of finding the two electrons at the same position $\mathbf{r}_1 = \mathbf{r}_2$ vanishes, because the interchange of identical coordinates on the one hand should change the sign of the probability amplitude, but on the other hand constitutes no change. Two major consequences follow: (a) The vanishing of the wave function $(\mathbf{r}_1,\mathbf{r}_2\,|\,\beta,1)$ at $\mathbf{r}_1 = \mathbf{r}_2$ constitutes a "node." Insofar as any wave function with a node represents an excited state, a system of two electrons *cannot* be in its ground state if the spins are parallel, (b) The exclusion of $\mathbf{r}_1 = \mathbf{r}_2$ for electrons with parallel spins implies that, other circumstances being equal, these electrons keep further apart than if their spins were opposite, that is, the mutual spin orientation of a pair of electrons influences the probability distribution of their positions through the exclusion principle.

The formulation of the exclusion principle for a pair of electrons, expressed by Eq. 10, can be extended to a system of many electrons. A complete set of eigenstates of the position and spin orientation of N electrons, labeled as though the electrons were different, is $(\mathbf{r}_1,m_{s1}; \mathbf{r}_2,m_{s2}; \cdots; \mathbf{r}_N,m_{sN})$. As for the case of two electrons, any actual state a of the system must be represented as a superposition of states obtained by interchanging the position coordinates and spin orientations of all possible pairs among the N electrons. The superposition must have probability amplitudes obeying the law

$$P(\mathbf{r}_1,m_{s1}; \mathbf{r}_2,m_{s2}; \cdots; \mathbf{r}_N,m_{sN}\,|\,a)$$

$$= -(\mathbf{r}_1,m_{s1}; \mathbf{r}_2,m_{s2}; \cdots; \mathbf{r}_N,m_{sN}\,|\,a), \quad (13)$$

where P indicates the interchange of the position and spin orientation of *any two* among the N particles. This property constitutes the usual formulation of the exclusion principle for electrons.

Equation 13 implies that the probability amplitude vanishes whenever the positions and spin orientations of two electrons coincide, because here again interchange of the electrons constitutes no change, but should nevertheless reverse the sign of the probability amplitude.

As an initial complete set of states of the individual electrons one may take, instead of the position eigenstates, the eigenstates of any other variable, for example, stationary states of motion under the attraction by a nucleus. The probability amplitudes $(\mathbf{r}_1,m_{s1}; \mathbf{r}_2,m_{s2}; \cdots; \mathbf{r}_N,m_{sN}\,|\,a)$ may then be replaced with

$$(n_1,l_1,m_1,m_{s1}; n_2,l_2,m_2,m_{s2}; \cdots; n_N,l_N,m_N,m_{sN}\,|\,a)$$

$$= \Sigma_{\mathbf{r}_1} \Sigma_{\mathbf{r}_2} \cdots \Sigma_{\mathbf{r}_N}(n_1,l_1,m_1\,|\,\mathbf{r}_1)(n_2,l_2,m_2\,|\,\mathbf{r}_2) \cdots (n_N,l_N,m_N\,|\,\mathbf{r}_N)$$

$$\times (\mathbf{r}_1,m_{s1}; \mathbf{r}_2,m_{s2}; \cdots; \mathbf{r}_N,m_{sN}\,|\,a). \quad (14)$$

It follows then that the property stated by Eq. 13 holds also for the probability amplitudes (14). That is, the exclusion principle may be formulated equally well with reference to any complete set of states of the individual particles. In particular, the probability amplitude vanishes whenever any two electrons are in the same state, that is, whenever $(\mathbf{r}_i,m_{si}) = (\mathbf{r}_k,m_{sk})$ or, alternatively, $(n_i,l_i,m_i,m_{si}) = (n_k,l_k,m_k,m_{sk})$. States with equal sets of quantum numbers are thereby excluded, in accord with the elementary formulation of the exclusion principle given in Sect. 17.1.

17.4 The Spectrum of the Helium Atom

Analysis of the emission spectrum of helium according to the Rydberg-Ritz combination principle (page 49) shows that the helium atom has two distinct sets of spectral terms, that is, of energy levels. Each observed line frequency corresponds to the energy difference between two levels of one set.[4] The spectrum appears thus as if it were emitted by a mixture of two substances; the two "substances" thus identified by empirical analysis of the spectrum were called "parahelium" and "orthohelium." The ground state of helium belongs to the parahelium set of levels and lies nearly 20 ev lower than any other level. Orthohelium appears to constitute a metastable form of helium, whose conversion back into parahelium occurs hardly at all by emission of radiation but rather by less easily observable mechanisms such as collisions among gas atoms or with the containers' walls.

The parahelium spectrum exhibits no fine structure and a normal Zeeman effect (see pages 228 and 244). It follows that the spin currents of the two electrons in the parahelium states have opposite directions, that is, combine with resultant spin quantum number $S = 0$. The orthohelium spectrum exhibits a fine structure and an anomalous Zeeman effect, which indicate parallel spin currents and a spin quantum number $S = 1$. The extreme faintness of the intercombination lines between the two spectra stems from the low probability that the spin orientation changes in the course of an emission process. (The probability increases with the increasing strength of spin-orbit coupling in successive elements of the periodic system.)

Figure 17.3 shows the diagram of energy levels of the He atom. The arrows indicate transitions observed with appreciable intensity in the emission spectrum. The para- and ortho-systems of levels are separated inasmuch as no arrow interconnects them, and are similar except that

---

[4] "Intercombination lines" corresponding to transitions between levels of different sets are observed only with difficulty since their intensity is exceedingly low.

the deep-lying ground level of parahelium has no counterpart in ortho-helium.   The levels are arranged in columns, so that arrows join only levels of adjacent columns.   The levels of each column constitute a series which "converges" to the limit of ionization like the single series of

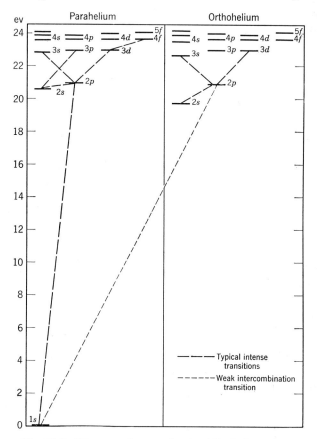

Fig. 17.3   Diagram of energy levels of the helium atom.

levels of the H spectrum (see page 50).   The fine structure of the ortho-helium spectrum is not indicated in Fig. 17.3; each group of levels that differ only in their spin-orbit coupling is indicated as a single level.

The subdivision of the helium levels into para- and ortho-systems and the main characteristics of these systems follow directly from the exclusion principle, as formulated in Sect. 17.3 and particularly from the remarks on page 258.[5]   States of the two electrons of the He atom with

_____

[5] In fact, the formulation of Sect. 17.3 was first developed by Heisenberg through the theory of the helium spectrum.

opposite or parallel spins are subject to the conditions expressed by Eq. 12 for $S = 0$ or $S = 1$. In particular, it has been noted that all ortho-states are excited states and that the two electrons keep further apart in ortho- than in para-states, other conditions being equal. Since the electrons repel each other, their potential energy is lower when they keep further apart, other conditions being equal; the excited states of the ortho-system are, in fact, lower than the corresponding ones of the para-system, as shown in Fig. 17.3.

The levels in each system are classified by pairs of quantum numbers (n,l) which characterize the radial motion and the rotational energy of a single electron attracted toward a center of force, as in the hydrogen atom. The classification implies that one regards the He atom in its excited states as the combination of a single electron and of a He$^+$ ion. Justification for this model derives from the fact that He$^+$ is very small and the probability of its electron position is distributed with spherical symmetry about the nucleus as in the ground state of the H atom. An electron outside a He$^+$ ion is therefore attracted toward the center of the ion as though the ion were a H nucleus. The attraction becomes stronger than in the H atom when the electron penetrates close to the nucleus of the He$^+$ ion; it follows that states with equal quantum number n and different l have somewhat different energies, as in the alkaline atoms. Notice that the quantum number l is the same for all levels of each column of Fig. 17.3, and differs by one in adjacent columns. The classification agrees thus with the general rule that an electron emits light intensely only in transitions between stationary states whose quantum numbers l differ by one (see Appendix IX).

The qualitative description of the He atom in its excited states as a combination of a He$^+$ ion and of an outer electron can be extended into a systematic approximation theory which yields quantitative results and applies also to the ground state, although with lower accuracy. Each electron is initially assumed to move independently of the other one and to be attracted toward the nucleus by a force which is not quite the same as either in a H atom or in a He$^+$ ion. The schematized attraction is represented by a potential energy $U(r)$ which depends only on the distance r from the nucleus and whose optimum determination will be discussed in Sect. 18.1. Stationary states of motion of a single electron are then represented, for example, by wave functions $(\mathbf{r} \mid n,l,m)$ which are similar to the hydrogen wave functions (18), page 211 and differ from them only in the radial factor $(r \mid n,l)$, owing to the difference in the potential energy.

We consider stationary states of the He atom with one electron in the ground state, $(n = 1, l = m = 0)$, and the other one in some excited state with unspecified quantum numbers n, l, and m. The energy of such a state may be indicated in the initial approximation as [6]

$$E_{1,0} + E_{n,l}. \tag{15}$$

The numbers n and l in this formula coincide with those that label the levels in Fig. 17.3, including the ground state of the atom for which $n = 1$ and $l = 0$. Disregarding the spin coordinates and indicating the position coordinates by $\mathbf{r}_1$ and $\mathbf{r}_2$, as though the electrons were not identical, one may write the wave functions of two states with the energy (15), in which one or the other electron is excited, namely,

$$(\mathbf{r}_1 \,|\, 1{,}0{,}0)(\mathbf{r}_2 \,|\, n{,}l{,}m) \quad \text{and} \quad (\mathbf{r}_2 \,|\, 1{,}0{,}0)(\mathbf{r}_1 \,|\, n{,}l{,}m). \tag{16}$$

For $n = 1$, $l = m = 0$, both electrons are in the ground state, the whole atom is in its ground state, and the two wave functions (16) coincide.

Starting from the energy eigenvalues (15) and eigenfunctions (16), one considers the disturbance, or "perturbation," represented by the difference between the schematized potential energy and the actual potential energy of the two electrons, due to their attraction by the nucleus and to their mutual repulsion. This difference is

$$V(\mathbf{r}_1\mathbf{r}_2) = -\frac{2e^2}{r_1} - \frac{2e^2}{r_2} + \frac{e^2}{|\mathbf{r}_1 - \mathbf{r}_2|} - [U(r_1) + U(r_2)]. \tag{17}$$

According to the procedure of Chapter 16, (pages 231–2) we assume that this disturbance combines the two states represented by (16) with one another, because they have the same energy, but with no other state.

The second step of the procedure consists of identifying a characteristic property of the eigenstates of the total energy, which must identify the correct combinations of the eigenfunctions (16). This is the property (12) imposed by the exclusion principle. Since the wave functions (16) result from one another by an interchange of the electron position, that is $P(\mathbf{r}_1 \,|\, 1{,}0{,}0)(\mathbf{r}_2 \,|\, n{,}l{,}m) = (\mathbf{r}_2 \,|\, 1{,}0{,}0)(\mathbf{r}_1 \,|\, n{,}l{,}m)$, the correct combinations of the two which obey Eq. 12 are

$$(\mathbf{r}_1,\mathbf{r}_2 \,|\, 1{,}0{,}0;\, n{,}l{,}m{,}S)$$

$$= \sqrt{\tfrac{1}{2}}[(\mathbf{r}_1 \,|\, 1{,}0{,}0)(\mathbf{r}_2 \,|\, n{,}l{,}m) + (-\,1)^S(\mathbf{r}_2 \,|\, 1{,}0{,}0)(\mathbf{r}_1 \,|\, n{,}l{,}m)], \tag{18}$$

with $S = 0$ or $S = 1$. (The factor $\sqrt{\tfrac{1}{2}}$ serves to fulfill the condition $\Sigma_{\mathbf{r}_1}\Sigma_{\mathbf{r}_2} |\,(\mathbf{r}_1\mathbf{r}_2 \,|\, 1{,}0{,}0;\, n{,}l{,}m{,}S)\,|^2 = 1$.) The wave function (18) with either value of S yields a probability distribution of the positions of the two

---

[6] The energy does not depend on the quantum number m, which characterizes only the orientation of the orbital currents.

electrons which is no longer the product of two separate distributions of r_1 and r_2, and therefore describes a state of correlated, rather than independent, electrons. The ground state is a special case in that there is only one wave function (16) and therefore no combination (18); the single wave function (16) obeys the condition (12) provided S is taken equal to zero in that equation.

The final step of this stage of the approximation procedure consists of calculating the mean value of the potential energy difference (17) in the states represented by the wave functions (18). The mean value is, for excited states,

$$\langle V(\mathbf{r}_1,\mathbf{r}_2)\rangle$$

$$= \Sigma_{\mathbf{r}_1}\Sigma_{\mathbf{r}_2} V(\mathbf{r}_1,\mathbf{r}_2) \tfrac{1}{2} |(\mathbf{r}_1|1,0,0)(\mathbf{r}_2|n,l,m) + (-1)^S (\mathbf{r}_2|1,0,0)(\mathbf{r}_1|n,l,m)|^2$$

$$= \tfrac{1}{2} \{ \Sigma_{\mathbf{r}_1}\Sigma_{\mathbf{r}_2} V(\mathbf{r}_1,\mathbf{r}_2) |(\mathbf{r}_1|1,0,0)|^2 |(\mathbf{r}_2|n,l,m)|^2$$

$$+ \Sigma_{\mathbf{r}_1}\Sigma_{\mathbf{r}_2} V(\mathbf{r}_1,\mathbf{r}_2) |(\mathbf{r}_2|1,0,0)|^2 |(\mathbf{r}_1|n,l,m)|^2$$

$$+ (-1)^S \Sigma_{\mathbf{r}_1}\Sigma_{\mathbf{r}_2} (1,0,0|\mathbf{r}_1)(n,l,m|\mathbf{r}_2) V(\mathbf{r}_1,\mathbf{r}_2)(\mathbf{r}_2|1,0,0)(\mathbf{r}_1|n,l,m)$$

$$+ (-1)^S \Sigma_{\mathbf{r}_1}\Sigma_{\mathbf{r}_2} (1,0,0|\mathbf{r}_2)(n,l,m|\mathbf{r}_1) V(\mathbf{r}_1,\mathbf{r}_2)(\mathbf{r}_1|1,0,0)(\mathbf{r}_2|n,l,m) \}. \quad (19)$$

The first two terms on the right have the same value because $V(\mathbf{r}_1,\mathbf{r}_2)$ is unaffected by interchange of the two particles. Each of these terms, to be called $V_{1,0,0;n,l,m}$, represents the mean value of V when the positions of the two electrons have, respectively, the probability distributions $|(\mathbf{r}|1,0,0)|^2$ and $|(\mathbf{r}|n,l,m)|^2$. The last two terms are also equal to one another. Each of these terms, to be called $W_{1,0,0;n,l,m}$, is called the "exchange energy" or "exchange integral" because it relates to the interchange of the electrons (see also Appendix X) and is appropriately represented as a multiple integral rather than as a sum. The mean energy (19) is therefore expressed in the form

$$\langle V(\mathbf{r}_1,\mathbf{r}_2)\rangle = V_{1,0,0;n,l,m} + (-1)^S W_{1,0,0;n,l,m}. \quad (20)$$

The energy difference of the para- and ortho-states equals, in this approximation, twice the exchange integral.

The result (20), obtained by Heisenberg in 1926, constituted an early important success of quantum mechanics because the distinction of ortho- and para-levels had been a complete puzzle until then. Indeed, the exchange energy results from the interference of the two initial states which are superposed in (18), that is, from a phenomenon that has no classical analog. The Heisenberg treatment also emphasized non-stationary states which result from the superposition of ortho-para pairs and which coincide periodically with one or the other of the initial states (16). A classical analog of this periodic alternation is seen in the periodic exchange of oscillatory motion between two coupled pendulums which have the same oscillation frequency, that is, which are at *resonance*. The analogy applies also to spin-orbit coupling and to all situations where one considers initially a number of states with equal, or nearly equal, energy and subsequently their combination due to a disturbance. From this analogy stems the widespread use in atomic and quantum physics of "resonance" and "exchange" and related terms. The non-stationary aspect of the treatment and the mechanical analog are discussed in Appendix X.

PROBLEM

17.1 Two electrons are confined to the vicinity of a center of force by an elastic attraction represented by the potential energy $V(\mathbf{r}) = \frac{1}{2}kr^2 = \frac{1}{2}k(x^2 + y^2 + z^2)$, the force being so strong that the repulsion between the electrons may be disregarded. One electron is in its ground state, the other one in its first excited state of motion along the x axis. The wave functions of single-electron motion along each axis may be taken from Problem 13.4. Write the wave function of the pair of electrons for the para and for the ortho state, (*a*) as a function of the separate electron positions $\mathbf{r}_1$ and $\mathbf{r}_2$, and (*b*) as a function of the joint coordinates $\mathbf{R} = \frac{1}{2}(\mathbf{r}_1 + \mathbf{r}_2) = (X, Y, Z)$ and $\mathbf{r} = \mathbf{r}_1 - \mathbf{r}_2 = (\mathsf{x}, \mathsf{y}, \mathsf{z})$.

PART 2 | Aggregates of particles

Introduction

The following chapters deal with the structure of familiar substances, regarded as aggregates of nuclei and electrons, considering first single atoms with many electrons and then combinations of two or more atoms. This introduction indicates the types of questions which will be asked, the general methods utilized in answering them, and the necessary background information. Even qualitative answers require most, if not all, of the concepts of quantum physics developed in the preceding chapters.

Any particular type of aggregate of particles which is encountered frequently in nature or technology must be sufficiently stable against external disturbances. The *stability* and the *size* and *shape* of aggregates in their ground state constitute our main subject. Excited states will not be considered much. An aggregate is stable if it takes a substantial amount of energy to change its composition, size, or shape. "Substantial" means here large as compared to the amounts—of the order of 1000 cal/mole $= \frac{1}{20}$ ev—that are readily provided by thermal agitation; it is well known that energies of the order of electron volts, that is, of scores of kcal/mole, are required to disrupt atoms or molecules. The size and shape of an aggregate of atomic particles are, of course, characteristics of the *probability distribution* (Chapter 6) of the particle positions.

The study of an aggregate of electrons and nuclei concerns primarily the motion of its electrons. This motion is governed by the electric attraction toward the nuclei, by the repulsion among the electrons, and by the quantum-mechanical effects of *reaction to confinement* (Chapter 11) and of *exclusion* (Chapter 17), which oppose the nuclear attraction. The motion of nuclei has a minor influence on the aggregation of atoms because nuclei, owing to their larger mass, are readily confined within narrowly defined positions in an aggregate, while nevertheless their kinetic energy remains much lower than that of electrons. The magnetic interactions among orbital and spin currents have a very minor influence on the gross properties of an aggregate because they are weak. Spin orientations have, however, a major influence indirectly through the exclusion effects.

As a main index of stability we shall consider how the lowest energy eigenvalue of the whole electron body of an aggregate depends on its constitution, on its size and shape, and on external disturbances. For example, the energy is nowhere near a minimum unless the total number of electrons in the aggregate equals, at least approximately, the number of positive unit charges of the nuclei. A main characteristic of atomic systems is the substantial separation among the lower energy levels of their electrons. Therefore, the energy of atomic systems cannot be raised in separate very small steps by transient external actions; also the effect of a steady external disturbance on the electrons remains small unless it involves an energy change comparable to the difference between the two lowest energy eigenvalues. By the same token, an aggregate yields to external actions the more readily the lower is its first level of excitation, and is stiff when the first level is high.

Rather simple approximation methods prove adequate for a qualitative analysis of most of the problems we shall consider, even though they provide satisfactory quantitative estimates only in a minority of problems. The motion of electrons will be treated primarily in the independent-particle approximation: each electron is regarded as subject to an average electric force which depends on the average distribution in space of the nuclei and of all other electrons. Thereby, one considers probability *distributions* of the position of *individual electrons*, whose qualitative features can be analyzed by the criteria indicated in Chapter 13. The shapes of the probability distributions of electrons belonging to a single atom can be taken from the treatment of the H atom in Chapter 14. In further analogy with the treatment of H, one also considers stationary states of individual electrons moving through a whole molecule, and the probability distributions of their positions.

The motion of nuclei will be treated in an approximation—called "Born-Oppenheimer approximation"—based on the fact that the nuclei move much more slowly than electrons, owing to their larger mass. (Particles with different masses, confined by mutual attraction within comparable volumes of space, have momenta of the same order of magnitude and velocities in inverse ratio to their masses.)   Because the electrons move faster than the nuclei, one may consider initially their motion and calculate their energy eigenvalues for each conceivable position of all nuclei within the aggregate, as though the nuclei were at rest.   The nuclei actually move, but remain near the positions for which the electron energy attains a minimum value; the electron energy for each set of positions may be treated as a potential energy which confines the motion of the nuclei.   One concludes that the probability distribution of the nuclear positions, and hence the shape of an entire molecule, is controlled primarily by the motion of the electrons and by the resulting shape of the electron distributions.

When an initial approximation yields two or more stationary states of the electrons with nearly equal energy eigenvalues, the actual stationary states are usually combinations of the initial states, as discussed in Chapter 16.   The lowest among the actual energy eigenvalues is lower than any of the approximate ones.   The actual stationary states are often characterized by properties foreign to the initial states, such as being eigenstates of the total angular momentum in the example of Chapter 16.   Remember in this connection that a combination of states may differ as radically from its components as, for example, circularly polarized light differs from its linearly polarized components.

chapter 18

Atoms with
many electrons

It is well known that the physical and chemical properties of atoms follow a periodic pattern in their variation as the atomic number increases. This pattern, called the "periodic system" of elements and shown in Fig. 18.1, was first established on the basis of chemical evidence, that is of the behavior of atoms in combination with one another. In particular, the atomic radius—defined, for example, as the mean distance of the electrons from the nucleus—increases sharply from each rare gas to the following element, which is an alkali; this rise is accompanied by a drop in ionization potential, as shown in Fig. 4.7. In the sequence of elements along each row of the periodic system, from an alkali to a rare gas, the atomic radius decreases and the ionization potential increases, gradually though not always regularly. A progressive decrease in radius, that is, an increasing confinement of the atomic electrons, can be attributed to the increasing attraction by the nucleus. The steplike increase of radius between each rare gas and the next element has been considered for the case of helium and lithium in Sect. 17.1, and has been interpreted as an effect of the exclusion principle. It appears that, when the number of electrons in an atom has reached a critical limit, equal to the atomic number of one of the rare gases, additional electrons can no longer be packed in the same volume, but are forced to stay further away from the nucleus.

This phenomenon, and the general periodicity of atomic properties, are readily explained by the treatment of atoms in the independent-electron approximation (Sect. 18.1). In this approximation, individual electrons have stationary states characterized by the same quantum numbers (n,l,m,m_s) as the electron of a hydrogen atom. To each stationary state there corresponds an energy level and a mean distance from the nucleus which depend primarily on the principal quantum number n in an atom of a given element. (The mean distance is essentially the radius of the outermost interference fringe of the radial motion.) States of electrons with approximately equal energy and distance from the nucleus, but with different rotational motion and spin orientation, are said to belong to a "shell."

The nuclear attraction strives to confine the electrons close to the nucleus, but the exclusion principle allows only a limited number of electrons in the same space, that is, in the same shell. This number equals the number of states in the shell and is $2n^2$ for the shell characterized by the quantum number n. A group of electrons which fills every state of a shell has great stability and stiffness. The electrons of an atom in its ground state are in the states of lowest energy consistent with the exclusion principle, and are therefore distributed among the innermost shells. The distribution can be determined by assigning to each shell, beginning with the innermost one, the number of electrons required to fill it, and proceeding to outer shells until all electrons have been assigned; the last group of electrons in general fills a shell only partially. An increasing number of shells gets filled as the atomic number increases.

The experimental evidence appears to indicate that the rare gases have the exact numbers of electrons to complete the filling of successive shells. Since the atomic numbers of the rare gases are 2, 10, 18, 36, 54, and 86, successive shells should contain 2, 8, 8, 18, 18, and 32 electrons. This result agrees only partially with the characterization of shells according to the quantum number n, since the values of $2n^2$ are 2, 8, 18, 32 $\cdots$ without any repeats. The discrepancy is removed by a closer analysis of the energies and radii of one-electron states which turn out to depend appreciably also on the azimuthal quantum number l (Sect. 18.2).

The major physical and chemical properties of an atom are determined by the number of electrons in its outermost shell. Atoms with different numbers of filled shells but with equal numbers of electrons in their outermost shell have similar chemical properties and belong to the same *column* of the periodic table of elements (Fig. 18.1). Successive *rows* in the table correspond to successive numbers of filled inner shells.

Atoms in each column of the periodic table also have similar optical (infrared, visible and ultraviolet) spectra. That is, the optical spectra of successive elements follow the same pattern of periodic variation as chemical properties. The emission and absorption of radiation in the optical range derives, in fact, like the chemical properties, from the outermost atomic electrons whose energy level differences are equal to photons of optical frequencies. (The excitation of inner electrons requires more energy and yields, in general, different effects.) In most cases of interest, radiation is emitted or absorbed in transitions between stationary states that differ primarily by the level of excitation of a single electron whose quantum numbers n and l change in the course of the transition. The analysis of spectra leads to a classification of the stationary states of atoms according to eigenvalues of the angular momenta (orbital, spin, and total). The eigenvalues of the energy and of the angular momenta for the various stationary states depend on the interaction among electrons. Their theoretical determination requires, therefore, a more detailed treatment of electron interaction than in the independent electron approximation (Sect. 18.3). The angular momenta of the ground state of an atom and of its successive excited states, are determined, in general, by the number of electrons in the outermost shell and by their quantum numbers l. Therefore, the same pattern of angular momenta is found, in general, in the spectra of atoms along each column of the periodic system. The same pattern is also found in the spectra of "isoelectronic" ions, that is, of ions with the same number of electrons as a given neutral atom.

X rays are emitted in transitions in which a single electron drops into an inner shell to fill a vacancy caused by a preceding phenomenon. Since the quantum numbers of inner shell states are the same for atoms in successive columns of the periodic table, X-ray spectra do not exhibit any periodic variations, in contrast to optical spectra. On the other hand, the energy of the emitted X-ray photon depends greatly upon the shell into which the electron drops. X-ray spectra thus provide direct evidence on the existence and energy levels of inner shells (see also page 46).

18.1 Independent-electron Approximation

The motion of many electrons within a single atom is complicated because the potential energy of each electron at any one time and place depends on the position of all other electrons at that time. Hence, the motion of all electrons should be considered simultaneously. However, it is possible to obtain significant results by a simplified approximation procedure.[1]

In the independent-electron approximation, the electric force applied to one electron is represented initially as though the positions of all other electrons had a probability distribution uniform in all directions around the nucleus and independent of the position of the electron one considers. This electron is then attracted toward the nucleus by a force approximately equal to Ze^2/r^2 (Z = atomic number, r = distance from the nucleus) when it is close to the nucleus and the repulsion by all other outlying electrons cancels out. The attraction is approximately equal to e^2/r^2 when the electron under consideration lies farther from the nucleus than the other $Z - 1$ electrons, so that their repulsions add up, that is, when the nucleus and the $Z - 1$ electrons can be regarded together as a pointlike ion of unit charge. The attraction at any distance may be expressed as $Z_{\text{eff}} e^2/r^2$, where Z_{eff} is called the "effective nuclear charge" and is a function of the distance from the nucleus which decreases from Z at $r = 0$ down to one. The attraction is represented by a potential energy $U(r)$ approximately equal to $-e^2/r$ for large r and to $-Ze^2/r + V_0$ near the nucleus, where V_0 is a constant equal to the energy spent in bringing an electron from infinite distance to the center of the atom against the repulsion by the other electrons. The determination of the function $U(r)$ in the main range of interest of r through the atom offers a serious problem.

This problem is best solved by Hartree's "self-consistent" method. Starting from a trial function $U_0(r)$, one calculates the motion of all electrons, the combined probability distribution of their positions, and hence the average electric force which they would generate. Thus one obtains a new estimate $U_1(r)$ of the potential energy. This estimate agrees with $U_0(r)$ if U_0 was a good trial function; otherwise $U_1(r)$ serves as a new trial function and the calculation is repeated until a satisfactory estimate is attained. Simpler but cruder methods of estimating $U(r)$ are available.

Once the potential energy of an electron is specified by a function $U(r)$, its motion is analyzed like the motion of the electron of the hydrogen atom. Stationary states of this motion are called "one-electron states," to distinguish them from the states of the whole atom. Since the potential energy depends only on r, the rotational motion of the

---

[1] Conditions are favorable to a schematization in atoms of high atomic number where the effect of nuclear attraction is dominant and irregularities in the distribution of electrons tend to cancel out owing to the large number of electrons.

electron is unaffected by torques and the eigenstates of its squared orbital angular momentum $\mathbf{l}^2$ are the same as for the hydrogen atom. The radial motion is subjected to an attractive force, stronger at most places than in the hydrogen atom, and is therefore confined into a narrow space. A one-electron stationary state is classified by the same set of quantum numbers (n,l,m,m_s) as for the hydrogen atom (see page 233) if the spin-orbit coupling is disregarded.[2]

The energy of a one-electron state (n,l,m,m_s) is independent of the quantum numbers m and m_s, which identify only the orientation of the orbital and spin currents, and will be called E_{nl}. In the hydrogen atom, E_{nl} is also independent of the azimuthal quantum number l, but in other atoms states with higher l have higher energy for equal n. The potential energy $U(r)$ decreases more rapidly than in hydrogen, when an electron approaches the nucleus, as indicated by the increase of Z_{eff}. This decrease of potential energy reduces the energy of electrons with low angular momentum (small l) to a greater extent than the energy of electrons with higher angular momentum, which are kept away from the immediate vicinity of the nucleus by the centrifugal force. For given values of n and l and increasing atomic number Z, the energy E_{nl} decreases rapidly.[3] The mean distance from the nucleus of an electron in a given state also decreases with increasing Z.

A state of a complete atom with Z electrons is identified, in the initial approximation, by Z sets of quantum numbers (n,l,m,m_s) which identify the one-electron states of all electrons. No two of these sets of quantum numbers ever coincide, according to the exclusion principle. The orientation of the electron currents, represented by the quantum numbers m and m_s, has no bearing on the energy of the individual electrons, or on that of the whole atom, in the independent-electron approximation. States of the whole atom which differ only in the orientation of the electron currents have therefore the same energy and are said to have the same "configuration." A configuration is identified by the numbers of electrons in states with any given pair of quantum numbers n and l. It is usually represented by a formula in which the values of n and l are indicated by a number and a letter, respectively, according to the code given on pages 202 and 208, and the number of electrons with any given n and l is indicated as a superscript. For example, the con-

---

[2] The spin-orbit coupling should be taken into account in the initial approximation for the inner electrons of medium and heavy atoms and sometimes for the outer electrons of heavy atoms. In this event, the one-electron states are identified by the quantum numbers (n,l,j,m_j) utilized for the hydrogen atom on page 240.

[3] When the spin-orbit coupling is considered the energy eigenvalue depends also on the quantum number j and is called E_{nlj}.

figuration of the ground state of the silicon atom is

$$(1s)^2(2s)^2(2p)^6(3s)^2(3p)^2, \tag{1}$$

meaning that there are two electrons with $n = 1$, $l = 0$, two electrons with $n = 2$, $l = 0$, six electrons with $n = 2$, $l = 1$, etc.

The states of whole atoms identified by Z sets of one-electron quantum numbers (n,l,m,m_s) are not, in general, stationary states because of the interactions among different electrons which are disregarded in the independent-electron approximation. The actual stationary states of a whole atom may be represented as combinations of first approximation states (identified by one-electron quantum numbers) whose energies are equal, or nearly equal, according to the procedure of pages 231 ff. The combination includes usually only states with the same configuration, and occasionally states with different configurations whose energies differ by a small amount.

The number of states of an atom with any given configuration is limited by the exclusion principle, which requires all sets of quantum numbers (n,l,m,m_s) with equal (n,l) to have different pairs (m,m_s). If the number of (n,l) electrons in a configuration equals the available number of pairs (m,m_s), their state is uniquely defined. For each pair of quantum numbers (n,l), the number of possible values of m is $(2l + 1)$, while m_s can have the values $\pm\frac{1}{2}$; hence there are $2(2l + 1)$ different pairs of values of (m,m_s), that is, 2 for s states, 6 for p states, 10 for d states, etc. Therefore, a group of $2(2l + 1)$ electrons with quantum numbers n and l has only one state which is identified by the $2(2l + 1)$ different sets of quantum numbers (n,l,m,m_s) with the given values of n and l. For instance, the neon atom in its ground state has the configuration $(1s)^2(2s)^2(2p)^6$ which consists of three groups of $2(2l + 1)$ electrons. Since each of these groups has a single state, the ground state of the whole atom is uniquely defined by its configuration. In the example of the ground state of silicon, with the configuration $(1s)^2(2s)^2(2p)^6(3s)^2(3p)^2$, the groups of electrons $(1s),(2s),(2p)$, and $(3s)$ have a uniquely defined state; the two remaining $(3p)$ electrons may be in any of the states identified by two among the $2(2 \times 1 + 1) = 6$ possible pairs of quantum numbers (m,m_s). This yields 15 different states with the same configuration and with energies equal in first approximation. The ground state of the Si atom is, therefore, a combination of these states.

18.2   Shell Structure and the Periodic System of Elements

The ground state of an atom has the configuration whose energy is lowest in first approximation.[4] The lowest-energy configuration for a neutral atom with Z electrons is determined by the following procedure: One considers the sequence of energies E_{nl} of one-electron states, which runs basically in order of increasing n, and, for a given n, of increasing l, namely $E_{10}, E_{20}, E_{21}, E_{30}, \cdots$. Then one assigns to each of these energy levels, in succession of increasing energy, the maximum number of electrons consistent with the exclusion principle, namely, $2(2l + 1)$, until all Z electrons are assigned. After a certain number of levels are filled, a residue of the Z electrons is left, in general, smaller than the number of states in the next level; for example, in the ground state configuration of Si, shown in (1), two electrons are left in the $3p$ level which has six states available.

In general, one-electron states with different quantum number n have quite different energy levels, whereas the energy difference between states with equal n and different l are minor. The mean distance of an electron from the nucleus depends on its energy level.[5] Therefore, the one-electron states with the same quantum number n are said to constitute one "shell." The one-electron states with the same n and l values, that is, belonging to the same level, are said to constitute a "subshell." The different shells, particularly the first ones, are often identified by code letters, rather than by the values of n, as follows:[6]

$$n = 1 \quad 2 \quad 3 \quad 4 \quad 5 \quad 6$$
$$\text{code} = K \quad L \quad M \quad N \quad O \quad P$$

The shell structure of atoms will be discussed here by considering in turn the atoms with increasing atomic number. Following H, the He atom has its two electrons in the first shell, which consists of the single subshell $1s$. The two electrons fill the shell, so that there is only one

---

[4] Exceptions to this rule may occur if different configurations have nearly equal energy.

[5] The mean distance is approximately equal to the radius of the outermost interference fringe of the radial probability distribution at its brightest point (see the distribution of the electron in the H atom in Fig. 14.9). When $n > l + 1$, the distribution consists of more than one bright fringe, corresponding to a non-vanishing, but low probability, of finding the electron at a distance from the nucleus much lower than the mean.

[6] A roman numeral subscript is sometimes used to indicate a subshell identified by spin-orbit coupling quantum numbers l and j; for example, L_{II} means $n = 2$, $l = 1$, $j = \frac{1}{2}$; L_{III} means $n = 2$, $l = 1$, $j = \frac{3}{2}$, etc.

state with the configuration $(1s)^2$, with opposite spin orientation, as discussed in Chapter 17. The energy difference between the ground state and the lowest excited states of He, with the configurations $(1s)^1(2s)^1$ and $(1s)^1(2p)^1$, is approximately 20 ev, that is, substantially larger than for any other atom. Therefore, any variation of the ground state of He, represented by a combination of the ground state with excited states, involves a variation of energy proportionately higher than in other atoms; the He atom in its ground state is the most stable and stiff of all atoms. In particular the fact that the ground state has a one-state configuration prevents the formation of chemical bonds and thereby classes helium as a rare gas.

The short periods. The next two atoms, Li and Be, have, respectively, one and two electrons in the subshell $2s$. The subshell is filled in Be, whose configuration is $(1s)^1(2s)^2$. However, the single state of this configuration is not very stable because the energy difference $E_{21} - E_{20}$ is small and a small disturbance suffices to combine the ground state configuration with $(1s)^2(2s)^1(2p)^1$.

The atoms from B to Ne have the ground state configuration $(1s)^2(2s)^2(2p)^n$, with n increasing from one to six. The subshell $2p$ is filled at Ne, and with it the whole L shell $(n = 2)$. Ne atoms are therefore similar to He atoms, that is, are very stable and stiff, and exhibit the properties of a rare gas. Let us reemphasize that the recurrence of rare gas properties, when Z has increased by eight units beyond He, derives from the capacity of the shell with $n = 2$, which is $2n^2 = 8$. Notice also that, even though the probability distribution of any one p electron is not uniform around the nucleus, the combined distribution of all electrons in a filled subshell is exactly uniform [7]; moreover, the resultant spin of the subshell vanishes.

The eight atoms from Na to A have increasing numbers of electrons in the subshells $3s$ and $3p$ of the M shell $(n = 3)$, following the same pattern as the eight atoms from Li to Ne. Pairs of elements whose atoms have equal numbers of electrons in incomplete shells with $n = 3$ and $n = 2$, have very similar physical and chemical properties and are accordingly arranged in the same columns of the periodic table. These eight pairs of elements, Li and Na, Be and Mg, $\cdots$ to Ne and A, constitute the two "short periods" of the table. It is remarkable, at this point of the sequence of elements, that A shares the special stability of

---

[7] This property is verified by calculating, with the wave functions of page 211, that $\Sigma_m |(\theta|l,m)(\phi|m)|^2 = (2l + 1)/4\pi$, independently of the direction (θ,ϕ), or by noticing that the sum of the quantum numbers m of all states of a subshell vanishes, whatever coordinate axis has been chosen.

Ne and He, that is, is a rare gas, even though its electrons fill only the levels up to the $3p$ subshell, leaving unoccupied the remaining subshell, $3d$ ($l = 2$), of the M shell. The stability of A is very high, though not quite as high as that of Ne, because the energy of the $3d$ states lies much higher than the energy of the $3p$ states for the reasons indicated on page 274. The energy of the A configuration with one electron in the $3d$ subshell exceeds by 11.5 ev the energy of the ground state configuration. Therefore, the effects generally associated with completion of a shell are associated here, and also in the remaining rare gases, with completion of a p subshell.

The long periods. Proceeding beyond A, a departure from the basic regularity of shells is encountered, namely, the energy of the $3d$ states exceeds that of the $4s$ states. Therefore, the atom following A, namely K, has the ground state configuration $(1s)^2(2s)^2(2p)^6(3s)^2(3p)^6(4s)^1$, that is, it consists of a rare gas core and of a single electron in the next shell. Potassium is thus similar to Li and Na. The next atom, Ca ($Z = 20$), has two electrons in the $4s$ subshell and is thus analogous to Be and Mg.

The states of the $3d$ subshell begin to be occupied in the atoms following Ca. The atoms from Sc ($Z = 21$) to Mn ($Z = 25$) have three to seven electrons with comparable energies in the $4s$ and $3d$ subshells. These atoms are somewhat similar to those of the sequence Al to Cl which also have three to seven outer electrons with comparable energies. The difference between the $3d$ states in one sequence and the $3p$ states in the other causes, however, the elements in the two sequences to be increasingly different. The $3d$ subshell has 10 states, as compared with 6 states for the $3p$ subshell, and the elements following Mn, namely, Fe, Co, and Ni, have additional $3d$ electrons and therefore have no analog in the earlier portion of the periodic table.

As the nuclear charge increases and the $3d$ subshell gets filled, its energy level E_{32} decreases somewhat faster than the level E_{40} of the $4s$ subshell, and becomes eventually lower than it (Fig. 18.2). This crossover of energy levels stems from the following circumstance. Once the nuclear attraction has become sufficiently strong to overcome the centrifugal force on $3d$ electrons and to draw their probability distribution inside the atom, these electrons are attracted toward the nucleus with increasing strength, represented by a high value of the effective nuclear charge Z_{eff}. The effect indicated on page 274 to explain the dependence of E_{nl} upon the quantum number l becomes less important. Actually the energy level E_{32} becomes more nearly comparable to E_{31} and E_{30} as Z increases beyond 30.

When the subshells $4s$ and $3d$ hold jointly 11 electrons, that is, at Cu $(Z = 29)$, the ground state configuration formula includes, besides the rare gas core of A, a factor $(3d)^{10}(4s)^1$, whereas the preceding Ni atom has $(3d)^8(4s)^2$. Thus the filling of the $3d$ subshell—and of the whole M shell—gets completed when another subshell is already started,

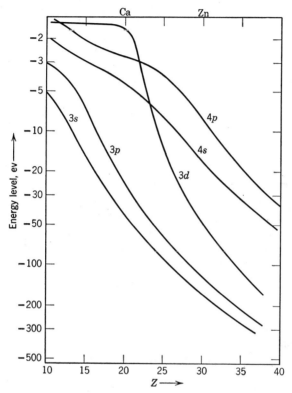

Fig. 18.2 Typical variations of one-electron energy levels as functions of the atomic number. (Adapted from R. Latter, *Phys. Rev.*, **99**, 515, 1955.)

and no remarkable stability is associated with its completion. The $(3d)^9(4s)^2$ configuration of Cu has an energy only about 1.5 ev higher than the $(3d)^{10}(4s)^1$ configuration.

The filling of the $4s$ and $4p$ subshells resumes regularly after the $3d$ subshell is completed. From Cu to Kr $(Z = 29$ to $36)$ we have a sequence of eight atoms with one to eight s and p electrons, which become increasingly similar to the corresponding atoms of the short period sequences from Li to Ne and from Na to A. The increasing similarity derives from the increasing stability of the filled $3d$ subshell which is being drawn in with the rest of the M shell and has a diminishing influence on the outer electrons. Completion of the $4p$ subshell at $Z = 36$ is quite analogous to the completion of the $3p$ subshell at $Z = 18$, and indeed the Kr element is a rare gas like A.

Thus 18 electrons have been added along the sequence of atoms from A to Kr, as many as belong in the $n = 3$ shell, according to the $2n^2$ formula. However, these electrons have occupied the subshells $4s$, $3d$, and $4p$ instead of a single shell.

The filling of the $4d$ subshell is delayed like that of the $3d$ subshell. Beyond Kr the sequence of configurations parallels closely the sequence that follows A. From Rb ($Z = 37$) to Xe ($Z = 54$) we have 18 atoms which form a "long period" of the periodic table, quite analogous to the preceding period from K to Kr. The subshells $5s$, $4d$, and $5p$ are filled along the sequence which terminates, upon filling of the $5p$ subshell, with the rare gas Xe similar to Kr and A. The subshell $4f$ is still unfilled at this point, as well as $5d$.

The rare earths. A new long period starts with Cs ($Z = 55$) in which the $6s$ subshell is filled first, and then the $5d$ is started. However, the filling of the $4f$ subshell sets in after La ($Z = 57$) which has two $6s$ electrons and one $5d$. As the atomic number increases in this range, the energy level E_{43} of the $4f$ electrons decreases faster than the levels E_{52} and E_{60}, much as the level E_{32} decreases faster than the other levels in Fig. 18.2. Still more striking is the rapid decrease of the mean distance of $4f$ electrons from the nucleus. It follows that, however many electrons are in the $4f$ states of the atoms following La, they are substantially closer to the nucleus than the $6s$ and $5d$ electrons. In these atoms the configuration of the ground state, shown in Fig. 18.1, provides no adequate indication of the chemical properties. It turns out that owing to the characteristics of $4f$ states, all the elements following La have chemical properties closely similar to those of La and of the other analogous elements with three outer electrons ("earth elements"), namely Sc and Y. The filling of the 14 states of the $4f$ subshell extends over the group of elements from $Z = 58$ to $Z = 71$, which are called the "rare earths."

The "long period" which begins at Cs resumes its course after the $4f$ subshell has been filled and remains quite similar to the preceding long periods. Including the rare earths, this period consists of 32 elements, as many as the states of the shell with $n = 4$. The period terminates upon completion of the $6p$ subshell, at Rn ($Z = 86$) which is another rare gas. The $5f$ and $6d$ subshells are still unfilled at this point, besides $5g$, $6f$, $6g$, and $6h$.

Following Rn, a new long period starts with Fr and Ra which have, respectively, one and two $7s$ electrons. There follows Ac and a long group of elements, called actinides, which are analogous to the rare earths. This group includes the "transuranic" elements, with atomic number higher than 92, which are not found in nature but have been produced by laboratory transformation of atomic nuclei.

Atomic ions. Atoms can exist in various states of positive ionization, in which the number of electrons is smaller than the number of unit charges on the nucleus. Ions with a net positive charge of a dozen units exist on the sun. Positive ions are stable, of course, insofar as no electrons are available to be captured.

The ground state of a positive ion may be characterized by its configuration which is generally the same as that of a neutral atom with the same number of electrons. A typical exception to this rule is the Cu^+ ion which has an outermost complete subshell of ten $3d$ electrons, whereas the neutral Ni atom has the same number of electrons in a $(4s)^2(3d)^8$ configuration.

Positive ions with one or a few unit charges are produced in electric discharges. Certain species of positive ions also exist as stable constituents of large aggregates of matter (crystals or solutions), when the conditions around the ion prevent it from capturing an electron without expenditure of energy. Some examples of this stability will be given in Chapter 22. The ions for which these conditions obtain have particularly stable configurations, namely, those of the rare gases, and are called "isoelectronic" to rare gases. Typical examples are Li^+ and Be^{++}, isoelectronic to He, Na^+, Mg^{++}, and Al^{+++}, isoelectronic to Ne, K^+, and Ca^{++}, isoelectronic to A. Ions of the Cu^+ and Zn^{++} groups, whose configuration has an outermost complete d subshell, have also considerable stability, whereas the isoelectronic neutral atoms of the Ni group have different ground state configurations and are not particularly stable.

Atoms of a few elements are apt to capture an additional electron and to form with it a stable negative ion. Consider that an electron outside a neutral atom is attracted to it by no net electric charge but only by a weak induced electric force (to be discussed in Sect. 22.3). The weak force is not sufficient to confine an electron. Therefore, a negative ion cannot exist with an electron substantially farther away from the nucleus than the other electrons. On the other hand, if an atom has a partially filled outer shell, an additional electron can be at a distance from the nucleus comparable to that of the other electrons and experience a strong net attraction toward the nucleus. The conditions are most favorable to the formation of a negative ion in neutral atoms that lack a single electron to complete a rare-gas configuration. Typical negative ions have in fact a rare-gas configuration, namely, H^- with 2 electrons, F^- with 18 electrons, and similarly Cl^-, Br^-, and I^-. The neutral O atom lacks 2 electrons to achieve a rare gas configuration, but nevertheless forms a stable O^- ion. The O^{--} ion is stable only in crystals.

18.3 Stationary States in Normal-coupling Approximation

The states of whole atoms identified by Z sets of one-electron quantum numbers (n,l,m,m_s) are not, in general, stationary, as mentioned in Sect. 18.1, because of the interactions among the electrons. The procedure to identify the actual stationary states depends on the relative strength of different types of interaction. In the independent-electron approximation, the electric repulsion among electrons has been strongly schematized and the magnetic interactions among orbital and spin currents have been disregarded. Most frequently, the departures from the schematized electric repulsion have a dominant effect, and are appropriately taken into account ahead of the magnetic interactions. The interaction among electrons under these conditions is called "normal coupling." Magnetic interactions become increasingly important as the atomic number increases and substantial departures from conditions of normal coupling are encountered; however, the present treatment is limited to normal coupling.

The state of an atom with a configuration consisting only of complete subshells is completely identified by its configuration, as mentioned in Sect. 18.1. The interactions among electrons do not modify this stationary state unless they are sufficiently strong to combine different configurations. In general, the complication of the interaction of many electrons depends on the number of states of the whole atom in the same configuration. The number of states depends on the number of electrons in the partially filled subshell (or subshells); it increases with increasing number of electrons until the subshell is half-filled, and decreases thereafter. For a subshell with given quantum number l, the number of states is the same whether it contains r electrons or r vacancies.[8]

States with a single electron in an unfilled shell, which are typical of the alkali atoms, present no special interaction problem. The electric repulsion between the electrons of completed subshells and the single "outer" electron in the unfilled shell does not modify the magnetic quantum number m of the outer electron; the magnetic spin-orbit interaction of this electron has been treated in Chapter 16. The ground state of the halogen atoms, whose configuration lacks one electron to complete a subshell, is analogous to the states of the alkali atoms. The treatment of electron interaction in subshells containing more than one electron is beyond the scope of this book; only highlights of its results are outlined below.

The energy of the electric repulsion among electrons depends on the mutual orientation of the separate probability distributions of their positions and on the correla-

---

[8] With reference to the example on page 275, it can be seen that the number of states of the whole atom equals the number of ways in which the $2(2l + 1)$ one-electron states of the subshell can be divided into two groups of r and $2(2l + 1) - r$ states. It is immaterial whether r indicates the number of filled states or the number of vacancies.

tions between the positions of different electrons which are established by the exclusion principle. The orientation effects arise only for electrons in states with an azimuthal quantum number $l \neq 0$, because states with $l = 0$ have probability distributions uniform in all directions. The mutual orientation of probability distributions may be expressed in terms of the mutual orientation of the orbital currents of different electrons, and therefore depends on the squared resultant orbital angular momentum $\mathbf{L}^2$ of all electrons. Under conditions of normal coupling, stationary states of a whole atom are eigenstates of $\mathbf{L}^2$. The eigenvalues of $\mathbf{L}^2$ are indicated by $L(L + 1)\hbar^2$, where L is called total orbital quantum number as in Chapter 17. The possible values of the quantum number L for a given configuration are obtained by applying the procedure of addition of angular momenta, indicated in Sect. 16.2, to the orbital angular momenta 1 of the individual electrons in the incomplete subshell. The mutual orientation of orbital currents is restricted by the exclusion principle, which therefore restricts also the possible resultant values of L. For example, the ground state of nitrogen has three $2p$ electrons but the value $L = 3$, corresponding to parallel orbital momenta, is excluded as all three electrons cannot be in states with $m = 1$. Often, though not always, the quantum number L specifies completely the mutual orientation of the orbital currents and the probability distribution of the interacting electrons. States of an atom with many electrons are usually designated with capital letters which identify the value of L according to the same code as for one-electron states, namely,

L value	0	1	2	3	4	$\cdots$
code name	S	P	D	F	G	$\cdots$

The correlations between the positions of different electrons arising from the exclusion principle depend on the mutual orientation of the electron spins, and therefore on their squared resultant angular momentum $\mathbf{S}^2$. Under conditions of normal coupling, stationary states of a whole atom are eigenstates of $\mathbf{S}^2$; the eigenvalues of $\mathbf{S}^2$ are indicated by $S(S + 1)\hbar^2$, as in Chapter 17. The possible values of S are determined by addition of the spin angular momenta $\mathbf{s}$ of the individual electrons in the incomplete subshell. Here again, the mutual orientation of spin currents is restricted by the exclusion principle, which therefore restricts also the possible values of S. Within this limitation, the higher is the value of S, the larger is the average distance of the electrons and the lower is the average potential energy due to their repulsion. Therefore, the ground state of an atom has generally the highest permissible value of S. In the example of the ground state of the nitrogen atom, the three $2p$ electrons have parallel spins ($S = \frac{3}{2}$); the electrons must therefore occupy the states with quantum numbers $m = 1, 0$ and -1, their resultant angular momentum vanishes ($L = 0$), and the ground state is therefore fully defined.

Eigenstates of $\mathbf{L}^2$ and $\mathbf{S}^2$ with quantum numbers L and S other than zero exist with different mutual orientations of their orbital and spin currents, that is, with different squared total angular momenta $\mathbf{J}^2 = |\mathbf{L} + \mathbf{S}|^2$. These states have different energy of spin-orbit coupling. Energy levels of states with equal L and S and different J constitute the fine structure multiplets of the spectra, analogous to the doublets of alkali spectra (see Chapter 16).

In conclusion, stationary states of atoms with many electrons under conditions of normal coupling are eigenstates of $\mathbf{L}^2$, $\mathbf{S}^2$, and $\mathbf{J}^2$ characterized by quantum numbers L, S, and J. The mutual orientation of the orbital currents and probability distributions of several electrons may require further specification than is provided by the value of L. A state with quantum numbers L, S, and J is usually indicated by a code symbol which specifies the values of these numbers. The symbol consists of the code letter corresponding to the value of L, with a superscript on the left equal to $2S + 1$ (which is the number of fine structure levels for $L \geq S$) and a subscript on the right equal to J. For example, $^4D_{5/2}$ means $L = 2$, $S = \frac{3}{2}$, and $J = \frac{5}{2}$.

When the interactions among electrons cause an appreciable combination of states of different configurations, only states with the same quantum numbers L, S, and J intercombine under conditions of normal coupling.

Under conditions of normal coupling, intense emission or absorption of radiation occurs only in transitions between states with the same quantum number S. Therefore, the spectral levels of an atom are subdivided into separate sets of terms corresponding to different values of S, as the levels of He are subdivided into parahelium ($S = 0$) and orthohelium ($S = 1$) levels (Sect. 17.4). The S value of each set of levels is determined by experimental observation of the multiplicity of fine structure levels.

chapter 19

The simplest molecules

The hydrogen molecule, H_2, is the simplest electrically neutral molecule. It consists of two hydrogen atoms, that is, of two hydrogen nuclei and of two electrons. Still simpler is the hydrogen molecular ion, H_2^+, which consists of two nuclei and of a single electron.

The stability of the H_2^+ ion results from the tendency of its electron to expand, that is, from the complementarity relationship between the volume in which the electron is confined and its kinetic energy (see Chapter 11). The electron of a H atom finds itself under reduced confinement when a second H nucleus approaches the atom, because it can pass from the proximity of one nucleus to the proximity of the other without any increase of its potential energy. An electron in the space surrounding two H nuclei can therefore be in a stationary state such that its mean potential energy is comparable to that in the ground state of the H atom, but its mean kinetic energy is substantially lower. Experiments show that the total energy of the ion H_2^+ in its ground state is 2.65 ev lower than the sum of the energies of a H atom and of a

H nucleus at infinite distance, as represented by the equation.

$$H_2^+ = H + H^+ - 2.65 \text{ ev.} \tag{1}$$

To study the mechanics of the H_2^+ ion, it is appropriate to consider the energy eigenvalues of its electron for each possible distance of the two nuclei (see page 269). If this distance greatly exceeds the size of the H atom, the potential energy of the electron at the mid-point between the two nuclei is considerably higher than its average value in the H atom, and the electron's energy eigenvalue is not much lower than in the H atom. If the internuclear distance is much smaller than the size of the H atom, the electron is not less confined than in the H atom and its kinetic energy fails to be reduced; moreover, to the electron's energy eigenvalue one must add a high potential energy of repulsion between the two nuclei. Between the two high-energy regions for small and large internuclear distances there lies a minimum of the total energy for an internuclear distance comparable to the size of the H atom. A calculation outlined in Sect. 19.1 yields the plot of energy versus distance shown in Fig. 19.1 with a minimum at the internuclear distance of 1.06 A. The calculation also yields an energy eigenvalue for the ground state of the ion which agrees with the experimental value given in Eq. 1.

The normal hydrogen molecule, H_2, is regarded in the independent-electron approximation as a system of two electrons, each of which moves under the attraction of two nuclei much as the single electron of the H_2^+ ion. The two electrons, being in the same state of motion, must have opposite spin orientation on account of the exclusion principle. The molecule has, therefore, the complete shell characteristics of a He atom in its ground state.

The stability of the H_2 molecule may also be understood by considering first two adjacent H atoms. The close approach of the two atoms reduces the confinement of each electron because they can both pass from the vicinity of one nucleus to the vicinity of the other without increasing their potential energy. Since the two electrons have their kinetic energy decreased by decreasing confinement, the energy released in the formation of the H_2 molecule is roughly twice as large as in the formation of the H_2^+ ion,

$$H_2 = H + H - 4.48 \text{ ev.} \tag{2}$$

The internuclear distance which yields the minimum of the total energy is smaller than that of the H_2^+ ion, namely 0.74 A.

The formation of the H_2 molecule involves a full interpenetration of the electron "bodies" of the two H atoms, that is, a full overlapping of the probability distributions of electron positions. The interpenetration is possible only if the electrons have opposite spin orientation. If two H atoms approach one another with parallel electron spins, their combined state may be regarded as an excited state of the H_2 molecule, analogous to the ortho-states of the He atom discussed in Sect. 17.4. The total energy of the molecule in this excited state is higher than the energy of the separate H atoms for all values of the internuclear distance. Therefore, H atoms with parallel electron spins fail to interpenetrate and to form a stable molcule. (If, however, one of the two H atoms happens to be initially in an excited state, a molecule can be formed in a state with parallel electron spins without violation of the exclusion principle. The resulting molecule is in an excited state.)

In general, the state of a system of two approaching atoms is not an eigenstate of their squared total spin angular momentum, that is, the spins are neither certainly parallel nor opposite. The state can, however, be represented as a superposition of component eigenstates with parallel and opposite spin orientation. The intensities of the component states represent the probability that the atoms interpenetrate or fail to do so. Interpenetration leads to the formation of a molecule only if the system can release excess energy, usually through simultaneous collision with another molecule; otherwise interpenetration merely results in an elastic collision of the two atoms.

Because the two electrons of a H_2 molecule are in states that constitute a complete shell, no further electron can be confined in the same region of space without being in an excited state. Therefore, a further H atom which approaches a H_2 molecule does not penetrate it with formation of a H_3 molecule. The H_2 molecule constitutes a closed system, with no tendency to form additional bonds with other atoms. For the same reason, a H atom does not penetrate a He atom with formation of a HHe molecule. The electron of a H atom cannot be confined in a ground state in the same space as the two electrons of He, just as the third electron of a Li atom does not stay in the $1s$ shell together with the other two electrons.

Three electrons can be confined to form a molecule in the space around two nuclei if one of the electrons is not in the ground state, in analogy to the Li atom configuration $(1s)^2(2s)^1$. As shown in Sect. 19.1, the one-electron energy level immediately above the ground state of the molecule is "antibonding." This energy level decreases steadily as the internuclear distance increases; therefore the presence of an electron in the antibonding state reduces the stability of the molecule. The molecule can nevertheless be stable, provided the energy gain from the "bonding" action of two electrons in the ground state overcompensates the effect of the electron in the antibonding state. Whether the aggregate of three electrons and two nuclei is stable or not depends on whether its total energy is smaller or larger than the sum of energies of any other possible aggregate of the same constituents. For instance, the H_2 molecule does not hold an additional electron to form H_2^-, and an HHe molecule would be less stable than the separate atoms of H and He. Conversely, the He_2^+ ion is stable and constitutes a typical example of molecule with a "three-electron bond." Its stability is comparable to the stability of the H_2^+ molecular ion whose bond is called a "one-electron" bond. Addition of a fourth electron to the He_2^+ ion into the lowest energy state available, which is antibonding, leads to decomposition of the molecule into two neutral He atoms. However, if the fourth electron is added in a bonding state of higher excitation, it forms an excited metastable He_2 molecule. The temporary existence of this molecule can be observed experimentally before it loses its excitation energy and breaks up into two He atoms.

This discussion of the states of simple molecules has been based on the independent-electron approximation, which assigns each electron to a one-electron state with a probability distribution extended throughout the molecule. A one-electron state of orbital motion, that is, a stationary state of electron motion irrespective of spin orientation is called an "orbital." A "molecular orbital" is an orbital in which the electron distribution extends over a molecule (or over a part of a polyatomic molecule). Two electrons with opposite spin orientation may be in the same orbital.

The independent-electron approximation provides a very direct description of molecular stability and is therefore convenient for qualitative analysis. However, it underestimates substantially the effects of repulsion among electrons. Not even the average effect of this repulsion is conveniently taken into account in the first approximation treatment of the H_2 molecule. As mentioned in Chapter 18, the independent-electron approximation yields reasonably good quantitative results when the attraction by a single nucleus is predominant and when many electrons perform similar motions. These conditions are not met in the H_2 molecule. Other approximation methods are commonly utilized for the calculation of energies of molecules with two or more electrons. Different methods of approximation lead to different points of view on the mechanism of bond formation. Section 19.2 indicates alternative approaches and their relationships.

19.1   Stationary States of the H_2^+ Ion

The stationary states of the electron in the H_2^+ ion are studied according to the Born-Oppenheimer approximation by assuming initially that the nuclei lie at a fixed distance R from one another. For each value of the internuclear distance one solves the Schroedinger equation for the electron motion, seeking the distance that yields the lowest energy eigenvalue. The Schroedinger equation is expressed as in Eq. 2, page 170, by

$$-\frac{\hbar^2}{2m_e}\left[\frac{\partial^2(\mathbf{r}\,|\,E_n)}{\partial x^2} + \frac{\partial^2(\mathbf{r}\,|\,E_n)}{\partial y^2} + \frac{\partial^2(\mathbf{r}\,|\,E_n)}{\partial z^2}\right] + V(\mathbf{r},R)(\mathbf{r}\,|\,E_n) = (\mathbf{r}\,|\,E_n)E_n,$$

(3)

where E_n is an energy eigenvalue, $(\mathbf{r}\,|\,E_n)$ the corresponding eigenfunction, and the potential energy $V(\mathbf{r},R)$ represents the attraction on the electron by the two nuclei. The equation is to be solved separately for each value R of the internuclear distance. The potential energy due to the repulsion between the nuclei may be included in the expression of $V(\mathbf{r},R)$, so that the energy eigenvalues of the electron will include this contribution. If the nuclei lie on the z axis at equal distances from the origin of coordinates, we have

$$V(\mathbf{r},R) = V(x,y,z,R) = -\frac{e^2}{\sqrt{x^2 + y^2 + (z - \tfrac{1}{2}R)^2}}$$

$$-\frac{e^2}{\sqrt{x^2 + y^2 + (z + \tfrac{1}{2}R)^2}} + \frac{e^2}{R}. \quad (4)$$

The mathematical solution of the Schroedinger equation with this potential energy must be conducted by approximation methods, because the motion of the electron cannot be resolved completely into motions in different directions as was done for the H atom. The solution yields the energy eigenvalues plotted as functions of R in Fig. 19.1. Maximum stability of the molecule corresponds to the internuclear distance $R_{\min}$ at which the lowest eigenvalue E_0 is a minimum. The total energy of the molecule in its ground state includes, besides the eigenvalue of the electron's energy $E_0(R_{\min})$, the energy of relative motion of the two nuclei.

The relative motion of the nuclei consists of a rotation about their center of mass and of oscillatory variations of the internuclear distance about the equilibrium value $R_{\min}$. The energy eigenvalue $E_0(R)$ of the electron's motion may be treated as the potential energy of the nuclei, in the same way as the kinetic energy of rotation of the electron in the H atom is treated as potential energy of the radial motion in

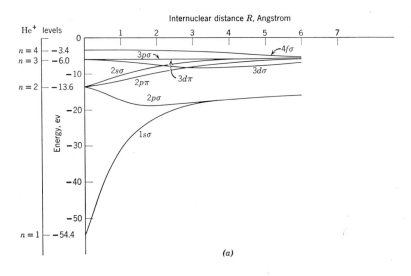

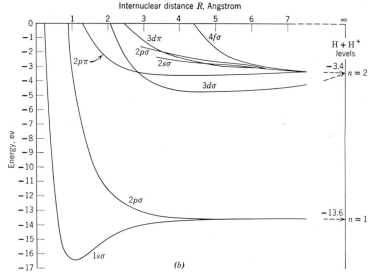

Fig. 19.1   Energy levels of the electron in the H_2^+ ion as functions of the internuclear distance.   The energy of internuclear repulsion is included in the levels shown in (b), while it is not in (a).   (After E. Teller, Z. *Physik*, **61**, 474, 1930.)

Sect. 14.1*a*. The stationary states of the nuclear motion are eigenstates of a Schroedinger equation which has the same form as (3) and the following variables and parameters: (*a*) the relative coordinates **R** of the two nuclei in place of the electron's coordinates **r**; (*b*) the reduced mass of the two nuclei, that is, $\frac{1}{2}$ the mass of one nucleus (see Appendix II and Sect. 14.5) in place of the electron's mass; and (*c*) $E_0(R)$ in place of $V(\mathbf{r})$. The stationary states of the nuclear motion are then quite analogous to those of the electron in the H atom, because the potential depends only on the magnitude of **R** and not on its direction, except that the radial motion is now governed by the potential energy shown in Fig. 19.1*b* with its lowest point at $R_{\min}$ rather than at zero. Eigenvalues of the Schroedinger equation for the relative motion of the two nuclei represent the total energy of the H_2^+ ion, since the electron's energy is already included as potential energy of the nuclei. The lowest eigenvalue, corresponding to vanishing rotational motion and to a single bright interference fringe in the probability distribution of the internuclear distance, equals $E_0(R_{\min}) + 0.15$ ev.

As mentioned on page 254, an H nucleus has a spin angular momentum equal to that of electrons. This spin angular momentum does not influence directly the mechanics of the H_2^+ ion, or of the H_2 molecule. However, the exclusion principle requires that the orientation of the two nuclear spins be opposite or parallel ($S = 0$ or $S = 1$) depending on whether the quantum number of the rotational motion is even or odd. In particular, the spin orientations are opposite for the ground state of the molecule in which the rotational motion vanishes.

The motion of the electron in the H_2^+ ion can be analyzed as for the H atom with a resulting complete classification of its stationary states. Part of the results thus obtained is applicable to other molecules with two equal nuclei. The electron moves freely around the line that joins the nuclei ("nuclear axis"), and thereby generates a centrifugal force which influences the motion in other directions. This motion is analogous to the motion along parallel circles in the H atom (Sect. 14.1*b* and 14.3). It is characterized for each stationary state by an eigenvalue of the squared angular momentum component $l_z^2 = m^2\hbar^2$,[1] where z indicates the nuclear axis as in Eq. 4. Eigenstates of rotational motion with $m^2 = 0, 1, 4, \cdots$ are designated respectively as σ, π, δ, $\cdots$, that is, by Greek letters corresponding to the letters s, p, d, $\cdots$, used for the one-electron states of atoms. Eigenstates of l_z^2 which are also eigenstates of l_z with eigenvalue other than zero involve a net electron flow around the nuclear axis. Eigenstates σ, π, δ, $\cdots$ of l_z^2 without any electron flow have electron distributions with respectively zero, one, two, $\cdots$ dark interference fringes centered on planes through the nuclear axis. (Notice the analogy with the eigenstates of l_z^2 in the H atom in Fig. 14.4.)

After this classification of the electron's motion around the nuclear axis, there remains to be considered the motion within planes through this axis. The existence of two centers of attraction hampers, in general,

---

[1] The quantum number m is often called λ when applied to molecules, as here.

the further analysis of this motion, except in the special case of the H_2^+ ion. Here the mathematical form (4) of the potential energy makes it possible to treat separately different components of the electron motion in the same way as the motion of the electron in the H atom is resolved into the motion along meridian and radial directions. In the H_2^+ ion the appropriate directions are no longer singled out by a system of polar coordinates but by elliptical coordinates. It follows that each stationary state of the H_2^+ ion is characterized by two sets of dark interference fringes in its electron distribution (see Chapter 13). One set is centered on ellipsoids with the nuclei at their foci, the other one on hyperboloids which cross the nuclear axis and have the same foci (Fig. 19.2). A sta-

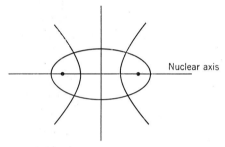

Fig. 19.2 Intersection of centers of dark fringes with a plane through the nuclear axis for H_2^+.

tionary state with no electron flow around the z axis is identified by three quantum numbers: the number m of plane dark fringes containing the nuclear axis, the number of hyperboloid dark fringes crossing this axis (namely, three in Fig. 19.2), and the number of ellipsoid dark fringes wrapped around both nuclei. The sum of these numbers, increased by one, is called the "principal quantum number" n, as in the H atom. The sum of the first two numbers (of planes and hyperboloids) is indicated by an azimuthal quantum number l or by the corresponding code letters s, p, d, $\cdots$, again as in the H atom. For example, the set of quantum numbers $n = 4$, $l = 2$, $m = 1$, or the corresponding symbol $4d\pi$, indicates, for a state without any flow, one dark fringe along the z axis, one across it, and one around the nuclei.

The number and type of interference fringes remains unchanged in the H_2^+ ion if the internuclear distance R varies. For analytical purposes one considers conveniently the extreme limits of $R = \infty$ and $R = 0$. At $R = \infty$ a state of the H_2^+ ion reduces to a combination of states of a H^+ ion and of a H atom, at $R = 0$ to a state of a He^+ ion (which is isoelectronic to the H atom, as we know). In the limit $R = 0$ the hyperboloid fringes reduce to cones and the ellipsoid fringes to spheres, so that the quantum numbers n and l resume their usual meaning of Chapter 14. The characterization of the H_2^+ states by quantum numbers n and l is actually based on the limiting case of $R = 0$, which is called the "united atom" limit.

Of special importance for molecular mechanics is the presence of a dark or bright fringe centered on the plane perpendicular to the nuclear axis at its midpoint. This plane is a degenerate hyperboloid, as seen in Fig. 19.2, and must be the center of a dark or of a bright fringe of the electron distribution owing to the symmetry of the molecule. States with a bright fringe on this "central" plane are stable because the electron has then a high probability of being in the space between the two nuclei where its potential energy is low. The ground state has no dark interference fringe and is clearly a state of this type. The explanation of the stability of the H_2^+ ion on the basis of reduced confinement of its electron applies to all its states with a bright fringe on the central plane. Conversely, a dark fringe across the middle of the molecule excludes the electron from the region of low potential energy and, in a way, keeps it confined to the separate halves of the molecule. Any increase of the internuclear distance results in a broadening of the bright fringes on either side of the central dark fringe and thereby reduces the mean kinetic energy of the electron (see page 177) without any decrease of mean potential energy. Therefore, the energy eigenvalue of any state with a central dark fringe is a steadily decreasing function of the internuclear distance, as shown in Fig. 19.1, and has no minimum corresponding to molecular stability. For this reason, stationary states are called "bonding" or "antibonding" depending on whether their electron distribution has a bright or a dark fringe on the central plane of the molecule. A dark central fringe occurs when the number $l - m$ of dark hyperboloid fringes is odd, a bright fringe when $l - m$ is even. The dependence of the molecular stability on $l - m$ is illustrated by the presence or absence of a minimum in the curves of Fig. 19.1.

In a molecule with many electrons, the potential energy is complicated so that the one-electron states are no longer classified and described by definite numbers of dark fringes across the nuclear axis and around the nuclei. The energy and other characteristics of each stationary state may still be considered as functions of the internuclear distance R, so that each state may be identified by the quantum numbers n,l,m, which pertain to the united atom limit $R = 0$. However, the number and type of interference fringes may vary as a function of R so that a designation such as $4d\pi$ is useful but not necessarily descriptive of the state of the actual molecule. Two important classification features remain invariant and meaningful: (a) for all molecules with an internuclear axis of symmetry the motion *around* the nuclear axis is independent of other motions and of the value of R, and is characterized by the symbol $\sigma, \pi, \delta, \cdots$; (*b*) all molecules symmetrical with respect to a plane perpendicular to this axis have in each stationary state a bright or dark fringe centered on this plane and therefore a *bonding* or *antibonding* character represented by an even or odd value of $l - m$ for the united atom limit.

The low-energy stationary states of molecules with two nuclei and a small number of electrons can be characterized, aside from electron spin orientation, by configuration formulas analogous to (1), page 275, in terms of their one-electron states. The ground state of the H_2 molecule has the configuration $(1s\sigma)^2$ and spin quantum number $S = 0$. The system of two H atoms in their ground states approaching with parallel spins has the configuration $(1s\sigma)^1(2p\sigma)^1$ and $S = 1$. The ground state of the $He_2{}^+$ ion has the configuration $(1s\sigma)^2(2p\sigma)^1$ and $S = \frac{1}{2}$. The molecule of He_2, which exists only in excited states, has a state of lowest energy $(1s\sigma)^2(2p\sigma)^1(2s\sigma)^1$ and $S = 1$.

19.2   The Atomic Orbital Approximation and Chemical Resonance

The description of the H_2 molecule on the basis of molecular orbitals does not yield very good quantitative results, as mentioned on page 288. The molecular orbital approximation attributes to each electron a stationary state in which the electron's position has a probability distribution spread throughout the molecule and independent of the position of other electrons. A different approximation was utilized in the first interpretation of the stability of the H_2 molecule by Heitler and London in 1928 and has found widespread applications. This approximation initially regards the H_2 molecule as consisting of two separate atoms, each with its own electron in the ground state, and is therefore called the "atomic orbital" approximation.

Even at the start of this approximation, the probability distributions of the positions of the two electrons cannot be treated as independent in the region between the two nuclei where the distributions overlap. Since the two electrons are indistinguishable, the probability of finding an electron at any one point within this region must be determined by a combination of the probability distributions pertaining to the two atoms, and the combination involves interference effects. The appropriate treatment of identical particles is governed by the general formulation of the exclusion principle and has been discussed in Chapter 17. The exclusion principle introduces a statistical correlation between the positions of the two electrons. The correlation increases the probability of finding an electron in the region of overlap if the electrons have opposite spin orientation, and decreases it if the spins are parallel. The potential energy of the electron is particularly low in the region of overlap, which is close to both nuclei. Therefore, a state represented initially by atomic orbitals and modified by the correlation pertaining to opposite spin orientation has a mean energy lower than the sum of the energies of the two separate atoms.

The mathematical calculation of the mean energy of the molecule in this approximation is fully analogous to the calculation for the excited states of the He atom in Sect. 17.4. The He atom has one electron in the ground state, with quantum numbers (1,0,0), and one in the excited state (n,l,m); here we consider initially one electron in the ground state ("atomic orbital") of each separate H atom.[2] The wave functions of the two atoms can be indicated initially by a and b, as though the atoms were distinguishable, and the positions of the two electrons are indicated by $\mathbf{r}_1$ and $\mathbf{r}_2$, as though the electrons were distinguishable. One writes then two wave functions of the whole molecule, corresponding to alternative assignments of electrons 1 and 2 to the two atomic orbitals and analogous to the He wave functions (16) page 262, namely,

$$(\mathbf{r}_1 \mid a)(\mathbf{r}_2 \mid b) \quad \text{and} \quad (\mathbf{r}_2 \mid a)(\mathbf{r}_1 \mid b). \tag{5}$$

The correlation of electron positions is introduced by representing the state of the H_2 molecule, in first approximation, as a superposition of the wave functions (5), analogous to the He wave function (18) page 262, namely,

$$(\mathbf{r}_1,\mathbf{r}_2 \mid a,b,S) = \sqrt{\tfrac{1}{2}}\,[(\mathbf{r}_1 \mid a)(\mathbf{r}_2 \mid b) + (-1)^S\,(\mathbf{r}_2 \mid a)(\mathbf{r}_1 \mid b)] \tag{6}$$

with $S = 0$ or 1 for opposite or parallel spins. Electrons in a state represented by this formula have a mean potential energy which is given, as the He energy (20), page 263, by the sum or the difference of two terms, depending on the value of S:

$$\langle E \rangle = V_{ab} + (-1)^S W_{ab}. \tag{7}$$

In this equation the term W_{ab} represents the effect of interference in the region of overlap of the two atoms. This term is negative because the potential energy is negative in the region of overlap (the corresponding term in the He problem is positive). Therefore, a decrease of the internuclear distance, increasing the region of overlap, decreases the mean potential energy of electrons with opposite spin orientations. This

---

[2] Conversely, the molecular orbital approximation represents the state of the H_2 molecule in analogy with the ground state of the He atom, with identical probability distributions for the positions of both electrons.

energy decrease represents the chemical bond that draws the atoms together. The atoms approach until the bond attraction is balanced by
the increasing nuclear repulsion.

An important difference between the independent-electron molecular-orbital approximation and the atomic-orbital approximation lies in the treatment of the
repulsion among electrons, which is fully disregarded in the former approximation.
This difference is illustrated by representing the molecular-orbital wave functions
schematically as combinations of one-electron atomic orbitals. The electron in the
ground state $1s\sigma$ of the H_2^+ ion is regarded as belonging with equal probability to
either nucleus. The wave function of this state is accordingly represented as a super-
position of the wave functions $(\mathbf{r}\,|\,a)$ and $(\mathbf{r}\,|\,b)$ with equal probability amplitudes,[3]

$$(\mathbf{r}\,|\,1s\sigma) = \sqrt{\tfrac{1}{2}}\,[(\mathbf{r}\,|\,a) + (\mathbf{r}\,|\,b)]. \tag{8}$$

The ground state of the H_2 molecule may be represented in the molecular-orbital
approximation in terms of the wave function (8) of one-electron states,

$$(\mathbf{r}_1,\mathbf{r}_2\,|\,(1s\sigma)^2) = (\mathbf{r}_1\,|\,1s\sigma)(\mathbf{r}_2\,|\,1s\sigma)$$

$$= \tfrac{1}{2}[(\mathbf{r}_1\,|\,a)(\mathbf{r}_2\,|\,a) + (\mathbf{r}_1\,|\,b)(\mathbf{r}_2\,|\,b) + (\mathbf{r}_1\,|\,a)(\mathbf{r}_2\,|\,b) + (\mathbf{r}_1\,|\,b)(\mathbf{r}_2\,|\,a)]. \tag{9}$$

This wave function is a superposition of the wave functions $(\mathbf{r}_1\,|\,a)(\mathbf{r}_2\,|\,b)$ and $(\mathbf{r}_1\,|\,b)$
$(\mathbf{r}_2\,|\,a)$, which are the same as in the atomic-orbital wave function (6), and also of the
functions $(\mathbf{r}_1\,|\,a)(\mathbf{r}_2\,|\,a)$ and $(\mathbf{r}_1\,|\,b)(\mathbf{r}_2\,|\,b)$, which represent both electrons as belonging to
the same atom. The inclusion of the latter wave functions on a par with the other
ones is unrealistic, as the electrons are unlikely to be in the same atom owing to their
repulsion. Conversely, the complete exclusion of the terms $(\mathbf{r}_1\,|\,a)(\mathbf{r}_2\,|\,a)$ and $(\mathbf{r}_1\,|\,b)$
$(\mathbf{r}_2\,|\,b)$ from the atomic-orbital wave function (6) is also unrealistic. A better approximation should include these terms with a smaller probability amplitude than the
others.

The atomic-orbital approximation method has the advantage of starting from states that are completely identified in terms of the well-known
stationary states of the H atom. The initial wave functions (5) are
unrealistic in so far as the position coordinates of the two electrons are
treated as independent distinguishable variables; but this initial error
is compensated by replacing the wave functions (5) with their combinations (6). Similarly, in the treatment of molecules more complicated
than H_2 it is often convenient to consider initially states of different
parts of a molecule. The stationary states of the whole molecule are
then described approximately by no single initial state but by a combination of two or more states. The determination of the actual stationary states and of their energy eigenvalues follows the general procedure outlined in Chapter 16.

---

[3] The $2p\sigma$ state is represented by $\sqrt{\tfrac{1}{2}}\,[(\mathbf{r}\,|\,a) - (\mathbf{r}\,|\,b)]$. A state in which the elec-
tron belongs definitely to one atom, as it must when the internuclear distance is very
large, is represented by $(\mathbf{r}\,|\,a) = \sqrt{\tfrac{1}{2}}\,[(\mathbf{r}\,|\,1s\sigma) + (\mathbf{r}\,|\,2p\sigma)]$.

As indicated in connection with the helium atom and discussed in Appendix X, the quantum mechanical treatment of the combinations of a few states is analogous to the classical treatment of a few coupled pendulums. The initial set of quantum mechanical states have equal, or nearly equal, energies, and the pendulums have equal, or nearly equal, frequencies, that is, are at or near *resonance* with one another. One speaks particularly of resonance when the oscillation energy is transferred periodically from one pendulum to another one; similarly, there are non stationary quantum mechanical states which approximate in turn now one and then another of the initial states. A set of coupled pendulums can perform a steady harmonic combined oscillation with minimum frequency lower than the frequency of the separate pendulums; similarly, the combinations of initial quantum mechanical states include a stationary state of minimum energy lower than the energy of the initial states. The existence of such a combined state of highest stability is often called an "effect of resonance." Sometimes it is also said inappropriately that a system in a stationary state resonates among the initial states; such a concept refers rather to a non-stationary state.

In the atomic-orbital treatment of the H_2 molecule, the initial states with the wave functions (5) differ in the assignment of electrons among the two atoms. A non-stationary state that approximates first one and then the other of the initial states represents an exchange of electrons between the two atoms. Owing to this aspect of the approximate treatment, which is common to the treatment of the He atom in Sect. 17.4, it is said that the exchange of the electrons between the atoms stabilizes their aggregation into a single molecule. Even in the molecular-orbital treatment the stability of the molecule derives from the ability of each electron to move from one to the other atom.

The frequency of the exchange of electrons between the atoms in a non-stationary state is determined by the same energy term W_{ab} in Eq. 7 which determines the stability of the molecule. This term is called the "exchange energy," as mentioned on page 264. The energy W_{ab} is a part of the electric potential energy of the electrons. It is the part which the atomic-orbital method singles out as due to the interference of the states with the alternative distributions of electrons between the two atoms.

chapter 20 ....

Chemical bonds

Atoms are held together in molecules by bonds which resemble, to a greater or smaller extent, the bond between the two atoms in the H_2 molecule. Many atoms may be connected chainwise into molecules of different sizes and shapes.

Molecules consisting of two alkali atoms are particularly similar to the H_2 molecule, inasmuch as each alkali atom has a single electron in its outermost shell. To discuss the formation of chemical bonds by an atom with more than one electron in its outermost shell, the state of the atom is appropriately identified at the outset, in the independent-electron approximation, by assigning a full set of quantum numbers to each electron, as on page 275. (The portion of electron interaction disregarded in this approximation is smaller than the interaction with other atoms which gives rise to the bond formation.) Any one-electron state of orbital motion irrespective of spin orientation, identified for example, by quantum numbers n,l,m, is called an "atomic orbital." A bond similar to the bond in the H_2 molecule can be formed whenever two atoms approach under the following conditions: (a) each atom has an atomic orbital with a single electron assigned to it, that is, an unfilled orbital; (b) the probability distributions of the electron position in unfilled orbitals of the two atoms overlap; (c) the electrons in the overlapping orbitals have opposite spin orientation. These two electrons can then pair up, each expanding into the space assigned to the other one. The combined state of the two electrons is identified, in the independent-electron approximation, by assigning both electrons to the same "molecular orbital" (see page 288) with opposite spin orientation. Alternatively, the state of the two electrons may be represented, in the atomic-orbital approximation, as a combination of a pair of states with alternative assignment of the two electrons to the two atoms, in analogy to the treatment of H_2 on pages 294–297.

Notice that, in the bond formation by atoms other than H, the interpenetration of the atoms is resisted not only by the repulsion between the nuclei but also by the effects of exclusion among the electrons of their inner shells. For purpose of orientation it is sufficient to assume that any two complete shells of different atoms are effectively impenetrable to each other. This obstacle to interpenetration often reduces the stability of bonds, particularly for atoms like the alkalis whose complete shells have a large radius.

One- and three-electron bonds, similar to those of the H_2^+ and He_2^+ ions, can also be formed between many-electron atoms. However, molecules with these types of bond are on the whole less stable than molecules with ordinary two-electron bonds and are seldom encountered. That is, chemical bonds are in the main two-electron bonds which result from the sharing of pairs of electrons by adjacent atoms.

An atom has an opportunity to form a chemical bond as long as it has an orbital with a single electron assigned to it; such an electron is called "unsaturated." Matter usually attains a stable state of aggregation when all its electrons are saturated. For this reason, and because of the predominance of two-electron bonds, stable molecules and ions have, in general, even numbers of electrons. Moreover, any two electrons that "saturate" each other have opposite spin orientation, in molecular as in atomic orbitals, so that the resultant spin angular momentum of most molecules vanishes. (Numerous molecules with unsaturated electrons are now being studied, even though they are unstable. They are called "free radicals" and are usually characterized by a nonvanishing resultant spin angular momentum.)

The stability of each chemical bond in a given molecule is characterized by the bond's energy, which is the energy required to break it by raising the internuclear distance up to infinity. The stability of a bond is also indicated by the mean value of the internuclear distance in the ground state of the molecule, particularly by the difference in internuclear distance when two atoms are linked together in different molecules.

Chemical bonds, although similar in general to the bond in the H_2 molecule, exhibit characteristics that do not occur in the simple case of hydrogen. First, the nature of the bond is modified and its stability increased when it links different atoms instead of identical ones (Sect. 20.1). Second, an atom with more than one electron in its outermost shell may form a number of simultaneous bonds with surrounding atoms; the geometrical characteristics of the atomic orbitals determine the relative positions of the atoms in the resulting molecule (Sect. 20.2). Third, two atoms with more than one unsaturated electron each may form a multiple bond by sharing more than one pair of electrons (Sect. 20.3).

20.1   Covalent and Ionic Bonds

The character of a bond depends on the similarity or dissimilarity of the atoms it links. A bond between identical atoms, as in the H_2 or Na_2 molecules, is called "covalent" or "homopolar." [1] A bond between two atoms apt to form ions of opposite sign has different character and greater stability than the basic covalent bond. The additional stability derives from the contribution of a different bonding mechanism, namely, from the electric attraction between ions of opposite sign. Consider the approach of two atoms, like Na and Cl, which have particularly stable ionized forms of opposite sign. An electron transfer from one neutral atom to the other one would generate a pair of ions which are then held together by electric attraction. This kind of bond is called "ionic" or "heteropolar." A purely ionic bond exists only in crystals and not in molecules.

To assess the stability of an ionic bond, compare the energy of a Na^+Cl^- combination with the energy of separate atoms of Na and Cl. Starting from separate atoms, the stripping of an electron from Na to yield Na^+ and a free electron at infinite distance absorbs 5.1 ev. The subsequent attachment of the electron to a Cl atom to form a stable Cl^- ion releases 3.7 ev. Finally, the approach of the ions Na^+ and Cl^- from infinite distance to the limit of interpenetration of their complete electron shells, about 2.8 A, reduces their potential energy by 5.3 ev. Therefore, the sequence of three processes releases about $-5.1 + 3.7 + 5.3 = 3.9$ ev. That is, the structure Na^+Cl^- has an energy lower than

---

[1] A bond between different atoms is also called "covalent" or "homopolar" whenever its character is not altered substantially by the difference between the atoms.

Na + Cl by an amount comparable to the energy released in the formation of a covalent bond.

On the other hand, the Na and Cl atoms have each an unsaturated
electron, and thus are capable of forming a bond of the covalent type.
The bond between Na and Cl differs from the bond between two like
atoms in that the mean potential energy of the unsaturated electron of
Cl is lower than that of the unsaturated electron of Na.   Therefore,
after bond formation each electron has a greater probability to be found
in the Cl than in the Na atom.   This is to say that the bond partakes
of the ionic character.

In the molecular-orbital approximation the probability distribution
of the positions of the two bond electrons is modified by the lower potential energy in the Cl atom.   It is no longer distributed evenly with
respect to the mid-point between the two nuclei, but is shifted toward
the Cl nucleus.   The electron concentration in the region of low electric
potential adds stability to the NaCl molecule.   More specifically, the
energy eigenvalue of the molecular orbital of NaCl is lower than the
arithmetic mean of the corresponding eigenvalues of Na_2 and Cl_2.   In
the atomic orbital approximation, the state of the two electron system
is no longer adequately represented by a superposition of the states
with wave functions $(\mathbf{r}_1|Na)(\mathbf{r}_2|Cl)$ and $(\mathbf{r}_2|Na)(\mathbf{r}_1|Cl)$, correspond-
ing to formula (5), page 295.   The superposition must also include,
with substantial probability amplitude, a state with wave function
$(\mathbf{r}_1|Cl)(\mathbf{r}_2|Cl)$ which represents both electrons in the Cl orbital and
thus attributes to the molecule the ionic structure Na^+Cl^-.   It is often
said that the NaCl molecule is "stabilized by resonance" between the
covalent structure, represented by the formula Na—Cl and the wave
function $\sqrt{\frac{1}{2}}[(\mathbf{r}_1|Na)(\mathbf{r}_2|Cl) + (\mathbf{r}_2|Na)(\mathbf{r}_1|Cl)]$, and the ionic struc-
ture, represented by the formula Na^+Cl^- and the wave function
$(\mathbf{r}_1|Cl)(\mathbf{r}_2|Cl)$.

A chemical bond between any two different atoms always partakes,
to a greater or lesser extent, of the covalent and of the ionic character.
One way to specify the extent of the ionic character of the bond between
two atoms α and $\mathcal{B}$ consists of comparing the stability of the bonds
α—$\mathcal{B}$, α—α, and $\mathcal{B}$—$\mathcal{B}$, by calculating the energy difference

$$E_{\alpha\mathcal{B}} - \tfrac{1}{2}(E_{\alpha\alpha} + E_{\mathcal{B}\mathcal{B}}). \tag{1}$$

The ionic character of a bond derives from the greater tendency of one
of the atoms to form a negative ion.   Atoms that form stable negative
ions are called "electronegative."   One says, therefore, that the energy
difference (1) is an index of the difference in electronegativity between
the atoms α and $\mathcal{B}$.   It is possible to construct empirically a table of the

electronegativity of chemical elements by examining the relative stability of the bonds which they form.

The electronegativity of elements increases along each row of the Periodic Table (Fig. 18.1) as one approaches the halogens, which lack one electron to achieve a complete shell configuration. In each column of the periodic system the lighter elements are the more electronegative ones, because shell completion has a more marked effect in the upper rows of the periodic system. (The stability of the rare gases decreases with increasing atomic weight.) The strongly electronegative elements are the few ones in the upper right hand corner of the Periodic Table, the most strongly electronegative one being fluorine.

The strongly electronegative elements combine with other elements into the most stable known molecules, and the combination reactions are correspondingly exothermic. These reactions proceed readily, and often spontaneously, particularly when they involve fluorine. They are called, in general, "combustions." Among the strongly electronegative elements, oxygen is widespread and combustions with oxygen provide the most common sources of chemical energy.

The ionic character of a chemical bond is also indicated by the electric dipole moment of the resulting molecule, or, more specifically, of the

TABLE 20.1

DIPOLE MOMENTS OF MOLECULAR GROUPS

Molecular Group	Dipole Moment $\mu(10^{-18}$ esu)	Internuclear Distance $R(10^{-8}$ cm)	$\dfrac{\mu}{eR}$
HN (in NH_3)	0.63	1.01	0.13
HO (in H_2O)	1.51	0.97	0.32
HF	1.91	0.92	0.43
HCl	1.05	1.27	0.17
HBr	0.80	1.41	0.11
HI	0.42	1.62	0.05
KF	7.3	2.55	0.60
CsF	7.6	2.34	0.68

pair of atoms linked by the bond. One calls "electric dipole" the combination of two distributions of electric charge of equal magnitude and opposite sign and centered at different positions; for example, a pair of ions Na^+ Cl^- constitutes a dipole. The product of the magnitude of the charge in either distribution and of the distance between their centers is called the "moment of the dipole." The dipole moment is a vector directed from the center of the negative to the center of the positive charges.   The dipole moment of a molecular aggregate is defined as follows: Given an aggregate of N electrons at positions $\mathbf{r}_i$ and of nuclei with atomic numbers Z_k at positions $\mathbf{R}_k$, its dipole moment $\boldsymbol{\mu}$ is Ne times the vector distance between the centers of positive and negative charges, that is, $\boldsymbol{\mu} = Ne(\Sigma_k Z_k \mathbf{R}_k/N - \Sigma_i \mathbf{r}_i/N)$.   The dipole moment of an atomic system is the mean value of $\boldsymbol{\mu}$ averaged over the probability distribution of particle positions.   The dipole moment of a molecule can be measured experimentally by various methods.   If a chemical bond were fully ionic, the atoms it links would have a dipole moment equal to the product of the unit charge e and of the internuclear distance.   Table 20.1 gives a few examples of dipole moments of molecules, or parts of molecules, with partially ionic bonds.

20.2   Atoms with Many Bonds and the Shape of Molecules

An atom can form chemical bonds with a number of different atoms equal to the number of its unsaturated electrons.   This number is the *chemical valence* of the atom.[2]

The state of an isolated atom which determines the number and type of its bonds is not necessarily the ground state.   The approach of other atoms capable of forming bonds with the atom under consideration disturbs this atom, primarily by beginning to reduce the confinement of its electrons.   The perturbed state may be represented as a superposition of stationary states of the isolated atom.   The component state with largest probability amplitude is the one which yields the largest net energy release upon bond formation.   One may say that the disturbance drives the atom into the state which permits the formation of the largest number of bonds and of the bonds of greatest stability, provided that the improvement in bond formation releases more energy than is required to modify the ground state of the atom.   With this proviso, the state of the atom which determines the number and type of bonds has the maximum number of unsaturated electrons for its configuration, it has the configuration with the highest number of unsaturated electrons, and the one-electron atomic orbitals which overlap most with those of the approaching atom.

The highest number of unsaturated electrons in a given configuration is the same as the highest number of electrons with parallel spins.[3]

---

[2] Only a limited number of atoms can fit around a given atom so as to form bonds with it.   This number is not always as large as the number of unsaturated electrons, so that the number of bonds may not attain its theoretical maximum.

[3] States with a maximum number of parallel spins are particularly stable for an isolated atom, as discussed on page 283.

It equals either the number of electrons in partially filled subshells, or the number of vacancies in these subshells, whichever is smaller. For example, the O atom has four $2p$ electrons in its outer shell, that is, two electrons fewer than would fill this shell; its valence is accordingly two.

The number of unsaturated electrons is increased by distributing the outer electrons among more than one incomplete subshell. Such a redistribution requires, in general, much energy, but electrons shift readily from s to p states of the same shell, or between nd and $(n + 1)s$ or $(n + 1)p$ states in atoms of the long periods with unfilled d subshells. In particular, the ground state configurations $(ns)^2$, $(ns)^2(np)$, and $(ns)^2(np)^2$, of atoms like Be, B, and C, are normally raised, respectively, to $(ns)(np)$, $(ns)(np)^2$, and $(ns)(np)^3$. The valence of these atoms increases thereby from 0, 1, and 2 to the familiar values 2, 3, and 4 which are indicated, for example, by the existence of fluoride molecules BeF_2, BF_3, and CF_4.

Consider now the overlapping of the atomic orbitals. One-electron states characterized by a quantum number l have electron positions distributed with equal probability in any two directions opposite with respect to the nucleus. For example, in the p_z state ($l = 1$, $m = 0$) the probability distribution of the electron position has maxima of equal brightness in the directions of the positive and negative z axis. This probability distribution is favorable to bond formation with an atom approaching along the z axis; nevertheless, the concentration of probability distribution in the negative z direction does not contribute to the overlap of the orbitals. A larger overlap of probability distribution is afforded by one-electron states with off-center electron distribution of the type described in Sect. 14.4. In particular, for the configuration $(2s)(2p)$ there is a complete set of two one-electron states with off-center probability distribution, one of which is concentrated in the region of positive z and the other in the region of negative z. These states are represented by the wave functions (23) and (25) on pages 213–4. Similarly, for the $(2s)(2p)^2$ configuration there is a set of three one-electron states whose probability distributions are concentrated, respectively, in three directions forming a plane, symmetrical, three-pointed star. These states have wave functions of the form (26) and (27), on page 214. Finally, in the $(2s)(2p)^3$ configuration there is a complete set of four states with off-center probability distributions concentrated, respectively, in the directions of the vertices of a regular tetrahedron centered at the atomic nucleus. The four wave functions have the form (28) and (29) on page 214. The fluoride molecules BeF_2, BF_3, and CF_4 have in fact, respectively, the linear, triangular, and tetrahedral shapes indicated in Fig. 20.1.

Bond formation along axes arranged in a straight line, in a triangular, or in a tetrahedral pattern is normal for elements of the Be, B, and C groups, respectively. In particular, carbon atoms are linked in long chains of aliphatic (saturated [4]) compounds with hydrogen atoms, or other groups, as side branches. Each carbon atom in these chains is sur-

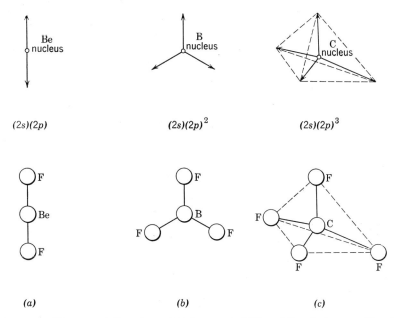

$(2s)(2p)$ $(2s)(2p)^2$ $(2s)(2p)^3$

(a)   (b)   (c)

Fig. 20.1 Diagram of directions of highest probability of the electron position for sets of off-center orbitals of different configurations. The arrows represent the central axes of the brightest fringes, the circles the positions of the atoms in typical molecules.

rounded by four other atoms in a tetrahedral pattern. The methane molecule, CH_4, constitutes a basic example of tetrahedral structure. Notice that this molecule has, in all, ten electrons like the Ne atom and that the set of its molecular orbitals partakes of the symmetry and stability of a closed shell. These characteristics are shared also by the ammonium ion, NH_4^+, which differs from methane only by the replacement of a carbon with a nitrogen nucleus. The higher electric charge of the N nucleus draws the probability distribution of all electron positions

---

[4] The adjective "saturated" refers here not to the absence of unsaturated electrons but rather to the formation by each C atom of a maximum number of bonds with a maximum number of different atoms. It distinguishes the aliphatic hydrocarbons from the ethylenic and acetylenic ones which have multiple bonds; see footnote 8.

closer to the center of the molecule, giving the bonds a greater ionic character than they have in the CH_4 molecule.[5]

In atoms like N, with five electrons in s and p subshells, only three electrons can be unsaturated irrespective of their subdivision among the two subshells. Therefore, the neutral N atom is trivalent, whereas the ion N^+, with one less electron, is tetravalent.[6] In particular, N is trivalent in its ground state with the configuration $(2s)^2(2p)^3$. An atom with the three unsaturated electrons in the orbitals $2p_x$, $2p_y$, and $2p_z$, respectively, can form bonds with three other atoms approaching in the directions of the three coordinate axes. According to this model, the resulting molecule would have a pyramidal shape with 90° angles between the bond directions. On the other hand, the bonds formed starting from the p orbitals of the ground state configuration are not as strong as the bonds formed starting from orbitals with off-center electron distributions. In particular, one may consider for the N atom the same set of four orbitals in the tetrahedral pattern as for the C atom.[7] The five electrons in the outer shell of the N atom fill completely one of these orbitals, leaving the other three available for bond formation. This model also yields a pyramidal shape for a molecule like NH_3, however, with the "tetrahedral angle" of 109.5° instead of 90° between the bond directions. The bond angle of the NH_3 molecule is known experimentally to be 108°. This value would indicate that the bonds of this molecule are formed starting from orbitals quite similar to those of carbon. One must also consider in this connection that the NH bond is partially ionic (see Table 20.1) with an excess positive charge on the H atom. The repulsion between the H atoms strives to increase the bond angles. The actual state of the NH_3 molecule appears thus to partake of the characteristics of the two models considered above.

The problem of bond formation by oxygen is quite analogous to that of nitrogen, except that the number of unsaturated electrons is now reduced to two, instead of three. The simple compound H_2O has V-shaped molecules, with a bond angle of 105°. The ground state con-

---

[5] In the atomic orbital approximation, the state of the NH_4^+ molecular ion is represented as a combination of five states described by the structural formulas

$$
\begin{matrix}
\text{H} & & \text{H} & & \text{H}^+ & & \text{H} & & \text{H} \\
| & & | & & | & & | & & | \\
\text{H—N}^+\text{—H,} & & \text{H}^+\ \ \text{N—H,} & & \text{H—N—H,} & & \text{H—N}\ \ \text{H}^+, & & \text{H—N—H.} \\
| & & | & & | & & | & & | \\
\text{H} & & \text{H} & & \text{H} & & \text{H} & & \text{H}^+
\end{matrix}
$$

[6] The alternative apparent pentavalence of N will be discussed in Sect. 21.1.

[7] The bonds formed starting from C orbitals are stronger than those formed starting from Be or B type orbitals.

figuration of oxygen $(2s)^2(2p)^4$ can form two bonds at an angle of $90°$. A state with carbon-type orbitals has two of these orbitals completely filled and two with one electron each available to form bonds at an angle of $109.5°$. Here again the molecule appears to partake of the characteristics of both models. The HO bond is more strongly ionic than the NH bond (see Table 20.1).

Atoms in states with a partially filled d subshell can form a larger number of bonds than atoms of the short periods which have only s and p electrons. A theoretical maximum of nine bonds could be formed starting from a configuration $(ns)(np)^3(n-1\ d)^5$. However, nine atoms cannot fit around a central atom sufficiently close to it for bond formation. The highest number of single bonds an atom actually forms in a molecule is usually six.

20.3 Multiple Bonds

Two atoms, each possessing more than one unsaturated electron, can form a multiple bond by sharing two or three pairs of electrons. The molecules thus formed are quite stable, even though the formation of a second or third bond does not usually release as much energy as the formation of the first one. Some typical examples of multiple bonds occur in the oxygen and nitrogen molecules and in the "unsaturated" [8] hydrocarbons.

Different pairs of electrons taking part in a multiple bond are in different one-electron states, owing to the exclusion principle. Since the pairs of electrons are confined in the same region of space, they have usually different energy levels, one pair being in the ground state, the others in excited states. Therefore, the structure of a molecule with multiple bonds is conveniently analyzed by considering first the formation of single bonds by pairs of electrons in their ground state, and then the formation of additional bonds by the remaining pairs of bonding electrons. In the molecular orbital approximation, the states of the electrons in the first bonds are classified as σ states, while the additional electrons shared by atoms can generally be classified as π electrons (see Sect. 19.1). This situation is illustrated by the following examples.

The ethylenic double bond. Ethylene, C_2H_4, is a prototype of unsaturated hydrocarbon molecule. Its saturated counterpart, the ethane molecule, C_2H_6, has one additional hydrogen atom attached to each carbon. In ethylene, the fourth valence electron of each carbon,

---

[8] "Unsaturated" means in this case that the carbon atoms are not linked to a maximum number of hydrogen atoms. The electrons in the molecule are, however, all saturated by the formation of multiple bonds.

which is not utilized in a C—H bond, is shared by the two carbons in the formation of a second C—C bond. The resulting structural formula is

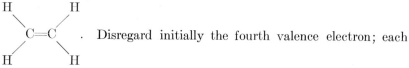

. Disregard initially the fourth valence electron; each

carbon atom forms bonds like a trivalent atom, namely, like B, starting from the atomic configuration $(2s)(2p)^2$ (see page 304). Each carbon is therefore surrounded by three atoms (two hydrogens and a carbon) in the plane triangular configuration of Fig. 20.1b. (The triangle need

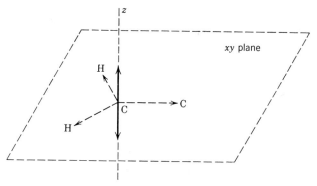

Fig. 20.2 Diagram of directions of highest probability distribution of the electron position for the p_z atomic orbital of a carbon atom in ethylene.

not be exactly equilateral when the three atoms are not identical.) The second C—C bond is formed starting from an orbital of each carbon atom which is orthogonal (that is, mutually exclusive, see page 97) to the orbitals involved in the other three bonds. These last orbitals have electron distributions concentrated along the three coplanar directions of the atoms surrounding the carbon. The fourth orbital has, therefore, its electron distribution concentrated in the directions perpendicular to this plane. It is the p orbital whose electron distribution has a dark interference fringe centered on the plane of the atoms surrounding the carbon (see Fig. 20.2). Notice that this orbital has two bright interference fringes above and below the plane of the other nuclei, centered along directions perpendicular to this plane, neither of which points toward the other C atom. These directions are usually designated as $\pm z$ and the orbital as the p_z orbital. The bright fringes of the p_z orbitals of the two carbon atoms overlap sideways above and below the C—C axis. Since the two C atoms are held at close distance by the first C—C bond, this overlap reduces sufficiently the confinement of each electron to yield a bond with substantial energy release. It is essential, however, for good overlap that the bright fringes of the p_z orbitals of the two C atoms have parallel axes (that is, that the z directions for the two atoms coincide). Therefore, the formation of a double bond constricts the whole ethylene molecule into a planar configuration. This constriction is, of course, not a rigid one; the two halves of the molecule can twist about the C—C axis, but any twist is resisted because it forces up the kinetic energy of the p_z electrons.

In the molecular-orbital approximation, the states of the four electrons in the double bond can be classified according to their motion about the bond axis, as was done for the states of the H_2^+ ion (see Sect. 19.1). The electrons of the first bond have their position distributed uniformly about the bond axis and no rotational motion around this axis; their state is accordingly classified as σ. The electrons of the second C—C bond have a distribution with a dark interference fringe centered on the molecular plane which contains the bond axis. Their states are accordingly classified as π.

The internuclear C=C distance in the ethylenic double bond is 1.34 A, as compared to 1.54 A for singly bonded carbons. Double bonds analogous to the ethylenic C=C bond occur in organic molecules between carbon and nitrogen and between carbon and oxygen atoms.

The 14-electron molecules C_2H_2, N_2, and CO. Acetylene, C_2H_2, has two hydrogen atoms less than ethylene; the valence electron thus left unsaturated in each C atom is taken up in the formation of an additional C—C bond. The structure formula is accordingly H—C≡C—H.

Disregard initially the electrons forming the second and third C—C bond; each carbon atom forms bonds like a bivalent atom, namely, like Be, starting from the atomic configuration $(2s)^1(2p)^1$ (see page 304). Each carbon is therefore linked to two atoms in a straight line.

Since the molecule is linear, the one-electron states (atomic and molecular) are classified according to rotational motion about the molecular axis. The electrons forming the C—H and the first C—C bonds have no rotational motion, that is, are in σ states. The electrons forming the second and third bonds have therefore a non-vanishing rotational motion. Specifically, their two atomic orbitals are p states which may be characterized either by dark interference fringes centered on two perpendicular planes through the molecular axis, or by opposite directions of electron flow about this axis. The bright fringes of these orbitals extend in directions transverse to the molecular axis, and the second and third bond are formed in the same way as the second bond of ethylene. In the molecular orbital approximation, the electrons of the second and third bond are assigned to four π states, each of them identified by one of two alternative orbitals and one of two alternative spin orientations. The C≡C internuclear distance in the acetylene molecule is 1.20 A.

The N_2 molecule is held together by a very stable triple bond, quite analogous to that of acetylene, with internuclear distance 1.10 A. Each N atom has an electronic structure very similar to that of the C—H group and is equivalent to this group in many organic compounds. (Even NH_3 has the structure of CH_4, with the N atom in place of CH.) The C—H group and the N atom have the same number of nuclear charges and of electrons, namely seven. One may regard the electronic structure of the N atom as a limiting case of the structure of the molecular group C—H, when the internuclear distance is brought to zero. The two electrons forming the C—H bond in acetylene remain paired, in the case of nitrogen, in a single atomic orbital homologous to the carbon atomic orbital from which the C—H bond was originated.

Since the N_2 molecule is diatomic, its one-electron molecular orbitals can be classified like the orbitals of the H_2^+ ion by complete sets of quantum numbers which pertain to the "united atom" limit of vanishing internuclear distance (Sect. 19.1). Out of the 14 electrons, two pairs are in the $1s$ shells of the separate atoms and take no part in the formation of bonds; their states can nevertheless be classified as molecular orbitals $1s\sigma$ and $2p\sigma$, one of which is bonding and one antibonding. The triple bond stems from three pairs of electrons in bonding orbitals, one of which is classified as $2s\sigma$ and two as $2p\pi$. The $2s\sigma$ molecular orbital is formed from N atomic orbitals of the off-center type which are combinations of $2s$ and $2p$ with $m = 0$; the $2p\pi$ orbitals are formed from $2p$ atomic orbitals with $m = \pm 1$. There remain the two electron pairs, one for each atom, in the atomic orbitals which are homologous to those in the C—H bond of acetylene and are also combinations of $2s$ and $2p$ with $m = 0$; these electrons take no part in the bond but their states can nevertheless be classified as molecular orbitals $3s\sigma$ and $3p\sigma$, one of which is bonding and one antibonding. The complete state of the 14 electrons is accordingly described by the configuration $(1s\sigma)^2(2p\sigma)^2(2s\sigma)^2(2p\pi)^4$ $(3s\sigma)^2(3p\sigma)^2$.

The carbon monoxide molecule, CO, is diatomic with the same number of electrons as the N_2 molecule. Its remarkable stability and short internuclear distance indicate that it partakes of the stability of the triply bonded N_2 molecule. Whereas N_2 has seven unit charges on each nucleus, CO has six charges on one nucleus and eight on the other one. The structure formula of CO analogous to that of N_2 would therefore be C^-≡O^+. The triple bond stabilizes this structure, but it takes a large amount of energy to shift an electron from electronegative oxygen to carbon. Experimentally, the CO molecule has a very small dipole moment. On the other hand, the usual formula C=O does not account for the stability of the molecule or for the short internuclear distance, which is 1.13 A, as compared to about 1.21 A for C=O groups in organic molecules. In addition, the C=O structure implies that the C atom has two unsaturated valences. The actual state of the CO molecule may be regarded as a superposition of $C^-\!\!\equiv\!\!O^+$ and of C—O, stabilized by resonance; the superposition probably also includes the structure $C^+\!\!-\!\!O^-$ with appreciable probability amplitude. The molecular orbital approximation affords a simple qualitative description of this state. The probability distribution of the positions of the six electrons $(2s\sigma)^2(2p\pi)^4$ need not be symmetrical with respect to the midpoint between the two nuclei, but may be shifted toward the O nucleus to an extent commensurate to the strength of its attraction.

The H—C≡N molecule and the (C≡N)$^-$ ion have electronic structures analogous to those of C_2H_2 and CO.

The oxygen molecule. The oxygen atom with six electrons in its outer shell is bivalent because it has only two unsaturated electrons. Accordingly, the atoms in the O_2 molecule are connected by a double bond. This bond has, however, the singular characteristic that the electrons forming it have a net spin angular momentum. The circulating current associated with the angular momentum causes the O_2 gas to be paramagnetic.[9]

The structure of O_2 is conveniently described in the molecular orbital approximation. Two electrons are added to the configuration of N_2 to yield the full complement of electrons of O_2. The states of lowest energy available for these two electrons are antibonding states $3d\pi$. The addition of two electrons in an antibonding orbital counterbalances almost exactly the bonding action of two among the six bonding electrons, thus leaving the molecule with the stability of a double bond. The antibonding electrons occupy two of the four $3d\pi$ states, each of which is identified by one of two alternative orbitals and by one of two alternative spin orientations. The repulsion between the two antibonding electrons causes their joint state to be most stable when their spin angular momenta are parallel and they are assigned to different orbitals. This effect is analogous to the greater stability of orthohelium as compared to parahelium excited states (see Sect. 17.4).

---

[9] A substance is called paramagnetic when under the action of an external magnetic field it acquires a magnetic moment due to prevalent parallel orientation of net intramolecular currents.

The O_2 molecule has a state of low excitation which has the same configuration as the ground state, but has zero resultant spin angular momentum and the two antibonding electrons in the same $3d\pi$ orbital. This state is equivalent to the state described by assigning two pairs of electrons to form an ethylene-type double bond and two additional pairs, one for each atom, to non-bonding atomic orbitals.

···

chapter 21

Non-localized bonds

The chemical bonds described in the last chapter link any one atom of a molecule only to atoms immediately adjacent to it. Thereby distant atoms of a molecule are linked only indirectly through a chain of bonds, and physical actions are transmitted through molecules only stepwise from one atom to its neighbors. The ordinary structure formulas of chemistry emphasize this stepwise linkage by representing each bond as a dash between the symbols of two elements. This concept of localized chemical bond goes a long way toward a realistic description of chemical structures but fails to account for the properties of many important aggregates of atoms.

The basic mechanism of chemical bonds, namely, the relaxation of the confinement of electron motion, is not exploited fully when separate electron pairs expand over separate pairs of atoms. Additional stability accrues to many molecules when a number of electron pairs spread smoothly over a number of atoms, thus welding all atoms together by a single diffuse bond. Electrons moving throughout the volume of many atoms can also concentrate in regions where the potential energy is particularly low, with a resulting further gain of stability. This gain extends the gain derived from partial ionic character of localized bonds.

The combination of a number of electron pairs into a single system gives molecules certain characteristic properties besides increased stability. In the first place, the motion of electrons over an extended volume transmits readily throughout that volume the effects of external disturbances. Second, the larger the volume is through which electrons can move, the closer are their one-electron energy levels (see the example on page 189). Therefore, the spacing of the energy levels of the whole system decreases with increasing volume, even though the number of electrons is proportional to the volume and consequently the average energy per electron is constant. It follows that a system becomes increasingly sensitive to external disturbances (see page 268) and acquires the properties which characterize a conductor.

A series of examples will be given in this chapter, in which the range of electronic motion within an aggregate increases from a few atoms to macroscopic distances. Examples of motion through small molecules are described in Sect. 21.1 and examples of motion along chains and plane networks of atoms in Sect. 21.2. Metals may be regarded as limiting cases of large molecules with unrestricted range of electronic motion (Sect. 21.3). Molecules with non-localized bonds are utilized in physicochemical processes owing to their sensitivity to disturbances and to their ability to transmit them. Organic molecules with non-localized bonds as, for example, the tetrapyrrole ring shown in Fig. 21.1 are found to be key ingredients of biochemical catalysis.

Polyvalent atoms usually form bonds, as explained in Sect. 20.2, starting from atomic orbitals with off-center electron distributions, concentrated in the direction of bond formation. There result molecular orbitals in which the electrons have small probability of being outside the region between the nuclei and little opportunity of expanding in other directions. Accordingly, non-localized bonds occur normally in molecules as modifications of *multiple* bonds, in which the electron distribution is not quite concentrated between two nuclei. Non-localized bonds do not occur, for example, in saturated hydrocarbons. In metals, molecular orbitals between pairs of atoms would not be very stable and no electron remains localized in such a state.

Non-localized bonds are not represented directly by chemical structure formulas. The state of a molecule with a non-localized bond is usually regarded, according to the quantum mechanical approximation method (page 297), as a combination of a number of states, each represented by a structure formula. The molecule is portrayed by the collection of these formulas and is said to be stabilized by resonance.

21.1   A Simple Example: Carbon Dioxide

As seen in Sect. 20.3, multiple bonds originate in part from atomic orbitals with electron distributions extending transversally to the bond axis. Such orbitals of two adjacent atoms have electron distributions extending not toward but mainly parallel to each other. They nevertheless overlap sufficiently to reduce the electrons' confinement with formation of a bond.

Consider now the situation of a molecule, like CO_2, in which an atom, carbon, forms multiple bonds with two equal atoms. Any carbon orbital with electron distribution extending transversally to the bond axes overlaps equally on two sides with a similar orbital of each O atom. An electron initially in the carbon orbital may thus move through all three atoms linking them all, instead of linking only a pair of them.

The motion of an electron through three atoms has stationary states which are represented approximately as combinations of orbitals of the three atoms and are analogous to the states $2p\pi$ and $3d\pi$ of motion restricted to two atoms. The two-atom states $2p\pi$ and $3d\pi$ are, respectively, bonding and antibonding and have, respectively, no dark fringe and one dark fringe perpendicular to the molecular axis. It can be shown that the three-atom system has three types of states, respectively, with 0, 1, and 2 dark fringes perpendicular to the molecular axis, which may be designated as π_0, π_1 and π_2. There are four states of each type, identified by one of two alternative orbitals (for example, with opposite directions of electron flow about the bond axis) and by one of two alternative spin orientations. The π_0 states have lowest energy and are strongly bonding, more strongly than the $2p\pi$, the π_1 have no bonding action, and the π_2 are strongly antibonding.

The electronic structure of the CO_2 molecule is described by the procedure of Sect. 20.3, that is, by considering first the formation of two single bonds between carbon and the two oxygens. The C atom forms these bonds like a bivalent atom and is therefore linked to the two O atoms in opposite directions, forming a linear molecule. The C atom has thus two residual outer electrons for assignment in the π molecular orbitals. Each oxygen has six electrons in its outer shell, one of which is taken up by the first CO bond. Two of the remaining electrons saturate each other in one atomic orbital, as in O_2 and N_2, with its bright fringe centered in a direction opposite to the CO bond. There remain three electrons in each O atom for assignment to the π molecular orbitals. In all, the CO_2 molecule has eight electrons (two from C, and three from each O) for assignment to π orbitals. The ground state configuration of these electrons is therefore $(\pi_0)^4(\pi_1)^4$.

The pairing of four electrons in the two π_0 orbitals yields two bonds, which, together with the two initial CO bonds, make a total of four bonds for the CO_2 molecule. As noted above, the π_0 bonds, distributed over the whole molecule, are more stable than the $2p\pi$ bonds of diatomic molecules. The molecule is therefore more stable than indicated by the ordinary formula O=C=O, with two localized double bonds. Experimentally, the total bond energy of the molecule exceeds by 1.4 ev the sum of the energies of two localized double bonds between carbon and oxygen such as occur, for example, in aldehydes and ketones. The internuclear CO distance in the CO_2 molecule is 1.15 A, as compared to about 1.21 A in molecules with localized bonds.

The special stability of CO_2 can be accounted for qualitatively by regarding the state of the molecule as a combination of states represented by O=C=O and by the alternative formulas $O^+\equiv C-O^-$, and $O^--C\equiv O^+$. The combination gives each bond a partial triple bond character. A transition between states represented by the three formulas involves a shift of electrons from one to the other end of the molecule. Therefore, a combination of these states represents, like the description by molecular orbitals, a state of the molecule in which electrons move throughout its length and weld all atoms together by means of a single non-localized bond.

The special stability of the CO_2 molecular structure accounts for the structure and stability of two molecules isoelectronic to CO_2, namely, the nitrogen monoxyde N_2O and the azide ion $N_3{}^-$. The structure formulas of these molecules analogous to O=C=O are respectively $N^-=N^+=O$ and $N^-=N^+=N^-$.

The borate, carbonate, and nitrate ions. The ions $BO_3{}^{---}$, $CO_3{}^{--}$, and $NO_3{}^-$ constitute an isoelectronic sequence. Their atoms are arranged in plane triangular patterns, with the oxygens at the vertices and the other atom at the center. This structure derives from the formation of three single bonds by the central atom with trivalent behavior, starting from the $(2s)(2p)^2$ configuration (see page 304, Fig. 20.1b). It corresponds to the structure formulas

$$
\begin{array}{ccc}
\text{O}^- & \text{O}^- & \text{O}^- \\
| & | & | \\
\text{B} & \text{C}^+ & \text{N}^{++} \\
\diagup\;\diagdown & \diagup\;\diagdown & \diagup\;\diagdown \\
\text{O}^-\quad\text{O}^- & \text{O}^-\quad\text{O}^- & \text{O}^-\quad\text{O}^-
\end{array}
\qquad (1)
$$

All atoms of these ions have an atomic orbital with a dark interference fringe centered on the plane of the nuclei. This orbital is the one from which is formed the second bond of ethylene (see page 308) and is designated by p_z when the z axis is perpendicular to the plane of the molecule. The formulas (1) imply electronic structures in which the central atom is trivalent and surrounded by monovalent O^- ions. The p_z orbital of the central atom is wholly unoccupied and the p_z orbital of each O^- ion is occupied by a pair of electrons with opposite spin orientation. In fact, the p_z orbitals of the central and outer atoms overlap and the p_z electrons of each O^- can expand toward the center of the molecule. In the molecular orbital approximation one considers a set of four π orbitals, each with a dark fringe centered on the plane of the molecule, in which the probability distribution of the electron position extends over all four atoms. The probability of finding the electron in the central atom is low for the BO_3^{---} ion and increasingly large for CO_3^{--} and NO_3^-. Three of the four π orbitals are fully occupied by the six electrons which would be assigned to the O atoms according to the formulas (1).

The shift of the electrons toward the center of the ions is taken into account by regarding the state of each ion as a combination of states represented by (1) and by formulas of the type

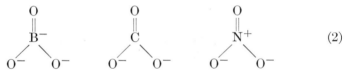

$$(2)$$

(There are three sets of formulas with the double bond in the three positions.) Notice that, from the standpoint of electronic structure, there is

no state represented by the formula $O^- \!\!-\!\! N \!\!\begin{smallmatrix} \diagup O \\ \diagdown O \end{smallmatrix}$ in which the N atom

appears to be pentavalent, because the outer shell of the N atom possesses only four independent orbitals from which bonds can be formed.

The distance between the central nucleus and the nuclei of the outer atoms is 1.35, 1.31, and 1.21 A respectively for the three ions. These distances are shorter than would be expected for single bonds, and their decrease along the sequence parallels the increasing double-bond character of the bonds and the increasing stability of the ions.

21.2   Conjugated Ethylenic Bonds.   Graphite

Very important classes of organic molecules contain non-localized bonds which result from the merger of double bonds similar to the ethylene bond described in Sect. 20.3. The smallest molecule of this type is butadiene whose basic structure formula is indicated schematically by $CH_2{=}CH{-}CH{=}CH_2$, and more explicitly in the alternative *cis* and *trans* forms

$$\tag{3}$$

cis   *trans*

Each of the double bonds indicated in these formulas may be described like the bond of ethylene. The "second" bond of each double bond arises from the overlap of atomic orbitals of the C atoms with a dark fringe of the electron distribution centered on the plane of the molecule; these orbitals are designated by p_z, with reference to a z axis perpendicular to the plane of the molecule. The p_z orbitals of the two middle atoms of the molecule overlap each other as well as the orbitals of the end atoms, so that a non-localized bond is formed throughout the chain of four C atoms.

Four π molecular orbitals, with electron distribution extended over the whole chain of C atoms and with a dark fringe centered on the plane of the molecule, are formed starting from the p_z orbitals of the four C atoms. The four electrons, one from each atom, which would form the second bonds in the structures (3) fill the two extended π orbitals with lowest energy. The first of these orbitals has bonding action throughout the molecule and particularly at its mid-point, the second has a dark fringe across the middle of the molecule and is antibonding there. Therefore, the resulting non-localized bond is weaker in the middle of the chain than in its outer links. In fact, the internuclear CC distance is 1.46 A for the middle bond, as compared to 1.54 A for a single bond and to 1.34 A for the double bond in ethylene. Owing to the non-localized bond, the total bond energy of butadiene is $\frac{1}{3}$ ev higher than it would be if its structure were represented accurately by one of the formulas (3) with separate double bonds.

The actual state of the butadiene molecule may be regarded as a combination of states represented by the schematic formulas $CH_2{=}CH{-}CH{=}CH_2$ and $CH_2{-}CH{=}CH{-}CH_2$. The structure with the double bond in the middle has one bond less than the normal structure; therefore, its probability amplitude is rather small, in accordance with the fact that the middle bond has only a weak double-bond character.

The formation of a non-localized bond along the whole chain stabilizes the molecule to a configuration with all its nuclei in a plane. In the absence of this bond, the two halves of the molecule could twist with respect to one another about the axis of the middle bond. There are two alternative plane configurations, with equal bond energies, namely, those indicated as *cis* and *trans* in the formulas (3). The non-localized bond is, however, not very strong in the middle and fails to prevent the occurrence of transitions between the *cis* and *trans* forms, so that these forms are not isolated as distinct structure isomers of butadiene.

Double bonds which are separated by a single C—C bond, as indicated in the butadiene formulas (3), are called "conjugated double bonds." Sequences of conjugated double bonds of various lengths occur in numerous organic molecules. Simple chains of CH groups, represented by formulas —CH=CH—CH=CH—CH=CH— $\cdots$, or —$(CH=CH)_n$—, are called "polymethine" chains. The non-localized bonds formed along these chains become increasingly uniform as the chain length increases, that is, they show no longer any weak spot as marked as the one in the middle of the butadiene molecule. As the chain length increases, the electrons forming the non-localized bond become capable of oscillating with lower frequency, in non-stationary states, as it generally happens to mechanical systems of increasing dimensions. The low-frequency oscillations of non-stationary states may be represented as effects of interference between stationary states whose energy differences are small for the reason indicated on page 314. The electrons of polymethine chains with more than four conjugated bonds oscillate with frequencies in the visible and infrared range of the spectrum, and therefore absorb light of characteristic frequencies in this range. Substances having these chains in their molecules act as dyes; they include the carotene pigments.

The benzene molecule, C_6H_6, consists of a closed ring of six methine groups with three conjugated double bonds. These groups are welded into a regular hexagon by a non-localized bond whose electrons are distributed uniformly all around the ring. The total bond energy of benzene exceeds by 1.7 ev the value corresponding to the structure

$$
\begin{array}{ccc}
 & CH & \\
 \diagup & & \diagdown \\
CH & & CH \\
\| & & | \\
CH & & CH \\
 \diagdown & & \diagup \\
 & CH &
\end{array}
$$

with alternate single and double bonds. The complete uniformity and stability of the benzene ring is often taken into account by structure formulas which symbolize the whole molecule as a regular hexagon ⬡.

The organic polycyclic hydrocarbons consist of two or more benzene rings condensed into a plane network with common sides. The structures of the simplest substances of this series are indicated by the schematic structural formulas

Naphthalene   Anthracene   Phenanthrene

Vertices of these diagrams common to different rings indicate the positions of C atoms, vertices belonging to a single ring indicate the positions of CH groups. Each atom of the network is linked to the adjacent atoms by an ordinary covalent localized bond. All atoms are further welded into a single system by a non-localized bond formed by electrons which move all over the network in states with a dark interference fringe centered on the plane of the network.

There is a great variety of polycyclic compounds, in which CH groups are often replaced with N atoms and some rings consist of five atoms

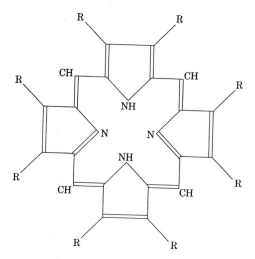

Fig. 21.1 Structure formula of tetrapyrrole ring. Numerous substances have this structure with various radicals at positions R. Carbon atoms lie at unmarked corners of the network of conjugated bonds.

only. There are also combinations of rings and of polymethine chains again welded into single systems by non-localized bonds. Figure 21.1 shows, as an example, the structure formula of a tetrapyrrole ring. This basic ring, with an iron or magnesium ion added in the middle and with different minor modifications, constitutes the pigment and key functional element of hemoglobin and of chlorophyll.

Networks of hexagonal benzene rings of any size can exist, up to macroscopic dimensions, because they are structurally strong and less liable to accidental breakage than polymethine chains. A large network consists almost entirely of C atoms, since CH groups are confined to its edges. As the size of the network increases, the electronic system of the non-localized bond becomes increasingly sensitive to disturbances, as indicated on page 314, and capable of oscillating at progressively lower frequencies. A macroscopic network of this type acts as a laminar *metallic* conductor and constitutes the basic structural unit of graphite crystals. It will be seen in the next chapter that a graphite crystal consists of a stack of such laminar units held together by weak cohesive forces.

21.3   The Metallic Bond

We have seen that non-localized bonds are formed starting from atomic orbitals whose electron distributions extend equally in the directions of different adjacent atoms. Conversely, bonds localized between two atoms are strongest when the electron distribution of an orbital of each atom is concentrated in the direction of the other atom. Formation of a non-localized bond also implies an equal, or nearly equal, overlap of orbitals between an atom and two or more adjacent atoms and therefore implies that the adjacent atoms are equal or at least similar to one another. Formation of a bond which welds many atoms uniformly, as in the carbon chains and networks, implies that all these atoms are similar to one another, as they are in typically covalent bonds.

In the examples described thus far, non-localized bonds are subsidiary to an underlying system of localized covalent, or partially ionic, single bonds. This system of bonds determines the kind, number, and relative positions of the adjacent atoms among which a non-localized bond can be formed. In particular under these conditions, atoms with only s and p electrons in their outer shell, and therefore with four independent orbitals, can form non-localized bonds with no more than three adjacent atoms. On the other hand, non-localized bonds become increasingly stable if the confinement to the motion of atomic electrons is reduced by the approach of an increasing number of atoms from different directions. Therefore, maximum spread of a non-localized bond is inconsistent with an underlying network of localized bonds and occurs when the circumstances cause a non-localized bond to replace localized bonds altogether, namely in metals.

A metal consists of a lattice of atoms, usually of the same element, held together by a non-localized bond formed by electrons that move throughout the lattice in all directions. This type of non-localized bond, which results from reduced confinement of all unsaturated electrons in a three-dimensional array of directions, is called a "metallic bond." A system of conjugated double bonds constitutes an intermediate case between the covalent and metallic bonds. The total bond energy of a metal lattice is of the order of a few electron volts per pair of electrons taking part in the bond.

Most of the chemical elements are metals, that is, under normal conditions of pressure and temperature their atoms form an aggregate held together by a metallic bond. On the other hand, a number of important elements, like hydrogen and oxygen, are stable when their atoms combine in pairs to form molecules held together by covalent bonds. Some metallic elements, for example, the alkalis, also form diatomic molecules in their vapor form, but upon condensation their molecules merge into a lattice and the covalent bonds into a metallic bond, whereas this merger does not occur, for example, in oxygen. The elements whose molecular form persists upon condensation are those that form strong covalent bonds, whereas the covalent bonds of metal atoms are weak. That is, the metallic bond prevails only when the covalent bond is weak; or, in other words, the metallic bond is never very strong.

The reason for the limited strength of the metallic bond is indicated in Fig. 21.2. The figure shows the cross section of a lattice of atoms, each atom being represented schematically by a circle. The electron distribution of each atom overlaps equally with the electron distributions of several other atoms. The strength of the metallic bond is derived from the number of separate overlaps, but no single overlap can be very extensive. In a regular lattice of atoms an extensive overlap would imply a simultaneous overlap of the electron distributions of more than two atoms, and would violate the exclusion principle since no more than two electrons can occupy the same space and have opposite spin orientations. (More specifically, the probability distributions of the positions of three or more electrons can overlap only if their joint state is so combined as to yield a partially antibonding effect.)

In a covalent bond the extent of overlap between the electron distributions of two atoms is not limited by the exclusion principle, as far as the bond-forming electrons are concerned, but it is limited by the impenetrability of inner shells (see page 299). Therefore, the extent of overlap and the covalent bond strength are significantly limited in atoms whose core of inner shells is not much smaller than the whole atom. This condition holds for all atoms with few outer electrons and also, in general, for atoms of high atomic number; atoms with these characteristics belong to the elements that are, in fact, metals.   The limited interpenetration of these atoms in any one direction allows simultaneous interpenetration in many directions and makes the metallic bond energetically convenient.   Conversely, elements in the upper right hand corner of the Periodic

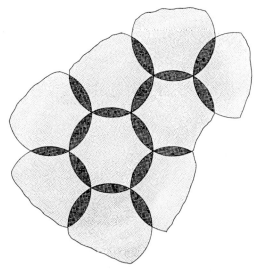

Fig. 21.2 Schematic diagram of overlap of electron distributions for atoms packed in a metal lattice.

Table, that is, the electronegative elements, have atoms with small inner-shell cores which can interpenetrate extensively and form strong covalent bonds.   These are just the elements whose molecules are stable even in condensed states.   There are, of course, elements which are neither strongly electronegative nor typically metallic; their state of aggregation will be considered in the next chapter.

chapter **22** ··

Macroscopic aggregates of atoms

Chemical bonds—covalent, ionic, or metallic—can hold together indefinitely large numbers of atoms. The resulting aggregates may be regarded as giant molecules. An aggregate of this kind is usually a crystal, that is, its atoms are arranged in a regular lattice whose structure determines the external shape of the whole aggregate. Diamond is a typical crystal consisting of carbon atoms linked by covalent bonds into a rigid three-dimensional lattice. Other examples of crystals with different types of bonds and different types of macroscopic properties will be discussed in Sect. 22.1.

The majority of substances in solid or liquid form are, however, aggregates of molecular groups bound to each other by mechanisms less strong than chemical bonds. Water consists, for example, of small molecules, whereas graphite consists of extended layers of carbon atoms (page 321). The water molecules and the graphite layers are held together by a combination of electric forces between the nuclei and electrons of different molecules, or layers. These forces, being partly attractive and partly repulsive, tend to cancel out, but the cancellation is

324

not exact. The net resulting force turns out to be attractive, although some 10 to 100 times weaker than the forces due to chemical bonds.

Molecules containing "polar groups," that is, with partially ionic bonds, exert a net force on any external electric charge because their electrons and nuclei are, on the average, at different distances from that charge. The positively charged portion of any polar group is thus drawn toward any negative ion or negatively charged portion of another polar group. The structure of water and the stability of ions in water solution originate from this mechanism. Polar groups containing hydrogen, such as O—H and N—H, become attached to other groups with particular firmness because the small size of the H atom affords a close approach; this attachment is called a "hydrogen bond" (Sect. 22.2).

An ever-present cohesive force exists also between non-polar groups. This force derives from simultaneous deformations of the electron distributions of adjacent atoms or group of atoms. Its existence was argued by Van der Waals on the basis of the departure of real gas properties from the perfect gas laws, but its nature was first explained by quantum-mechanical analysis. It is the Van der Waals force which holds the molecules together when gases liquefy or solidify at low temperatures. In substances consisting of extended molecules, the Van der Waals forces between many molecular groups contribute to hold each molecule close to other molecules against the action of thermal agitation and are thus adequate to stabilize a condensed state even at moderately high temperatures (Sect. 22.3).

The structural variety of materials and of their macroscopic properties derives largely from the possible coexistence of different mechanisms of aggregation having widely different strengths. Marked changes of macroscopic properties may be brought about by minor changes in the proportion of chemical bonds within an aggregate. For example, rubber is hardened by the process of vulcanization in which a comparatively few covalent cross-linkages are established between long molecular chains of hydrocarbon groups.

22.1   Crystals with Covalent, Ionic, and Metallic Bonds

A diamond constitutes the typical example of an aggregate of atoms held in a regular lattice by covalent bonds. Each carbon atom is surrounded by four other atoms arranged at the vertices of a tetrahedron (Fig. 22.1) and is linked to them by bonds of the type described in Sect. 20.1 and Fig. 20.1c. The lattice thus formed is braced in all directions and is very strong because any distortion alters the distances between the atoms and the angles between the bond directions.

Only a very few substances exist which form stable crystal lattices with purely covalent bonds. These substances consist of tetravalent elements of average electronegativity, like carbon. Thus silicon carbide, with alternate atoms of C and Si, is most nearly similar to diamond. The sequence of elements of the C group, namely, Si, Ge, and Sn, have solid forms analogous to diamond but with bonds having an increasingly metallic character.

Substances, like NaCl, whose molecules are held together by strongly ionic bonds, form crystalline aggregates with purely ionic bonds. For

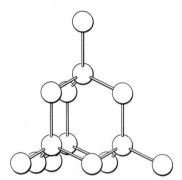 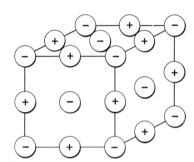

Fig. 22.1 Crystal structure of diamond.

Fig. 22.2 Crystal structure of NaCl.

example, when several NaCl molecules approach one another, each positively charged Na atom attracts to its proximity the negatively charged Cl atoms of other molecules. The negative charges surrounding a Na atom drive then the electrons of the NaCl bond farther away from Na and completely onto the Cl atom, so that the bond becomes completely ionic. The initial single bond of any one NaCl molecule is thereby weakened, by loss of its partial covalent character, but the resulting Na^+ ion becomes attached by an ionic bond to each of the surrounding Cl^- ions of other molecules. Therefore, the crystalline state of aggregation of the substance is more stable than its molecular vapor state.[1]

The lattice type of any particular ionic crystal depends on the relative size of the constituent ions, and also on their shape if they consist of several atoms. For example, in a NaCl crystal the ions are arranged in a cubic lattice (Fig. 22.2) in which each Na^+ or Cl^- is surrounded respectively, by six Cl^- or Na^+ ions. The arrangement of monoatomic ions

---

[1] Ionic crystals form usually by precipitation of separate ions from a solution in which the ions are stable, rather than by condensation of molecules in vapor form.

in crystal lattices can generally be predicted by regarding each type of ion as a hard sphere of given radius and considering what is the most compact possible packing of any given set of spheres.   Table 22.1 shows

TABLE 22.1

IONIC RADII (ANGSTROM)

		Li^+	Be^{++}		
		0.70	0.30		
O^{--}	F^-	Na^+	Mg^{++}	Al^{+++}	Si^{++++}
1.35	1.33	1.00	0.75	0.55	0.40
S^{--}	Cl^-	K^+	Ca^{++}	Sc^{+++}	
1.82	1.80	1.33	1.05	0.83	
Se^{--}	Br^-	Rb^+	Sr^{++}	Y^{+++}	
1.93	1.96	1.52	1.18	0.95	
Te^{--}	I^-	Cs^+	Ba^{++}	La^{+++}	
2.12	2.20	1.70	1.38	1.15	
		Cu^+	Zn^{++}		
		0.58	0.83		
		Ag^+	Cd^{++}		
		0.97	0.99		

Data from R. W. G. Wyckoff, *Crystal Structures*, Interscience, New York, 1948.

the radii of hard spheres which represent adequately various kinds of ions.   The halogenides, oxides, and sulphides of most metals form typical ionic crystals.   Polyatomic ions of either sign, for example, CO_3^{--}, SO_4^{--}, or NH_4^+, participate in the formation of ionic crystals in the same manner as monoatomic ions, with due regard to their size and shape.   The packing of ions into a regular lattice is often facilitated by the inclusion of water molecules, oriented with their negatively charged O atoms next to positive ions and their H atoms next to negative ions.   Ionic crystals are very rigid because the attractions between ions of opposite sign brace their lattices with great strength and in all directions.

As described in Sect. 21.3, the atoms of most elements tend to aggregate in crystals held together by a metallic bond.   This happens when the atoms are electropositive, that is, when they have rather large cores of closed shells and cannot form strong covalent bonds.   Simple metals consist of atoms of a single element, and therefore of equal size; consequently, they form the types of lattice which yield the highest density of equal hard spheres. "Alloys" are aggregates consisting of mixtures of atoms of different elements packed together and joined by a single metallic bond. Atoms of nearly equal size, like Cu and Zn, form alloys by mixing in practically any proportion. Atoms of greatly different size form "intersticial" alloys in which a few of the smaller atoms fill holes in interstices between larger atoms.

The metallic bond is not very strong, as noted in Sect. 21.3, and its strength does not depend critically on the lattice shape. Therefore, metallic crystals yield to stresses more readily than covalent or ionic crystals by experiencing small elastic deformations. Following an elastic

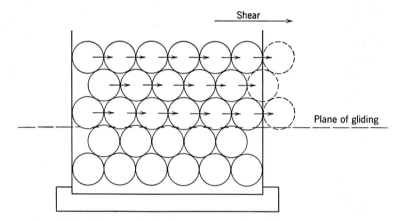

Fig. 22.3 Diagram of plastic deformation by gliding of metal atoms.

deformation, a crystal lattice returns spontaneously to its original arrangement of atoms when the stress subsides. Metallic crystals also experience a different type of deformation, which is "plastic," that is, not spontaneously reversible, when they are subjected to sufficiently high stresses. Inasmuch as the atoms of a metal are all equal, or nearly equal, their aggregate remains just as stable if the atoms of a section of a crystal shift each to replace one of its nearest neighbors as shown, for example, in Fig. 22.3. This collective shift amounts to a gliding of the atoms on one side of a plane over the adjacent layer of atoms across the plane. The combination of numerous gliding processes along parallel planes yields a macroscopic plastic deformation. The ductility of metals derives from their ability to experience such plastic deformations. Plastic deformations of crystals with covalent or ionic bonds are possible, but meet with stronger resistance on account of the greater bond strength; therefore these crystals tend to break at points of imperfection when subjected to very high stresses rather than to glide plastically. The addition of foreign atoms to a metal to form an intersticial alloy, for example, the addition of a small proportion of carbon to iron to form steel, inhibits its ductility.

The shift of atoms indicated in Fig. 22.3 requires an initial expenditure of energy, until it is half-accomplished. The minimum stress required to bring about the initial half-shift is called the "yield strength." The remainder of the shift proceeds spontaneously and returns the energy spent initially, except for some dissipation into heat. The dissipation is represented macroscopically as the work performed against a resistance which opposes the plastic deformation and limits its rate of progress when a metal is subjected to a stress in excess of the yield strength. This resistance constitutes, therefore, the viscosity of the metal. The yield strength and the viscosity vary greatly from one metal to another. They are low, for example, in lead and still lower in mercury, which is a liquid flowing under the stresses caused by its own weight and by thermal agitation.

22.2 Aggregation of Polar Groups

A polar group within a molecule exerts a net force on any charge in the surrounding space, because the electric fields generated by its nuclei and electrons nowhere compensate each other exactly in strength and in direction. The interaction of a polar group with other charges may be represented in first approximation as the interaction of a "dipole" (page 303) of given moment and negligible dimensions. A dipole and a single charge exert on one another a force, whose strength is proportional to the magnitudes of the charge and of the dipole moment and decreases in inverse ratio to the cubed distance between charge and dipole.[2] Two dipoles also exert on one another a force, whose strength decreases in inverse ratio to the fourth power of their distance. In addition, polar groups are subject to torques since the electric field generated by other groups of particles pulls their positive and negative charges in opposite directions. The torque acting on a dipole strives to orient it so that its positive (or negative) charge is closest to the negative (or, respectively, positive) charges of other groups. When this orientation occurs, the net force on a polar group *attracts* it toward other groups (Fig. 22.4).

Isolated neutral atoms in stationary states, and molecules with purely covalent bonds, have no dipole moment.[3] They may, however, have

---

[2] This decrease is more rapid than for the force between charges because the separate charges of a dipole appear so close to one another, when seen from a great distance, as to nearly cancel out.

[3] The H states with off-center electron distributions are exceptional in this respect.

electric moments of higher order which are represented schematically by combinations of dipoles with different orientations, called "multipoles."

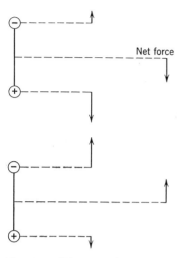

(The combination of two dipoles is called a "quadrupole," of four dipoles an "octupole," etc.) Atoms, or groups of atoms, with quadrupole or higher multipole moments and with appropriate mutual orientation attract one another as shown, for example, in Fig. 22.5. The strength of these attractions decreases very rapidly with increasing distance.

The potential energy due to dipole, or multipole, interactions between adjacent atoms or molecules may be as large as about $\frac{1}{10}$ of the potential energy of interaction between ions. It may amount to 10,000 cal/mole and thus exceed greatly the energy of thermal agitation and produce a stable aggregation of molecules at ordinary temperatures.

Fig. 22.4 Diagram of net attraction between two properly oriented dipoles.

For example, forces between the polar OH groups of H_2O molecules influence the molecular orientation to form networks in which the negatively charged side of any one molecule, namely its O atom, remains

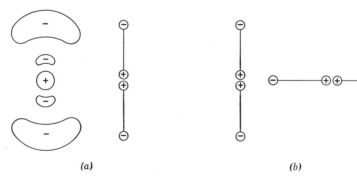

(a)   (b)

Fig. 22.5 (a) Charge distribution within an atom, analogous to that of Fig. 14.10, and its schematic representation as a quadrupole consisting of two dipoles. (b) Orientation of two quadrupoles yielding net attraction.

close to the positively charged H atom of another molecule. Several types of H_2O network exist; they constitute solid or liquid structures depending on their stability and rigidity. Besides adhering to each other, water molecules adhere to polar molecules or to larger aggregates, called "hydrophilic," whose surfaces contain polar groups. Hydrophilic molecules mix readily with water to form solutions.

Solvation of ions. Ions are particularly stable in water solution. The ionic charge orients the surrounding water molecules so that the portion of each molecule with charge opposite to that of the ion is closest to it. The combined potential energy of the ion and of the water molecules is thereby reduced. This orientation of water molecules around an ion extends over a radius of several molecular diameters and is called "solvation." Solvation releases an amount of energy of the order of one electron volt per ion and increases the stability of isolated ions in solution against their aggregation into molecules or crystals. By the same token, molecules and crystals with wholly or partially ionic bonds "dissociate" into separate solvated ions when in contact with water. The tendency of any given substance to dissociate depends, of course, also upon the stability of the electronic structure of the resulting ions. For

example, the $-\overset{|}{\underset{|}{C}}-O-H$ group of an alcohol does not dissociate into

$-\overset{|}{\underset{|}{C}}-O^-$ and H^+, whereas the related carboxyl group $O=\overset{|}{C}-O-H$

behaves as an "acid" by releasing readily an H^+ ion in water, because the carboxyl radical is stabilized by a non-localized bond represented by

combination of the bond structures $O=\overset{|}{C}-O^-$ and $O^-—\overset{|}{C}=O$.

Hydrogen bond. The dipole interaction between water molecules is enhanced by the circumstance that the H atom is small and its nucleus can approach closely the negatively charged portion of another molecule. The interactions of all polar groups containing hydrogen, particularly in O—H, N—H, F—H, and Cl—H combinations, are similarly enhanced. The link between molecules due to this interaction is called a "hydrogen bond." The formation of this type of bond releases about $\frac{1}{4}$ ev = 6,000 cal/mol. The hydrogen bond has great practical importance. It accounts for the remarkable properties not only of water but also of the related substances NH_3 and HF as well as of organic substances containing alcoholic and carboxylic groups, $-\overset{|}{\underset{|}{C}}-O-H$ and

$O=\overset{|}{C}-O-H$. For example, it causes HF and carboxylic acids to form stable dimers with the structures

$$\text{H---F}$$
$$\vdots \quad \vdots \quad \text{and}$$
$$\text{F---H}$$

$$\begin{array}{c} \text{O----H---O} \\ -\text{C} \qquad \text{C---} , \\ \text{O---H----O} \end{array}$$

where the dots indicate the hydrogen bonds.

22.3 Aggregation of Non-polar Groups

Induced dipole moments. Single atoms, and molecular groups with purely covalent bonds,[4] have normally no electric dipole moment. However, the approach of an ion or of a polar group deforms atoms and molecules by pulling their electrons in one direction and their nuclei in the opposite direction, and thereby "induces" a dipole moment in non-polar atoms or groups of atoms. The induced moment is directed so that a net attraction results between the inducing agent and the initially non-polar group (Fig. 22.6). A cohesive force arises thus between ions,

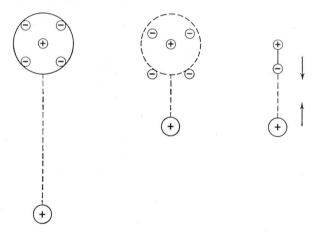

Fig. 22.6 Schematic representation of induced dipole moment in an atom.

or polar groups, and any sort of surrounding atoms or molecules. This force is weaker than it would be if these atoms or molecules possessed a non-vanishing dipole moment in their undisturbed stationary states.

The strength of the cohesive force arising from induced dipole moments may be estimated by a standard procedure of quantum mechanics. The procedure serves to calculate the effect of any weak disturbance applied

---

[4] A bond is understood here to be "purely covalent" insofar as it has no dipole moment.

to an atomic system. Its results are readily visualized in our present problem, where the disturbance consists of an electric field generated by an ion or dipole external to the atomic system.

The ground state of an atom subject to an electric field is regarded as a combination of stationary states of the undisturbed atom. The probability amplitudes of this combination are to be calculated. The total energy of the atom includes a term V equal to the product of the electric field strength and of the atom's dipole moment. The dipole moment vanishes if the atom is in one of the states, 0, 1, 2, $\cdots$, i, $\cdots$, which are stationary in the absence of the electric field. When these states are combined, their interference yields a new probability distribution of the electron positions which may be off-center with respect to the nucleus, as for the H states of Sect. 14.4, and may therefore have a non-vanishing dipole moment (see also Appendix IX). One may consider a set of standard combinations, each one consisting of the superposition of the ground state 0 and of one of the excited states i of the undisturbed atom with equal probability amplitudes, and call their dipole moments $e\xi_{0i}$; in this expression e is the charge of an electron and ξ_{0i} has the dimensions of a distance whose value may range up to nearly 1 A. Calling V_{0i} the product of this dipole moment and of the electric field strength, the disturbance caused by this field is "weak" provided V_{0i} is much smaller than the difference $E_i - E_0$ of the zero-field energy eigenvalues, for each state i. In this event, one finds that the actual ground state of the atom in presence of the field includes the state i as a component with *probability amplitude equal to the energy ratio* $V_{0i}/(E_i - E_0)$. The inclusion in the combination of the component state i contributes to reduce the energy eigenvalue of the ground state by the product of V_{0i} and of the ratio $V_{0i}/(E_i - E_0)$, that is, by

$$\frac{V_{0i}{}^2}{E_i - E_0}. \tag{1}$$

The contributions (1) due to combination of the zero-field ground state with each of the states i must be added to calculate the new energy eigenvalue in the presence of the electric field.

The electric field generated by an ion with charge e at a distance r has strength e/r^2, which yields $V_{0i} = e^2\xi_{0i}/r^2 = (e^2/r)(\xi_{0i}/r)$, equal to the potential energy of two ions with unit charge at distance r reduced by the ratio ξ_{0i}/r. This ratio may be of the order of, or somewhat larger than, $\frac{1}{10}$ in cases of interest. The sum of the energy contributions (1) for all states i becomes then

$$\frac{e^4}{r^4}\Sigma_i \frac{(\xi_{0i})^2}{E_i - E_0} = \frac{e^2}{r}\Sigma_i \frac{e^2/r}{E_i - E_0}\left(\frac{\xi_{0i}}{r}\right)^2 \tag{2}$$

In the summation on the right side, the first factor may be of the order of a few electron volts, the second of the order of 1, and the third of the order of, or somewhat larger than, $\frac{1}{100}$.

The expression (2) represents the potential energy corresponding to the cohesive force between an ion and a non-polar atom or group of atoms. This energy decreases in inverse ratio to the fourth power of the distance between the ion and the non-polar system. When the cohesive force derives from the field of a polar group, which has a dipole moment and no net charge, the strength of this field is inversely proportional to the third power and the potential energy of cohesion to the sixth power of the distance.

Van der Waals force. Electric dipole moments arise in neutral atoms, or groups of atoms, whenever there are other atoms in their proximity, owing to interaction between the electron motions in different

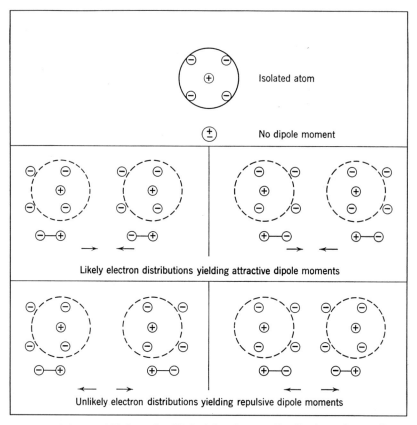

Fig. 22.7 Scheme of likely and unlikely joint electron distributions of two adjacent atoms.

atoms without any intervention of ions or other sources of constant electric fields. The effect of this interaction becomes apparent by treating a pair of adjacent atoms first as separate systems and then as a single system. The statement that each atom in its ground state has vanishing dipole moment means that the mean position of all its electrons, averaged over their probability distribution, coincides with the position of the nucleus. When the two atoms are considered simultaneously, their dipole moments still vanish if the probability distributions of the electrons of the two atoms are regarded as independent, that is, if the whole system is treated in an "independent-atom approximation" analogous to the independent-electron treatment of single atoms. Actually, the positions of the electrons of the two atoms are bound to be correlated. For example, the probability of finding the electrons of *both* atoms concentrated in the space between the two nuclei is small owing to the repulsion among electrons. If the electrons of one atom are found predominantly in that space, those of the other atom are likely to be found concentrated on the opposite side of its nucleus, as shown in Fig. 22.7. That is, a distribution of the electrons of one atom yielding a dipole moment in the direction of the internuclear axis is likely to occur jointly with a distribution in the other atom yielding a dipole moment with equal orientation. The mean value of the dipole moment of each atom vanishes, but the mean value of their product does not vanish. Two aligned dipoles of equal orientation attract each other. Therefore, the correlation between electron positions in the two atoms yields a net attraction, and the total energy eigenvalue of the two atoms is lower when they are close to one another than when they are far away.

The magnitude of this attraction is calculated by the method utilized to calculate the attraction of an ion upon a neutral atom. In the treatment of two neutral atoms we consider, instead of a simple sequence $0, 1, 2 \cdots i \cdots$ of zero-field stationary states, a double sequence $0, 1, 2 \cdots j \cdots, 0, 1, 2 \cdots k \cdots$ of stationary states of the separate atoms with separate energies $E_0, \cdots E_j \cdots$ and $E'_0 \cdots E'_k$. We also consider standard combinations of states $0j$ and $0k$ for the two separate atoms and call their dipole moments respectively $e\xi_{0j}$ and $e\xi'_{0k}$. The energy V_{0j} of a standard dipole in an external field is replaced here by the potential energy of two aligned dipoles, which is $V_{0j0k} = -2e\xi_{0j}e\xi'_{0k}/r^3$, and the energy difference $E_j - E_0$ is replaced by $(E_j - E_0) + (E'_k - E'_0)$. The combination of the ground states of the separate atoms with their various excited states then reduces the ground state energy of the whole system by the quantity analogous to (2)

$$\Sigma_j\Sigma_k \frac{V_{0j0k}{}^2}{E_j + E'_k - E_0 - E'_0} = \frac{4e^4}{r^6}\Sigma_j\Sigma_k \frac{(\xi_{0j}\xi'_{0k})^2}{E_j + E'_k - E_0 - E'_0}$$

$$= 4\frac{e^2}{r}\Sigma_j\Sigma_k \frac{e^2/r}{E_j + E'_k - E_0 - E'_0}\left(\frac{\xi_{0j}}{r}\right)^2\left(\frac{\xi'_{0k}}{r}\right)^2. \quad (3)$$

The attraction between any two atoms or groups of atoms is thus found to be represented by a potential energy inversely proportional to the sixth power of their distance. The structure of the formulas indicates the order of magnitude of the potential energy; closer evaluations show this energy to be about 0.1 ev for a pair of adjacent atoms of average properties.

Molecular crystals and aggregates of large molecules. Gases consisting of small molecules with tight covalent bonds solidify, at low temperatures, into crystalline aggregates of molecules ("molecular crystals") held together by Van der Waals forces. The solid forms of the rare gases may also be regarded as molecular crystals. The molecules are packed with low density in these crystals, because the Van der Waals forces are much weaker than chemical bonds or even than the forces between polar groups. For the same reason, the Van der Waals forces suffice to keep small molecules packed in a crystal only at low temperatures, that is, when thermal agitation is weak.

Molecules of increasing size attract each other through an increasing multiplicity of Van der Waals bonds, acting between all pairs of adjacent atoms, or groups of atoms, of different molecules. The molecules form, accordingly, aggregates of increasing stability. These aggregates are crystalline if individual molecules have a regular and rigid shape which allows them to be packed into a regular lattice. Graphite crystals consist, as mentioned before, of extended molecular layers of carbon atoms held in a stack by Van der Waals forces; each layer is held together in a flat shape by a combination of covalent and non-localized bonds (see Sect. 21.2). The weakness of Van der Waals forces and the resulting large distance between adjacent layers permit the layers to glide on one another plastically when subjected to a low shearing stress in the appropriate direction. This structure accounts for the characteristic properties of the material.

Long stringy molecules with no definite shape generally form "amorphous" aggregates in which they intertwine irregularly. Typical among these molecules are the saturated hydrocarbons, consisting of chains of —CH_2— groups which may rotate freely about each C—C chain link. Paraffins are substances of this type. They are readily subjected to plastic flow, in which portions of different molecules glide on one another.

APPENDICES

Deflection
of charged particle beams

Consider a beam of particles with charge e, mass m, and velocity v, which traverse a region of length l where they are subjected to an electric field of strength E perpendicular to the beam. (In a narrow gap between the plates of a flat condenser, E equals the potential difference of the plates divided by their distance.) The deflecting force on each particle is eE and the resulting acceleration is eE/m. The particle remains exposed to the field for a time l/v and hence acquires a crosswise velocity $(eE/m)(l/v)$. If this velocity is much smaller than v, the resulting angle of deflection is approximately

$$\delta_E = \frac{(eE/m)(l/v)}{v} = \frac{eEl}{mv^2}. \tag{1}$$

If the same beam traverses a magnetic field of strength H perpendicular to the beam direction, it experiences a force perpendicular to the field and to the beam of strength evH/c, where c is the velocity of light. The corresponding acceleration is evH/mc. If the field acts over a dis-

339

tance l', that is, for a time l'/v, and the total deflection remains small, it will impart to each particle a crosswise velocity $(evH/mc)(l'/v)$ and therefore a deflection

$$\delta_H = \frac{(evH/mc)(l'/v)}{v} = \frac{eHl'}{mcv}. \qquad (2)$$

In a beam of canal rays the velocities are not uniform because ions may have been generated at different points of the potential between the electrodes and they may have lost different amounts of energy in collisions against gas molecules. To eliminate the influence of this lack of uniformity J. J. Thomson applied an electric and a magnetic field in parallel directions so that the deflections δ_E and δ_H would be perpendicular to each other. These deflections could then be measured as ordinates and abscissas on a screen or photographic plate which registered the arrival of the beam after deflection. Beam components with different velocities and equal specific charges arrived at different points whose coordinates obeyed the equation of a parabola

$$\frac{\delta_E}{\delta_H{}^2} = \left(\frac{eEl}{mv^2}\right) \Big/ \left(\frac{eHl'}{mcv}\right)^2 = \frac{m}{e} \frac{Ec^2}{H^2} \frac{l}{l'^2}, \qquad (3a)$$

that is,

$$\delta_E = \frac{m}{e} \frac{Ec^2}{H^2} \frac{l}{l'^2} \delta_H{}^2. \qquad (3b)$$

Measurement of the constants of this parabola yielded the value of e/m, since E, H, c, l, and l' were known.

Relative motion of two particles

Consider two particles, for example an α particle and the nucleus of an atom, or an electron and the nucleus of the same atom, which attract or repel each other. The attraction or repulsion is represented by a potential energy $U(r)$ which depends only on the distance r of the two particles.

We indicate the position coordinates of the two particles, with respect to an arbitrary origin, respectively, by vectors $\mathbf{r}_1$ and $\mathbf{r}_2$ and their velocities and accelerations by $\mathbf{v}_1$, $\mathbf{a}_1$ and $\mathbf{v}_2$, $\mathbf{a}_2$. The distance of the two particles is then,

$$r = |\mathbf{r}_1 - \mathbf{r}_2| \tag{1}$$

and the velocity and acceleration of particle 1 with respect to particle 2 are

$$\mathbf{v} = \mathbf{v}_1 - \mathbf{v}_2 \tag{2}$$

$$\mathbf{a} = \mathbf{a}_1 - \mathbf{a}_2 \tag{3}$$

The force $\mathbf{F}_1$ acting on particle 1 may be indicated by $-\mathrm{grad}_{\mathbf{r}_1} U(r)$, where $\mathrm{grad}_{\mathbf{r}_1}$ is the gradient with respect to variations of the coordinate vector $\mathbf{r}_1$. Since U depends on the magnitude of $\mathbf{r} = \mathbf{r}_1 - \mathbf{r}_2$, we may write

$$\mathbf{F}_1 = -\operatorname{grad}_{\mathbf{r}_1} U(r) = -\operatorname{grad}_{\mathbf{r}} U(r) \qquad (4)$$

$$\mathbf{F}_2 = -\operatorname{grad}_{\mathbf{r}_2} U(r) = \operatorname{grad}_{\mathbf{r}} U(r) \qquad (5)$$

The equations of motion of the two particles are then

$$m_1 \mathbf{a}_1 = -\operatorname{grad}_{\mathbf{r}} U(r), \qquad (6)$$

$$m_2 \mathbf{a}_2 = \operatorname{grad}_{\mathbf{r}} U(r). \qquad (7)$$

The relative motion of one particle with respect to the other is studied by calculating their relative acceleration (3). To do this, we divide (6) by m_1 and (7) by m_2 and then subtract the second equation from the first, which gives:

$$\mathbf{a} = \mathbf{a}_1 - \mathbf{a}_2 = -\left(\frac{1}{m_1} + \frac{1}{m_2}\right) \operatorname{grad}_{\mathbf{r}} U(r) = -\frac{m_1 + m_2}{m_1 m_2} \operatorname{grad}_{\mathbf{r}} U(r). \qquad (8)$$

This equation may also be written

$$\mu \mathbf{a} = -\operatorname{grad}_{\mathbf{r}} U(r), \qquad (9)$$

where

$$\mu = \frac{m_1 m_2}{m_1 + m_2} \qquad (10)$$

is called the "reduced mass" of the two particles. Equation 9 coincides with the equation of motion of a *single particle* of mass μ attracted or repelled toward the origin of the coordinates $\mathbf{r}$ by a force corresponding to the potential $U(r)$. Notice that the reduced mass is always smaller than either m_1 or m_2, and approaches the smaller one of the two if the other particle is much heavier than it.

The sum of (6) and (7) yields

$$m_1 \mathbf{a}_1 + m_2 \mathbf{a}_2 = 0. \qquad (11)$$

This equation may also be written as

$$M\mathbf{A} = 0, \qquad (12)$$

where

$$M = m_1 + m_2 \qquad (13)$$

is the total mass, and

$$\mathbf{A} = \frac{m_1}{M} \mathbf{a}_1 + \frac{m_2}{M} \mathbf{a}_2 \qquad (14)$$

represents the acceleration of the center of mass of the two particles, which lies at

$$\mathbf{R} = \frac{m_1}{M}\mathbf{r}_1 + \frac{m_2}{M}\mathbf{r}_2. \tag{15}$$

Equation 12 states that a force acting between the two particles does not affect the motion of their center of mass.

The total kinetic energy of the two particles may also be decomposed into kinetic energy of relative motion and kinetic energy of the motion of their center of mass. The velocity of the center of mass is

$$\mathbf{V} = \frac{m_1}{M}\mathbf{v}_1 + \frac{m_2}{M}\mathbf{v}_2, \tag{16}$$

and it follows from (2) and (16) that

$$\mathbf{v}_1 = \mathbf{V} + \frac{m_2}{M}\mathbf{v} \tag{17}$$

$$\mathbf{v}_2 = \mathbf{V} - \frac{m_1}{M}\mathbf{v}. \tag{18}$$

The kinetic energy is then

$$K = \tfrac{1}{2}m_1 v_1{}^2 + \tfrac{1}{2}m_2 v_2{}^2 = \tfrac{1}{2}MV^2 + \tfrac{1}{2}\mu v^2. \tag{19}$$

The total energy, kinetic plus potential, also splits into two components

$$E = K + U(r) = \tfrac{1}{2}MV^2 + [\tfrac{1}{2}\mu v^2 + U(r)], \tag{20}$$

the first of which depends only on the center of mass coordinates and the second only on the relative coordinates.

Relation between deflection and impact parameter in Rutherford scattering

This appendix gives two proofs of Eq. 1 of Chapter 3; one utilizes the knowledge that the α particle follows a hyperbolic track and the other does not. It will also be indicated how that equation must be adjusted to take into account the recoil of the nucleus.

(**1**) Call ρ the distance of closest approach to the nucleus and $\bar{v}$ the α-particle velocity at this distance. The total energy, kinetic and potential, of the α particle at this distance must equal its kinetic energy before the collision,

$$\frac{1}{2} m\bar{v}^2 + \frac{zZe^2}{\rho} = \frac{1}{2} mv^2. \tag{1}$$

The angular momenta before the collision and at the distance ρ must also be equal. Before the collision the particle is aimed to pass at the distance b from the nucleus, at distance ρ its velocity $\bar{v}$ is perpendicular to the direction of ρ. Hence the angular momentum equation is

$$mvb = m\bar{v}\rho, \tag{2}$$

which gives $\bar{v} = v(b/\rho)$. Substituting this value of $\bar{v}$ in (1) and dividing that equation by $\frac{1}{2}mv^2$ gives

$$\left(\frac{b}{\rho}\right)^2 + 2\frac{zZe^2}{mv^2b}\frac{b}{\rho} = 1. \tag{3}$$

This is an equation of the second degree in b/ρ with the solution

$$\frac{b}{\rho} = -\frac{zZe^2}{mv^2b} + \sqrt{\left(\frac{zZe^2}{mv^2b}\right)^2 + 1}. \tag{4}$$

On the other hand, for any hyperbola the ratio b/ρ is a function of the angle θ between the asymptotes (see Fig. III.1), which can be expressed in the form

$$\frac{b}{\rho} = -\operatorname{tg}\tfrac{1}{2}\theta + \sqrt{1 + \operatorname{tg}^2\tfrac{1}{2}\theta}. \tag{5}$$

Equation 1 of Chapter 3 follows by comparing (5) with (4).

(2) The repulsion exerted by the nucleus on the α particle is a force $F = zZe^2/r^2$ pushing the particle always away from the nucleus, and

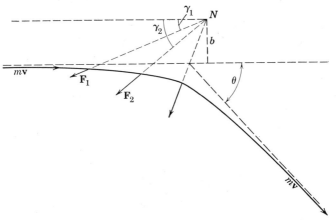

Fig. III.1 Variation of repulsion along an α-particle track.

therefore acting in different directions depending on the instantaneous position of the particle with regard to the nucleus (see Fig. III.1). Each of the angles γ shown in the figure characterizes the direction of **F** for a position of the α particle along its track.

The force **F** acting during a small interval of time, Δt, contributes to the particle a momentum **F** Δt, in the direction determined by γ, which must be added vectorially to the momentum of the α particle prior to Δt. When the particle is still far away from the nucleus, γ is approximately equal to zero and hence the direction of **F** is approximately opposite to that of the momentum **p** $= m\mathbf{v}$ of the incoming particle. The initial effect of the force is thus simply to slow down the particle, that is, to reduce the value of its momentum. As the particle approaches the nucleus, the angle γ differs appreciably from zero and therefore the momentum contributed by the repulsion **F** is oblique to the momentum previously possessed by the particle. The resulting momentum after the push **F** Δt has a new direction corresponding to the partial deflection of the particle.

This process of deflection due to the addition of successive momentum contributions by the repulsive force in different directions proceeds as shown in Fig. III.2 while the particle approaches the nucleus and then while it draws away. It terminates when the particle is again very far from the nucleus, so that the repulsive force is again parallel to the track of the particle, but this time directed so as to increase the particle's momentum.

There remain to be calculated the quantitative features of the vector diagram in Fig. III.2. Consider successive small but unequal intervals of

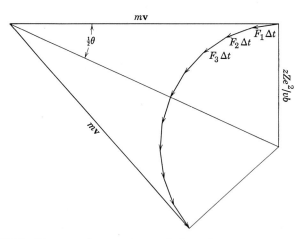

Fig. III.2 Diagram of momentum variations along an α-particle track.

time Δt, during which the direction of the force **F** varies by equal small amounts $\Delta \gamma$. The ratio $\Delta \gamma / \Delta t$ is the rate (angular velocity) ω at which the α particle goes around the nucleus. The successive momentum contributions by the repulsion have therefore magnitudes:

$$F \, \Delta t = F \, \Delta\gamma/\omega = \frac{zZe^2}{r^2\omega} \, \Delta\gamma. \tag{6}$$

The quantity $r^2\omega$ in the denominator of (6) is the angular momentum of the particle with respect to the nucleus divided by the particle's mass m; it is called the "areal velocity." The angular momentum is constant throughout the motion of the particle and is equal to mvb, according to (2). Hence we may replace $r^2\omega$ in (6) with vb, which gives

$$F \, \Delta t = \frac{zZe^2}{vb} \, \Delta\gamma = \text{const.} \, \Delta\gamma. \tag{7}$$

This equation states that the momentum contributions $F \, \Delta t$ in successive time intervals during which γ varies by equal amounts $\Delta\gamma$ are all equal in magnitude. These momentum contributions can therefore be entered in the diagram of Fig. III.2 as small arrows of equal length each of which is rotated with respect to the previous one by an equal angle $\Delta\gamma$. The arrows form, therefore, a circle of radius zZe^2/vb. The total deflection θ is obtained by considering that in the triangle

$$\text{tg} \, \frac{1}{2} \, \theta = \frac{zZe^2/vb}{mv}, \tag{8}$$

which coincides with (1) of Chapter 3.

(3) According to Appendix II, the relationship (1) of Chapter 3 between the deflection and the impact parameter is correct, in the frame of reference of the center of mass of the α particle and the nucleus, provided m represents the reduced mass of the α particle and the nucleus. Equation 10 of Appendix II specifies that

$$m = \frac{m_\alpha m_N}{m_\alpha + m_N}, \tag{9}$$

where m_α and m_N are the masses of the α particle and of the nucleus. The deflection Θ in the laboratory frame of reference, in which the nucleus was at rest before recoiling, can be expressed in terms of the deflection θ (in the center of mass system) and of the mass ratio m_α/m_N,

$$\text{tg}^2 \, \frac{1}{2} \, \Theta = \frac{\text{tg}^2 \frac{1}{2}\theta}{1 + \dfrac{m_\alpha}{m_N} (1 + \text{tg}^2 \frac{1}{2}\theta)}. \tag{10}$$

Analysis of a phenomenon into sinusoidal oscillating components (Fourier analysis)

Numerous physical phenomena, described by the plot of a function of one variable, may be regarded as combinations of sinusoidal oscillations with different frequencies. For example, the radio disturbance emitted by a spark affects receivers tuned to different frequencies; the response of each receiver indicates the presence in the disturbance of an oscillatory component of its proper frequency, even though the spark may involve a simple surge of current directed from one electrode to another. Similarly, the sound track obtained by recording any noise may be analyzed into a superposition of records of pure notes.

This analysis of physical phenomena constitutes an application of the mathematical process of expansion of functions $f(t)$, where t indicates any variable, in the form

$$f(t) = \Sigma_\nu\, c_\nu \sin(2\pi\nu t + \phi_\nu) \tag{1}$$

or

$$f(t) = \Sigma_\nu\, [a_\nu \sin 2\pi\nu t + b_\nu \cos 2\pi\nu t], \tag{2}$$

where c_ν is the amplitude of the oscillating component with frequency

ν, ϕ_ν is its phase constant, $a_\nu = c_\nu \cos\phi_\nu$ and $b_\nu = c_\nu \sin\phi_\nu$. The sum over different frequencies ν contains, in general, terms corresponding to all possible values of ν, which range with continuity from zero to infinity, and is properly represented by an integral. The Fourier expansion (1) or (2) is possible for all continuous functions which are finite throughout and vanish outside a finite range of values of t. (These conditions have been stated for simplicity in a form unnecessarily restrictive.) The expansion can be extended to functions of several variables.

The existence of the Fourier expansion of a given function and the calculation of the coefficients a_ν, b_ν (or c_ν and ϕ_ν) hinge on the following properties of the sine and cosine functions. The square of each of these functions is, of course, non-negative, and its mean value, averaged over a range of values of t extending to infinity, equals $\frac{1}{2}$. For definiteness, the averaging may be carried out over a finite range of t, from the value $t = -T$ to $t = T$, and then one takes the limiting value of the average when T increases to infinity. We write then

$$\lim_{T=\infty} \frac{1}{2T} \int_{-T}^{T} \sin^2 2\pi\nu t \, dt$$
$$= \lim_{T=\infty} \frac{1}{2T} \int_{-T}^{T} \cos^2 2\pi\nu t \, dt = \frac{1}{2}, \qquad \text{for } \nu \neq 0. \quad (3)$$

For $\nu = 0$ the average of the squared sine vanishes and the squared cosine equals one. The product of two sine (or cosine) functions with different frequencies ν_1 and ν_2, or of a sine and a cosine function with any frequencies, is an oscillating function whose mean value, defined as in (3) vanishes:

$$\lim_{T=\infty} \frac{1}{2T} \int_{-T}^{T} \sin 2\pi\nu_1 t \, \sin 2\pi\nu_2 t \, dt$$
$$= \lim_{T=\infty} \frac{1}{4T} \int_{-T}^{T} [\cos 2\pi(\nu_1 - \nu_2)t - \cos 2\pi(\nu_1 + \nu_2)t] \, dt$$
$$= 0, \qquad\qquad \text{for } \nu_1 \neq \nu_2, \qquad (4)$$

$$\lim_{T=\infty} \frac{1}{2T} \int_{-T}^{T} \cos 2\pi\nu_1 t \, \cos 2\pi\nu_2 t \, dt = 0, \qquad \text{for } \nu_1 \neq \nu_2$$

$$\lim_{T=\infty} \frac{1}{2T} \int_{-T}^{T} \sin 2\pi\nu_1 t \, \cos 2\pi\nu_2 t \, dt = 0.$$

The coefficients a_ν and b_ν are calculated conveniently by considering again large but finite intervals from $-T$ to T, in which case the frequency ν must be replaced with $n/2T$, where n is an integer. With these values of ν, (3) and (4) hold even though T is finite. Assuming also, initially, that the expansion (2) exists, one multiplies each side of this equation by $(1/2T) \sin 2\pi(n/2T)t$ or $(1/2T) \cos 2\pi(n/2T)t$ and integrates from $-T$ to T. All terms of the sum on the right side, but one, vanish owing to (4), and the residual term is given by (3). One finds

$$\left. \begin{aligned} \frac{1}{2T} \int_{-T}^{T} f(t) \sin\left(2\pi \frac{n}{2T} t\right) dt &= \frac{1}{2} a_n, \\ \frac{1}{2T} \int_{-T}^{T} f(t) \cos\left(2\pi \frac{n}{2T} t\right) dt &= \frac{1}{2} b_n, \end{aligned} \right\} \text{for } n \neq 0 \qquad (5)$$

$$0 = a_0, \qquad \frac{1}{2T} \int_{-T}^{T} f(t) \, dt = b_0, \qquad \text{for } n = 0.$$

To show that the right side of (2) is actually equal to $f(t)$, when the coefficients are given by (5), one checks whether the difference of the right and left side of (2), squared and integrated over t, vanishes. The integration represents the sum of possible discrepancies over all values of t; the squaring of the discrepancies ensures against accidental cancellation of discrepancies with opposite signs. It follows from (3), (4), and (5) that

$$\int_{-T}^{T} \left[f(t) - \Sigma_{n=0}^{\infty} \left(a_n \sin\frac{2\pi nt}{2T} + b_n \cos\frac{2\pi nt}{2T} \right) \right]^2 dt$$

$$= \int_{-T}^{T} [f(t)]^2 \, dt - T[2b_0^2 + \Sigma_{n=1}^{\infty}(a_n^2 + b_n^2)]. \quad (6)$$

By entering in (6) the values of a_n and b_n from (5) and carrying out the sum over n, it is verified that the right side of (6) actually vanishes.

Equation 6 indicates a physical interpretation of the expansion procedure. The integrated square of a function is often a quantity of interest. For example, if $f(t)$ represents the current intensity in a wire, as a function of time, $\int_{-T}^{T} [f(t)]^2 \, dt$ is proportional to the energy dissipated into heat in the time interval from $-T$ to T. Each term on the right of (6) represents similarly the energy dissipated by one of the sinusoidal components of the current. The essential point is that, if two or more sinusoidal components are combined, the total energy dissipation is simply the sum of the dissipations of the separate components; all "cross terms" vanish, owing to (4). Similarly, one may consider that an oscillating current performs no work against a potential that oscillates with a different frequency, or with the same frequency but 90° off phase; this again follows from (4). To determine how much of a certain sinusoidal component is contained in a current intensity $f(t)$, one calculates simply how much work would be performed by this current against a test potential $V(t)$ oscillating in step with that component; the coefficients a_n and b_n have the form $\int_{-T}^{T} f(t) V(t)\, dt$ according to (5).

A sinusoidal oscillation is understood, by definition, to extend over the whole range of the variable t, from $-\infty$ to ∞. Any oscillation with frequency ν which follows a sine law but lasts only for N cycles, from $t = -N/2\nu$ to $t = N/2\nu$ is not really sinusoidal. It may be regarded as a combination of sinusoidal oscillations with somewhat different frequencies which remain "in step" for N cycles and cancel out outside that time interval. To examine the contribution to this combination from oscillations with different frequencies, we calculate the expansion (2), taking $f(t) = \sin 2\pi\nu t$ for t between $-N/2\nu$ and $N/2\nu$, and $f(t)=0$ for t outside this range. Equation 5 yields

$$a_0 = b_0 = b_n = 0.$$

$$
\begin{aligned}
a_n &= \frac{1}{T} \int_{-N/2\nu}^{N/2\nu} \sin(2\pi\nu t) \sin\left(2\pi \frac{n}{2T} t\right) dt \\
&= \frac{1}{2T} \int_{-N/2\nu}^{N/2\nu} \left\{ \cos\left[2\pi\left(\nu - \frac{n}{2T}\right)t\right] - \cos\left[2\pi\left(\nu + \frac{n}{2T}\right)t\right]\right\} dt \\
&= \frac{1}{2T} \left[\frac{\sin\left(N\pi \dfrac{\nu - n/2T}{\nu}\right)}{\pi\left(\nu - \dfrac{n}{2T}\right)} - \frac{\sin\left(N\pi \dfrac{\nu + n/2T}{\nu}\right)}{\pi\left(\nu + \dfrac{n}{2T}\right)} \right].
\end{aligned}
\tag{7}
$$

The second term of the last expression is usually negligible for practical purposes, but the first one is of nearly constant magnitude $N/2\nu T$ as long as $N\pi(\nu - n/2T)/\nu$ is much smaller than one, that is, over the whole range of frequencies $n/2T$ which differ from ν by much less than ν/N.

This range of frequencies, which are contained in the combination with nearly equal coefficients is called the "band width" of the oscillation of limited duration. The band width ν/N is the reciprocal of the duration of the oscillation. *Any phenomenon of limited duration exhibits, when analyzed into sinusoidal oscillations, a frequency spectrum with a band width equal to the reciprocal of its duration.*

appendix **V** ....

Notes on
statistical distributions
and tests

Statistics serves to describe and analyze phenomena in which the result of any single experiment is not predictable in full detail but regularities are nevertheless observed in the combined results of numerous experiments. The following notes summarize some concepts and procedures of statistics with reference to typical examples.

Probability distributions. Consider the predictions that can be made about a series of throws of a pair of dice. The predictions derive from the initial statement that all faces of each die have "equal probability" of turning upwards in a throw; the implications of this statement are discussed in Sect. 6.2. Since each die has six faces, each face of a die has the probability $\frac{1}{6}$ of turning up in any one throw. There are 36 combinations of faces of two dice, all "equally probable;" therefore each combination has probability $\frac{1}{36}$ of turning up in any one throw. Out of the 36 combinations, the combination of the two faces with the number 1, which we call the (1,1) combination, yields a total score of 2. Two combinations, namely (2,1) and (1,2), yield a score of 3, three combinations, namely (3,1), (2,2), and (1,3), yield a score of 4, etc. A 4-point throw has a total probability $\frac{3}{36}$ because it can result from 3 combinations, each with equal probability $\frac{1}{36}$. One can thus construct a table of the number of combinations for each score, and of the corresponding probability:

Score	n	2	3	4	5	6	7	8	9	10	11	12
Combinations	C_n	1	2	3	4	5	6	5	4	3	2	1
Probability	p_n	$\frac{1}{36}$	$\frac{2}{36}$	$\frac{3}{36}$	$\frac{4}{36}$	$\frac{5}{36}$	$\frac{6}{36}$	$\frac{5}{36}$	$\frac{4}{36}$	$\frac{3}{36}$	$\frac{2}{36}$	$\frac{1}{36}$

The set of values p_n, given in this table as a function of the score n, is called the "probability distribution" of the number scored in a throw. In a long series of N throws, an n-point throw occurs a number of times ν_n such that the ratio ν_n/N, called the experimental "frequency" of n-point throws, approaches the probability p_n very closely.

In quantum physics, as discussed in Sect. 6.2, the probability distribution $p_1, p_2 \cdots p_r \cdots$ of alternative events $E_1, E_2 \cdots E_r \cdots$ is determined either by experimental observation of the frequency of occurrence of events, or by theory, though not necessarily from an initial statement of equal probability.

Means and mean deviations. An important quantity in a series of dice throws is the arithmetic mean of the scores observed in a series of throws. If a 2-point throw occurred ν_2 times, a 3-point throw ν_3 times, etc., the mean score is

$$\frac{2\nu_2 + 3\nu_3 + \cdots + 12\nu_{12}}{\nu_2 + \nu_3 + \cdots \nu_{12}} = \frac{\Sigma_n n\nu_n}{\Sigma_n \nu_n} = \frac{\Sigma_n n\nu_n}{N} \tag{1}$$

Since the "frequency of occurrence" of an n-point throw, namely, the ratio ν_n/N, approaches the probability p_n, the arithmetic mean score (1) approaches the quantity

$$\langle n \rangle = \Sigma_n n p_n = 2\tfrac{1}{36} + 3\tfrac{2}{36} + \cdots + 12\tfrac{1}{36} = 7. \tag{2}$$

This quantity is called the "average" or the "mean" score in a throw, whether determined by experimental observation of frequencies or by calculation of probabilities. It is a "parameter," that is, a numerical characteristic, of the probability distribution. In the problem of dice throwing, a 7-point throw is also the most probable result, according to the table, because scores larger and smaller than 7 by equal amounts are equally probable. However, probability distributions do not possess in general this symmetry, and their mean does not coincide, in general, with the most probable value. The probability distribution of the dice point has many characteristic parameters beside the mean, such as the mean square score $\langle n^2 \rangle = \Sigma_n n^2 p_n$, the mean cube $\langle n^3 \rangle = \Sigma_n n^3 p_n$, etc.

It is often more interesting to characterize the distribution of the deviation of the score from its mean, that is, the distribution of $n - \langle n \rangle$, than the distribution of n itself. The mean deviation vanishes, of course, because deviations by excess or defect cancel out on the average. The mean square deviation is the most interesting parameter, next to the mean of n itself and is related to the mean square of n,

$$\langle (n - \langle n \rangle)^2 \rangle = \Sigma_n \, p_n(n - \langle n \rangle)^2 = \langle n^2 \rangle - \langle n \rangle^2. \tag{3}$$

This "mean square deviation" is also indicated by Δn^2. In the example of dice throws we have

$$\langle (n - \langle n \rangle)^2 \rangle = \tfrac{1}{36}(2 - 7)^2 + \tfrac{2}{36}(3 - 7)^2$$

$$+ \cdots + \tfrac{1}{36}(12 - 7)^2 = 5.83. \tag{4}$$

The "root mean square deviation" Δn, equal to 2.41 in our example, indicates the order of magnitude of the deviations from the mean which are likely to occur.

Repeated trials. Consider an experiment in which a certain event has a probability p to occur; for example, a dice throw in which the 4-point event has the probability $\tfrac{3}{36} = \tfrac{1}{12}$. In a series of N experiments, the number of times, ν, in which the event occurs, approaches the product of N and of the probability p, as noted above. If various "trial" series of N experiments are performed, the value of ν varies in general from one trial to the next. We consider here the distribution of ν in successive trials.

The probability $P(\nu)$ that the event occurs exactly ν times in a trial can be calculated as follows: In a sequence of N experiments, ν occurrences may be distributed differently; the number of alternative sequences with different distributions is $N(N - 1) \cdots (N - \nu + 1)/1 \times 2 \times 3 \times \cdots \times \nu$. Each experiment has the probability p of yielding the event, and a probability $1 - p$ of not yielding it. The probability that the event occurs in ν experiments at specified positions in a sequence is p^ν; the probability that it does not occur in any of the $N - \nu$ remaining experiments is $(1 - p)^{N-\nu}$. The probability that the event occurs just in ν specified experiments, and no more, is $p^\nu(1 - p)^{N-\nu}$. This probability multiplied by the number of alternative sequences with the same number ν yields

$$P(\nu) = \frac{N(N - 1)(N - 2) \cdots (N - \nu + 1)}{1 \times 2 \times 3 \times \cdots \times \nu} p^\nu(1 - p)^{N-\nu}. \tag{5}$$

This probability, as a function of ν, is called the "binomial distribution." The mean number of events is

$$\langle \nu \rangle = \Sigma_\nu \, \nu P(\nu) = Np, \tag{6}$$

as expected. The mean square deviation of ν is

$$\langle (\nu - \langle \nu \rangle)^2 \rangle = \Sigma_\nu (\nu - Np)^2 P(\nu) = Np(1 - p). \tag{7}$$

If both Np and ν are large numbers, the probability distribution (5) is represented approximately by the "Gaussian distribution"

$$P(\nu) \sim \frac{1}{\sqrt{2\pi Np(1 - p)}} \, e^{-\frac{1}{2}(\nu - Np)^2 / Np(1 - p)}. \tag{8}$$

The approximation is surprisingly good when Np and ν are only as large as 5 or 10.

Poisson distribution. The study of the time distribution of atomic events may be regarded as a study of repeated trials. A period of observation of t seconds constitutes a "trial" consisting of a very large number N of "experiments," each of them lasting for a very small interval $\Delta t = t/N$. The probability p of occurrence of an event in one experiment is, therefore, extremely small, but the mean number of events in a trial, $\langle \nu \rangle = Np$, need not be small. Under these conditions, ν is negligible as compared to N, and p is conveniently represented in the form $\langle \nu \rangle / N$. The distribution (5) reduces then to the simpler approximate form

$$P(\nu) = \frac{\langle \nu \rangle^\nu}{\nu!} \, e^{-\langle \nu \rangle}, \tag{9}$$

where $\nu! = 1 \times 2 \times 3 \times \cdots \times \nu$. The mean of the distribution is, of course, $\langle \nu \rangle$ and its mean square deviation reduces also to $Np = \langle \nu \rangle$.

A correlation test. Consider a set of balls, contained in a box, which are of several colors, for example, white, red, and blue, and are marked with different numbers of spots, for example, 1, 2, 3, or 4 spots. To determine whether the number of spots and the color of each ball are correlated, one may extract a sample of N balls from the box and classify them according to color and number of spots. Call the total number of balls of each color N_w, N_r, and N_b, respectively, the total number of balls with each number of spots N_1, N_2, N_3, or N_4 and, for example, ν_{r3} the number of red balls with 3 spots. All these numbers may be arranged in rows and columns as in the following "contingency table":

Number of spots / Color	1	2	3	4	Total
White	ν_{w1}	ν_{w2}	ν_{w3}	ν_{w4}	N_w
Red	ν_{r1}	ν_{r2}	ν_{r3}	ν_{r4}	N_r
Blue	ν_{b1}	ν_{b2}	ν_{b3}	ν_{b4}	N_b
Total	N_1	N_2	N_3	N_4	N

An analysis of possible correlations between color and spot number starts usually from the initial assumption that there is no correlation. One regards then the N balls as distributed among the 12 boxes of the table with equal probability subject only to the condition that the totals for the boxes in each row and column have the observed values N_w, N_r, N_b, N_1, N_2, N_3, and N_4. The probability of any set of values of ν_{w1}, $\nu_{w2} \cdots \nu_{b4}$ can then be calculated, and from the distribution of this probability the mean of each number ν is obtained. The mean number, for example, of red balls with 3 spots equals the total number of balls N multiplied by the fraction of all balls which are red, namely N_r/N, and by the fraction of all balls which have 3 spots, namely N_3/N,

$$\langle \nu_{r3} \rangle = N \frac{N_r}{N} \frac{N_3}{N} = \frac{N_r N_3}{N}. \tag{10}$$

Any correlation between color and spot number brings about systematic deviations of the numbers in the table from their mean values (10) calculated on the basis of no correlation. In the absence of correlation there are deviations due to sampling accidents. An index of the expected magnitude of these deviations for each number, like ν_{r3}, is provided by the mean square deviation according to the Poisson distribution. A convenient index of the aggregate deviation of all numbers in the table from their means is found to be the expression

$$\chi^2 = \frac{(\nu_{w1} - \langle \nu_{w1} \rangle)^2}{\langle \nu_{w1} \rangle} + \frac{(\nu_{w2} - \langle \nu_{w2} \rangle)^2}{\langle \nu_{w2} \rangle} + \cdots + \frac{(\nu_{b4} - \langle \nu_{b4} \rangle)^2}{\langle \nu_{b4} \rangle}. \tag{11}$$

The value of this expression depends on sampling accidents, besides possible correlations. The sums of the deviations of the numbers ν in each row and in each column must vanish, so that only 6 out of the 12 numbers in the table are independent. A value of the index χ^2 comparable to the number of independent deviations (6 in our example) is likely to arise from sampling accidents alone. A much larger value is unlikely. The number of independent variations is called the "number of degrees of freedom" in the table. Statistical tables give the probability that χ^2 exceed any given value, owing to sampling accidents only, for each number of degrees of freedom. If this probability is very small, one concludes that a systematic correlation exists.

Correlation coefficient. When two variables, like the color and number of spots of balls in the preceding example, are correlated, it is useful to describe the kind and magnitude of the correlation by some suitable index, to signify, for example, that the blue color is preferentially associated with 4 spots. There is a general procedure to investigate and describe correlations called "analysis of variance." Here we consider the correlation coefficient which is defined only for pairs of variables represented by numerical indices.[1]

Consider then two variables x and y, whose values can be determined by a single observation but vary in successive observations with some probability distribution, and consider their deviations $x - \langle x \rangle$ and $y - \langle y \rangle$. A correlation of these variables may be such that positive deviations of both variables ($x - \langle x \rangle > 0$, $y - \langle y \rangle > 0$) are frequently found in single observations and so are negative deviations ($x - \langle x \rangle < 0$, $y - \langle y \rangle < 0$), whereas simultaneous occurrence of a positive and a negative deviation (for example, $x - \langle x \rangle > 0$, $y - \langle y \rangle < 0$) is infrequent. The correlation is then called "positive." This qualitative characteristic of the correlation is represented by the sign of the mean product of the deviations

$$\Delta xy = \langle (x - \langle x \rangle)(y - \langle y \rangle) \rangle. \tag{12}$$

The magnitude of this mean product is also a characteristic of the correlation but acquires a meaning only when compared to the expected magnitude of the separate deviations $x - \langle x \rangle$ and $y - \langle y \rangle$.

A correlation coefficient should then be suitably defined as a combina-

---

[1] The color of a ball does not fall in this class even though it may be represented by a numerical index according to an arbitrary code, for example, blue = 1, white = 2, red = 3; it would then be generally meaningless to consider an "average" value of the color index.

tion of Δxy and of the root mean square deviations Δx and Δy. The definition

$$r = \frac{\Delta xy}{\Delta x\,\Delta y} \tag{13}$$

is convenient, because, as shown below,

$$r^2 \le 1, \tag{14}$$

so that the magnitude of r constitutes an absolute index of the strength of the correlation. A value $r = \pm 1$ indicates that pairs of deviations $x - \langle x \rangle$ and $y - \langle y \rangle$ are in a constant ratio and indicates a complete correlation.

To prove Eq. 14, one may consider the mean value of the combination of deviations $[(\Delta y^2)(x - \langle x \rangle) - (\Delta xy)(y - \langle y \rangle)]$. The square of this expression cannot be negative and neither can its mean value. We write therefore

$$0 \le \langle [(\Delta y^2)(x - \langle x \rangle) - (\Delta xy)(y - \langle y \rangle)]^2 \rangle$$

$$= \Delta y^4 \langle (x - \langle x \rangle)^2 \rangle + (\Delta xy)^2 \langle (y - \langle y \rangle)^2 \rangle$$

$$\quad -2(\Delta y^2)(\Delta xy)\langle (x - \langle x \rangle)(y - \langle y \rangle) \rangle$$

$$= \Delta y^4 \Delta x^2 - \Delta y^2 (\Delta xy)^2 = \Delta y^2 [\Delta x^2\,\Delta y^2 - (\Delta xy)^2]. \tag{15}$$

Since Δy^2 is itself non-negative, it follows from (15) that

$$(\Delta xy)^2 \le \Delta x^2\,\Delta y^2 \tag{16}$$

which is equivalent to (14).

Complex numbers

Algebra introduces negative numbers to represent conveniently the operations of addition and subtraction. In order to define the square root of negative numbers, algebra introduces a further kind of number, called "imaginary." The sum of an imaginary number and of an ordinary ("real") number constitutes a "complex" number, which is equivalent in many respects to a pair of positive real numbers. The algebra of complex numbers is not only more general than the algebra of real numbers but also remarkably compact. As a by-product it serves to deal with a pair of real numbers combined in the form of a single complex number. The following notes summarize the main definitions and properties of complex numbers.

The *unit of imaginary numbers* is defined as $\sqrt{-1}$ and is indicated usually by the letter i. The product of the imaginary unit i and of a real number a constitutes an *imaginary number* ia of magnitude a. The square of ia is the negative real number $(ia)^2 = i^2a^2 = (-1)a^2 = -a^2$.

The sum of a real (positive or negative) number a and of an imaginary number ib (with b positive or negative) constitutes a *complex number*, indicated simply by $a + ib$. The number a is called the "real part" and b the "imaginary part" of the complex number $a + ib$. The number $a - ib$ is called the *complex conjugate* of $a + ib$ and is usually indicated, in physics, by $(a + ib)^*$.

Complex numbers are added and multiplied according to the usual rules of algebra, keeping in mind the special property of the imaginary unit $i^2 = -1$. Notice in particular

$$(a_1 + ib_1) + (a_2 + ib_2) = (a_1 + a_2) + i(b_1 + b_2), \tag{1}$$

$$(a + ib)^2 = (a^2 - b^2) + i2ab, \tag{2}$$

$$(a - ib)^2 = (a^2 - b^2) - i2ab, \tag{3}$$

$$(a + ib)(a - ib) = a^2 + b^2. \tag{4}$$

The positive real number $a^2 + b^2$ in Eq. 4 is called the "squared magnitude" or "squared modulus" of the number $a + ib$ and is indicated by $|a + ib|^2$. Notice that

$$|a + ib|^2 = |a - ib|^2. \tag{5}$$

Plane diagram of complex numbers. It is often convenient to represent complex numbers as points of a plane (see Fig. VI.1). With a

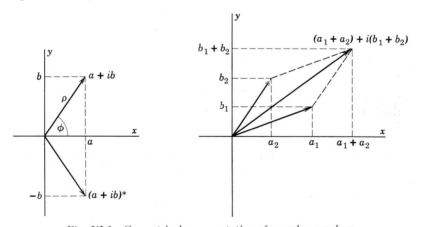

Fig. VI.1 Geometrical representation of complex numbers.

system of cartesian coordinates (x,y) one may represent a real number a as a point of the x axis, at the abscissa $x = a$, an imaginary number ib as a point of the y axis at the ordinate $y = b$, and a complex number $a + ib$ as the point with coordinates $(x = a, y = b)$. The sum of two complex numbers, defined according to Eq. 1, is represented in Fig. VI.1 by a diagram of vector addition.

The point with cartesian coordinates ($x = a$, $y = b$) may also be identified by polar coordinates which represent the distance of the point from the origin of coordinates and its direction with respect to a reference direction which is usually that of the positive x axis (Fig. VI.1). The polar coordinates are

$$\rho = \sqrt{x^2 + y^2} = \sqrt{a^2 + b^2} = |a + ib|,$$

$$\phi = \text{arctg} \frac{y}{x} = \text{arctg} \frac{b}{a}$$

(6)

and are called, respectively the "magnitude" or "modulus" (see Eq. 4), and the "azimuth" or "phase," of the complex number $a + ib$. The relationship (6) between polar and cartesian coordinates can be inverted to yield $x = \rho \cos\phi$ and $y = \rho \sin\phi$, so that

$$a + ib = \rho(\cos\phi + i \sin\phi).$$

(7)

Product of complex numbers. The identification of a complex number by its magnitude and phase permits a simple formulation of the rule for constructing products of complex numbers. Given two complex numbers $a_1 + ib_1$ and $a_2 + ib_2$, their product is defined as

$$a + ib - (a_1 + ib_1)(a_2 + ib_2) = (a_1 a_2 - b_1 b_2) + i(b_1 a_2 + a_1 b_2). \quad (8)$$

The magnitude and phase of this product are

$$\rho = \sqrt{(a_1 a_2 - b_1 b_2)^2 + (b_1 a_2 + a_1 b_2)^2}$$

$$= \sqrt{a_1^2 a_2^2 + b_1^2 b_2^2 + b_1^2 a_2^2 + a_1^2 b_2^2}$$

$$= \sqrt{(a_1^2 + b_1^2)(a_2^2 + b_2^2)} = \rho_1 \rho_2 \quad (9)$$

$$\phi = \text{arctg} \frac{b_1 a_2 + a_1 b_2}{a_1 a_2 - b_1 b_2} = \text{arctg} \frac{b_1/a_1 + b_2/a_2}{1 - (b_1/a_1)(b_2/a_2)}$$

$$= \text{arctg} \frac{\text{tg}\phi_1 + \text{tg}\phi_2}{1 - \text{tg}\phi_1 \text{tg}\phi_2} = \phi_1 + \phi_2. \quad (10)$$

That is, the magnitude of the product is the product of the magnitudes of the factors, and the phase of the product is the sum of the phases of the factors.

In particular, the square of an imaginary number ib, with magnitude b and phase $90° = \frac{1}{2}\pi$ radians, has the magnitude b^2 and the phase $180° = \pi$ radians, in accordance with the fact that it is real and negative. Complex conjugate numbers have phases of opposite sign according to (6); when they are multiplied by each other, as in (4), their phases cancel out and their product is real and positive.

Exponential form of complex numbers. The phase of a complex number is akin to the logarithm of a real number in that the phase of a product of two numbers equals the sum of their phases. To specify the connection between phases and logarithms, we consider numbers of magnitude 1, whose products, quotients, powers, and roots also have magnitude one. In particular the Nth root of a number z of magnitude one and phase ϕ has the phase ϕ/N. If N is a very large number, and ϕ is expressed in radians, the number with magnitude 1 and phase ϕ/N is very approximately $1 + i\phi/N$ because the magnitude of this number, namely $\sqrt{1 + \phi^2/N^2}$, and its phase, $\text{arctg}(\phi/N)$, differ respectively from 1 and from ϕ/N by amounts proportional to $1/N^2$ and $1/N^3$. Therefore, the number z is represented exactly, in the limit of very large N, by

$$z = \lim_{N = \infty} \left(1 + i\frac{\phi}{N}\right)^N. \tag{11}$$

The $\lim_{N = \infty} (1 + 1/N)^N$ is the number $e = 2.718\cdots$, which is the base of "natural logarithms." The $\lim_{N = \infty} (1 + a/N)^N$, where a is any number, is the ath power of e. Therefore, the representation (11) of the number is equivalent to

$$z = e^{i\phi}. \tag{12}$$

A general complex number $a + ib$ of magnitude ρ and phase ϕ may be regarded as the product of the real number ρ and of the number z of magnitude 1, and is therefore represented by

$$a + ib = \rho e^{i\phi}. \tag{13}$$

This representation combines the magnitude and phase of a complex number into a single algebraic expression by means of the number e. The product of two numbers, calculated according to (9) and (10), can now be represented in condensed form by the ordinary rules of algebra,

$$\rho_1 e^{i\phi_1} \rho_2 e^{i\phi_2} = \rho_1\rho_2 e^{i(\phi_1+\phi_2)}. \tag{14}$$

Finally, according to (13), the natural logarithm of the number $a + ib$, that is, its logarithm in the base e, must be defined as

$$\ln(a + ib) = \ln\rho + i\phi. \tag{15}$$

That is, the phase of a complex number is the imaginary part of its natural logarithm.

Geometrical calculation of probability amplitudes

The problem of calculating the probability amplitudes for pairs of eigenstates of atomic orientation was outlined in Sect. 8.3. The calculation is to utilize Eq. 9, page 111,

$$(\mathbf{B}\tilde{m} \,|\, \mathbf{P}m) = \Sigma_{\bar{m}}(\mathbf{B}\tilde{m} \,|\, \mathbf{A}\bar{m})(\mathbf{A}\bar{m} \,|\, \mathbf{P}m), \tag{1}$$

among the probability amplitudes pertaining to the eigenstates of three analyzers with orientations **P**, **A**, and **B**. The angles which identify these orientations with respect to one another, with the help of reference planes, are defined as follows (see Fig. 8.5):

$\phi_\mathbf{A}$ and $\phi_\mathbf{B}$ are the azimuth angles about the axis **P** from the reference plane of this axis to the planes **PA** and **PB** respectively;

$\bar{\phi}_\mathbf{B}$ is the azimuth angle about **A** from its reference plane to the plane **AB**;

$\theta_\mathbf{AP}$, $\theta_\mathbf{BP}$, and $\theta_\mathbf{BA}$ are the angles between the axes indicated as subscripts;

$\psi_\mathbf{A}$ is the azimuth angle about **A** from the plane **PA** to the reference plane of **A**;

ψ_B and $\bar{\psi}_B$ are azimuth angles about $\mathbf{B}$ from the planes $\mathbf{PB}$ and $\mathbf{AB}$, respectively, to the reference plane of $\mathbf{B}$. The probability amplitudes $(\mathbf{A}\bar{m}\,|\,\mathbf{P}m)$, $(\mathbf{B}\bar{m}\,|\,\mathbf{A}\bar{m})$, and $(\mathbf{B}\bar{m}\,|\,\mathbf{P}m)$ should be, respectively, functions of the three sets of Euler angles $(\phi_A,\theta_{AP},\psi_A)$, $(\bar{\phi}_B,\theta_{BA},\bar{\psi}_B)$, and $(\phi_B,\theta_{BP},\psi_B)$.

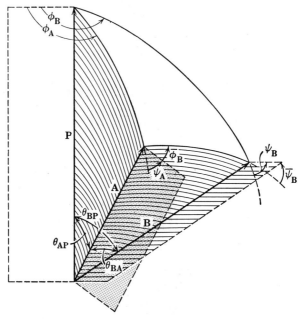

Fig. 8.5 Angles relating the orientations of the axes $\mathbf{P}$, $\mathbf{A}$, and $\mathbf{B}$ and of their respective reference planes.

The functional dependence of the probability amplitude $(\mathbf{A}\bar{m}\,|\,\mathbf{P}m)$ on the Euler angles can be factored into three functions of the separate angles by the expedient of considering additional reference systems $\mathbf{P'}$ and $\mathbf{A'}$ whose axes coincide respectively with $\mathbf{P}$ and $\mathbf{A}$ and whose reference planes coincide with the plane $\mathbf{PA}$. Repeated application of Eq. 1 yields then

$$(\mathbf{A}\bar{m}\,|\,\mathbf{P}m) = \Sigma_{m'}(\mathbf{A}\bar{m}\,|\,\mathbf{P'}m')(\mathbf{P'}m'\,|\,\mathbf{P}m)$$

$$= \Sigma_{\bar{m}'}\,\Sigma_{m'}(\mathbf{A}\bar{m}\,|\,\mathbf{A'}\bar{m}')(\mathbf{A'}\bar{m}'\,|\,\mathbf{P'}m')(\mathbf{P'}m'\,|\,\mathbf{P}m). \quad (2)$$

Because the reference system $\mathbf{P'}$ corresponds to an analyzer with field parallel to that of $\mathbf{P}$, the probability amplitude $(\mathbf{P'}m'\,|\,\mathbf{P}m)$, which depends on ϕ_A only, vanishes unless $m' = m$, and has magnitude 1 if $m' = m$. It has, therefore, the mathematical form

$$(\mathbf{P'}m'\,|\,\mathbf{P}m) = \delta_{m'm}e^{i\,f_m(\phi_A)}, \quad (3)$$

where the symbol [1]

$$\delta_{m'm} = \begin{cases} 1 & \text{for } m' = m \\ 0 & \text{for } m' \neq m, \end{cases} \tag{4}$$

and $f_m(\phi_A)$ is a real function yet to be determined. Similarly, we have

$$(\mathbf{A}\bar{m} \,|\, \mathbf{A}'\bar{m}') = \delta_{\bar{m}\bar{m}'} e^{i\, f_{\bar{m}}(\psi_A)}. \tag{3'}$$

Equation 2 reduces now to

$$(\mathbf{A}\bar{m} \,|\, \mathbf{P}m) = e^{i\, f_{\bar{m}}(\psi_A)} (\mathbf{A}'\bar{m} \,|\, \mathbf{P}'m) e^{i\, f_m(\phi_A)} \tag{5}$$

The probability amplitude $(\mathbf{A}'\bar{m} \,|\, \mathbf{P}'m)$ depends only on the angle θ_{AP}, besides the quantum numbers $\bar{m}'$ and m and the quantum number j, defined on page 90, which identifies the number of components separated from the atomic beam under consideration. This function is usually indicated by $\mathfrak{d}^{(j)}{}_{\bar{m}m}(\theta)$. It is the only function required to represent probability amplitudes when the axes of all magnets are coplanar. When the axes $\mathbf{P}$, $\mathbf{A}$ and $\mathbf{B}$ lie in the same plane, only two values of θ_{BP} are consistent with given values of θ_{BA} and θ_{AP}, namely, $\theta_{BP} = \theta_{BA} \pm \theta_{AP}$, and interference occurs only with phase differences $\delta = 0$ or $\delta = \pi$ as pointed out on page 107. This interference effect is analogous to the addition of parallel or antiparallel vectors and can be represented by the combination of real probability amplitudes. Accordingly the function $\mathfrak{d}^{(j)}{}_{\bar{m}m}(\theta)$ can be real, as will be verified below. We then write (5) in the form

$$(\mathbf{A}\bar{m} \,|\, \mathbf{P}m) = e^{i\, f_{\bar{m}}(\psi_A)} \, \mathfrak{d}^{(j)}{}_{\bar{m}m}(\theta_{AP}) \, e^{i\, f_m(\phi_A)}, \tag{5'}$$

where the functions f and $\mathfrak{d}^{(j)}$ are yet to be determined but are understood to be real.

The mathematical form of the function $f_m(\phi)$ is determined by considering two additional reference systems $\mathbf{P}'$, and $\mathbf{P}''$ whose axes coincide with the axis $\mathbf{P}$ and whose reference planes form angles ϕ' and ϕ'' with the reference plane of $\mathbf{P}$. Application of (1) and (3) yields

$$(\mathbf{P}''m \,|\, \mathbf{P}m) = e^{i\, f_m(\phi'')} = (\mathbf{P}''m \,|\, \mathbf{P}'m)(\mathbf{P}'m \,|\, \mathbf{P}m)$$
$$= e^{i\, f_m(\phi'' - \phi')} \, e^{i\, f_m(\phi')} = e^{i[f_m(\phi'' - \phi') + f_m(\phi')]}. \tag{6}$$

This equation requires that $f_m(\phi)$ be a linear function of ϕ. Since, moreover, $f_m(\phi')$ must vanish when $\phi' = 0$ and $\mathbf{P}'$ coincides with $\mathbf{P}$, we have

$$f_m(\phi) = \alpha_m \phi, \tag{7}$$

where α_m is a constant that remains to be determined.

---

[1] This standard symbol is called the "Kronecker delta," and should not be confused with the phase differences.

Let us now reexpress Eq. 1 utilizing the results obtained thus far. We select for simplicity the reference planes of **A** and **B** to coincide, respectively, with the planes **PA** and **AB**, as shown in Fig. VII.1, which makes $\psi_A = 0$ and $\bar{\psi}_B = 0$. The probability amplitudes to be entered in (1) have then the form

$$(\mathbf{B}\bar{m} \,|\, \mathbf{P}m) = e^{i\alpha_{\bar{m}}\psi_B} \, \mathfrak{d}^{(j)}{}_{\bar{m}m}(\theta_{BP}) \, e^{i\alpha_m\phi_B},$$

$$(\mathbf{B}\bar{m} \,|\, \mathbf{A}\bar{m}) = \mathfrak{d}^{(j)}{}_{\bar{m}\bar{m}}(\theta_{BA}) \, e^{i\alpha_{\bar{m}}\bar{\phi}_B}, \quad (\mathbf{A}\bar{m} \,|\, \mathbf{P}m) = \mathfrak{d}^{(j)}{}_{\bar{m}m}(\theta_{AP}) \, e^{i\alpha_m\phi_A}, \tag{8}$$

and Eq. 1 becomes

$$e^{i\alpha_{\bar{m}}\psi_B} \, \mathfrak{d}^{(j)}{}_{\bar{m}m}(\theta_{BP}) \, e^{i\alpha_m\phi_B} = \Sigma_{\bar{m}} \, \mathfrak{d}^{(j)}{}_{\bar{m}\bar{m}}(\theta_{BA}) \, e^{i\alpha_{\bar{m}}\bar{\phi}_B} \, \mathfrak{d}^{(j)}{}_{\bar{m}m}(\theta_{AP}) \, e^{i\alpha_m\phi_A}. \tag{9}$$

By evaluating the squared magnitudes of both sides of this equation, we obtain an expression of the Eq. 7, page 108, among probabilities, namely,

$$[\mathfrak{d}^{(j)}{}_{\bar{m}m}(\theta_{BP})]^2 = \Sigma_{\bar{m}} \, [\mathfrak{d}^{(j)}{}_{\bar{m}\bar{m}}(\theta_{BA})]^2 \, [\mathfrak{d}^{(j)}{}_{\bar{m}m}(\theta_{AP})]^2$$

$$+ 2\Sigma^j_{\bar{m}=-j}\Sigma^{\bar{m}-1}_{\bar{m}'=-j} \, \mathfrak{d}^{(j)}{}_{\bar{m}\bar{m}'}(\theta_{BA}) \, \mathfrak{d}^{(j)}{}_{\bar{m}'m}(\theta_{AP}) \, \mathfrak{d}^{(j)}{}_{\bar{m}\bar{m}}(\theta_{BA}) \, \mathfrak{d}^{(j)}{}_{\bar{m}m}(\theta_{AP})$$

$$\times \cos[(\alpha_{\bar{m}'} - \alpha_{\bar{m}})\bar{\phi}_B]. \tag{10}$$

Notice now that the angle θ_{BP}, on the left side of (10), is related to the angles θ_{BA}, θ_{AP}, and $\bar{\phi}_B$ on the right side by the formula of spherical trigonometry

$$\cos\theta_{BP} = \cos\theta_{BA} \cos\theta_{AP} - \sin\theta_{BA} \sin\theta_{AP} \cos\bar{\phi}_B. \tag{11}$$

In particular, the magnitude of θ_{BP}, and the probability $[\mathfrak{d}^{(j)}{}_{\bar{m}m}(\theta_{BP})]^2$ that depends on it, must be periodic functions of $\bar{\phi}_B$ with the period of 2π radians, as can also be seen from Fig. VII.1. In order that Eq. 10 fulfill this condition, all *the constants $\alpha_{\bar{m}}$ must differ from one another by whole numbers.*

This requirement allows some of the $\alpha_{\bar{m}}$ to be equal, but such equality does not in fact occur in the problem we are considering. We assume that there are as many different values of $\alpha_{\bar{m}}$ as there are values of $\bar{m}$, so that each eigenstate of the analyzer **A** may be identified by its value of $\alpha_{\bar{m}}$ or by the corresponding symbol, rather than by $\bar{m}$ itself.[2] The constant $\alpha_{\bar{m}}$, defined as the ratio of the phase of $(\mathbf{B}\bar{m} \,|\, \mathbf{A}\bar{m})$ to the azimuth

---

[2] If there were several eigenstates of **A** with the same value of α, each of them could be identified by the value of α and by the value of some other variable. It could then be proved that any additional variable remains unaffected when the molecular beam is split by Stern-Gerlach analyzers of different orientation, and that the problem of beam decomposition by analyzers of different orientation can be treated separately for each value of the additional variable. No such additional variable has been relevant to the description of phenomena in Chapters 7 and 8.

angle $\bar{\phi}_B$, will turn out to coincide with the quantum number $\bar{m}$ which was introduced simply to enumerate the eigenstates of an analyzer.

The properties which determine the constants $\alpha_{\bar{m}}$ and the functions $\mathfrak{d}^{(j)}{}_{\bar{m}m}$ are brought out by considering the situation in which the axes $\mathbf{P}$, $\mathbf{A}$, and $\mathbf{B}$ are nearly parallel. The angles θ_{AP}, θ_{BA}, and θ_{BP} are then

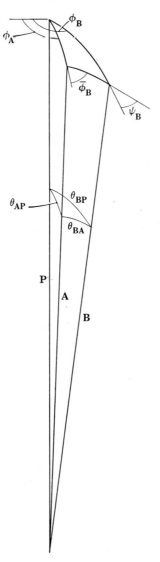

Fig. VII.1 Angles relating the orientations of nearly parallel axes $\mathbf{P}$, $\mathbf{A}$, and $\mathbf{B}$, and of their respective reference planes.

small and the functions $\mathfrak{d}^{(j)}{}_{\bar{m}m}(\theta)$ are expressed adequately by an expansion in powers of these angles. From the equations (9) and (10) we shall calculate the coefficients of the first few terms of the expansion, determine the values of $\alpha_{\bar{m}}$, and then formulate equations whose solution yields the complete functions $\mathfrak{d}^{(j)}{}_{\bar{m}m}(\theta)$.

For $\theta = 0$, the function $\mathfrak{d}^{(j)}{}_{\bar{m}m}$ reduces to $\delta_{\bar{m}m}$, which equals 1 or 0, according to (3). Its expansion has, therefore, the form

$$\mathfrak{d}^{(j)}{}_{\bar{m}m}(\theta) = \delta_{\bar{m}m} + b_{\bar{m}m}\theta + c_{\bar{m}m}\theta^2 + \cdots. \tag{12}$$

Entering this expansion into (10), and disregarding terms which contain more than two factors θ_{BP}, θ_{BA}, or θ_{AP}, we obtain

$$\delta_{\bar{m}m}(1 + 2b_{mm}\theta_{BP} + 2c_{mm}\theta_{BP}{}^2 + \cdots) + b_{\bar{m}m}{}^2\theta_{BP}{}^2 + \cdots$$

$$= \delta_{\bar{m}m}\{1 + 2b_{mm}(\theta_{BA} + \theta_{AP}) + b_{mm}{}^2\theta_{BA}\theta_{AP} + 2c_{mm}(\theta_{BA}{}^2 + \theta_{AP}{}^2)$$

$$+ 2\Sigma_{\bar{m}}^{\bar{m} \neq m} b_{m\bar{m}}b_{\bar{m}m}\theta_{BA}\theta_{AP} \cos[(\alpha_{\bar{m}} - \alpha_m)\bar{\phi}_B] + \cdots\}$$

$$+ b_{\bar{m}m}{}^2\{\theta_{BA}{}^2 + \theta_{AP}{}^2 + 2\theta_{BA}\theta_{AP} \cos[(\alpha_{\bar{m}} - \alpha_m)\bar{\phi}_B]\} + \cdots. \tag{13}$$

This equation is fulfilled for arbitrary values of the angles θ_{BP}, θ_{BA}, and θ_{AP}, if, and only if, the groups of terms with 0, 1, 2 $\cdots$ factors θ fulfill it separately. The terms with no such factor are $\delta_{\bar{m}m}$ on each side of the equation and are identical. The terms with one factor θ would be different, since $\theta_{BP} \neq \theta_{BA} + \theta_{AP}$, unless the coefficient b_{mm} vanishes; our first result is then $b_{mm} = 0$. Among the terms with two factors θ, those with $\bar{m} \neq m$ fulfill the equation provided either $b_{\bar{m}m} = 0$, or $\theta_{BP}{}^2 = \theta_{BA}{}^2 + \theta_{AP}{}^2 + 2\theta_{BA}\theta_{AP} \cos[(\alpha_{\bar{m}} - \alpha_m)\bar{\phi}_B]$. Now the angles θ_{BP}, θ_{BA}, θ_{AP}, and $\bar{\phi}_B$ are related by (11) which reduces to $\theta_{BP}{}^2 = \theta_{BA}{}^2 + \theta_{AP}{}^2 + 2\theta_{BA}\theta_{AP} \cos\bar{\phi}_B$ when the angles θ are small, a result which follows directly by solving the triangle in Fig. VII.1 according to plane geometry. Therefore, the coefficients $b_{\bar{m}m}$ can *differ from zero only for values of $\bar{m}$ and m such that $\alpha_{\bar{m}} - \alpha_m = \pm 1$*. Once this condition is established, the terms of (13) with $\bar{m} = m$ and with two factors θ are seen to fulfill the equation provided $c_{mm} = \frac{1}{2}\Sigma_{\bar{m}} b_{m\bar{m}}b_{\bar{m}m}$. Notice that the condition (14), on page 113 requires that $\Sigma_{\bar{m}} \mathfrak{d}^{(j)}{}_{m\bar{m}}(\theta) \mathfrak{d}^{(j)}{}_{\bar{m}m}(\theta) = 1$, a condition which is fulfilled by the expansion (12) only if $b_{m\bar{m}} = -b_{\bar{m}m}$; we have therefore $c_{mm} = -\frac{1}{2}\Sigma_{\bar{m}} b_{\bar{m}m}{}^2$. Since we have assumed that all values α_m are different, the $\Sigma_{\bar{m}}$ consists of only two non-vanishing terms, namely those for which $\alpha_{\bar{m}} = \alpha_m \pm 1$.

The coefficients $b_{\bar{m}m}$ and α_m will be determined by the requirement that not only the magnitudes but also the phases of the two sides of (9) be equal when the expansion (12) is utilized. We write then once more Eq. 9 for $\bar{m} = m$, with the expansion (12), utilizing the simplifications already established, such as $b_{mm} = 0$, and multiplying both sides by $e^{-i\alpha_m(\bar{\phi}_B + \phi_A)}$,

$$(1 + c_{mm}\theta_{BP}^2 + \cdots)\, e^{i\alpha_m(\psi_B + \phi_B - \bar{\phi}_B - \phi_A)}$$

$$= [1 + c_{mm}(\theta_{BA}^2 + \theta_{AP}^2) + \cdots]$$

$$- \Sigma_{\bar{m}}\, b_{\bar{m}m}^2\, \theta_{BA}\, e^{i(\alpha_{\bar{m}} - \alpha_m)\bar{\phi}_B}\, \theta_{AP} + \cdots. \quad (14a)$$

We know that the $\Sigma_{\bar{m}}$ has only two terms, with $\alpha_{\bar{m}} - \alpha_m = \pm 1$; it is therefore convenient, and permissible since all values $\alpha_{\bar{m}}$ are assumed to be different, to replace the indices m and $\bar{m}$ with indices α and $\alpha \pm 1$, and thus to rewrite (14a) in the form

$$(1 + c_{\alpha\alpha}\theta_{BP}^2 + \cdots)e^{i\alpha(\psi_B + \phi_B - \bar{\phi}_B - \phi_A)}$$

$$= [1 + c_{\alpha\alpha}(\theta_{BA}^2 + \theta_{AP}^2) + \cdots] - (b_{\alpha+1\,\alpha})^2\, \theta_{BA}\, e^{i\bar{\phi}_B}\, \theta_{AP}$$

$$- (b_{\alpha-1\,\alpha})^2\, \theta_{BA}\, e^{-i\bar{\phi}_B}\, \theta_{AP} + \cdots$$

$$= 1 + c_{\alpha\alpha}(\theta_{BA}^2 + \theta_{AP}^2)$$

$$- [(b_{\alpha+1\,\alpha})^2 + (b_{\alpha-1\,\alpha})^2]\theta_{BA}\theta_{AP}\cos\bar{\phi}_B + \cdots$$

$$- i[(b_{\alpha+1\,\alpha})^2 - (b_{\alpha-1\,\alpha})^2]\theta_{BA}\theta_{AP}\sin\bar{\phi}_B \cdots. \quad (14b)$$

Consider now the difference of angles $\psi_B + \phi_B - \bar{\phi}_B - \phi_A$ in the exponent on the left side of (14b). This difference would vanish if the triangle in Fig. VII.1 were plane and the sum of its angles were $180° = \pi$ radians. Actually, the sum of the angles of a spherical triangle exceeds π by an amount equal to the solid angle subtended by the triangle, expressed in steradians. This angle equals, in our approximation, $\frac{1}{2}\theta_{BA}\theta_{AB}\sin\bar{\phi}_B$, so that

$$e^{i\alpha(\psi_B + \phi_B - \bar{\phi}_B - \phi_A)} = e^{i\alpha\frac{1}{2}\theta_{BA}\theta_{AP}\sin\bar{\phi}_B}$$

$$= 1 + i\alpha\frac{1}{2}\theta_{BA}\theta_{AP}\sin\bar{\phi}_B + \cdots. \quad (15)$$

When this result is entered in (14b), the terms of the two sides without any factor i are seen to be equal, taking into account the earlier results $c_{\alpha\alpha} = -\frac{1}{2}[(b_{\alpha+1\,\alpha})^2 + (b_{\alpha\,\alpha-1})^2]$ and $(b_{\alpha\,\alpha-1})^2 = (b_{\alpha-1\,\alpha})^2$; the terms with the factor i will be equal, provided

$$\frac{1}{2}\alpha = -[(b_{\alpha+1\,\alpha})^2 - (b_{\alpha-1\,\alpha})^2] = (b_{\alpha\,\alpha-1})^2 - (b_{\alpha+1\,\alpha})^2. \quad (16)$$

The condition (16) proves fundamental. It relates the values of any two successive coefficients of the sequence $b_{\alpha+1\,\alpha}$, $b_{\alpha\,\alpha-1}$, $b_{\alpha-1\,\alpha-2}$, etc.

This sequence cannot extend indefinitely, because each coefficient belongs to a pair of eigenstates and there is only a finite number of eigenstates, namely $2j + 1$ eigenstates for molecules with the quantum number j. There must therefore exist one maximum value of α, let's call it β, for which there is no state with $\alpha = \beta + 1$, that is, such that $(b_{\beta+1\ \beta})^2 = 0$. Equation 16, with $\alpha = \beta$ and $(b_{\beta+1\ \beta})^2 = 0$, gives $(b_{\beta\ \beta-1})^2 = \frac{1}{2}\beta$; the same equation, with $\alpha = \beta - 1$, gives then $(b_{\beta-1\ \beta-2})^2 = \frac{1}{2}(\beta - 1) + (b_{\beta\ \beta-1})^2 = \frac{1}{2}(2\beta - 1)$. Continued application of this procedure yields

$$(b_{\beta-n\ \beta-n-1})^2 = \tfrac{1}{2}(\beta - \tfrac{1}{2}n)(n + 1), \tag{17}$$

where n is any non-negative integer. The sequence of coefficients b thus obtained would continue indefinitely for increasing values of n, *unless* the value of β is such that 2β is an integer. In this event the sequence stops when $n = 2\beta$, because (17) yields $(b_{-\beta\ -\beta-1})^2 = 0$. The condition $2\beta = $ integer yields thereby a finite sequence of coefficients $b_{\alpha\alpha'}$ whose indices α and α' differ by one and take the $2j + 1$ values β, $\beta - 1$, $\beta - 2$, $\cdots$, $-\beta + 1$, $-\beta$. Since we were to find the values of α for a sequence of $2j + 1$ states with quantum numbers m ranging from j to $-j$, it follows that the value of β *must coincide with the quantum number j* and that the values of α *must coincide with the values of the quantum number m*. Accordingly, we may replace in (17) the index β with j and n with $j - m$, which yields

$$(b_{m\ m-1})^2 = \tfrac{1}{4}(j + m)(j - m + 1). \tag{17'}$$

All requirements are fulfilled by assigning to the coefficients α_m, $\alpha_{\bar{m}}$, $\alpha_{\tilde{m}}$ in Eq. 8 the values m, $\bar{m}$, and $\tilde{m}$, and to $b_{\bar{m}m}$ in the expansion (12) the values

$$b_{\bar{m}m} = \tfrac{1}{2}\sqrt{(j + \bar{m})(j - m)} \qquad \text{for } m = \bar{m} - 1,$$

$$b_{\bar{m}m} = -\tfrac{1}{2}\sqrt{(j + m)(j - \bar{m})} \qquad \text{for } m = \bar{m} + 1, \tag{18}$$

$$b_{\bar{m}m} = 0 \qquad \text{otherwise.}$$

The earlier result

$$c_{mm} = -\tfrac{1}{2}\Sigma_{\bar{m}}b_{\bar{m}m}^2 \text{ yields now } c_{mm} = -\tfrac{1}{4}[j(j + 1) - m^2].$$

Having thus calculated $\mathfrak{d}^{(j)}{}_{\bar{m}m}(\theta)$ for small values of θ, one may determine complete functions $\mathfrak{d}^{(j)}{}_{\bar{m}m}(\theta)$ by considering again Eq. 9, but under conditions where only one of the angles θ, for example θ_{BA}, is regarded as small. We replace then, in (9), $\mathfrak{d}^{(j)}{}_{\bar{m}\bar{m}}(\theta_{BA})$ with the expansion (12), disregarding the term with θ_{BA}^2. Owing to (18), the $\Sigma_{\bar{m}}$ reduces to three terms, with $\bar{m} = \tilde{m}$, $\tilde{m} + 1$, and $\tilde{m} - 1$, and we have

$$e^{i\tilde{m}\psi_{\mathbf{B}}}\, \mathfrak{d}^{(j)}{}_{\tilde{m}m}(\theta_{\mathbf{BP}})\, e^{im\phi_{\mathbf{B}}}$$

$$= [e^{i\tilde{m}\bar{\phi}_{\mathbf{B}}}\, \mathfrak{d}^{(j)}{}_{\tilde{m}m}(\theta_{\mathbf{AP}}) + b_{\tilde{m}\ \tilde{m}+1}\,\theta_{\mathbf{BA}}\, e^{i(\tilde{m}+1)\bar{\phi}_{\mathbf{B}}}\, \mathfrak{d}^{(j)}{}_{\tilde{m}+1\ m}(\theta_{\mathbf{AP}})$$

$$+ b_{\tilde{m}\ \tilde{m}-1}\,\theta_{\mathbf{BA}}\, e^{i(\tilde{m}-1)\bar{\phi}_{\mathbf{B}}}\, \mathfrak{d}^{(j)}{}_{\tilde{m}-1\ m}(\theta_{\mathbf{AP}})]\, e^{im\phi_{\mathbf{A}}} + \cdots. \qquad (19)$$

The angles $\theta_{\mathbf{BP}}$, $\psi_{\mathbf{B}}$, and $\phi_{\mathbf{B}}$ can now be expressed as functions of $\theta_{\mathbf{AP}}$, $\bar{\phi}_{\mathbf{B}}$, $\phi_{\mathbf{A}}$, and of the small angle $\theta_{\mathbf{BA}}$; one finds

$$\theta_{\mathbf{BP}} = \theta_{\mathbf{AP}} + \theta_{\mathbf{BA}}\cos\bar{\phi}_{\mathbf{B}} + \cdots,$$

$$\psi_{\mathbf{B}} = \bar{\phi}_{\mathbf{B}} - \theta_{\mathbf{BA}}\sin\bar{\phi}_{\mathbf{B}}\,\frac{\cos\theta_{\mathbf{AP}}}{\sin\theta_{\mathbf{AP}}} + \cdots, \qquad (20)$$

$$\phi_{\mathbf{B}} = \phi_{\mathbf{A}} + \theta_{\mathbf{BA}}\sin\bar{\phi}_{\mathbf{B}}\,\frac{1}{\sin\theta_{\mathbf{AP}}} + \cdots.$$

The value of $\mathfrak{d}^{(j)}{}_{\tilde{m}m}(\theta_{\mathbf{BP}})$ can be expressed as the sum of $\mathfrak{d}^{(j)}{}_{\tilde{m}m}(\theta_{\mathbf{AP}})$ and of a series in powers of the small difference

$$\theta_{\mathbf{BP}} - \theta_{\mathbf{AP}} \doteq \theta_{\mathbf{BA}}\cos\bar{\phi}_{\mathbf{B}} + \cdots,$$

$$\mathfrak{d}^{(j)}{}_{\tilde{m}m}(\theta_{\mathbf{BP}}) = \mathfrak{d}^{(j)}{}_{\tilde{m}m}(\theta_{\mathbf{AP}}) + \frac{d\mathfrak{d}^{(j)}{}_{\tilde{m}m}(\theta_{\mathbf{AP}})}{d\theta_{\mathbf{AP}}}\,\theta_{\mathbf{BA}}\cos\bar{\phi}_{\mathbf{B}} + \cdots. \qquad (21)$$

Upon substitution of these results, and expansion into powers of $\theta_{\mathbf{BA}}$, Eq. 19 reduces to

$$\left[1 - i\tilde{m}\theta_{\mathbf{BA}}\sin\bar{\phi}_{\mathbf{B}}\,\frac{\cos\theta_{\mathbf{AP}}}{\sin\theta_{\mathbf{AP}}} + im\theta_{\mathbf{BA}}\sin\bar{\phi}_{\mathbf{B}}\,\frac{1}{\sin\theta_{\mathbf{AP}}}\right]\mathfrak{d}^{(j)}{}_{\tilde{m}m}(\theta_{\mathbf{AP}})$$

$$+ \frac{d\mathfrak{d}^{(j)}{}_{\tilde{m}m}}{d\theta_{\mathbf{AP}}}\,\theta_{\mathbf{BA}}\cos\bar{\phi}_{\mathbf{B}} + \cdots = \mathfrak{d}^{(j)}{}_{\tilde{m}m}(\theta_{\mathbf{AP}})$$

$$+ \theta_{\mathbf{BA}}\{\cos\bar{\phi}_{\mathbf{B}}\,[b_{\tilde{m}\ \tilde{m}+1}\,\mathfrak{d}^{(j)}{}_{\tilde{m}+1\ m}(\theta_{\mathbf{AP}}) + b_{\tilde{m}\ \tilde{m}-1}\,\mathfrak{d}^{(j)}{}_{\tilde{m}-1\ m}(\theta_{\mathbf{AP}})]$$

$$+ i\sin\bar{\phi}_{\mathbf{B}}\,[b_{\tilde{m}\ \tilde{m}+1}\,\mathfrak{d}^{(j)}{}_{\tilde{m}+1\ m}(\theta_{\mathbf{AP}}) - b_{\tilde{m}\ \tilde{m}-1}\,\mathfrak{d}^{(j)}{}_{\tilde{m}-1\ m}(\theta_{\mathbf{AP}})]\} + \cdots. \qquad (22)$$

This equation must be fulfilled separately by the terms without the factor i, and by those with the factor i. One obtains thus the separate equations

$$\frac{d\mathfrak{d}^{(j)}{}_{\tilde{m}m}}{d\theta_{\mathbf{AP}}} = b_{\tilde{m}\ \tilde{m}+1}\,\mathfrak{d}^{(j)}{}_{\tilde{m}+1\ m}(\theta_{\mathbf{AP}}) + b_{\tilde{m}\ \tilde{m}-1}\,\mathfrak{d}^{(j)}{}_{\tilde{m}-1\ m}(\theta_{\mathbf{AP}}),$$

$$-\frac{\tilde{m}\cos\theta_{\mathbf{AP}} - m}{\sin\theta_{\mathbf{AP}}}\,\mathfrak{d}^{(j)}{}_{\tilde{m}m}(\theta_{\mathbf{AP}})$$

$$= b_{\tilde{m}\ \tilde{m}+1}\,\mathfrak{d}^{(j)}{}_{\tilde{m}+1\ m}(\theta_{\mathbf{AP}}) - b_{\tilde{m}\ \tilde{m}-1}\,\mathfrak{d}^{(j)}{}_{\tilde{m}-1\ m}(\theta_{\mathbf{AP}}). \qquad (23)$$

The angle θ_{AP} may now be indicated simply by θ, and the values of the coefficients $b_{\tilde{m}m}$ may be taken from (18). We also replace the two equations (23) with their sum and their difference, and find

$$\frac{d\mathfrak{d}^{(j)}_{\tilde{m}m}}{d\theta} - \frac{\tilde{m}\cos\theta - m}{\sin\theta}\,\mathfrak{d}^{(j)}_{\tilde{m}m}(\theta)$$

$$= -\sqrt{(j+\tilde{m}+1)(j-\tilde{m})}\,\mathfrak{d}^{(j)}_{\tilde{m}+1\,m}(\theta), \quad (24a)$$

$$\frac{d\mathfrak{d}^{(j)}_{\tilde{m}m}}{d\theta} + \frac{\tilde{m}\cos\theta - m}{\sin\theta}\,\mathfrak{d}^{(j)}_{\tilde{m}m}(\theta)$$

$$= \sqrt{(j+\tilde{m})(j-\tilde{m}+1)}\,\mathfrak{d}^{(j)}_{\tilde{m}-1\,m}(\theta). \quad (24b)$$

In the special case $\tilde{m} = m = j$, the right side of (24a) vanishes and the equation reduces to

$$\frac{d\mathfrak{d}^{(j)}_{jj}}{d\theta} + j\frac{1 - \cos\theta}{\sin\theta}\,\mathfrak{d}^{(j)}_{jj}(\theta) = 0. \quad (25)$$

The function $\mathfrak{d}^{(j)}_{jj}(\theta)$ which obeys this equation, and which equals 1 at $\theta = 0$ in accordance with (12), is

$$\mathfrak{d}^{(j)}_{jj}(\theta) = \left(\frac{1 + \cos\theta}{2}\right)^j = (\cos\tfrac{1}{2}\theta)^{2j}. \quad (26)$$

When one enters this result on the left side of (24b), with $\tilde{m} = m = j$, the right side yields $\mathfrak{d}^{(j)}_{j-1\,j}(\theta) = -\sqrt{2j}\sin\tfrac{1}{2}\theta(\cos\tfrac{1}{2}\theta)^{2j-1}$. Repeated application of (24b) yields in sequence all the functions $\mathfrak{d}^{(j)}_{\tilde{m}j}(\theta)$. To find the remaining functions $\mathfrak{d}^{(j)}_{\tilde{m}m}(\theta)$, with $m \neq j$, one must utilize an additional equation, analogous to (24b). The additional equation is obtained by developing once more the application of Eq. 9, to the case where θ_{AP} is small instead of θ_{BA}. One finds the equations

$$\frac{d\mathfrak{d}^{(j)}_{\tilde{m}m}}{d\theta} + \frac{\tilde{m} - m\cos\theta}{\sin\theta}\,\mathfrak{d}^{(j)}_{\tilde{m}m}(\theta)$$

$$= \mathfrak{d}^{(j)}_{\tilde{m}\,m+1}(\theta)\sqrt{(j+m+1)(j-m)}, \quad (27a)$$

$$\frac{d\mathfrak{d}^{(j)}_{\tilde{m}m}}{d\theta} - \frac{\tilde{m} - m\cos\theta}{\sin\theta}\,\mathfrak{d}^{(j)}_{\tilde{m}m}(\theta)$$

$$= -\mathfrak{d}^{(j)}_{\tilde{m}\,m-1}(\theta)\sqrt{(j+m)(j-m+1)}. \quad (27b)$$

Since (24b) and (27b) can be expressed in the form

$$\mathfrak{d}^{(j)}{}_{\tilde{m}-1\,m}(\theta) = -\frac{1}{2\sqrt{(j+\tilde{m})(j-\tilde{m}+1)}}\left\{\sin\tfrac{1}{2}\theta\,\frac{d\mathfrak{d}^{(j)}{}_{\tilde{m}m}}{d\cos\tfrac{1}{2}\theta}\right.$$

$$\left.+\left[(\tilde{m}+m)\,\frac{\sin\tfrac{1}{2}\theta}{\cos\tfrac{1}{2}\theta}-(\tilde{m}-m)\,\frac{\cos\tfrac{1}{2}\theta}{\sin\tfrac{1}{2}\theta}\right]\mathfrak{d}^{(j)}{}_{\tilde{m}m}(\theta)\right\},$$

$$\mathfrak{d}^{(j)}{}_{\tilde{m}\,m-1}(\theta) = \frac{1}{2\sqrt{(j+m)(j-m+1)}}\left\{\sin\tfrac{1}{2}\theta\,\frac{d\mathfrak{d}^{(j)}{}_{\tilde{m}m}}{d\cos\tfrac{1}{2}\theta}\right.$$

$$\left.+\left[(\tilde{m}+m)\,\frac{\sin\tfrac{1}{2}\theta}{\cos\tfrac{1}{2}\theta}+(\tilde{m}-m)\,\frac{\cos\tfrac{1}{2}\theta}{\sin\tfrac{1}{2}\theta}\right]\mathfrak{d}^{(j)}{}_{\tilde{m}m}(\theta)\right\}, \quad (28)$$

repeated application of these formulas replaces factors $\cos\tfrac{1}{2}\theta$ with factors $\sin\tfrac{1}{2}\theta$, or vice versa, and thereby transforms the initial expression (26), $\mathfrak{d}^{(j)}{}_{jj} = (\cos\tfrac{1}{2}\theta)^{2j}$, into a homogeneous polynomial of degree $2j$ in $\cos\tfrac{1}{2}\theta$ and $\sin\tfrac{1}{2}\theta$. For small values of j these polynomials have only a few terms as shown in Table 8.1. For a general value of j they are represented by the formula

$$\mathfrak{d}^{(j)}{}_{\tilde{m}m}(\theta) = \Sigma_n\,(-1)^n\,\frac{\sqrt{(j+\tilde{m})!(j-\tilde{m})!(j+m)!(j-m)!}}{(j+\tilde{m}-n)!(j-m-n)!n!(n+m-\tilde{m})!}$$

$$\times\,(\cos\tfrac{1}{2}\theta)^{2j-2n+\tilde{m}-m}(\sin\tfrac{1}{2}\theta)^{2n-\tilde{m}+m}. \quad (29)$$

Mathematical formulation of quantum laws

Quantum mechanics constitutes an elaboration of the concepts and laws developed in Chapters 6 to 9, namely: (a) the concepts of incompatible variables and of their eigenstates and eigenvalues (Chapter 7); (b) the superposition of states, represented by the combination of probability amplitudes (Chapter 8); (c) the law of variation of states in the course of time (Chapter 9); (d) the interpretation of the laws of macroscropic physics as equations among the mean values of variables. On this basis a complete theory of atomic phenomena can be developed utilizing only the mathematical symbols that represent eigenvalues and probability amplitudes, but it proves convenient to utilize more condensed types of symbols.

Matrix equations. Macroscopically, the total energy E of a particle is the sum of its kinetic and potential energies, $K = \frac{1}{2}mv^2 = p^2/2m$ and $V(x,y,z) = V(\mathbf{r})$. For an atomic particle in an arbitrary state a the cor-

374

responding relationship holds among mean values and is expressed in the forms:

$$\langle E \rangle_a = \langle K \rangle_a + \langle V \rangle_a, \tag{1a}$$

$$\Sigma_E E \,|\,(E\,|\,a)\,|^2 = \Sigma_\mathbf{p} \frac{p^2}{2m} \,|\,(\mathbf{p}\,|\,a)\,|^2 + \Sigma_\mathbf{r} V(\mathbf{r})\,|\,(\mathbf{r}\,|\,a)\,|^2, \tag{1b}$$

$$\Sigma_E (a\,|\,E) E(E\,|\,a) = \Sigma_\mathbf{p}(a\,|\,\mathbf{p}) \frac{p^2}{2m} (\mathbf{p}\,|\,a) + \Sigma_\mathbf{r}(a\,|\,\mathbf{r}) V(\mathbf{r})(\mathbf{r}\,|\,a). \tag{1c}$$

Since this relationship constitutes a general law, it must hold independently of the values of probability amplitudes which identify the arbitrary state a. In the Eqs. 1b and 1c, the state a is identified by various sets of probability amplitudes, namely $(E\,|\,a)$, $(\mathbf{p}\,|\,a)$, and $(\mathbf{r}\,|\,a)$, which are not independent of one another since, for example, $(E\,|\,a) = \Sigma_\mathbf{r}(E\,|\,\mathbf{r})(\mathbf{r}\,|\,a)$. To obtain a form of (1) which holds irrespective of the specification of the state a, this specification has to be given by a single set of probability amplitudes, for example, in terms of $(\mathbf{r}\,|\,a)$ and $(a\,|\,\mathbf{r}) = (\mathbf{r}\,|\,a)^*$. We write then (1) once more in the form

$$\Sigma_E \,[\Sigma_{\mathbf{r}'}(a\,|\,\mathbf{r}')(\mathbf{r}'\,|\,E)]\,E\,[\Sigma_\mathbf{r}(E\,|\,\mathbf{r})(\mathbf{r}\,|\,a)]$$

$$= \Sigma_\mathbf{p} \,[\Sigma_{\mathbf{r}'}(a\,|\,\mathbf{r}')(\mathbf{r}'\,|\,\mathbf{p})] \frac{p^2}{2m} [\Sigma_\mathbf{r}(\mathbf{p}\,|\,\mathbf{r})(\mathbf{r}\,|\,a)] + \Sigma_{\mathbf{r}'}\Sigma_\mathbf{r}(a\,|\,\mathbf{r}')\delta_{\mathbf{r}'\mathbf{r}} V(\mathbf{r})(\mathbf{r}\,|\,a), \tag{2a}$$

where, in the last term, the symbol [1]

$$\delta_{\mathbf{r}'\mathbf{r}} = \begin{cases} 1 & \text{when } \mathbf{r}' = \mathbf{r} \\ 0 & \text{otherwise,} \end{cases} \tag{2'}$$

and $(a\,|\,\mathbf{r})$ has been expressed as $\Sigma_{\mathbf{r}'}(a\,|\,\mathbf{r}')\delta_{\mathbf{r}'\mathbf{r}}$ to achieve formal analogy with the other terms. The analogy is still more obvious if we regroup the summation terms in (2a) and write

$$\Sigma_{\mathbf{r}'}\Sigma_\mathbf{r}(a\,|\,\mathbf{r}')\,[\Sigma_E(\mathbf{r}'\,|\,E) E(E\,|\,\mathbf{r})]\,(\mathbf{r}\,|\,a)$$

$$= \Sigma_{\mathbf{r}'}\Sigma_\mathbf{r}(a\,|\,\mathbf{r}')\,[\Sigma_\mathbf{p}(\mathbf{r}'\,|\,\mathbf{p}) \frac{p^2}{2m} (\mathbf{p}\,|\,\mathbf{r}) + \delta_{\mathbf{r}'\mathbf{r}} V(\mathbf{r})]\,(\mathbf{r}\,|\,a). \tag{2b}$$

Each term on the left or on the right of this equation contains a product of probability amplitudes $(a\,|\,\mathbf{r}')(\mathbf{r}\,|\,a) = (\mathbf{r}'\,|\,a)^*(\mathbf{r}\,|\,a)$. The statement

---

[1] This symbol is called the "Kronecker delta;" it does *not* indicate a phase difference.

that (2b) holds for an arbitrary set of probability amplitudes $(\mathbf{r}|a)$ is mathematically equivalent to the statement that

$$\Sigma_E(\mathbf{r}'|E)E(E|\mathbf{r}) = \Sigma_\mathbf{p}(\mathbf{r}'|\mathbf{p})\frac{p^2}{2m}(\mathbf{p}|\mathbf{r}) + \delta_{\mathbf{r}'\mathbf{r}}V(\mathbf{r}) \tag{3}$$

for each pair of possible positions $\mathbf{r}'$, $\mathbf{r}$, of the particle.

The new Eq. 3 relates the probability amplitudes of the eigenstates of the total, kinetic, and potential energies, and the eigenvalues E, $p^2/2m$, and $V(\mathbf{r})$ of these variables. Only the existence of these eigenvalues and probability amplitudes is assumed, but no advance knowledge of their numerical values. Equation 3 constitutes, therefore, a general law, that is, a quantum analog of the macroscopic formula $E = p^2/2m + V(\mathbf{r})$. The values of the sums in the equation may be considered even when the actual eigenvalues and probability amplitudes are unknown. It is therefore convenient to represent each sum by a suitably abbreviated symbol, defining for example, for any pair of positions $\mathbf{r}'$ and $\mathbf{r}$ of a particle,

$$(\mathbf{r}'|E|\mathbf{r}) = \Sigma_E(\mathbf{r}'|E)E(E|\mathbf{r}). \tag{4}$$

Eq. 3 takes then the more condensed form

$$(\mathbf{r}'|E|\mathbf{r}) = (\mathbf{r}'|\ p^2/2m\ |\mathbf{r}) + (\mathbf{r}'|V|\mathbf{r}). \tag{3'}$$

The set of quantities $(\mathbf{r}'|E|\mathbf{r})$ can be arranged in a square arrays of rows and columns such that the quantities $(\mathbf{r}'|E|\mathbf{r}_1)$ corresponding to a single given position $\mathbf{r} = \mathbf{r}_1$ and to alternative positions $\mathbf{r}' = \mathbf{r}'_1$, $\mathbf{r}'_2$, $\mathbf{r}'_3$, $\cdots$, lie in a column labeled by the position $\mathbf{r}_1$, and the quantities $(\mathbf{r}'|E|\mathbf{r})$ corresponding to a single position $\mathbf{r}' = \mathbf{r}'_2$ and to alternative positions $\mathbf{r} = \mathbf{r}_1, \mathbf{r}_2, \cdots$, lie in a row labeled by the position $\mathbf{r}'_2$. Such an array is called a "matrix," and each of the quantities $(\mathbf{r}'|E|\mathbf{r})$ is called a "matrix element."

Row index \ Column index		$\mathbf{r}_1$	$\mathbf{r}_2$	$\mathbf{r}_3$	
$\cdots$	$\cdots$	$\cdots$	$\cdots$	$\cdots$	$\cdots$
$\mathbf{r}'_1$	$\cdots$	$(\mathbf{r}'_1\|E\|\mathbf{r}_1)$	$(\mathbf{r}'_1\|E\|\mathbf{r}_2)$	$(\mathbf{r}'_1\|E\|\mathbf{r}_3)$	$\cdots$
$\mathbf{r}'_2$	$\cdots$	$(\mathbf{r}'_2\|E\|\mathbf{r}_1)$	$(\mathbf{r}'_2\|E\|\mathbf{r}_2)$	$\cdots$	$\cdots$
$\mathbf{r}'_3$	$\cdots$	$(\mathbf{r}'_3\|E\|\mathbf{r}_1)$	$(\mathbf{r}'_3\|E\|\mathbf{r}_2)$	$\cdots$	$\cdots$
$\cdots$	$\cdots$	$\cdots$	$\cdots$	$\cdots$	$\cdots$
$\cdots$	$\cdots$	$\cdots$	$\cdots$	$\cdots$	$\cdots$
$\cdots$	$\cdots$	$\cdots$	$\cdots$	$\cdots$	$\cdots$

Equation 3′ holds among any three elements of the matrices $(\mathbf{r}'|E|\mathbf{r})$, $(\mathbf{r}'|p^2/2m|\mathbf{r})$, $(\mathbf{r}'|V|\mathbf{r})$ that occupy identical positions in the arrays. Such an equation is called an "equation among matrices" or, briefly, a a "matrix equation."

Owing to the definition (4) of $(\mathbf{r}'|E|\mathbf{r})$ and to the facts that the eigenvalues E are real and the probability amplitudes $(E|\mathbf{r})$ are the complex conjugates of their reciprocals $(\mathbf{r}|E)$, an interchange of rows and columns in the matrix (4) yields

$$(\mathbf{r}|E|\mathbf{r}') = (\mathbf{r}'|E|\mathbf{r})^*. \tag{5}$$

A matrix with this property is called "hermitian."

Equation 3, or 3′, was obtained from $(2a)$ after the arbitrary state a was specified by the probability amplitudes $(\mathbf{r}|a)$. Alternative specification through the probability amplitudes $(\mathbf{p}|a)$, or through $(E|a)$, leads respectively to the matrix equations

$$(\mathbf{p}'|E|\mathbf{p}) = (\mathbf{p}'|p^2/2m|\mathbf{p}) + (\mathbf{p}'|V|\mathbf{p}), \tag{3''}$$

$$(E'|E|E) = (E'|p^2/2m|E) + (E'|V|E). \tag{3'''}$$

Further expressions can, of course, be obtained in correspondence to still different sets of eigenstates, pertaining to variables other than position, momentum, or total energy. Equations 3′, 3″, and 3‴ are said to represent the same equation in different "schemes" of eigenstates.

Determination of eigenvalues and eigenstates. The matrix elements $(\mathbf{r}'|V|\mathbf{r})$ of the potential energy have the mathematical form $\delta_{\mathbf{r}'\mathbf{r}}V(\mathbf{r})$, as seen by comparing (3′) with (3). That is, when the matrix elements are arranged in a square array, only those elements of the array differ from zero that lie on the "main diagonal" of the array, from the upper left to the lower right corner. A matrix with this special form is called a "diagonal matrix." The matrix $(\mathbf{r}'|V|\mathbf{r})$ is diagonal because the eigenstates of the position $\mathbf{r}$ of a particle are also eigenstates of its potential energy (the potential energy being a function of position only). In Eq. 3″ the matrix of the kinetic energy is diagonal, as is the matrix of the total energy in Eq. 3‴. A "scheme" of eigenstates always exists in which the matrices of two or more *compatible* variables are diagonal; no simultaneously diagonal matrices exist for incompatible variables.

The matrix of a variable is diagonal when the scheme adopted is a scheme of eigenstates of that variable; the non-vanishing elements of the diagonal matrix are simply the eigenvalues of the variable. Therefore, the problem of determining the eigenvalues and the eigenstates of a variable can be defined mathematically as the problem of finding a diagonal matrix of that variable. For example, if the probability amplitudes $(\mathbf{r}'|\mathbf{p})$ and $(\mathbf{p}|\mathbf{r})$ are known and the potential energy function $V(\mathbf{r})$ is given, the matrices $(\mathbf{r}'|p^2/2m|\mathbf{r})$ and $(\mathbf{r}'|V|\mathbf{r})$ in $(3')$ can be calculated. Equation $3'$ defines then the value of each matrix element $(\mathbf{r}'|E|\mathbf{r})$. The diagonal matrix $(E'|E|E) = \delta_{E'E}E$ of the total energy can be expressed in terms of the non-diagonal matrix $(\mathbf{r}'|E|\mathbf{r})$ if one knows the probability amplitudes $(E|\mathbf{r})$,

$$(E'|E|E) = \delta_{E'E}E$$
$$= \Sigma_{\mathbf{r}'\mathbf{r}}(E'|\mathbf{r}')(\mathbf{r}'|E|\mathbf{r})(\mathbf{r}|E)$$
$$= \Sigma_{\mathbf{r}'\mathbf{r}}(E'|\mathbf{r}')[(\mathbf{r}'|p^2/2m|\mathbf{r}) + \delta_{\mathbf{r}'\mathbf{r}}V(\mathbf{r})](\mathbf{r}|E). \tag{6}$$

Conversely, the requirement that (6) be fulfilled by the energy eigenvalues E and the corresponding probability amplitudes $(E'|\mathbf{r}')$, $(\mathbf{r}|E)$, is sufficient for the mathematical determination of these quantities once the matrix sum $(\mathbf{r}'|p^2/2m|\mathbf{r}) + \delta_{\mathbf{r}'\mathbf{r}}V(\mathbf{r})$ is given. The expression on the right of (6) is called a "transformation" of the sum of matrices that "diagonalizes" it. The determination of eigenvalues and eigenstates is thus expressed as the problem of "diagonalizing" a given matrix (or sum of matrices).

For the purpose of determining the eigenvalues E and the probability amplitudes $(\mathbf{r}|E)$, Eq. 6 is conveniently reduced to a linear form. This is done by multiplying each side of (6) by $(\mathbf{r}''|E')$ and taking a summation over E'. Considering that $\Sigma_{E'}(\mathbf{r}''|E')(E'|\mathbf{r}) = \delta_{\mathbf{r}''\mathbf{r}}$, one finds

$$\Sigma_{\mathbf{r}'}(\mathbf{r}''|p^2/2m|\mathbf{r}')(\mathbf{r}'|E) + V(\mathbf{r}'')(\mathbf{r}''|E) = (\mathbf{r}''|E)E. \tag{7}$$

This formula represents a system of infinitely many linear homogenous equations, one for each position $\mathbf{r}''$, with the infinitely many unknowns $(\mathbf{r}'|E)$. The equations are expressed in algebraic form, but are actually integral equations because the symbol $\Sigma_{\mathbf{r}}$ represents in fact a triple integral $\int d\mathbf{r} = \iiint dx\,dy\,dz$. A system of equations which has the form (7), but is truly algebraic, that is, which consists of a finite number of equations with a finite number of unknown probability amplitudes $(\mathbf{r}'|E)$, has non-vanishing solutions only if the determinant D formed by its coefficients vanishes. This condition constitutes an algebraic equation among the coefficients; since the coefficients include the unknown energy eigenvalues, these eigenvalues are determined as the roots of the equation $D = 0$. Once this equation is solved, the probability amplitudes are easily calculated. In general, the equation (7) is not truly algebraic and the determination of eigenvalues and eigenstates requires the solution of an integral or differential equation. It will be shown below that Eq. 7 is equivalent to the Schroedinger differential equation (2), page 170, which is also derived from $\langle E \rangle = \langle K \rangle + \langle V \rangle$.

Operator equations. The matrix equations 3′, 3″, and 3‴ represent the same relationship among matrices that pertain to the same variables but to different schemes of eigenstates. Since the relationship holds equally in different schemes, it is convenient to represent it by symbols that do not refer explicitly to any one scheme of eigenstates. Consider, in this connection, that matrices pertaining to the same variable but to different schemes are related by equations such as

$$(E' \,|\, K \,|\, E) = \Sigma_{\mathbf{r}'\mathbf{r}}(E' \,|\, \mathbf{r}')(\mathbf{r}' \,|\, K \,|\, \mathbf{r})(\mathbf{r} \,|\, E), \tag{8}$$

and that any two matrices so related are said to be "equivalent." We shall then indicate all equivalent matrices pertaining to any one variable by a single symbol. The symbol will be the letter which ordinarily indicates the variable, but in *sans serif* character, for example, **E, K, V**. We regard the matrix of the kinetic energy $(E' \,|\, K \,|\, E)$ as the representation of **K** in the scheme of energy eigenstates and $\delta_{\mathbf{p}'\mathbf{p}}\, p^2/2m$ as its representation in the scheme of momentum eigenstates. The three equations 3′, 3″, and 3‴ will be regarded as special forms of the general equation

$$\mathsf{E} = \mathsf{K} + \mathsf{V}. \tag{9}$$

Notice that this equation has the same form as the equation $E = K + V$ among macroscopic variables, but is not equivalent to it because the symbols **E, K,** and **V**, represent matrices rather than ordinary algebraic variables. Actually (9) indicates the fact that the mean value equation $\langle E \rangle_a = \langle K \rangle_a + \langle V \rangle_a$ holds for any state a of a particle. Any equation among macroscopic variables is replaced in quantum mechanics by an equation among matrices. We write, for example, $\mathsf{K} = \mathsf{p}^2/2m$, and therefore

$$\mathsf{E} = \frac{1}{2m}\,\mathsf{p}^2 + \mathsf{V}. \tag{9'}$$

Relationships that involve probability amplitudes as well as matrices are also represented by equivalent equations in different schemes of eigenstates. For example, Eq. 7, which determines the energy eigenvalues and eigenstates and pertains to the scheme of position eigenstates, is equivalent to the equation in the scheme of momentum eigenstates

$$\frac{p^2}{2m}\,(\mathbf{p} \,|\, E) + \Sigma_{\mathbf{p}'}(\mathbf{p} \,|\, V \,|\, \mathbf{p}')(\mathbf{p}' \,|\, E) = (\mathbf{p} \,|\, E)E. \tag{7'}$$

Because equivalent equations such as (7) and (7′) contain alternative sets of probability amplitudes, $(\mathbf{r} | E)$ and $(\mathbf{p} | E)$, which pertain to the same energy eigenstate, one utilizes a single symbol to indicate any set of probability amplitudes pertaining to a given state a. The symbol consists of the letter ψ, with a subscript which identifies the state, and is called "state representative" or "state vector." (A wave function $\psi_a(\mathbf{r}) = (\mathbf{r} | a)$ constitutes a special form of state representative.) Equations 7 and 7' also contain sets of quantities, such as $\Sigma_{\mathbf{p'}}(\mathbf{p} | V | \mathbf{p'})(\mathbf{p'} | E)$, obtained from probability amplitudes by linear combinations whose coefficients are matrix elements. The result of equivalent transformations of probability amplitudes performed in various schemes of eigenstates is indicated by a product symbol such as $\mathbf{V}\psi_E$. Because $\mathbf{V}\psi_E$ indicates the result of a transformation of the state representative ψ_E, the symbol $\mathbf{V}$ is usually called an "operator" rather than a matrix symbol. The general term operator is more appropriate than "matrix symbol" because a linear algebraic transformation whose coefficients are matrix elements may be replaced by any non-algebraic transformation of a given set of probability amplitudes which yields identical results. For example, the set of quantities $\Sigma_{\mathbf{r'}}(\mathbf{r} | K | \mathbf{r'})(\mathbf{r'} | E)$, which is represented by the operator symbol $\mathbf{K}\psi_E$, may also be obtained without the use of matrix elements by calculating derivatives of the probability amplitudes $(\mathbf{r} | E)$, as will be shown below.

The symbols of operators and state representatives permit us now to write a general equation, of which (7), (7'), and equivalent equations are special forms, namely,

$$\left(\frac{1}{2m}\, \mathbf{p}^2 + \mathbf{V}\right) \psi_E = \psi_E E. \tag{10a}$$

This equation may also be expressed in terms of the total energy operator $\mathbf{E} = \mathbf{p}^2/2m + \mathbf{V}$, in the form

$$\mathbf{E}\psi_E = \psi_E E. \tag{10b}$$

Equations among operators and state representatives are called "operator equations." They represent in compact and convenient form the complex quantitative relationships among the eigenvalues and eigenstates of incompatible physical variables. Some operator equations, for example, (9), are the analogs of macroscopic equations. Others, which derive from the law of motion, have no macroscopic analog but serve to define standard relations of incompatibility.

The law of motion. Commutators. We shall now express by means of an operator equation the fact that the time derivative of the mean position of a particle must equal the mean value of its velocity.

The time derivative of the mean value of a variable, for a system in an arbitrary non-stationary state, $a(t)$, can be obtained from the law of variation of probability amplitudes given by Eq. 10, page 128. For the velocity component in the x direction we write

$$\langle v_x \rangle_a = \frac{d}{dt} \langle x \rangle_a = \frac{d}{dt} \Sigma_r (a(t)|\mathbf{r}) \, x \, (\mathbf{r}|a(t))$$

$$= \frac{d}{dt} \Sigma_r [\Sigma_{E'}(a(t)|E')(E'|\mathbf{r})] \, x \, [\Sigma_E(\mathbf{r}|E)(E|a(t))]$$

$$= \frac{d}{dt} \Sigma_{E'} \Sigma_E (a(t)|E')(E'|x|E)(E|a(t))$$

$$= \Sigma_{E'} \Sigma_E \left\{ \frac{d(a(t)|E')}{dt} (E'|x|E)(E|a(t)) + (a(t)|E')(E'|x|E) \frac{d(E|a(t))}{dt} \right\}$$

$$= \Sigma_{E'} \Sigma_E \frac{i}{\hbar} \left\{ (a(t)|E')E'(E'|x|E)(E|a(t)) - (a(t)|E')(E'|x|E)E(E|a(t)) \right\}$$

$$= \Sigma_{E'} \Sigma_E (a(t)|E') \frac{i}{\hbar} \left\{ E'(E'|x|E) - (E'|x|E)E \right\}(E|a(t)). \tag{11}$$

Since the mean value $\langle v_x \rangle_a$ can also be expressed by means of the probability amplitudes $(E|a(t))$, in the form

$$\langle v_x \rangle_a = \Sigma_{\mathbf{v}}(a(t)|\mathbf{v})v_x(\mathbf{v}|a(t))$$

$$= \Sigma_{E'} \Sigma_E (a(t)|E')(E'|v_x|E)(E|a(t)), \tag{12}$$

the requirement that Eq. 11 hold for any state is equivalent to the matrix equation

$$(E'|v_x|E) = \frac{i}{\hbar} \left\{ E'(E'|x|E) - (E'|x|E)E \right\}. \tag{13a}$$

This equation is expressed in the scheme of energy eigenstates, but can equally well be expressed in other schemes; in operator notation it reads

$$\mathbf{v}_x = \frac{i}{\hbar} \left\{ \mathbf{E}x - x\mathbf{E} \right\}. \tag{13b}$$

The expression $\mathbf{E}x - x\mathbf{E}$ is called the "commutator" of the operators $\mathbf{E}$ and x. The commutator of two operators $\mathbf{A}$ and $\mathbf{B}$ vanishes if, and only if, the corresponding variables are compatible. In this event, there is a scheme of eigenstates in which the matrix form of both $\mathbf{A}$ and $\mathbf{B}$ is diagonal; the operator products $\mathbf{AB}$ and $\mathbf{BA}$ are then also represented in that scheme by matrices which are diagonal and equal. It follows that the matrix form of **AB** − **BA** vanishes, in any scheme. We conclude, then, from Eq. 13b that the position of a particle and its total energy cannot be compatible; if they were compatible, the velocity operators $\mathbf{v}_x$, $\mathbf{v}_y$, and $\mathbf{v}_z$ would vanish and the mean velocity would vanish for all states of the particle. As it is, Eq. 13b constitutes a quantum mechanical law which relates the operators corresponding to the energy, position, and velocity of a particle. The law applies generally to the operators corresponding to any variable Q of an atomic system, to its time derivative $\dot{Q} = dQ/dt$ and to the total energy of the system. It is stated by the equation

$$\dot{\mathbf{Q}} = \frac{i}{\hbar}\,\{\mathbf{EQ} - \mathbf{QE}\}, \tag{14}$$

which follows from $\langle \dot{Q} \rangle = d\langle Q \rangle/dt$ just as (13b) follows from $\langle v_x \rangle = d\langle x \rangle/dt$.

Uncertainty relations. As discussed in Chapter 11, the quantum mechanical uncertainty relations establish lower limits to the products of the mean square deviations of certain pairs of incompatible variables. An uncertainty relation can be formulated for an arbitrary pair of variables F and G in terms of the commutator of their operators, **FG** − **GF**, which vanishes for an arbitrary state only if the variables are compatible. The mean value of a variable F of an atomic system in an arbitrary state is expressed, in the notation of operators and state representatives, by

$$\langle F \rangle_a = \psi_a{}^+\mathbf{F}\psi_a \tag{15}$$

where $\psi_a{}^+$ indicates the set of probability amplitudes reciprocal to the set indicated by ψ_a. The mean square deviations of F and G are, then,

$$\Delta F^2 = \langle [F - \langle F \rangle_a]^2 \rangle_a = \psi_a{}^+[\mathbf{F} - \langle F \rangle_a]^2\psi_a, \tag{16a}$$

$$\Delta G^2 = \langle [G - \langle G \rangle_a]^2 \rangle_a = \psi_a{}^+[\mathbf{G} - \langle G \rangle_a]^2\psi_a \tag{16b}$$

The product of mean square deviations, whether in quantum mechanics or in macroscopic statistics, fulfills an inequality which in our case takes the form [2]

$$\Delta F^2 \Delta G^2 = (\psi_a{}^+[\mathbf{F} - \langle F \rangle_a]^2\psi_a)(\psi_a{}^+[\mathbf{G} - \langle G \rangle_a]^2\psi_a)$$

$$\geq |\psi_a{}^+[\mathbf{F} - \langle F \rangle_a][\mathbf{G} - \langle G \rangle_a]\psi_a|^2. \tag{17}$$

The characteristic property of quantum mechanical statistics lies in the fact that $\psi_a{}^+\mathbf{FG}\psi_a$ is not real, unless the variables F and G are compatible. One verifies that $\psi_a{}^+\mathbf{GF}\psi_a$ is the complex conjugate of $\psi_a{}^+\mathbf{FG}\psi_a$ by ex-

---

[2] Equation 17 is a generalization of Eq. 16, page 160, just as (16a) and (16b) are analogous to Eqs. 13 and 15 on that page.

pressing the operators in matrix form and utilizing the fact that the matrices are hermitian (Eq. 5). Therefore, $\psi_a{}^+\mathsf{GF}\psi_a$ does not represent the mean value of a physical quantity; it is a combination of two real quantities (its real and imaginary parts), which are physically meaningful. These parts are separated utilizing the identity $\mathsf{FG} = \frac{1}{2}(\mathsf{FG} + \mathsf{GF}) - i\frac{1}{2}i(\mathsf{FG} - \mathsf{GF})$, which yields

$$\psi_a{}^+[\mathsf{F} - \langle F\rangle_a][\mathsf{G} - \langle G\rangle_a]\psi_a$$
$$= \{\psi_a{}^+[\tfrac{1}{2}(\mathsf{FG} + \mathsf{GF}) - \langle F\rangle_a\langle G\rangle_a]\psi_a\} - i\{\psi_a{}^+\tfrac{1}{2}i(\mathsf{FG} - \mathsf{GF})\psi_a\}.$$

$$(18)$$

Here each of the separate expressions in the braces is real, as one verifies again expressing the operators in matrix form and utilizing the property (5) of the matrices. Equation 17 gives, then,

$$\Delta F^2\,\Delta G^2 \geq \{\psi_a{}^+[\tfrac{1}{2}(\mathsf{FG} + \mathsf{GF}) - \langle F\rangle_a\langle G\rangle_a]\psi_a\}^2 + \tfrac{1}{4}\{\psi_a{}^+i(\mathsf{FG} - \mathsf{GF})\psi_a\}^2.$$

$$(19)$$

Equation 21, page 161 constitutes a special case of this general formula. The first term on the right of (19) is analogous to the squared mean product of deviations $(\Delta xy)^2$ in the formula of macroscopic statistics (16), page 358. The second term represents the additional uncertainty due to the quantum mechanical effect of incompatibility. This term vanishes for an arbitrary state of the system only when the variables F and G are compatible and the commutator $\mathsf{FG} - \mathsf{GF}$ vanishes. In general, the value of the second term depends on the state of the system. However, there are pairs of incompatible variables, namely, those that are called "complementary," for which the commutator $\mathsf{FG} - \mathsf{GF}$ has a fixed value, independent of the state a of the system; there is then a lower limit to the possible values of $\Delta F^2\Delta G^2$. The position coordinates and the momentum components of a particle constitute typical pairs of complementary variables as discussed in Chapter 11 and further illustrated below.

Complementarity of position and momentum. The commutator equation 13b, or rather its more general form (14), constitutes a basic law, whose further implications are brought out by considering it together with the macroscopic relationships between energy, position, and velocity. Thereby one obtains a commutator equation which involves the operators of only two variables, such as the position and the momentum of a particle, and thus determines completely the relationships among their eigenstates.

Because the total energy of a particle is the sum of its kinetic and potential energies, and because the potential energy is compatible with the particle position, so that $\mathbf{Vx} - \mathbf{xV} = 0$, the commutator in Eq. 13b reduces to the commutator of $\mathbf{K}$ and $\mathbf{x}$.

$$\mathbf{Ex} - \mathbf{xE} = (\mathbf{Kx} - \mathbf{xK}) + (\mathbf{Vx} - \mathbf{xV}) = \mathbf{Kx} - \mathbf{xK}. \qquad (20)$$

Moreover, the kinetic energy is a function of the momentum or of the velocity components, so that the operator $\mathbf{K}$ may be expressed as $\frac{1}{2}m(\mathbf{v}_x{}^2 + \mathbf{v}_y{}^2 + \mathbf{v}_z{}^2)$, and (13$b$) becomes

$$\mathbf{v}_x = \frac{i}{\hbar}\,\tfrac{1}{2}m\{\mathbf{v}_x{}^2\mathbf{x} - \mathbf{xv}_x{}^2 + \mathbf{v}_y{}^2\mathbf{x} - \mathbf{xv}_y{}^2 + \mathbf{v}_z{}^2\mathbf{x} - \mathbf{xv}_z{}^2\}. \qquad (21)$$

Finally, the commutators of the squared velocity components on the right side of this equation may be reduced to the commutators of the components themselves by means of the identity $\mathbf{A}^2\mathbf{B} - \mathbf{BA}^2 = \mathbf{A}(\mathbf{AB} - \mathbf{BA}) + (\mathbf{AB} - \mathbf{BA})\mathbf{A}$, to yield

$$\mathbf{v}_x = \frac{i}{\hbar}\,\tfrac{1}{2}m\{\mathbf{v}_x(\mathbf{v}_x\mathbf{x} - \mathbf{xv}_x) + (\mathbf{v}_x\mathbf{x} - \mathbf{xv}_x)\mathbf{v}_x + \mathbf{v}_y(\mathbf{v}_y\mathbf{x} - \mathbf{xv}_y)$$
$$+ (\mathbf{v}_y\mathbf{x} - \mathbf{xv}_y)\mathbf{v}_y + \mathbf{v}_z(\mathbf{v}_z\mathbf{x} - \mathbf{xv}_z) + (\mathbf{v}_z\mathbf{x} - \mathbf{xv}_z)\mathbf{v}_z\}. \qquad (22)$$

This equation is fulfilled provided

$$\mathbf{v}_y\mathbf{x} - \mathbf{xv}_y = 0, \qquad \mathbf{v}_z\mathbf{x} - \mathbf{xv}_z = 0 \qquad (23)$$

and

$$\frac{i}{\hbar}\,m(\mathbf{v}_x\mathbf{x} - \mathbf{xv}_x) = \frac{i}{\hbar}\,(\mathbf{p}_x\mathbf{x} - \mathbf{xp}_x) = 1. \qquad (24a)$$

We have here typical examples of commutators which are equal to a constant rather than to another operator. (Actually a constant, such as $\hbar$, may be regarded as the operator corresponding to a physical variable whose eigenvalues are all equal to the constant and of which any state is an eigenstate.) It follows from Eq. 24a that when the uncertainty relation for the variables x and p_x is expressed in the form (19), the term $\frac{1}{4}[\psi_a{}^{+}i(\mathbf{p}_x\mathbf{x} - \mathbf{xp}_x)\psi_a]^2$ equals $\frac{1}{4}\hbar^2$ whatever be the state a, in agreement with Eq. 21, page 161.

Equations analogous to (24a) are found, of course, for the y and z components of the position, velocity, and momentum vectors, namely,

$$\frac{i}{\hbar}\,m(\mathbf{v}_y\mathbf{y} - \mathbf{yv}_y) = \frac{i}{\hbar}\,(\mathbf{p}_y\mathbf{y} - \mathbf{yp}_y) = 1, \qquad (24b)$$

$$\frac{i}{\hbar}\,m(\mathbf{v}_z\mathbf{z} - \mathbf{zv}_z) = \frac{i}{\hbar}\,(\mathbf{p}_z\mathbf{z} - \mathbf{zp}_z) = 1. \qquad (24c)$$

These equations are special cases of a general result that follows from Eq. 14. One proceeds in analogy with Eqs. 20 to 24, that is, considering the dependence of the total energy E of the system upon the variable $\dot{Q}$. Under rather broad assumptions [3] the relevant feature of this dependence is the derivative $\partial E/\partial \dot{Q}$, which is called the "momentum conjugate to Q," and is usually indicated by P.[4] One can show that (14) is fulfilled provided

$$\frac{i}{\hbar}(\mathbf{PQ} - \mathbf{QP}) = 1. \tag{25}$$

Equation 24a, $(i/\hbar)(\mathbf{p}_x\mathbf{x} - \mathbf{x}\mathbf{p}_x) = 1$, suffices to determine the mathematical form of the operators $\mathbf{x}$ and $\mathbf{p}_x$, and thereby to calculate the probability amplitudes $(x|p_x)$. In the scheme of eigenstates of the particle position, Eq. 24a takes the form

$$\frac{i}{\hbar}[(\mathbf{r}'|p_x|\mathbf{r})x - x'(\mathbf{r}'|p_x|\mathbf{r})] = \delta_{\mathbf{r}'\mathbf{r}}, \tag{26}$$

where the symbol $\delta_{\mathbf{r}'\mathbf{r}}$, defined by Eq. 2′, constitutes the matrix representation of an operator equal to 1. The matrix elements $(\mathbf{r}'|p_x|\mathbf{r})$ must vanish whenever $x' \neq x$, because the right side of (26) vanishes. They must, conversely, be infinite at $\mathbf{r}' = \mathbf{r}$; otherwise the left side would vanish since $x' = x$, whereas the right side does not vanish. A function of $\mathbf{r}$ and $\mathbf{r}'$ with this singular behavior exists and is completely determined by Eq. 26; it is called the "Dirac δ′ function." Instead of defining this function completely one may define only the result of calculating a linear combination of probability amplitudes $(\mathbf{r}|a)$ whose coefficients are the matrix elements $(\mathbf{r}'|p_x|\mathbf{r})$. One can prove that the value of this linear combination is obtained by calculating the derivative $\partial(\mathbf{r}|a)/\partial x$ as indicated by the equation

$$\Sigma_{\mathbf{r}}(\mathbf{r}'|p_x|\mathbf{r})(\mathbf{r}|a) = \frac{\hbar}{i}\Sigma_{\mathbf{r}}\,\delta_{\mathbf{r}'\mathbf{r}}\frac{\partial(\mathbf{r}|a)}{\partial x} = \frac{\hbar}{i}\frac{\partial(\mathbf{r}'|a)}{\partial x'}. \tag{27}$$

This indirect definition of the matrix elements $(\mathbf{r}'|p_x|\mathbf{r})$ is seen to comply with the requirements of Eq. 26 by verifying that

$$\frac{i}{\hbar}\Sigma_{\mathbf{r}}[(\mathbf{r}'|p_x|\mathbf{r})x - x'(\mathbf{r}'|p_x|\mathbf{r})]\,(\mathbf{r}|a)$$

$$= \Sigma_{\mathbf{r}}\,\delta_{\mathbf{r}'\mathbf{r}}\frac{\partial[(\mathbf{r}|a)x]}{\partial x} - x'\Sigma_{\mathbf{r}}\,\delta_{\mathbf{r}'\mathbf{r}}\frac{\partial(\mathbf{r}|a)}{\partial x}$$

$$= \Sigma_{\mathbf{r}}\,\delta_{\mathbf{r}'\mathbf{r}}\left[\frac{\partial(\mathbf{r}|a)}{\partial x}x + (\mathbf{r}|a)\right] - \Sigma_{\mathbf{r}}\,\delta_{\mathbf{r}'\mathbf{r}}\,x\frac{\partial(\mathbf{r}|a)}{\partial x}$$

$$= \Sigma_{\mathbf{r}}\,\delta_{\mathbf{r}'\mathbf{r}}\,(\mathbf{r}|a). \tag{28}$$

---

[3] The dependence must be representable by a series of powers of $\dot{Q}$.

[4] The momentum component p_x is equal to $\partial E/\partial v_x = \partial(\tfrac{1}{2}mv_x{}^2)/\partial v_x = mv_x$.

The content of Eq. 27 can be expressed by stating that the result of transforming the probability amplitude $(\mathbf{r}\,|\,a)$ by the operator $\mathbf{p}_x$ equals the derivative $\partial(\mathbf{r}\,|\,a)/\partial x$ multiplied by $\hbar/i$. Since calculating the derivative of a function constitutes a linear transformation, this transformation can be regarded as an operator and identified by the symbol $\partial/\partial x$. Accordingly, the product of $\hbar/i$ and of $\partial/\partial x$ constitutes a representation of the operator $\mathbf{p}_x$ in the scheme of position eigenstates, and one writes

$$\mathbf{p}_x = \frac{\hbar}{i}\frac{\partial}{\partial x}. \tag{29}$$

In the same scheme, the operator $\mathbf{x}$ is equivalent to the ordinary algebraic variable x. Indeed, $\mathbf{p}_x = (\hbar/i)\,\partial/\partial x$ and $\mathbf{x} = x$ fulfill the operator equation $(i/\hbar)(\mathbf{p}_x\mathbf{x} - \mathbf{x}\mathbf{p}_x) = 1$.

The equation analogous to (10b) which identifies the eigenstates of the momentum component p_x is

$$\mathbf{p}_x\psi_{p_x} = \psi_{p_x}p_x. \tag{30}$$

In the scheme of the position coordinate x one can utilize the form (29) of $\mathbf{p}_x$ and Eq. 30 takes the form

$$\frac{\hbar}{i}\frac{\partial\psi_{p_x}(x)}{\partial x} = \psi_{p_x}(x)p_x. \tag{31}$$

This equation coincides with Eq. 11, on page 145, and has the solution

$$\psi_{p_x}(x) = (x\,|\,p_x) = e^{i(p_x/\hbar)x}. \tag{32a}$$

Similarly one finds that

$$(y\,|\,p_y) = e^{i(p_y/\hbar)y}, \quad (z\,|\,p_z) = e^{i(p_z/\hbar)z}, \tag{32b}$$

that is,

$$(\mathbf{r}\,|\,\mathbf{p}) = (x\,|\,p_x)(y\,|\,p_y)(z\,|\,p_z) = e^{i(\mathbf{p}/\hbar)\cdot\mathbf{r}}. \tag{32c}$$

This is the fundamental expression of the momentum eigenfunctions which is derived in Chapter 10 from the analysis of diffraction experiments. It follows, from the independent determination of (32c) obtained here, that the diffraction experiments need not have been regarded as independent experimental evidence on the properties of atomic particles; on the contrary, their results can be predicted theoretically on the basis of (32c), which is based, in turn, on evidence presented ahead of the diffraction experiments. All the results developed in Chapters 11 and 12 on complementarity, on the uncertainty relations, and on the Schroedinger equation, can be obtained as applications of the formulas of this Appendix. In particular, Eq. 10 takes the form of the Schroedinger equation

(2), page 170, if one sets $\mathbf{p}^2 = \mathbf{p}_x{}^2 + \mathbf{p}_y{}^2 + \mathbf{p}_z{}^2 = (\hbar|i)^2[(\partial|\partial x)^2 + (\partial|\partial y)^2 + (\partial|\partial z)^2]$ in accordance with (29) and $\psi_E = \psi_E(\mathbf{r}) = (\mathbf{r}|E)$.

Application. The energy levels of radiation. We consider the example of the electromagnetic field in a rectangular cavity resonator with perfectly reflecting walls, for the purpose of determining its energy eigenvalues. Radiation in free space can be treated as a limiting case of the radiation enclosed in a very large cavity.

Call A, B, and C the dimensions of the cavity, and take coordinate axes directed along three of its edges with the origin at one vertex. The multiple reflection on the cavity walls restricts the possible distributions of the electric and magnetic field to certain "modes" with specified orientations of the fields $\mathbf{E}$ and $\mathbf{H}$ and specified numbers of interference fringes.[5] One possible distribution, with the electric field parallel to the z edge of the cavity and with m fringes in the x direction and n fringes in the y direction is

$$E_x = 0, \qquad E_y = 0, \qquad E_z = -\frac{1}{c} \dot{Q}(t) \sin\left(m\pi \frac{x}{A}\right) \sin\left(n\pi \frac{y}{B}\right),$$

$$H_x = \frac{n\pi}{B} Q(t) \sin\left(m\pi \frac{x}{A}\right) \cos\left(n\pi \frac{y}{B}\right),$$

$$H_y = -\frac{m\pi}{A} Q(t) \cos\left(m\pi \frac{x}{A}\right) \sin\left(n\pi \frac{y}{B}\right), \qquad H_z = 0. \quad (33)$$

In this formula, c is the light velocity and Q is a variable that indicates the amplitude and phase of the radiation: The strength of the magnetic field at any point is proportional to Q, the strength of the electric field to the time derivative $\dot{Q}(t) = dQ/dt$. The macroscopic Maxwell equations require that $Q(t)$ oscillate sinusoidally with the frequency

$$\nu = \frac{1}{2} c \sqrt{\frac{m^2}{A^2} + \frac{n^2}{B^2}}. \quad (34)$$

According to quantum mechanics, the Maxwell equations are fulfilled only by the mean values $\langle\mathbf{E}\rangle$ and $\langle\mathbf{H}\rangle$. The mean values $\langle Q\rangle$ and $\langle\dot{Q}\rangle$ must fulfill corresponding equations, and in particular $\langle\dot{Q}\rangle$ must equal $d\langle Q\rangle/dt$. Because of this requirement and because the radiation energy depends on both the magnetic and the electric fields, which are proportional to Q and $\dot{Q}$, respectively, the field strengths H and E are incompati-

---

[5] See, for example, P. Morse and H. Feshbach, *Methods of Theoretical Physics*, McGraw-Hill, New York, 1953, Sect. 13.3.

ble variables. Their incompatibility is characterized by the application of Eq. 25. To define the momentum conjugate to Q, one must express the energy of the radiation in the resonator as a function of Q and $\dot{Q}$. The energy stored per unit volume of space in the form of electric or magnetic fields equals the squared field strength divided by 8π. By taking this value at each point of the cavity for each of the fields as given by (33) and integrating over the volume of the cavity, one finds for the radiation energy the expression

$$E = \frac{1}{2}\frac{ABC}{16\pi c^2}\dot{Q}^2 + \frac{1}{2}\frac{ABC}{16\pi}\pi^2\left(\frac{m^2}{A^2} + \frac{n^2}{B^2}\right)Q^2, \tag{35}$$

where ABC represents the cavity volume. Since the energy is proportional to the squared time derivative $\dot{Q}$, the momentum P is proportional to $\dot{Q}$,

$$P = \frac{\partial E}{\partial \dot{Q}} = \frac{ABC}{16\pi c^2}\dot{Q}, \tag{36}$$

just as the momentum of a particle is proportional to its velocity. The operator **P** has the differential form $(\hbar/i)d/dQ$ analogous to (29). The electric and magnetic fields being proportional, respectively, to $\dot{Q}$ (that is, to P) and to Q are complementary variables, related to one another by quantum mechanical uncertainty relations analogous to those that apply to the velocity (or momentum) and the position of a particle.

It also follows that the energy eigenvalues of the radiation are determined by solving a Schroedinger equation that has the same mathematical form as the equation for the energy eigenvalues of a particle. The variable Q of the electromagnetic field corresponds to the position coordinate of a particle, the factor $(ABC/16\pi c^2)$ which multiplies $\frac{1}{2}\dot{Q}^2$ in (35) is analogous to the particle mass, and the term $\frac{1}{2}(ABC\pi^2/16\pi)$ $(m^2/A^2 + n^2/B^2)Q^2$ to a potential energy. Notice that a potential energy proportional to the squared position coordinate corresponds to an elastic force under whose influence a particle performs harmonic oscillations. The Schroedinger equation which one obtains in the radiation problem is analogous to Eqs. (9), page 183, for the one-dimensional motion of a particle and is

$$-\frac{\hbar^2}{2(ABC/16\pi c^2)}\frac{d^2(Q\,|\,E)}{dQ^2} + \frac{1}{2}\frac{ABC}{16\pi}\pi^2\left(\frac{m^2}{A^2} + \frac{n^2}{B^2}\right)Q^2(Q\,|\,E) = (Q\,|\,E)E. \tag{37a}$$

One simplifies this equation by replacing Q and E with the dimensionless variables $\xi = (ABC/16c)^{1/2}(m^2/A^2 + n^2/B^2)^{1/4}Q/\hbar^{1/2}$,

$\epsilon = 2E/\hbar\pi c(m^2/A^2 + n^2/B^2)^{1/2} = 2E/h\nu$, to obtain

$$-\frac{d^2(\xi|E)}{d\xi^2} + \xi^2(\xi|E) = (\xi|E)\epsilon. \tag{37b}$$

Since this equation corresponds to the motion of a particle fully confined within a "parabolic potential well," a qualitative discussion by the method of Chapter 13 shows that it has an infinite sequence of eigenfunctions $(\xi|E_N)$, where $N = 0, 1, 2 \cdots$, indicates the number of dark interference fringes in the probability distribution $|(\xi|E_N)|^2$. It is verified that the eigenvalues of (37b) are the odd numbers

$$\epsilon_N = 2N + 1, \tag{38a}$$

to which correspond the eigenvalues of the radiation energy

$$E_N = \tfrac{1}{2}h\nu\epsilon_N = (N + \tfrac{1}{2})h\nu. \tag{38b}$$

Successive eigenvalues of this sequence are separated by the constant interval $h\nu$, in agreement with the experimental evidence represented by Eq. 1, page 39. The eigenfunctions of (37b) have the form

$$(\xi|E_N) = \frac{1}{\sqrt{2^N N! \pi^{1/2}}} e^{-1/2\xi^2} H_N(\xi), \tag{39}$$

where

$$H_N(\xi) = \Sigma_{n=0}^{n \leq 1/2N} \frac{(-1)^n N!}{n!(N - 2n)!} (2\xi)^{N-2n} \tag{39'}$$

is called the "Hermite polynomial" of degree N.

By means of these results one can verify that the mean values of the electric and magnetic fields at each point of the cavity vary in the course of time in accordance with the macroscopic law. The magnetic field components are proportional to the variable Q, according to (33), and Q is proportional to ξ. Therefore, for radiation of the type (33) in an arbitrary state $a(t)$, the mean value of $\mathbf{H}$ at each point of the cavity is proportional to

$\langle \xi \rangle = \Sigma_\xi(a(t)|\xi)\xi(\xi|a(t))$

$\quad = \Sigma_N\Sigma_{N'}(a(t)|E_N)[\Sigma_\xi(E_N|\xi)\xi(\xi|E_{N'})](E_{N'}|a(t))$

$\quad = \Sigma_N\Sigma_{N'}(a(0)|E_N)e^{i(E_N/\hbar)t}(E_N|\xi|E_{N'})e^{-i(E_{N'}/\hbar)t}(E_{N'}|a(0))$

$\quad = \Sigma_N(E_N|\xi|E_N)(E_N|a(0))^2$

$\quad + 2\Sigma_{N=0}^{\infty}\Sigma_{N'=0}^{N-1}(a(0)|E_N)(E_N|\xi|E_{N'})(E_{N'}|a(0))\cos\dfrac{E_N - E_{N'}}{\hbar} t,$

$$\tag{40}$$

where the probability amplitudes $(E_N | a(0))$ have been assumed to be real for simplicity. This general formula represents $\langle \xi \rangle$ as the sum of a constant term and of sinusoidal terms oscillating with frequencies $(E_N - E_{N'})/h = (N - N')\nu$, which are multiples of the macroscopic frequency ν given by (34). In fact, the only non-vanishing terms on the right of (40) are those that oscillate with frequency ν; no constant term and no multiples of ν occur because the values of the matrix elements are found to be

$$
(E_{N'} | \xi | E_N) = \left[\begin{array}{ll} \sqrt{\tfrac{1}{2}N'} & \text{for } N' = N + 1 \\ \sqrt{\tfrac{1}{2}N} & \text{for } N' = N - 1 \\ 0 & \text{otherwise.} \end{array} \right. \tag{41}
$$

One also finds, in analogy with (13),

$$
(E_{N'} | \dot{\xi} | E_N)
$$
$$
= i \frac{(E_{N'} - E_N)}{\hbar} (E_{N'} | \xi | E_N) = \left[\begin{array}{ll} 2\pi i\nu \sqrt{\tfrac{1}{2}N'} & \text{for } N' = N + 1 \\ - 2\pi i\nu \sqrt{\tfrac{1}{2}N} & \text{for } N' = N - 1 \\ 0 & \text{otherwise,} \end{array} \right.
$$

so that the mean value of the electric field, being proportional to $\langle \dot{\xi} \rangle$, also oscillates sinusoidally with frequency ν. Notice, in particular, that the mean values $\langle \mathbf{E} \rangle$ and $\langle \mathbf{H} \rangle$ vanish when the radiation is in a stationary state.

Electron oscillations
in non-stationary states
of the hydrogen atom

Atoms absorb or emit radiation in transitions between stationary states, that is, while they are in non-stationary states. In a non-stationary state the probability distribution of an electron's position varies in the course of time. The variation may be described, according to Chapter 9, as a combination of sinusoidal oscillations which constitute the alternating currents responsible for the emission and absorption of electromagnetic radiation. Each sinusoidal oscillation derives from the interference of two stationary states. The effect of interference can be studied in detail for the H atom utilizing the data of Chapter 14 on the stationary states and on their wave functions. The main results of this study are applicable to many-electron atoms because the emission and absorption of light is generally due to a single electron moving under conditions similar to those that prevail in the H atom (Chapter 18).[1]

Intraatomic currents yield only very weak emission or absorption of radiation if they flow in opposite directions in different parts of the same

---

[1] Analysis of the interference between stationary states of an undisturbed atom provides also information on the stationary states of an atom whose electron distribution is distorted by an electric field from external sources (Sect. 22.3).

atom so that their effects cancel out. A strong net effect results when the mean position of the electron oscillates; conversely, there is no strong effect when the mean position remains centered at the nucleus despite the oscillation of other statistical parameters of the electron distribution such as the mean square distance from the nucleus. It is, therefore, of interest to determine which pairs of stationary states yield, upon interference, an oscillating, off-center, mean position of the electron. Transitions between the states of such a pair are favored by the ready emission or absorption of light. It will be seen that the quantum numbers l, m, l', and m' of two states yielding an off-center mean position fulfill certain equations called "selection rules," namely:

$$l - l' = \pm 1 \tag{1}$$

and

$$m - m' = 0, 1, \text{ or } -1. \tag{2}$$

Consider a non-stationary state $a(t)$ of a H atom which is a combination of two stationary states with quantum numbers (n,l,m) and (n',l',m') belonging to the set described in Sect. 14.3. (The extension to a combination of many states is straightforward.) According to Sect. 14.3 and to Eq. 1, page 122, the wave function of this state is represented by

$$(r,\theta,\phi \,|\, a(t)) = (r,\theta,\phi \,|\, n,l,m)(n,l,m \,|\, a(t)) + (r,\theta,\phi \,|\, n',l',m')(n',l',m' \,|\, a(t))$$

$$= (r \,|\, n,l)(\theta \,|\, l,m)(\phi \,|\, m)e^{-iE_n t/\hbar}(n,l,m \,|\, a(0))$$

$$+ (r \,|\, n',l')(\theta \,|\, l',m')(\phi \,|\, m')e^{-iE_{n'} t/\hbar}(n',l',m' \,|\, a(0)). \tag{3}$$

One may assume without loss of generality that the phase difference of the probability amplitudes $(n,l,m \,|\, a(0))$ and $(n',l',m' \,|\, a(0))$ vanishes and that the probability amplitudes themselves are real. Considering also that $(\phi \,|\, m) = e^{im\phi}/\sqrt{2\pi}$ and that $(r \,|\, n,l)$ and $(\theta \,|\, l,m)$ are real, the probability distribution of the electron position may be expressed in the form of Eq. 7, page 127,

$$|\, (r,\theta,\phi \,|\, a(t)) \,|^2 = \frac{1}{2\pi} \Big\{ (r \,|\, n,l)^2 (\theta \,|\, l,m)^2 (n,l,m \,|\, a(0))^2$$

$$+ (r \,|\, n',l')^2 (\theta \,|\, l',m')^2 (n',l',m' \,|\, a(0))^2$$

$$+ 2(r \,|\, n,l)(r \,|\, n',l')(\theta \,|\, n,l)(\theta \,|\, n',l')$$

$$\times \cos\Big[\frac{E_{n'} - E_n}{\hbar} t - (m' - m)\phi\Big](n,l,m \,|\, a(0))(n',l',m' \,|\, a(0)) \Big\}. \tag{4}$$

The first two terms represent together a weighted mean of the stationary probability distributions of the two states (n,l,m) and (n',l',m'), with weights $(n,l,m \,|\, a(0))^2$ and $(n',l',m' \,|\, a(0))^2$. The last term represents the effect of interference between the two states, namely, a departure from the stationary mean probability of electron position, and oscillates sinusoidally with frequency $(E_{n'} - E_n)/h$. If the state a were a combination of N stationary states instead of two, the probability distribution (4) would include the mean of N stationary distributions and a number of oscillatory departures from the mean, one for each pair of states in the combination.

At each instant of time, for example, at $t = 0$, the departure of the probability distribution (4) from its stationary mean value is proportional to $(r\,|\,n,l)(r\,|\,n',l')(\theta\,|\,l,m)(\theta\,|\,l',m')$ and can be mapped utilizing the explicit form of $(r\,|\,n,l)$, $(\theta\,|\,l,m)$, $(r\,|\,n',l')$, and $(\theta\,|\,l',m')$, much as the stationary distributions are mapped in the figures of Chapter 14. Whereas the stationary probability is positive at all places and only its magnitude varies from point to point, the departures from the stationary distribution are positive at some point and negative at other points. Figure IX.1 shows sample maps of the regions of positive and negative departure for various pairs of states (n,l,m) and (n',l',m'). The variations of probability distribution in the course of time correspond to a net electron flow, defined as on page 181, ff., which oscillates back and forth between the regions marked with different hatchings.

When the quantum numbers m and m' are equal, the probability $|(r,\theta,\phi\,|\,a(t))|^2$ has the same distribution over all meridian planes through the z axis with different coordinates ϕ and oscillates in step on all these planes. When $m \neq m'$, the departures from the stationary mean differ in phase on different meridian planes, as shown in the figure by the fact that the equatorial sections are not uniform about their center. Instead of considering the off-phase oscillations in the various meridian planes, one may visualize the probability distribution (4) at each time instant t, for $m \neq m'$, as obtained from the distribution at $t = 0$ by rotation about the z axis at the uniform rate of $(E_{n'} - E_n)/h$ turns per second.

Let us first consider the necessary conditions for the mean electron position to lie off the center of the atom in the direction of the z axis of coordinates. The conditions are two: (a) that there is a mean departure upwards or downwards from the $z = 0$ (equatorial) line in the distribution pattern on the meridian xz-plane; and (b) that this departure does not average out when the mean is taken over all meridian planes (that is, over the coordinate ϕ). Figure IX.1 and Eq. 4 show that condition (b) is violated whenever the quantum numbers m and m' are different, that is, that condition (b) is expressed by the selection rule

$$m - m' = 0. \tag{5}$$

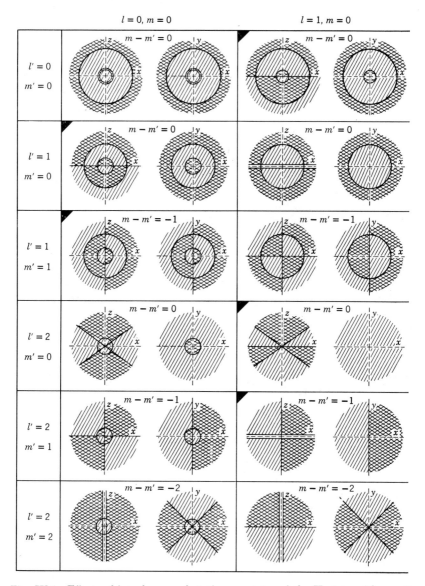

Fig. IX.1 Effects of interference of stationary states of the H atom with $n = 2$, $n' = 3$. The diagrams represent cross-sectional maps of the departures of electron distribution from its stationary components, for different pairs of interfering states $(n,l,m)(n',l',m')$. The cross-hatched areas represent positive departures in Eq. 4, at

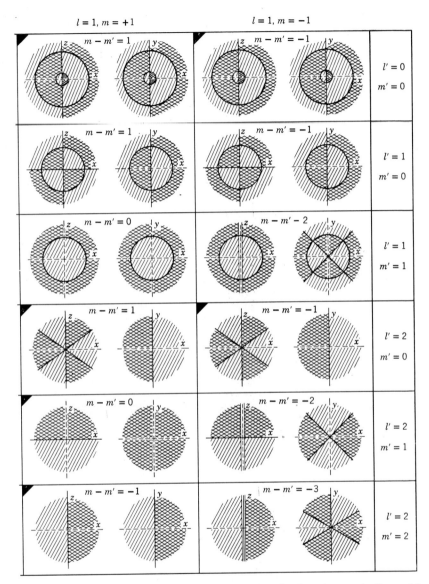

$t = 0$, the hatched areas negative departures. When the departures actually vanish on the xy plane, the xy map represents a cross section just above this plane. Interference patterns with an off-center electron distribution are marked with a black corner.

Condition (a) is certainly violated whenever the upper and lower halves of the xz pattern in Fig. IX.1 are identical, that is, whenever $(l - m) - (l' - m')$ is even, or, in view of (5), when $l - l'$ is even. To obtain a more complete formulation of condition (a), one must actually calculate the mean value of $z = r \cos\theta$ over the distributions shown schematically in Fig. IX.1, that is, the value of

$$\langle z \rangle = [\Sigma_r \, r(r \,|\, n,l)(r \,|\, n',l')] \, [\Sigma_\theta \, \cos\theta(\theta \,|\, l,m)(\theta \,|\, l',m)]. \tag{6}$$

The first factor on the right of this formula is generally different from zero, but the second factor is found to vanish unless Eq. 1 is satisfied. Equations 1 and 5 express the selection rule for a displacement of the mean electron position in the direction of the z axis.

Consider now the necessary conditions for the mean position of the electron to lie off the center of the atom in a direction perpendicular to the z axis. These conditions are also two: (a) that there is a mean departure crosswise, along the $z = 0$ line, in the distribution pattern on a meridian plane; and (b) that the effect of this departure does not average out when all meridian planes are considered. If $m - m'$ is even, the pattern on any meridian plane is symmetric with respect to the z axis and condition (a) is violated. The patterns in the xy-plane in Fig. IX.1 show that condition (b) is violated whenever m and m' differ by two or more. Therefore the quantum numbers m and m' must obey the condition

$$m - m' = \pm 1. \tag{7}$$

Condition (a) is certainly violated whenever the upper and lower halves of the pattern of Fig. IX.1 show departures of equal magnitude and opposite sign, that is, whenever $(l - m) - (l' - m')$ is odd, or, in view of (7), when $l - l'$ is even. To obtain a more complete formulation of condition (a), one must actually calculate the mean value of $r \sin\theta$ over the distributions shown schematically in Fig. IX.1, that is, the value of

$$\langle r \sin\theta \rangle = [\Sigma_r \, r(r \,|\, n,l)(r \,|\, n',l')] \, [\Sigma_\theta \, \sin\theta(\theta \,|\, l,m)(\theta \,|\, l',m')]. \tag{8}$$

The first factor on the right side of this formula is the same as in (6) and is generally different from zero, and the second factor vanishes, like the corresponding factor of (6), unless (1) is fulfilled. Therefore, Equations 1 and 7 express the selection rule for a displacement of the mean electron position in a direction perpendicular to the z axis. Since the conditions (5) and (7) are mutually exclusive, a displacement oblique to the z axis, with components parallel and perpendicular to it, occurs only in superpositions of more than two states (n,l,m).

The condition (1), $l - l' = \pm 1$, which applies in all circumstances, is of greatest importance for the analysis of spectra. It is referred to in Chapters 15, 17, and 18, and is illustrated particularly by the diagram of He levels (Fig. 17.3). The conditions (5) and (7) have particular importance for the emission or absorption of light in a magnetic field when the "normal" Zeeman effect obtains (see page 244). Under these circumstances, light emitted in transitions between pairs of states with given l and l' and various values of $m - m'$ has different frequencies. A transition with $m = m'$ radiates with the same intensity distribution and polarization as a linear radio antenna directed along the z axis. A transition with $m - m' = \pm 1$ radiates with the same intensity distribution and polarization as a single charge which rotates about the z axis. According to (4) the direction of rotation is indicated by the sign of the ratio $(E_{n'} - E_n)/(m' - m)$.

Notice finally that the selection rules represent a specification and limitation of the angular momentum gained or lost by an atom when it absorbs or emits radiation. Since the azimuthal quantum number l indicates an eigenvalue $l(l + 1)\hbar^2$ of the squared angular momentum $\mathbf{l}^2$ (page 200), Eq. 1 specifies that absorption or emission of radiation by an atom is accompanied by a variation of $\mathbf{l}^2$ equal to

$$[l(l + 1) - l'(l' + 1)]^2\hbar^2 = (l - l')(l + l' + 1)\hbar^2 = \pm(2l + 1 \pm 1)\hbar^2. \tag{9}$$

The component l_z of the angular momentum along the z axis has the eigenvalues $m\hbar$ specified by the quantum number m. The selection rule (2) specifies that l_z varies by $\pm\hbar$ or remains constant in a transition with ready absorption or emission of radiation. Moreover the change of l_z in the transition relates to the polarization of the radiation. A transition without change of l_z emits only linearly polarized radiation.

···

Resonance

In classical physics, "resonance" indicates a situation where two oscillation frequencies coincide. For example, a pendulum performs forced oscillations at resonance when the driving disturbance oscillates with a frequency equal to the frequency of free oscillation of the pendulum. The oscillation amplitude rises then until it is limited by friction or by its reaction on the driving agent. The forced oscillations impressed by one pendulum on another one under resonance conditions are of particular interest in connection with quantum mechanical analogs.

Consider the pair of identical pendulums shown in Fig. X.1, which are linked by a light spring. If one of the pendulums is initially set into motion, it drives the other one into oscillation through their coupling. Because of the resonance condition, the second pendulum increases its oscillation amplitude until it has absorbed the whole initial energy of the first pendulum, which comes thereby to rest. At this point, the roles of the two pendulums are interchanged and the "second" drives the "first" one. The exchange of oscillation energy from one to the other pendulum and back again is easily demonstrated experimentally and continues indefinitely, except of course for friction or other disturbances.

Mathematically, this phenomenon is described in the following manner. The pair of coupled pendulums has two "normal modes" of steady harmonic oscillation, namely, one in which the two pendulums oscillate "in step" with equal amplitude and never stretch their link, and one in which they oscillate with equal amplitude and opposite phase and stretch their link (the link then pulls them back towards their equilibrium positions). The first of these modes has the same frequency

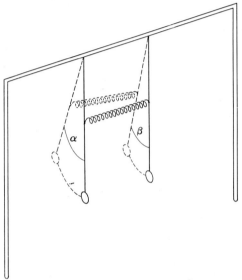

Fig. X.1 Coupled pendulums.

ν_1 as each pendulum would have in the absence of coupling; this frequency is a little lower than the frequency ν_0 of each pendulum when the other one is kept fixed at its equilibrium position and the pull of the link speeds up the oscillations. The second normal mode has a frequency ν_2 higher than ν_0 by an amount equal to $\delta = \nu_0 - \nu_1$, because the link is stretched here by the opposite displacement of both pendulums and thus pulls them twice as strongly as if one were fixed. The displacements from equilibrium, α and β, of the two pendulums are given as functions of time by

$$\alpha = A\ \cos 2\pi\nu_1 t, \qquad \beta = A\ \cos 2\pi\nu_1 t, \tag{1}$$

for one normal mode and by

$$\alpha = A\ \cos 2\pi\nu_2 t, \qquad \beta = -A\ \cos 2\pi\nu_2 t, \tag{2}$$

for the other one, where A indicates the amplitude of oscillation of either pendulum. Each normal mode may be regarded as an oscillatory variation of a single variable of the whole system, namely, in the first case, the sum $\xi = \alpha + \beta$ of the displacements of the two pendulums and in the second case, their difference $\eta = \alpha - \beta$. Therefore Eqs. 1 and 2 may be expressed respectively in the forms

$$\xi = \alpha + \beta = 2A \cos 2\pi\nu_1 t, \qquad \eta = 0 \tag{1'}$$

$$\xi = 0, \qquad \eta = \alpha - \beta = 2A \cos 2\pi\nu_2 t. \tag{2'}$$

If one pendulum starts at rest with a shift A and the other one with no shift, their subsequent motion is a combination of both normal modes, with equal amplitudes, namely,

$$\alpha = A[\tfrac{1}{2} \cos 2\pi\nu_1 t + \tfrac{1}{2} \cos 2\pi\nu_2 t]$$

$$\beta = A[\tfrac{1}{2} \cos 2\pi\nu_1 t - \tfrac{1}{2} \cos 2\pi\nu_2 t] \tag{3}$$

or

$$\xi = A \cos 2\pi\nu_1 t \qquad \eta = A \cos 2\pi\nu_2 t. \tag{3'}$$

The formulas of cosine addition and subtraction change (3) to the form

$$\alpha = A \cos\pi(\nu_2 - \nu_1)t \cos\pi(\nu_1 + \nu_2)t = A \cos 2\pi\delta t \cos 2\pi\nu_0 t$$

$$\beta = A \sin\pi(\nu_2 - \nu_1)t \cos\pi(\nu_1 + \nu_2)t = A \sin 2\pi\delta t \cos 2\pi\nu_0 t. \tag{4}$$

These formulas represent the motion of each pendulum as an oscillation with frequency ν_0 and with an amplitude that varies sinusoidally with frequency $\delta = \nu_0 - \nu_1$.

When the two pendulums differ slightly, for example, if one of them is a little shorter than the other, there is a near-resonance condition. The system of two coupled pendulums has still two normal modes of oscillation, which are, however, not as simple as in the case of exact resonance. If one of the pendulums starts at rest in a displaced position and the other one with no displacement, their subsequent motion is a combination of the two normal modes with slightly different coefficients. The first pendulum still drives the other one into a forced oscillation but not quite to the point of transferring to it all of its energy.

In quantum mechanics the two-pendulum system has characteristics quite similar to those described above. One schematizes usually a pendulum as a "harmonic oscillator," that is, as a particle of atomic size held in the vicinity of an equilibrium position by an elastic force. The elastic coupling of two equal oscillators consists of an additional weak force proportional to the difference between the displacements of the two particles from their respective equilibrium positions. In the absence of coupling, each oscillator has a sequence of stationary states with evenly spaced energy levels of oscillatory motion and with increasing mean square values of the displacement α or β respectively. (The same holds for each oscillator if there is a coupling, but the other oscillator is confined tightly by an additional strong force.) The stationary states of separate oscillators are *not* stationary states of the pair of coupled oscillators. The oscillator pair has an array of stationary states, each identified by a pair of quantum numbers n_ξ and n_η, where n_ξ characterizes the probability distribution of the normal mode variable $\xi = \alpha + \beta$ and n_η characterizes the distribution of $\eta = \alpha - \beta$. That is, the normal mode variables ξ and η may be regarded in quantum mechanics as in classical mechanics as displacement variables of two hypothetical, independent, compound oscillators. In particular, the first excited states $(n_\xi = 1, n_\eta = 0)$ and $(n_\xi = 0, n_\eta = 1)$ have nearly equal energies if the coupling is weak. The first excited state of one separate oscillator, for instance, the state $(n_\alpha = 1, n_\beta = 0)$, can be represented at a given time as a superposition of the first excited stationary states $(n_\xi = 1, n_\eta = 0)$ and $(n_\xi = 0, n_\eta = 1)$ of the coupled pendulums. Such a state is non-stationary because its stationary components have somewhat different energies. It varies slowly in the course of time and coincides alternately now with the first excited state of one separate oscillator and then with the corresponding state of the other oscillator, in analogy to the classical phenomenon represented by Eq. 4.

This relationship between a pair of stationary states with nearly equal energies and their non-stationary combinations is encountered frequently in quantum mechanics and is called a "resonance effect." In the first place, this effect occurs for any pair of identical weakly coupled systems, irrespective of whether they are harmonic oscillators. In the second place, it occurs for any single system with a pair of states that have equal—or nearly equal—energies in first approximation and that combine in higher approximation to yield a pair of actual stationary states, according to the procedure of Chapter 16. Call r and s the two first approximation states of the separate oscillators. Call 1 and 2 the stationary states obtained by combining r and s, and E_1 and E_2 their energy eigenvalues. A non-stationary state $a(t)$ which coincides with r at the time $t = 0$ may be represented as a combination of the stationary states 1 and 2 with probability amplitudes that vary according to the law (1), page 122, namely

$$(1\,|\,a(t)) = e^{-iE_1 t/\hbar}(1\,|\,a(0)) = e^{-iE_1 t/\hbar}(1\,|\,r)$$

$$(2\,|\,a(t)) = e^{-iE_2 t/\hbar}(2\,|\,a(0)) = e^{-iE_2 t/\hbar}(2\,|\,r). \tag{5}$$

In the course of time the magnitudes of these probability amplitudes remain constant, but their phase difference varies at the constant rate of

$(E_1 - E_2)\hbar$ radians per second. The state $a(t)$ returns, therefore, to coincide with r periodically, at time intervals $h/(E_1 - E_2)$, like the oscillation (4) of coupled pendulums returns to be concentrated on the pendulum with coordinate α at time intervals $1/2\delta = 1/(\nu_1 - \nu_2)$. In particular, if the non-stationary states r and s have exactly equal energy mean values E_0,[1] all the probability amplitudes $(r|1)$, $(s|1)$, $(r|2)$, and $(s|2)$ have the same magnitude, namely, $\sqrt{\frac{1}{2}}$, and differ only in phase. The state $a(t)$ coincides then alternately with r and s, as the oscillation (4) concentrates alternately on one and on the other pendulum.

The analogy between the oscillations of a macroscopic pendulum and the oscillations of a quantum mechanical variable is properly appreciated by considering non-stationary rather than stationary states of a quantum mechanical system. Consider, for any quantum system, the non-stationary states which can be represented as superpositions of only two stationary states. The superposition of stationary states with energies E_i and E_k yields a state in which the mean value of any variable, for example, of a particle position, oscillates in the course of time with frequency $(E_i - E_k)/h$ (unless that variable happens to be constant). That is, sinusoidal oscillations of a variable occur in any quantum mechanical system. The proper analog of the alternating oscillation of two coupled pendulums is not a quantum mechanical state of the type $a(t)$ represented by (5), but the superposition of the state $a(t)$ and of a stationary state 0 with energy E_0 quite different from E_1 and E_2. The superposition of the pair of stationary states 0 and 1 and the superposition of 0 and 2 constitute the analogs of the normal modes of coupled pendulums. Since $a(t)$ is itself a superposition of 1 and 2, the superposition of 0 and of $a(t)$ constitutes a further superposition of (0,1) and of (0,2) and is therefore the analog of a combination of normal modes.

The entire discussion of this Appendix is readily extended to the treatment of more than two macroscopic coupled pendulums or more than two quantum mechanical states. A system of n coupled pendulums has n normal modes of oscillation whose frequencies are nearly equal if the pendulums are themselves nearly equal and their coupling is weak. Similarly, a set of n quantum mechanical states with nearly equal first-approximation energies yields in higher approximation n stationary states with nearly equal energy eigenvalues.

---

[1] This value need not coincide with the first-approximation energy eigenvalue of the states r and s, just as the frequency ν_0 of the example of the classical pendulums does not coincide with their frequency in the absence of coupling.

Answers to problems

1.1. $N/A_{Fe} = 6.025 \times 10^{23}/55.84 = 1.079 \times 10^{22}$.

1.2. $6.0 \times 10^{23}/18 \times 4\pi(6.4 \times 10^8)^2 = 6500$.

1.3. (a) Layer contains 0.003 divided by $M_{BF_3} = 4.4 \times 10^{-5}$ moles/cm^2. Thickness equals $4.4 \times 10^{-5} \times$ volume of one mole $= 1.0$ cm. (b) Number of B atoms $= 4.4 \times 10^{-5} \times N = 2.7 \times 10^{19}$. Number of F atoms $= 3 \times 4.4 \times 10^{-5} \times N = 8.1 \times 10^{19}$. (c) $5 \times 2.7 \times 10^{19} + 9 \times 8.1 \times 10^{19} = 8.6 \times 10^{20}$.

2.1. $1.2 \times 4\pi(100)^2 = 1.5 \times 10^5$ particles/sec.

2.2. Current equals number of ionizations per second times charge of ion, e, that is, $1.5 \times 10^5 \times (5.2 \times 10^6/34) \times 1.6 \times 10^{-19} = 3.7 \times 10^{-9}$ amp.

2.3. Cross section equals number of observed events divided by length of track and by number of atoms per cm^3, that is, $60/2.1 \times 10^6 \times 0.057 \times 6.0 \times 10^{23} = 8 \times 10^{-28}$ cm^2.

2.4. B^{10} must be responsible because the neutron absorption is proportional to B^{10} concentration ($2:5 = 18:45$). B^{10} cross section equals fractional absorption divided by B^{10} absolute concentration, that is $0.02/0.18 \times 2.7 \times 10^{19} = 4 \times 10^{-21}$ cm^2.

3.1. (a) $t = 2\mu$, from Eq. 5, with $n/n_0 = 1/8 \times 10^5$, $d = 6.0 \times 10^{23} \times 19.3/197$ cm^{-3}, $\Omega = 0.5/10^2$, $z = 2$, $Z = 79$, $e = 4.8 \times 10^{-10}$ esu, $\frac{1}{2}mv^2 = 5 \times 10^6$ ev $= 8 \times 10^{-6}$ erg, $\sin^4(\theta/2) = \frac{1}{16}$. (b) $\rho = \sqrt{3}b = \sqrt{3}(2 \times 79e^2/mv^2)\sqrt{3} = 3 \times 79 \times 23 \times 10^{-20}/8 \times 10^{-6} = 6.8 \times 10^{-12}$ cm. from Eq. 4 Appendix III and from Eq. 2. (c) The number is reduced in proportion to $(Z_{Ag})^2/(Z_{Au})^2 = (47)^2/(79)^2 = 1/2.8$.

4.1. $K_M = h\nu - h\nu_0 = hc/\lambda - hc/\lambda_0 = 6.6 \times 10^{-27} \times 3 \times 10^{10}(1/1.7 \times 10^{-5} - 1/2.7 \times 10^{-5}) = 4.3 \times 10^{-12}$ erg $= 2.7$ ev.

4.2. Minimum potential difference in volts equals photon energy $h\nu = hc/\lambda$, expressed in ev. (a) 2.0×10^4 volts, (b) 2.0 volts, (c) 2.0×10^{-5} volts.

403

4.3. The collision is elastic since the electron energy is below the threshold of excitation for Hg. Conservation of energy and momentum requires the fraction of energy lost by the electron to be $2m_e/(M_{Hg} + m_e) = 5.5 \times 10^{-6}$.

4.4. The emitting atoms have been raised to their third energy level E_3 from which the red line is emitted but not to their fourth level. Therefore $E_3 - E_1 < K < E_4 - E_1$, that is, $12.1 < K < 12.7$ ev.

4.5. A diagram of levels and transitions, similar to Fig. 4.6, shows that the emissions L2 and B1 follow the collisions C_3 and the emission L1 follows either C_2 or the emission B1. Therefore, $C_3 : C_2 = (N_{L2} + N_{B1}) : (N_{L1} - N_{B1})$; further, $C_n = 0$ for $n > 3$.

4.6. The Rydberg constants for the isotopes are in the ratio of the reduced masses $R_{Li6} : R_{Li7} = m_{Li6} : m_{Li7} = (1 + 1/7.0 \times 1823) : (1 + 1/6.0 \times 1823) \sim 1 - 1/42 \times 1823 = 1 - 1.3 \times 10^{-5}$.

5.1. (a) $I = 7.9 \times 10^{-9}$ erg/cm^2 sec, (b) $I/h \times 10^6 = 1.2 \times 10^{12}$ photons/cm^2 sec, (c) $\int_0^{2\pi} d\phi \int_0^{\pi} \sin\theta \, d\theta \, r^2 I(\theta) = 8.8 \times 10^6$ erg/sec $= 0.88$ watt.

5.2. (a) 12.0 erg/sec, from 5.1 (c) above, with $I = 100(hc/\lambda)/10^{-3} = 6.7 \times 10^5$ ev/cm^{2}sec $= 10.7 \times 10^{-7}$ erg/cm^{2}sec, at 60° and 10 m, (b) $12.0/6.7 \times 1.6 \times 10^{-12} = 1.1 \times 10^{12}$ photons/sec, (c) 0.37 photons/sec, since 10^{-9}g of Hg with atomic weight 200 contain $10^{-9} \times 6.0 \times 10^{23}/200 = 3 \times 10^{12}$ atoms, (d) $\sqrt{\langle a^2 \rangle} = \sqrt{\langle i^2 \rangle l^2/2\pi\nu e} = 2.6 \times 10^{-13}$ cm, from the value of $\langle i^2 \rangle l^2 = 1.6 \times 10^{-12}$ CGS units per atom, obtained from the formula in Problem 5.1, considering that $I = 10.7 \times 10^{-7}$ erg/cm^{2}sec at 60° and at 10 m for 3×10^{12} atoms.

6.1. (a) Eq. 3 for $m = 0$ gives $n_0 = N \exp(-T/\tau)$; that is $0.10 = \exp(-10/\tau)$; $\tau = -10/\ln(0.10) = 4.3$ sec., (b) $n_3/N = 0.20$, from Eq. 3 with $m = 3$.

6.2. Any specified sequence of counts has the same probability $(\frac{1}{2})^6 = \frac{1}{64}$. (a) $\frac{1}{32}$, (b) $\frac{1}{32}$, (c) $\frac{5}{32}$, (d) $\frac{5}{16}$ because there are 20 distinct sequences of the specified kind.

6.3. (a) $\langle m \rangle = \Sigma_{m=0}^{\infty} m n_m/N = (T/\tau)\Sigma_{m=1}^{\infty} n_{m-1}/N = T/\tau = \frac{15}{5} = 3$, (b) $\langle m^2 \rangle = \Sigma_{m=0}^{\infty} m^2 n_m/N = (T/\tau)\Sigma_{m=1}^{\infty} m n_{m-1}/N = (T/\tau)\Sigma_{m=1}^{\infty} [(m-1)n_{m-1} + n_{m-1}]/N = (T/\tau)^2 + (T/\tau) = 9 + 3 = 12$, (c) $\Delta m^2 = \langle m^2 \rangle - \langle m \rangle^2 = T/\tau = 3$.

6.4. The expected number of counts is $\langle m \rangle = 1.04Nt$; the expected increase of counts is $\langle m \rangle - Nt = 0.04Nt$; the mean square deviation is (see Problem 6.3) $\Delta m^2 = \langle m \rangle = 1.04Nt$; the root mean square deviation is $\Delta m \sim \sqrt{Nt}$; criterion of significance $0.04Nt = 3\sqrt{Nt}$; $t = 5625/N$ sec.

7.1. Since the components have equal intensities, $\langle m \rangle = 0$ and $\Delta m^2 = \frac{1}{4}(\frac{3}{2})^2 + \frac{1}{4}(\frac{1}{2})^2 + \frac{1}{4}(-\frac{1}{2})^2 + \frac{1}{4}(-\frac{3}{2})^2 = \frac{5}{4}$.

7.2. (a) According to Eq. 18 the separation is $\mu H/j = 2.7 \times 10^{-20} \times 10^3/\frac{3}{2} = 1.8 \times 10^{-17}$ erg $= 1.1 \times 10^{-5}$ ev, (b) $\nu = 1.8 \times 10^{-17}/h = 2.7 \times 10^9$ cycles/sec.

7.3. (a) $\langle \bar{m} \rangle = m \cos\theta$, (b) $\Delta \bar{m}^2 = \frac{1}{2}[j(j+1) - m^2] \sin^2\theta = \frac{1}{2}(2 - m^2) \sin^2\theta$.

7.4. $K = 3$.

8.1. Eq. 9 with $\bar{m} = m = 1$ becomes $\cos\alpha_{BP} = \cos\alpha_{BA} \cos\alpha_{AP} - \sin\alpha_{BA} \sin\alpha_{AP}$, which holds for $\alpha_{BP} = \alpha_{BA} + \alpha_{AP}$.

8.2. For $j = \frac{1}{2}$, $\bar{m} = m = \frac{1}{2}$, Eq. 22 becomes $\exp(i\frac{1}{4}\pi) \cos\frac{1}{4}\pi \exp(i\frac{1}{4}\pi) = \cos\frac{1}{4}\pi \times \exp(i\frac{1}{4}\pi) \cos\frac{1}{4}\pi - \sin\frac{1}{4}\pi \exp(-i\frac{1}{4}\pi) \sin\frac{1}{4}\pi$, that is, $i\sqrt{\frac{1}{2}} = \frac{1}{2}(1+i)\sqrt{\frac{1}{2}} - \frac{1}{2}(1-i)\sqrt{\frac{1}{2}}$.

8.3. $f = |(\mathbf{B}1|\mathbf{P}1)|^2 = |\cos\alpha_{\mathbf{BA}} \cos\alpha_{\mathbf{AP}} - \sin\alpha_{\mathbf{BA}} \exp(i\tfrac{1}{3}\pi) \sin\alpha_{\mathbf{AP}}|^2 = \cos^2\alpha_{\mathbf{BA}} \times \cos^2\alpha_{\mathbf{AP}} + \sin^2\alpha_{\mathbf{BA}} \sin^2\alpha_{\mathbf{AB}} - 2 \cos\alpha_{\mathbf{BA}} \cos\alpha_{\mathbf{AP}} \sin\alpha_{\mathbf{BA}} \sin\alpha_{\mathbf{AP}} \cos\tfrac{1}{3}\pi = \cos^2\alpha_{\mathbf{BP}} + \tfrac{1}{4} \sin2\alpha_{\mathbf{BA}} \sin2\alpha_{\mathbf{AP}}.$

9.1. (a) Because the energy levels of the atoms in the field are evenly spaced, their differences are multiples of one another. (b) The largest difference among four evenly spaced levels is three times the spacing.

9.2. Enter in Eq. 4 the probability amplitude $(\mathbf{A}\bar{m}|\mathbf{P}m)$ for $\bar{m} = \pm\tfrac{1}{2}$, $m = \tfrac{1}{2}$, from Eq. 21 and Table 8.1 of Chapter 8. Choose the reference planes as in Problem 8.2. Enter in the exponential of Eq. 4 the value $\mu H/j\hbar = 1.7 \times 10^9$ radians/sec. Enter into Eq. 2 $(\mathbf{A}\bar{m}|\mathbf{Q}(t)m)$ from Eq. 4, and $(\mathbf{B}\tilde{m}|\mathbf{A}\bar{m})$ from Eq. 21 Chapter 8, for $\tilde{m} = \tfrac{1}{2}$ or $-\tfrac{1}{2}$. The result is $|(\mathbf{B}\tfrac{1}{2}|\mathbf{Q}(t)\tfrac{1}{2})|^2 = \cos^2(\tfrac{1}{4}\pi - 1.7 \times 10^9 t)$; $|(\mathbf{B}-\tfrac{1}{2}|\mathbf{Q}(t)\tfrac{1}{2})|^2 = \sin^2(\tfrac{1}{4}\pi - 1.7 \times 10^9 t)$.

10.1. (a) Application of Eqs. 3 and 4 for two crystal cells on adjacent lattice planes yields the Bragg condition in the form $2\,d \sin\tfrac{1}{2}\theta/\lambda = N$. The maximum value of λ, $\lambda_{\max} = 2d = 4.2$ A, corresponds to $N = 1$ and $\theta = 180°$, that is, to perpendicular incidence of the X rays on the lattice planes. (b) For particles the analogous Bragg condition is $2\,p\,d \sin\tfrac{1}{2}\theta/h = N$. $E_{\min} = p_{\min}^2/2m = h^2/8md^2$ for $N = 1$, $\theta = 180°$, that is, $E_{\min} = 8$ ev for electrons and $E_{\min} = 4 \times 10^{-3}$ ev for neutrons.

10.2. Owing to interference the intensity I is not proportional to s^2, but to a quantity $|S|^2$ to be calculated according to Eq. 14. Enter $\mathbf{d}$ in place of $\mathbf{r}_1 - \mathbf{r}_2$; notice that $\mathbf{p} \cdot \mathbf{d} = mv \sin\theta\, d$, where m is the neutron mass 1.7×10^{-24} g. Hence $I(\theta) = 2|S(\theta)|^2/r^2 = 2(s^2/r^2)[1 + \cos(6.4 \sin\theta)]$.

10.3. Equation 16 can be generalized to apply to molecules with different kinds and different numbers of atoms, as apparent from its derivation. For CO_2, Eq. 16 becomes $\sigma(\theta) = s_C^2 + 2s_O^2\{1 + \sin[2(mv/\hbar)2d_{CO} \sin\tfrac{1}{2}\theta]/2(mv/\hbar)2d_{CO} \sin\tfrac{1}{2}\theta\} + 4s_Os_C \times \sin[2(mv/\hbar)d_{CO} \sin\tfrac{1}{2}\theta]/2(mv/\hbar)d_{CO} \sin\tfrac{1}{2}\theta = [10.8 + 6.7 \sin(14.0 \sin\tfrac{1}{2}\theta)/14.0 \sin\tfrac{1}{2}\theta + 14.8 \sin(7.0 \sin\tfrac{1}{2}\theta)/7.0 \sin\tfrac{1}{2}\theta] \times 10^{-25}$ cm^2. In a plot of $\sigma(\theta)$ take as abscissa $x = 7.0 \sin\tfrac{1}{2}\theta$ and notice that $\sin x/x$ equals 1 at $x = 0$, vanishes at $x = n\pi$ and has maxima or minima near $(n + \tfrac{1}{2})\pi$.

11.1. The probability distributions of x, y, and z are given by Eq. 34, those of p_x, p_y, and p_z (which are stationary) by Eq. 32. The results are $\langle x \rangle = (q_x/m)t$, $\langle y \rangle = (q_y/m)t$, $\langle z \rangle = (q_z/m)t$, $\langle p_x \rangle = q_x$, $\langle p_y \rangle = q_y$, $\langle p_z \rangle = q_z$, $\Delta x^2 = \Delta y^2 = \Delta z^2 = d^2 + \hbar^2 t^2/4m^2 d^2$, $\Delta p_x^2 = \Delta p_y^2 = \Delta p_z^2 = \hbar^2/4d^2$, $\Delta x\, \Delta p_x = \Delta y\, \Delta p_y = \Delta z\, \Delta p_z = \tfrac{1}{2}\hbar(1 + \hbar^2 t^2/4m^2 d^4)^{1/2}$. Notice that the minimum value of $\Delta x\, \Delta p_x$, etc., consistent with the uncertainty principle occurs at $t = 0$.

11.2. $P(R) = \int_0^R \exp(-2r/a)(4\pi r^2/\pi a^3)\, dr = 1 - \exp(-2R/a)(1 + 2R/a + 2R^2/a^2)$; $R_{1/2} = 1.34a$.

13.1. Continuity of $(x|E)$ requires $1 + A = B$, continuity of $d(x|E)/dx$ requires $K(1 - A) = K'B$. Solution: $A = (K - K')/(K + K') = (K^2 - K'^2)/(K + K')^2 = V_0/(\sqrt{E} + \sqrt{E + V_0})^2$; $R(E/V_0) = 1/(\sqrt{E/V_0} + \sqrt{E/V_0 - 1})^4$.

13.2. The four continuity conditions are: $1 + A = B + C$, $K(1 - A) = K'(B - C)$, $B \exp(iK'a) + C \exp(-iK'a) = D \exp(iK'a)$, $K'[B \exp(iK'a) - C \exp(-iK'a)] = KD \exp(iKa)$. Solution: $A = (K^2 - K'^2)/(K^2 + K'^2 + 2iKK' \times \cot K'a)$, $|A|^2 = [1 + 4E(E - V_0)/V_0^2 \sin^2(\sqrt{2m(E - V_0)}\, a/\hbar)]^{-1}$. In plotting express $\sin^2(\sqrt{2m(E - V_0)}\, a/\hbar)$ as $- \sinh^2(\sqrt{2m(V_0 - E)}\, a/\hbar)$ when $V_0 > E$; this hyperbolic sine is very large, so that $|A|^2 \sim 1$, unless $\sqrt{2m(V_0 - E)}\, a/\hbar < 1$. At

$V_0 = E$, $|A|^2 = (1 + 4\hbar^2/2ma^2E)^{-1}$. For $V_0 < E$, $|A|^2$ vanishes whenever $\sqrt{2m(E - V_0)}\, a/\hbar = n\pi$, and has maxima at $\sqrt{2m(E - V_0)}\, a/\hbar \sim (n + \frac{1}{2})\pi$; $|A|^2$ also vanishes at $V_0 = 0$.

13.3. Equation 20 yields, in the limit of $V_0 = \infty$, $E_n = n^2h^2/8ma^2$, where $n = 1, 2,$ $\cdots$ is the number of bright fringes of the corresponding probability distribution. In this limit each wave function vanishes at the edges of the well, that is, at $x = \pm\frac{1}{2}a$ (see p. 186). The wave function is then, $(x|n) = \sqrt{2/a}\,\cos(n\pi x/a)$ for n odd, and $(x|n) = \sqrt{2/a}\,\sin(n\pi x/a)$ for n even. Notice that $\int_{-\frac{1}{2}a}^{\frac{1}{2}a} dx\,|(x|n)|^2 = 1$.

13.4. The eigenvalue E_N is obtained by entering the wave function $(x|N)$ in the Schroedinger equation 9a, with $V_x(x) = \frac{1}{2}kx^2$. The equation is seen to be fulfilled with the eigenvalue $E_N = (N + \frac{1}{2})\hbar(k/m)^{\frac{1}{2}}$. Note that a macroscopic particle under the influence of the force $-kx$ oscillates sinusoidally with frequency $\nu = \sqrt{k/m}/2\pi$; in terms of this frequency, $E_N = (N + \frac{1}{2})h\nu$. The mean potential energy $\langle V_x \rangle = \frac{1}{2}k\int_{-\infty}^{\infty} x^2|(x|N)|^2\,dx$ is found to be $\frac{1}{2}E_N$. Since $E_N = \langle K \rangle + \langle V_x \rangle$, the mean kinetic energy must also be $\frac{1}{2}E_N$. Note that when a macroscopic particle performs sinusoidal oscillations, its kinetic and potential energies are also equal to one another when averaged over a cycle of oscillation.

13.5. From Eq. 7: $E_{n_x n_y p_z} = E_{n_x} + E_{n_y} + E_{p_z} = n_x^2h^2/8ma^2 + n_y^2h^2/8mb^2 + p_z^2/2m$. From Eq. 8: $(x,y,z\,|\,n_x,n_y,p_z) = (x\,|\,n_x)(y\,|\,n_y)(z\,|\,p_z) = \sqrt{2/a}\,\cos(n_x\pi x/a) \times \sqrt{2/b}\,\cos(n_y\pi y/b)\,\exp(ip_z z/\hbar)$ for n_x and n_y odd; the cosine is replaced with a sine whenever n_x or n_y is even. In mapping for $n_x = 2$, $n_y = 3$, notice the three dark fringes across the conduit, centered at $x = 0$ and at $y = \pm 1$ A; there are six bright fringes with maximum probability equal to 0.22 per A^3 at the points with coordinates $(\pm 0.75$ A, 2 A$)$, $(\pm 0.75$ A, 0$)$, $(\pm 0.75$ A, -2 A$)$.

13.6. From the law of time dependence $(2|b(t)) = \exp(-iE_2t/\hbar)(2|b(0)) = \sqrt{\frac{1}{2}} \times \exp(-i\pi ht/ma^2)$, $(3|b(t)) = \exp(-iE_3t/\hbar)(3|b(0)) = \sqrt{\frac{1}{2}}\,\exp(-i9\pi ht/4ma^2)$. (a) $(x|b(t)) = (x|2)(2|b(t)) + (x|3)(3|b(t)) = a^{-\frac{1}{2}}\sin(2\pi x/a)\,\exp(-i\pi ht/ma^2) + a^{-\frac{1}{2}} \times \cos(3\pi x/a)\,\exp(-i9\pi ht/4ma^2)$, (b) $|(x|b(t))|^2 = a^{-1}[\sin^2(2\pi x/a) + \cos^2(3\pi x/a) + 2\sin(2\pi x/a)\cos(3\pi x/a)\cos(5\pi ht/4ma^2)]$, (c) $\langle x \rangle = -(48a/25\pi^2)\cos(5\pi ht/4ma^2)$.

14.1. Obtain the component wave functions $(r,\theta,\phi\,|\,n,l,m)$ from Eqs. 13, 15, 16, and 17, where $\mathfrak{m}$ coincides with m, since $m = 0$. Enter the time dependence of $(n,l,m|b(t))$ in the form $\exp(-iE_nt/\hbar) = \exp(i\omega t/n^2)$ where $\omega = -E_1/\hbar = 2.0 \times 10^{16}$ radians/sec. Combine the components. (a) $(r,\theta,\phi|b(t)) = (1/\pi a^3)^{\frac{1}{2}}[\sqrt{\frac{1}{2}}\,\exp(-r/a + i\omega t) + \frac{1}{8}\sqrt{\frac{1}{2}} \times \cos\theta\,(r/a)\,\exp(-\frac{1}{2}r/a + i\frac{1}{4}\omega t) + \frac{1}{2}\,(\frac{1}{3})^4\sqrt{\frac{1}{6}}(3\cos^2\theta - 1)(r/a)^2\,\exp(-\frac{1}{3}r/a + i\frac{1}{9}\omega t)]$, (b) $|(r,\theta,\phi|b(t))|^2 = (1/2\pi a^3)[\exp(-2r/a) + (\frac{1}{2})^6\cos^2\theta(r/a)^2\,\exp(-r/a) + \frac{1}{2}\,(\frac{1}{3})^9(3\cos^2\theta - 1)^2(r/a)^4\,\exp(-\frac{2}{3}r/a) + \frac{1}{4}\cos\theta\,(r/a)\,\exp(-\frac{3}{2}r/a)\,\cos(\frac{3}{4}\omega t) + (\frac{1}{3})^{\frac{9}{2}}(3\cos^2\theta - 1)(r/a)^2\,\exp(-\frac{4}{3}r/a)\,\cos(\frac{8}{9}\omega t) + \frac{1}{8}\,(\frac{1}{3})^{\frac{9}{2}}\cos\theta\,(3\cos^2\theta - 1)(r/a)^3\,\exp(-\frac{5}{6}r/a) \times \cos(\frac{5}{36}\omega t)]$, (c) $\langle x \rangle = \langle r \rangle\langle\sin\theta\rangle\langle\cos\phi\rangle = 0$, $\langle y \rangle = \langle r \rangle\langle\sin\theta\rangle\langle\sin\phi\rangle = 0$, $\langle z \rangle = \langle r \rangle\langle\cos\theta\rangle = (\frac{2}{3})^34a\cos(\frac{3}{4}\omega t) + (\frac{2}{3})^83\sqrt{3}\,a\cos(\frac{5}{36}\omega t)$, where $a = $ Bohr radius $= 0.53 \times 10^{-8}$ cm. Notice how the calculation of $\langle x \rangle$ and $\langle y \rangle$ and $\langle z \rangle$ reduces greatly. This is an example of the selection rules given in Appendix IX.

14.2. Because the potential energy depends only on the coordinate r, and the eigenfunctions depend on r, θ, and ϕ through separate factors (see Eq. 13), the general formula $\langle V \rangle = \Sigma_{\mathbf{r}}V(\mathbf{r})|(\mathbf{r}|n,l,m)|^2$ reduces to $\langle -e^2/r \rangle = -e^2\int_0^{\infty} r^2\,dr(1/r) \times |(r|n,l)|^2$. Because each wave function $(r|n,l)$ is the product of an exponential and of a polynomial in r, the integrand reduces to a sum of terms of the type $\xi^n \exp(-\xi)$. The result is $\langle V \rangle = -e^2/an^2 = -27.2/n^2$ ev $= 2E_n$, independently of l. From $E_n = \langle K \rangle + \langle V \rangle$ follows then for the eigenstates of energy E_n, $\langle K \rangle = E_n - \langle V \rangle = -E_n = 13.6/n^2$ ev.

15.1. Splitting into four components implies $j = \frac{3}{2}$. The gyromagnetic ratio, as defined by Eq. 2, is then $\gamma = \mu/j\hbar = 2.7 \times 10^{-20}/\frac{3}{2} \times 1.05 \times 10^{-27} = 1.7 \times 10^7$ CGS units $= -e/mc$. The magnetic moment stems entirely from spin currents.

15.2. The fractional wavelength shift of $0.0016/1849 = 1/1.2 \times 10^6$ due to the magnetic field implies a corresponding shift of the photon energy, which is normally 6.7 ev $= 10.7 \times 10^{-12}$ erg. An energy shift of $10.7 \times 10^{-12}/1.2 \times 10^6 = 9 \times 10^{-18}$ erg caused by a field of 1000 gauss implies a difference of 9×10^{-21} erg/gauss $= 1$ Bohr magneton between successive eigenvalues of μ_z; the Zeeman effect is accordingly normal and the magnetic moment is due to orbital currents.

16.1. There are four states (n,l,m) with $n = 2$: $(2,0,0)$, $(2,1,1)$, $(2,1,0)$, $(2,1,-1)$, with equal energy E_2 in absence of disturbance. Because the electric field $\mathbf{F}$ exerts a torque perpendicular to its own direction, it leaves unaffected the component l_z of l in the direction of $\mathbf{F}$. The single state with $l_z = \hbar$, $(2,1,1)$, and the single state with $l_z = -\hbar$, $(2,1,-1)$, remain energy eigenstates; their energies are unchanged by $\mathbf{F}$ because the mean position of the electron coincides with the nucleus. Two states with $l_z = 0$, combinations of $(2,0,0)$ and $(2,1,0)$ with off-center electron distribution (Sect. 14.4) are energy eigenstates in presence of $\mathbf{F}$, with eigenvalues $E_2 + e\langle z \rangle F$; according to Chapter 12 they are the combinations with maximum and minimum $\langle z \rangle$. These combinations and the corresponding $\langle z \rangle = \pm 3a$ are given by Eqs. 23, 25, 26, pp. 213–214; the energies of these off-center states are therefore $E_2 \pm 1.59 \times 10^{-5}$ ev.

16.2. From Eq. 13 the gyromagnetic ratio is $-\frac{1}{2}(e/mc)g$, and g is for each l and j:

l	0	1	1	2	2
j	$\frac{1}{2}$	$\frac{1}{2}$	$\frac{3}{2}$	$\frac{3}{2}$	$\frac{5}{2}$
g	2	$\frac{2}{3}$	$\frac{4}{3}$	$\frac{4}{5}$	$\frac{8}{7}$.

16.3. The fractional wavelength shift $6/5890 \sim 10^{-3}$ implies a spin orbit coupling energy of $1/1000$ of the photon energy $hc/5.9 \times 10^{-5} = 2.1$ ev $= 3.4 \times 10^{-12}$ erg. From Eq. 14 the energy shift due to the magnetic field for $j = \frac{3}{2}$ and $\frac{1}{2}$, respectively, is $9 \times 10^{-21} \frac{4}{3} H \frac{1}{2}$ erg and $9 \times 10^{-21} \frac{2}{3} H \frac{1}{2}$ erg, with H in Gauss. The required shift is produced by $H = 10^{-2} \times 10^{-3} \times 3.4 \times 10^{-12}/9 \times 10^{-21} \times \frac{2}{3} \times \frac{1}{2} = 1.1 \times 10^4$ gauss.

17.1. Wave functions of a single electron in the ground state from Problem 13.4: $(x|0)(y|0)(z|0) = a^{-\frac{1}{2}}\pi^{-\frac{1}{4}} \exp(-\frac{1}{2}x^2/a^2)\, a^{-\frac{1}{2}}\pi^{-\frac{1}{4}} \exp(-\frac{1}{2}y^2/a^2)\, a^{-\frac{1}{2}}\pi^{-\frac{1}{4}} \exp(-\frac{1}{2}z^2/a^2) = a^{-\frac{3}{2}}\pi^{-\frac{3}{4}} \exp(-\frac{1}{2}r^2/a^2)$; in the first excited state of motion along x: $(x|1) \times (y|0)(z|0) = 2^{\frac{1}{2}} a^{-\frac{5}{2}}\pi^{-\frac{3}{4}} x \exp(-\frac{1}{2}r^2/a^2)$. (a) Wave functions of the two-electron states from Eq. 18: $(\mathbf{r}_1,\mathbf{r}_2|100,000,S) = a^{-4}\pi^{-\frac{3}{2}} x_1 \exp[-\frac{1}{2}(r_1^2 + r_2^2)/a^2] + (-1)^S \times a^{-4}\pi^{-\frac{3}{2}} x_2 \exp[-\frac{1}{2}(r_1^2 + r_2^2)/a^2]$, (b) substituting $\mathbf{r}_1 = \mathbf{R} + \frac{1}{2}\mathbf{r}$, $\mathbf{r}_2 = \mathbf{R} - \frac{1}{2}\mathbf{r}$ gives $(\mathbf{R},\mathbf{r}|100,000,0) = 2a^{-\frac{5}{2}}\pi^{-\frac{3}{4}} X \exp(-R^2/a^2)\, a^{-\frac{3}{2}}\pi^{-\frac{3}{4}} \exp(-\frac{1}{4}r^2/a^2)$, $(\mathbf{R},\mathbf{r}|100,000,1) = a^{-\frac{3}{2}}\pi^{-\frac{3}{4}} \exp(-R^2/a^2)a^{-\frac{5}{2}}\pi^{-\frac{3}{4}} x \exp(-\frac{1}{4}r^2/a^2)$. Notice that these wave functions are products of an oscillator wave function of the center of mass coordinates $\mathbf{R}$ and of a wave function of the relative position $\mathbf{r}$ of the two particles. In the para state the motion of the center of mass is the same as the motion of a single particle in its first excited state, while in the ortho state the relative motion of the two particles is excited and the motion of the center of mass is in the ground state. This separation of the wave function is characteristic of motion under the influence of elastic forces.

Index